2009 EDITION

America's Best

GRADUATE SCHOOLS

Exclusive rankings of more than 1,500 programs

Business · Education · Engineering · Law
Health & Medicine · Arts & Humanities · Sciences
Social Sciences · Library & Information Studies

PLUS: Directory listings for more than 1,200
schools in the big five disciplines

SCHOOL OF EDUCATION
CURRICULUM LABORATORY
UM-DEARBORN

HOW TO ORDER: Additional copies of the 2009 edition of *U.S.News & World Report*'s *Best Graduate Schools* guidebook are available for purchase by phone at (800) 836-6397 and online at *www.usnews.com/grad/*. Bulk quantity custom reprints or E-prints are available through FosteReprints, (800) 771-6445, Ext. 118, *catherinew@fostereprints.com*.

Contents

UNIVERSITY OF CINCINNATI COLLEGE OF LAW. JEFFREY MACMILLAN FOR *USN&WR*

Stepping Up to Life in Grad School

Practical advice on programs, getting in, and managing families and money

By Kim Clark

Admit it: Maybe your choice of college *was* influenced by where your high school friends were going or the on-campus sushi bar. But graduate school is too important, too difficult, and too expensive for such kid stuff. Besides, most grad school applicants are adults with jobs and, often, families.

America's Best Graduate Schools and *www.us-news.com* have uniquely practical and realistic information for grad students. Our well-established rankings can help applicants narrow their search by identifying the nation's very best programs. And our newest rankings also shed light on some of the hottest grad programs, including occupational therapy, pharmacy, and public affairs. Applicants can search our database of thousands of schools for the right program for them—geographically, financially, and educationally.

The following pages also offer lots of real-world advice about admissions, juggling responsibilities, and finances.

And there's plenty of good news. Many grad schools are themselves becoming more practical. More of them are tweaking their schedules to make them friendlier to adults. Law schools are giving students more training in business. Medical schools are training doctors to succeed in the new managed-care world. There are new cheap loan and loan repayment programs to reduce the financial burden. And, best of all, employers are still clamoring for grad school grads. ●

First-year M.B.A. student Laura Jones turns in her last exam of the quarter at Stanford's Graduate School of Business.

WILLIAM MERCER MCLEOD FOR *USN&WR*

Debt Doesn't Have to Clip Your Wings

Asking the right questions will save you money

By Kim Clark

A bachelor's degree is becoming passé in the job market. Those who really want to set themselves apart need a graduate degree. Unfortunately, the educational ticket to the top is expensive. Annual tuition and books alone at a run-of-the-mill public university are reaching $9,000 a year. Anyone who aims at a private school should prepare to cough up $25,000 to $30,000 a year. And that's *before* living expenses, which usually add at least $8,000 a year to a student's budget.

Compounding the sticker shock is the dismaying reality that students can't count on the kinds of scholarships that helped them through their undergraduate years. Fewer than 4 percent of graduate students get a federal or state grant. Fewer than 20 percent get any kind of scholarship from their school. Fully 60 percent of grad students get no free money of any kind and have to borrow or otherwise raise the entire cost of their advanced degree themselves.

Luckily, a little financial help appears to be coming to students' rescue. The federal government is offering new and potentially lower-cost educational loans. A growing number of communities and government agencies are offering to repay loans for workers who agree to spend several years in lower-paying public-service jobs such as teaching. And more employers are subsidizing employees' tuition.

Most important, employers continue to reward better-educated workers with bigger paychecks, making the investment of time and money a good bet. While the average worker with a bachelor's degree makes a comfortable $42,000 a year, master's degree holders make about 25 percent more. And those with professional degrees earn, on average, more than twice the income of those who stopped at a B.A.

That's a key motivator for thousands of grad students like Doug Spencer, who is working on a Ph.D. in jurisprudence and social policy at the University of California–Berkeley. Spencer owes more than $100,000 in educational debt and says it sometimes feels like "a foot on top of my head pushing me deeper and deeper into the mud." But Spencer loves school, and as a law professor (his goal) he could start at $150,000 a year. "Maybe I'm just blindly optimistic," he says, but he's convinced that the education will pay off in a financially secure life for him, his wife, and their new child.

Of course, not all grad student optimism is blind. Financial aid for graduate students is much more decentralized, and thus more complicated, than aid for undergraduates,

> FINANCIAL AID FOR GRAD STUDENTS IS MUCH MORE DECENTRALIZED, AND THUS MORE COMPLICATED, THAN AID FOR UNDERGRADUATES.

says Karen Klomparens, the dean of Michigan State University's Graduate School. But three types of grad students can be reasonably optimistic about getting some free money to ease school bills, she says:

- Science, math, or technology specialists can shoot for funding from foundations or government agencies, such as the National Institutes of Health.
- Very low-income students can qualify for need-based aid.
- Top students who apply to several schools can hope schools will compete for them by bidding up financial aid packages.

Extra perks. Students who aren't showered with grants can turn to one of the fastest-growing sources of free money for school: employers. Today, half of all workers are eligible for tuition benefits, up from 38 percent in 2000. And many employers focus on graduate training. Several big ones, for example, have signed on to California's new EnCorps

program, which funds up to $15,000 of the educational costs for retiring workers who want to launch second careers as teachers. Even employers without formal programs can write off as a business expense any worker's tuition for a class that is job-related but doesn't qualify the worker for another job, says Bob Scharin, senior tax analyst for Thomson Tax & Accounting. It takes little more than a one-page description of an education plan for a business to take advantage of Section 127 of the IRS code and pay as much as $5,250 a year in tax-free tuition benefits for workers taking just about any course, Scharin says.

Many employers say education benefits pay corporate dividends by attracting and retaining top workers. UTC, the conglomerate that owns Sikorsky helicopters and Pratt & Whitney, has found that the workers who take advantage of its generous tuition program are retained at a 4 percent higher rate than

Cathi Blair took out a federal loan. After five years' teaching, most of her debt will be canceled.

those who don't. They also get about 4 percent more promotions than those who don't.

A growing number of students work part time while they are in grad school. Campus research jobs are ideal because students can get paid for working on their dissertations. But those plum assignments are hard to get, and many more grad students end up with teaching assistantships. Teaching can be fun, and it prepares the student for a future as a professor, but grading undergrads' finals just when grad exams loom can be stressful.

Alas, there is such a shortage of grants and high-paying campus jobs that most grad students have to borrow, often massively. Almost 60 percent of all grad students have some education debt, and the average such debt is more than $40,000. Those attending professional schools should expect to rack up far more than that. More than 90 percent of all medical and dental students borrow, and their typical debt load exceeds $90,000. Debt loads of $200,000 are not unusual.

Point shaving. With those kinds of numbers, students who shop around for loans that waive fees or knock a couple of points off the interest rate can save thousands of dollars. Grad students say one way to save big bucks is to stick with federal loans even when private loans seem to offer lower terms, since the federal loans can be deferred or even forgiven. That was a happy discovery for Cathi Blair, who started spending down her family's savings to fund her pursuit of a master's in education at Eastern Kentucky University. Blair, who has worked more than 20 years as a scientist for the state, is preparing to launch a second career as a science teacher. One of her fellow students pointed her to a program that will repay up to $17,500 worth of federal education loans for science teachers. So she borrowed to pay tuition instead, preserving the family nest egg. After five years of teaching, most of her debts will be canceled. "It would have been extremely hard on my family" to pay all the costs out of pocket, she says.

About 80 percent of schools allow students to shop around for Stafford and Grad PLUS loans. Many of these will steer students to loans offered by "preferred lenders." While those are no longer simply the lenders that pay the biggest kickbacks to the school, they are not necessarily the lenders that offer the best deal. Students can save thousands of dollars if they spend a few hours checking out deals on websites such as SimpleTuition or Graduate Leverage or from nonprofit lenders such as the Missouri Higher Education Loan Authority. MOHELA lends to students around the country and cuts 2 percentage points off many loans. A list of nonprofit lenders can be found at *www.efc.org*. Some pri-

DAVID BUTOW—REDUX FOR *USN&WR*

Berkeley grad student Doug Spencer helps manage an apartment complex in return for reduced rent.

their PLUS loans. Since standard PLUS loans last only 10 years, students won't get any advantage from this program unless, as soon as they finish school, they apply for the federal government's 25-year income-based repayment plan.

Top dollar. Many professionals don't need these repayment programs, however, because their degrees pay off so handsomely. Although physicians these days leave medical school with about $100,000 in debt, most can easily make the monthly payments of $800 to $1,300 (the higher payments eliminate the debt within 10 years) once they start work. Likewise, *Forbes* magazine calculates that M.B.A. holders from the top 100 business schools typically get such big raises that they earn their grad school outlays back in just four years or so.

Of course, there are plenty of students—those in, say, social work or the humanities—for whom an investment in grad school returns little financial profit. But, says Kevin Murphy, an economics professor at the University of Chicago who has studied returns on education, money shouldn't always be the deciding factor. "I hate to see people get discouraged," says Murphy, who won a MacArthur "genius" prize in 2005. "Education gets you a lot more than earnings. . . . You should go for a master's in poetry if you enjoy it." ●

vate lenders may offer similarly low-sounding terms. But most private loans have variable rates, which means payments may rise in the future.

Students who move on to low-paid or public-service professions can get many of their federal—but not private—student loans forgiven. Among the advantages of federal loans:

● Income-based repayment. Starting in 2009, graduate students who consolidate their federal loans with the federal government can apply for an income-based repayment plan that caps monthly payments at 15 percent of family income.

Some borrowers can have their remaining debts canceled in as little as five years.

● Public-service forgiveness. A host of programs will repay educational loans for teachers, healthcare workers, and other public servants. Some of the programs, however, are designed with so many loopholes that most students won't get much benefit. Last year, for example, Congress congratulated itself on agreeing to repay Grad PLUS loans for those who work at public-service jobs of almost any type for 10 years and who make 10 years' worth of on-time payments on

Three Programs to Check

Time to see what your government can do for you

These are three cheap loan programs for grad students:

Perkins loans. Available only to those with low incomes. Grad students who qualify can get up to $6,000 a year at a 5 percent interest rate. Better yet, there's no interest at all while you're in school. These loans are made only through schools. There is a maximum lifetime limit of $40,000, including undergraduate Perkins debt.

Stafford loans. The second-cheapest program will charge grad students entering in fall 2008 a maximum of 6.8 percent plus up to 2 percent in fees, for a maximum true annual rate of 7.25 percent. Students attending schools that allow them to shop for these loans can find lenders who will waive some of the fees and knock a couple of percentage points off the interest rate for those who pay automatically and on time, making Staffords an especially good deal. Low-income students can get "subsidized" Staffords, which charge no interest while the student is in school—a savings of several thousand dollars over the life of the loan. Staffords for grad students are capped at $20,500 a year ($138,500 lifetime). No more than $8,500 a year can be subsidized.

PLUS. In 2006, the federal government began allowing grad students to borrow their full educational costs (after other financial aid), including basic living expenses such as transportation, child care, etc., from the PLUS program. Lenders can charge as much as 8.5 percent a year and up to 4 percentage points as fees, giving a true maximum annual rate of 9.42 percent. Some lenders, however, will offer discounts for automatic and on-time payment. –K.C.

Are You Ready to Fill In the Blank?

The GRE has made some changes. They're worth checking out before you take the test

By Lucia Graves

Grad school applicants be warned: Students taking the GRE General Test should be aware of some changes. In November, the Educational Testing Service, which administers the exam, introduced new question types to the verbal and quantitative sections. These alterations, while relatively minor, were the first phase in a larger effort to make the exam more relevant.

In the verbal section, a new "text completion" question asks students to fill in a series of blanks within a short paragraph. Each blank has its own list of multiple-choice options; each option changes the overall meaning of the paragraph and, by extension, the answers for the blanks that follow.

The new "numeric entry" question asks students to type their answer into a box instead of choosing one from multiple-choice options. (The test is taken on a computer.)

"You won't be asked to pick from a multiple-choice list very often in life, but you might be asked to come up with a number," explains David Payne, executive director of the GRE program at ETS. "We're trying to adopt items that have a closer analog to what students will be doing in graduate school."

Rollout rollback. It was over a year ago that ETS first rolled out plans for an extensive GRE makeover. Among the biggest changes would have been the elimination of the antonym and analogy questions in the verbal section, and a switch to a more secure, Internet-based exam offered only occasionally throughout the year. (Currently, students may schedule exams at almost any time.)

Test makers scrapped the idea last spring when it became clear that testing centers lacked the resources to accommodate the large groups of test takers it would create. More than 550,000 applicants per year take the test.

Since then, ETS has taken a more gradual approach to improving the exam. The antonym and analogy questions may be eliminated eventually, but test makers say it could be years before they introduce alternatives. The process of changing the exam has been so sluggish that some education experts are concerned that the standardized testing industry, which over-

sees dozens of national and statewide exams, has too many balls in the air. Larger concerns, like bias, susceptibility to coaching, and predictive inaccuracy, have yet to be fully addressed, they feel.

Others think the admitted need for gradualism a sign of prudence, especially given the challenges ETS faced with implementing the new SAT for prospective college students. In 2002, ETS made several changes to the SAT after the University of California–Berkeley, one of its biggest customers, threatened to drop the test entirely.

Reading comprehension questions took the place of analogies, and quantitative comparisons were replaced with algebra II questions.

Still, critics felt it was misleading to call it a "new" SAT when the changes seemed relatively minor. Robert Schaeffer, public education director of the group FairTest, a Massachusetts-based organization that monitors standardized tests for signs of bias, compared the changes to "painting lipstick and eye shadow on a pig." But good change often evolves slowly, he admits. "Clearly, this incremental approach is better than having a disaster,"

says Schaeffer. "It creates an opportunity to get the bugs out."

Schaeffer's chief concern is that, in his view, the test is more about making money for the testing companies than about helping kids choose schools or helping colleges choose kids. "One can only surmise that such changes are done for the same reason that Ford needs to repackage its cars every year: to burnish the image and hold market share, to make it look modernized," he says.

Indeed, though question types have been slow to change, exam costs have not. Prices to take the GRE are currently $140 for students in the United States and $170 abroad. ●

New for This Year
See how you'd perform on the new types of questions that have been added to this year's test. View answers below.

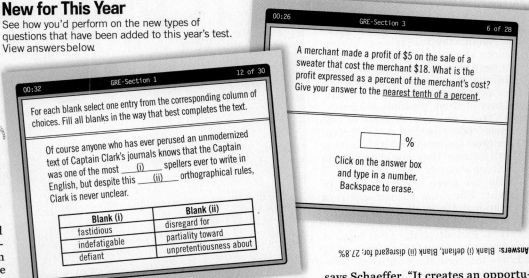

GRE-Section 1   12 of 30   00:32

For each blank select one entry from the corresponding column of choices. Fill all blanks in the way that best completes the text.

Of course anyone who has ever perused an unmodernized text of Captain Clark's journals knows that the Captain was one of the most ___(i)___ spellers ever to write in English, but despite this ___(ii)___ orthographical rules, Clark is never unclear.

Blank (i)	Blank (ii)
fastidious	disregard for
indefatigable	partiality toward
defiant	unpretentiousness about

GRE-Section 3   6 of 28   00:26

A merchant made a profit of $5 on the sale of a sweater that cost the merchant $18. What is the profit expressed as a percent of the merchant's cost? Give your answer to the <u>nearest tenth of a percent</u>.

[   ] %

Click on the answer box and type in a number. Backspace to erase.

Answers: Blank (i) defiant, Blank (ii) disregard for; 27.8%

Back-to-School Days, for Adults

Things to look for in a graduate school if your college days are long behind you

By Christopher J. Gearon

A Whittier, Calif., bookkeeper and 37-year-old mother dreams of becoming a volcanologist, while a 48-year-old District of Columbia attorney wants a new career in real-estate development. In Murfreesboro, Tenn., a former Army enlistee and 26-year-old father of five sees financial planning in his future. All three are in graduate school.

Today's grad student typically starts an advanced-degree program long after the traditional undergraduate-to-graduate student has finished. Nearly half of all grad students enroll between ages 24 and 35, according to the Council of Graduate Schools; one quarter start at age 36 or older. Most have real-world work experience. About a third are raising children.

Here's the rub: Many grad schools have been slow to accommodate nontraditional graduate learners. "Universities have failed to look at the demographics of their graduate students," says Carol Ann Baily, director of Off-Campus Student Services at Middle Tennessee State University in Murfreesboro. "That's because they would have to do something about it."

Baily has given the issue a lot of thought: She's the former chair of the National Academic Advising Association's Advising Adult Learners Commission. Too often, she says, support services are structured for young adults—full-time students whose lives revolve around campus. As a result, nontraditional students often confront advisers who keep banker's hours, a lack of prep classes, and little empathy from faculty about balancing work, family, school, and commuting.

Richard Denney, a former Army combat engineer with five kids, relies on his grad school for help. At Middle Tennessee State, where he is pursuing an M.B.A. at night, nontraditional students have their own resource center and lounge. A student organization called OWLs, for Older Wiser Learners, offers time-management workshops and adult-learning conferences; advice ranges from financial aid to stress-management seminars.

In Las Cruces, N.M., New Mexico State offers courses for older students in time management, speed-reading, and writing to reorient those who are rusty when it comes to hitting the books. "While [grad students] tend to be excellent students, they need to retool their study and comprehension skills," says Linda Lacey, dean of the university's graduate school. Nontraditional students "really do present a different set of issues," remarks Jean Morrison, vice provost of graduate programs at the University of Southern California. Child care and health insurance can be big distractions, she says, but "universities, by and large, are slow to come around to a family-friendly model." After USC re-examined its policies in 2005, its graduate school established a Center for Work and Family Life. Like many other schools, it offers health insurance—and struggles with how to make this affordable for older students.

Lisa Alpert, a USC Ph.D. candidate in geology and the mother of two toddlers, hadn't planned to pursue a Ph.D. at all. "I felt I was too old," she says. But a field trip during her master's work changed

Lisa Alpert (right) of USC with husband How and daughters Francesca (left) and Angelina

that; a professor encouraged her to apply, adding the magic words: "We pay you." Alpert is now immersed in "the insides of volcanoes and subduction zones"; she hopes to work for the U.S. Volcano Disaster Assistance Program.

WISE move. Alpert feels she struck gold at USC. Through an initiative called Women in Science and Engineering, or WISE, created by a $20 million gift to increase the numbers of women in science, math, and engineering, Alpert gets her tuition, plus a $4,000 stipend toward child care. As a result, Alpert's 3-year-old gets day care three times a week. In return, Alpert teaches 20 hours a week.

Some grad students think older is wiser. "It's a lot easier psychologically when you go back to school at this point in life," says Ronee McLaughlin, a 48-year-old Washington, D.C., attorney and real-estate investor working on a mas-

ter's in real-estate development at the University of Maryland. Besides, her graduate program "assumes people are working," McLaughlin says; required courses are offered in the evening. Maryland offers several programs and services for nontraditional students, including child care and an organization called Graduates as Parents.

Initially, McLaughlin applied to the executive M.B.A. program at Maryland's business school, only to find that it cost $89,000. "It was too expensive," she said. Instead, a grad school dean recommended she pursue a two-year master's: It was cheaper, and it fit her interests better. Now she's tackling the hardest part of going back to school, the technology—an experience that has created a bond between the mother and her 10-year-old daughter. "She certainly enjoys seeing me struggle with my homework," says McLaughlin. ●

DAVID BUTOW—REDUX FOR *USN&WR*

Finding Time for the Family

The fine art of convincing the kids it's all under control

You're in your 30s or 40s with a decent-paying job, a spouse, and kids, and you get an overwhelming urge to go back to school. What will your spouse think about this? Here are two possibilities: You'll quit your job or go part time (result: Your income will drop), or you'll keep working (result: You'll never be around to watch little Amanda).

"You've got to get the buy-in and support of your family. If you don't have that, it's very hard to be successful," says Gabe DeGabriele, a consultant with the Association for Non-Traditional Students in Higher Education. "I've seen marriages dissolve, and I've seen marriages get stronger" when a spouse goes to grad school.

Duty roster. At Middle Tennessee State, Richard Denney (story, left) and his wife, Monique, a full-time pre-med student, share responsibilities. They have five kids: He does days, she has night duty, and they share the cooking and cleaning.

Keeping chores straight is one thing, but remembering to be there when family members need you is crucial. DeGabriele says talking about expectations is a good start; so is scheduling time for your spouse and each child. "I know a couple who made date nights out of grocery shopping," DeGabriele says. It's also important for family members to support the returning student, which raises some wonderful opportunities for role reversal—asking the parental student how school was that day or taking kids to class occasionally.

Be careful about letting tests or papers interfere with family time. "As soon as you've taken that away, you've lost their support," DeGabriele says. –*C.J.G.*

11

The Infinite Variety of Humans

Why personalized medicine is revolutionizing what medical students will need to know

By Bernadine Healy, M.D.

What propels most students into medicine is the desire to relieve human suffering with knowledge, judgment, and skill. Noble aspirations quickly sour, however, when insurance companies deny care over the phone or when faceless bureaucrats penalize doctors' discretionary decisions on what's best for their patient based on some standardized guidelines. As pediatrician Mark Vonnegut stated recently in the *New England Journal of Medicine*, "U.S. doctors today have less and less to say about the care of their patients. All the complex lessons they learned in medical school are being swept aside for template care." Not much longer, I hope. Template care is increasingly at odds with the emergence of personalized medicine, a new discipline driven by the exploding knowledge of the human genome that guides treatment tailored to the individual patient. And this is what today's medical students will be practicing tomorrow.

Look at cancer, which offers a glimpse of what's to come. The wide arrays of genes that mastermind cancer have become targets for drug design. Herceptin, for example, counters a gene that occurs in 20 to 30 percent of women with breast cancer and makes it especially aggressive. For these women, Herceptin is lifesaving. For women who would not benefit and would face only side effects, the drug is avoided. This is what we want for every therapy. But the development of such personalized medicine requires that physicians actively integrate genomics into all fields, reaffirming the time-honored tenet that doctors always consider what's special about an individual patient as opposed to the textbook case.

Care would be easy if people fit some standard mold. When the sequence of the human genome was published in 2001, scientists pointed to our common humanity, with people being more similar than different. But seven years and a mountain of research show the opposite—an astonishing level of individual variety. In fact, *Science* magazine declared human genetic variation as the No. 1 breakthrough of 2007.

Thanks to ever better, faster, and cheaper sequencing technology, researchers have shown the many ways our 25,000 or so genes can vary. One little glitch—a misspelling, a hunk of DNA lost or added, or a gene altered by interplay with other genes or molecules—can affect disease susceptibility or treatment. Already, researchers have tied genetic differences to many diseases, including diabetes, heart failure, autism, restless leg syndrome, multiple sclerosis, and rheumatoid arthritis. Imagine this in medical practice. Knowing your patient's risk early on would bring more targeted prevention. And by knowing that some patients are more likely than others to become infected with certain viruses or other pathogens, patient care would be improved, as would the public-health management of epidemics—such as identifying priority groups for vaccination.

Case by case. It's downright humbling for physicians to learn that some patients with illnesses we label and treat as the same are just plain different and should not be expected to respond to standard therapy. These patients have not failed treatment; treatment has failed them. And so follows the mantra of the emerging personalized medicine industry in the hunt for personalized diagnostics and therapeutics: right treatment, right patient, right time—not one size fits all.

To the pharmaceutical industry, personalized medicine poses limitless opportunities. To insurers and government payers, it offers increased quality at lower cost, since treatments that don't work are not used. To patients, it's better care.

The medical establishment has been slow to catch on. As Ralph Snyderman, former chancellor at Duke University Medical Center, puts it, "physicians haven't yet grasped this as the great new wave in the practice of medicine." Although a few medical schools, including Duke, have developed programs in personalized medicine, they are scarce, as are the ranks of medical professionals trained in genetics.

But I have faith that personalized medicine will sweep the hallowed halls of medicine. A friend of mine in the telecommunications world tells me that all revolutions start with people in their 20s. Medicine is no exception. Students entering medical school now, encouraged by the needs of their patients, will be the ones to make personalized medicine happen. They will catch the wave and, no doubt, put an end to template care too. ●

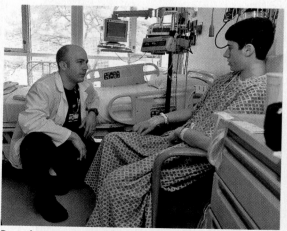

ONE LITTLE GLITCH—A MISSPELLING OR A HUNK OF DNA LOST OR ADDED—CAN AFFECT SUSCEPTIBILITY OR TREATMENT.

Doctoring one on one: University of Chicago Medical Center

How It's Done

Grad school is a juggling act. Linda Kulman asks six students about their choices, their finances, and how they pull it all off

Switch if It Makes Sense

Jasmine Brooks · Law

After seven years as a general surgeon in New York, Jasmine Brooks was fed up with HMOs that rewarded primary-care doctors for *not* referring patients to specialists and disciplining them when they did. In 2006, she enrolled in law school at Southern University in Baton Rouge, La. Not sure she had the drive to "give it my all," she signed up part time while teaching health and sciences to pad her landing. She didn't tell her mom and sister what she was doing "in case I failed." Brooks, 39, emigrated from Vietnam as a child; now a full-time student

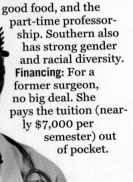

(though still squeezing in time to teach), she expects to graduate in 2009.

Goal: To change healthcare policy and protect doctors. Brooks loves to litigate and says she's good at it.
Aha moment: When her sister, a lawyer, had her second child. "It made me wonder if my choices were appropriate," says Brooks, who opted for a career over a family.
Why Southern: Warm weather, good food, and the part-time professorship. Southern also has strong gender and racial diversity.
Financing: For a former surgeon, no big deal. She pays the tuition (nearly $7,000 per semester) out of pocket.

Keep the Family Going on Less

Jesse French · Engineering

For Jesse French, a 35-year-old father of three, engineering has run in the family for four generations. But in 1996, after two quarters toward a master's in mechanical engineering, French entered the Army, which had footed his college bill. His stint as a helicopter pilot took him "all over the world," and after his discharge, he spent two years as an "engineering missionary" in South Korea, Mongolia, and China, teaching techniques such as harnessing wind power. When French's engineering-professor father found him a graduate research position in composite materials engineering at the University of Tulsa in 2005, he jumped at it—and expects to finish his Ph.D. next year.

Goal: French is interviewing as a mechanical engineer to do design work and consulting but ultimately plans to teach at the university level.
Education: B.S. in mechanical engineering (Rose-Hulman Institute of Technology, 1995); M.S.M.E. (University of Tulsa, 2007). He expects to earn his Ph.D. in mechanical engineering at Tulsa in 2009.
Finances: The school pays his annual tuition of $14,000, and French says that although the monthly stipend of $900 for teaching undergraduate engineering and supervising the machine shop doesn't make him rich, his family is fed, clothed, and owns two cars. There's pizza on Friday night, but "we're not at the ballet." One positive: He has no debt.

Reach for the Next Level

Jenni Mechem · Business

"I'm not a crafts mom," says Jennifer Mechem, who stayed home for five years with her kids before enrolling in business school. It's not the only time she has sidestepped convention: Mechem, now 43, dropped out of the University of Chicago and took a break before getting her undergraduate degree at age 30 from Evergreen State College. A babyhood bout with meningitis left her with hearing loss, and at Evergreen she concentrated on disability rights. She always had thoughts of law school, but she lost out in an interview for executive director of a nonprofit because of her lack of management experience: "If I wanted to get to the next level, I needed to fill the credential gap." Now she's in B-school at the University of Washington. "Ten years ago, I would have laughed and said, 'Fat chance!'"

Goal: To re-enter the workforce in the private sector. When she left Evergreen, she worked for the U.S. Department of Education in Washington, D.C.
Motivation: "I felt keenly that having only a B.A. was a barrier to advancement." She adds: "Life is uncertain. I want to make a reasonable amount of money if I have to support my family."
Finances: Even though her husband teaches law at U.Wash., she gets no break on the annual tuition of $17,000. A merit scholarship takes care of $7,000 a year, and, rather than blowing the family's savings, Mechem has borrowed $28,000 her first year. She will owe about $60,000 when she graduates.
Benefits of age: "I'm not intimidated by faculty. I look at them as peers."
Advice: Consider a full-time, daytime program over a part-time program in the evenings, because child care during the day is easier to find. It has worked for her.

Show Your Serious Side

Matt Soden · Medicine

In the 13 years since Matt Soden graduated from Columbia University with a degree in history, he has worked stints as a legal assistant in New York, as a financial analyst in Hong Kong, and with a reality TV show in L.A. The jobs were demanding and the cities exciting, but none made Soden, 35, feel he was living up to his potential. That's where med school comes in: He's a first-year student at Case Western Reserve University in Cleveland. Soden is fascinated by how things work, "and the human body beats them all."

Goal: Soden sees himself as a neurologist or a psychiatrist. He wants part of his practice to help underserved communities.
Aha moment: On 9/11 and the days after the towers fell, Soden watched on TV as rescuers sifted through the rubble. "Working to manufacture reality," he realized, "I'm not doing anything significant."
Education: B.A., Columbia, 1995; part-time premed classes at a local community college, Cal State-L.A., and SUNY–Stony Brook. He had no science background; Soden says that while there was no need for another four-year degree, med schools want proof that you're really dedicated.
Finances: This year, he has a $30,000 scholarship. He'll take out $35,000 in federal loans to meet the $64,000 tab for tuition, housing, food, books, and health insurance.

Make the Most of Your Talent

Ahmed Alsoudani · Fine Arts

If not for his drawings and paintings, Ahmed Alsoudani might still be in Syria. He grew up in Baghdad, and from elementary school on, he was always the best artist in his class. But after his escape to Damascus in 1995, he lived with no papers for four years. Then his art caught the attention of an American working with the United Nations, and in 1999, Alsoudani, now 32, came to the United States as a refugee, ending up in Portland, Maine. Four years ago, he was one of only 20 art students accepted to the six-week summer Yale–Norfolk program, and in 2006, he was one of 21 applicants (out of more than 1,100) accepted to the two-year Yale M.F.A. program. Last year, Alsoudani had a solo show in New York City—a rare honor for a student.

Goal: "It's important to me that my work be disturbing."
On his art: Alsoudani's portfolio contains apocalyptic, *Guernica*-like large-scale drawings and small-canvas paintings. He cares less about money than high visibility (he'd love to get his art into the Whitney Museum). His identity also matters. "I do not want to be an Iraqi artist in the U.S.," he says. "I want to be some guy from Iraq who paints."
Education: Maine College of Art (2005); spent $2^{1}/_{2}$ months at the Skowhegan School of Painting and Sculpture (2006). He will earn his M.F.A. from Yale this spring.
Why Yale: Studio facilities, faculty, visiting-artists program. "I feel spoiled at Yale."
Advice: Just because you're an artist doesn't mean you have talent. You have to know how to use your tools.

Let Your Conscience Guide You

Lynnette Parker · Education

Lynnette Parker (above, with nieces Kalia, 8, and Rayna, 6) was one of five kids in her family to be raised on welfare. She graduated from college in 1995 hoping to work in advertising. But that didn't pan out, and she found herself in a run-down classroom teaching high school English. "I was drawn to the kids, so it fell into place," she says. Still, it was tough. The school gave her a yellow pad, two pens, an eraser, and a box of chalk: "Every Friday I said, 'I'm quitting,' and every Monday I was back." She earned her master's in educational administration at New York University, but George Bush's No Child Left Behind Act led her to conclude that "politicians and policies were [too] removed from the classroom." Parker, now 35, is studying educational policy, organization measurement, and evaluation toward a Ph.D. at Berkeley.

Goal: "To be in that room" when educational programs are evaluated. She's "not opposed" to entering politics herself, especially if it helps poor children and minorities.
The administrator's dilemma: It's hard to know what's needed in the classroom if you're not there.
Education: B.A. in English (Cal State–Long Beach, 1995); M.S. in educational administration (NYU, 2003); M.S. in applied statistics and research (University of Northern Colorado, 2005). Parker expects to earn her Ph.D. by 2012. ●

How We Calculate the Rankings

Statistical indicators of quality are important, but so is the opinion of peers and recruiters

By Robert J. Morse and Samuel Flanigan

Each year, *U.S. News* ranks professional-school programs in business, education, engineering, law, and medicine. These rankings are based on two types of data: expert opinion about program quality and statistical indicators that measure the quality of a school's faculty, research, and students. These data come from surveys of more than 1,200 programs and some 14,000 academics and professionals that were conducted in fall 2007. As you research course offerings and weigh different schools' intangible attributes, *U.S. News*'s rankings can help you compare programs' academic excellence. It's important that you use the rankings to supplement—not replace—careful thought and your own inquiries.

We also rank programs in the sciences, social sciences, humanities, and many other areas, including selected health specialties. These rankings are based solely on the ratings of academic experts. This year we've updated our rankings of Ph.D. programs in computer science, mathematics, and physics (Pages 55–58) to correct a problem with 2006's survey that left some programs off the survey instrument. We've produced new rankings of graduate health programs in audiology (Page 39), clinical psychology (same page), occupational therapy (Page 41), pharmacy (same page), physical therapy (Page 42), social work (same page), and speech-language pathology (Page 43). We've also done new rankings for master's of public affairs and public policy (which now follow the business school rankings on Page 22) and master's of fine arts (Page 66).

In addition to these new rankings, we republish older rankings that are based solely on peer ratings in various health fields (Pages 39–43), Ph.D. programs in sciences (Pages 54–58), Ph.D. programs in social sciences and humanities (Pages 59–63), and master's of library and information studies (Page 64).

To gather the opinion data, we asked deans, program directors, and senior faculty to judge the academic quality of programs in their field on a scale of 1 ("marginal") to 5 ("outstanding"). In business,

WILLIAM MERCER MCLEOD FOR *USN&WR*

Pressure cooker: M.B.A. students at Stanford take a final exam.

education, engineering, law, and medicine, we also surveyed professionals who hire new graduates.

The statistical indicators used in our rankings of business, education, engineering, law, and medical schools fall into two categories: inputs, or measures of the qualities that students and faculty bring to the educational experience, and outputs, measures of graduates' achievements linked to their degrees.

Different output measures are available for different fields; as a result, the indicators we use in our models vary. In business, the value of students' education can be gauged by their starting salaries after graduation and by how long it takes them to find jobs. In law, we look at the time it takes new grads to get jobs, plus state bar exam passage rates.

This year, we modified our education school rankings. After consulting with deans of leading graduate education schools, we improved the methodology by making it more oriented toward the research aspect of graduate education.

Scoring. To arrive at a school's rank, we examined the data for each quality indicator. Where appropriate, we adjusted the indicators in which low values suggest higher quality, such as acceptance rates. We then standardized the value of each indicator about its mean. The weights applied to the indicators reflect our judgment about their relative importance, as determined in consultation with experts in each field. The final scores were rescaled: The highest-scoring school was assigned 100, and the other schools' scores were recalculated as a percentage of that top score. The scores were then rounded to the nearest whole number and schools placed in descending order. Every school's performance is presented relative to the other schools with which it is being compared. A school with an overall score of 100 did not necessarily top out on every indicator; rather, it accumulated the highest composite score. A school's rank reflects the number of schools that sit above it; if three schools are tied at 1, the next school will be ranked 4, not 2. Tied schools are listed alphabetically.

More details about the methodology can be found with the ranking tables and at *www.usnews.com*, which also has extended rankings in many categories. ●

Exclusive Rankings

Business • Public Affairs • Education • Engineering • Health & Medicine • Law
Arts & Sciences • Social Sciences & Humanities • Library & Information Studies
PLUS: Advice and admissions tips for graduate students in six top disciplines

FROM TOP: SCOTT GOLDSMITH—AURORA FOR *USN&WR*; JEFFREY MACMILLAN FOR *USN&WR*

Princeton: a graduate student "high table" (top) and a slice of campus life

Facing an Inconvenient Truth

Students tackle the problems of sustainable operations—with an eye on the bottom line

By Mindy Charski

Wal-Mart's goal is zero waste by 2025. General Electric is increasing its investment in cleaner-technology research. Coca-Cola Enterprises is reducing the raw materials it uses in packaging. Gone are the days when sustainability was a concern only of ecofriendly start-ups: Now, companies of all types are starting to realize that operating in a way that doesn't compromise future generations can be good for the bottom line.

"Sustainability is going to be the new paradigm for business," says John Joseph, 33, who will graduate from Stanford University in 2009 with a joint M.B.A./M.S. degree in environment and resources and plans to work or consult in the same field. "A lot of the business students are realizing they're going to have to deal with this whether or not they're interested in it."

Business schools are reflecting the changes in the marketplace by integrating studies of corporate citizenship into their programs. "Just as an M.B.A. is expected to know how to do financial modeling or how to read a balance sheet or develop a marketing strategy, increasingly there will be an expectation they can address the core society, educational, and environmental challenges," says Kevin Thompson, senior program manager for corporate citizenship and corporate affairs at IBM.

Schools take different approaches.

Sam Goldman (left) and Ned Tozun at Stanford created a power source for developing countries.

The Stanford Graduate School of Business offers several electives, including Environmental Entrepreneurship and Ethical Issues in the Biotech Industry, and students can earn a certificate in corporate social responsibility. Stanford has also incorporated social innovation into several required courses, including its new fall seminar, Critical Analytical Thinking. One session focused on Internet restrictions faced by Google in China. Likewise, the UCLA Anderson School of Management offers electives centered on topics like social entrepreneurship, business and the environment, and ethical considerations in business, but sustainability themes pop up in required classes like economics and strategy, too.

Maximum impact. "When a school is committed to having all students in all core courses touching on social and environmental themes, that's a sign the school is seriously committed to relevant issues," says Liz Maw, executive director of Net Impact, an organization with more than 100 B-school chapters that promotes using business for social good.

Both Stanford and Anderson complement classroom instruction with experiential learning, and so does the Johnson School at Cornell University, the alma mater of IBM's Thompson. There, for credit, M.B.A.'s can team up with a faculty mentor and students of other Cornell grad schools to work on company-sponsored projects throughout a semester.

"The issues we're trying to get students to wrestle with in the immersion are much more ambiguous, long term in nature," says Mark Milstein, director of Cornell's Center for Sustainable Global Enterprise. "You have to be very creative in problem-solving for those." Last spring, a team studied the potential glob-

Smart Choices

Real Estate. Forget the recent housing downturn; interest in this specialty is surging. The Wharton School at Penn offers a real-estate major; classes include Real Estate Development and Urban Real Estate Economics. **Healthcare.** B-schools including Columbia offer courses in this growing sector.

al market for clean-coal technologies for silicon producer Dow Corning.

Milstein says a program that allows an M.B.A. student to get some experience "gives you something to talk about with potential employers." Indeed, recruiters have asked Jessica Meyer, 30, about her ventures at the Kenan-Flagler Business School at the University of North Carolina: For credit, she and a team consulted with natural-products manufacturer Burt's Bees about additional sustainability strategies.

Calling all alums.
Meyer, who will graduate in 2008 with a concentration in sustainable enterprise, will begin a two-year program this summer working for Johnson & Johnson, where she hopes to be involved in procurement-focused sustainability initiatives. She says her school has a strong alumni network. "Kenan-Flagler was one of the first to build up its sustainable enterprise concentration," she says, "so we have a lot of alumni all over the country who are doing interesting things and are interested in talking to current M.B.A. students."

A helpful career center is important, too. Check if anyone is specifically assigned to help people find jobs in sustainability-related fields, suggests Net Impact's Maw, and ask about the strength of student clubs like hers on campus. Net Impact (*netimpact.org*) and the Aspen Institute Center for Business Education (*aspencbe.org*) both produce guides on how programs are addressing social and environmental issues.

Likewise, be sure to consider a school's commitment to the cause. Some universities have related research organizations on campus. Boston College, for instance, is the home of the Winston Center for Leadership and Ethics, which offers programming for M.B.A.'s in the Carroll School of Management.

It's also a good idea to ask schools how they are approaching sustainability. Is it through an environmental standpoint, for example, or through philanthropy? Cornell examines it through what Milstein describes as a "business-growth lens."

"It's much more, 'Let's think about how entrepreneurship and innovation serve as solutions to social and environmental issues and build that into the business.' It's not a particularly complicated concept, but it's not one that most programs take," Milstein says. "When students take the time to look at what those differences are, they start making decisions about what it is they want to study, and that tends to drive them toward where they want to go." ●

REALITY CHECK SOURCE: GRADUATE MANAGEMENT ADMISSION COUNCIL

Insider Tip

The University of Chicago's business school is one of several that require candidates to follow an honor code stating their application material is their own work. But admission consultants, whose services include essay help, aren't necessarily off limits. "Anyone who works with us can say it is their own work," says Graham Richmond, chief executive officer of Clear Admit in Philadelphia. His consultancy, which charges at least $200 an hour, doesn't write essays, and others shouldn't either. Find advisers who have agreed to follow ethical practices at *www.aigac.org.*

Getting In

Don't Hold Back. The majority of full-time M.B.A.'s who graduated in 2007 had more than three years' work experience before business school, according to the Graduate Management Admission Council, but 24 percent had less. If you're younger and have something remarkable to offer, apply. The University of Rochester's Simon Graduate School of Business actively seeks "early leaders," and students zero to three years out of college make up a third of entering classes.

Take an Exam. The GMAT is still the reigning standardized test for B-schools, but a growing number, including MIT's Sloan School of Management, accept GRE scores.

Be Honest. Don't fib about your salary, employment dates, grades, or other information on your application. And don't fabricate your references. Some schools, including the Fisher College of Business at Ohio State University, run verifications on everyone who enrolls full time.

Reality Check

Mean annual starting salary for '07 B-school graduates: $80,452 Mean number of job offers for full-time M.B.A. grads: 2.4% • Top job category for new hires: marketing/sales • Mean reimbursement in '06 by companies that help employees pay for part-time M.B.A. programs: $9,767; for executive M.B.A.'s: $27,374; for online programs: $4,042 • Increase in number of GMAT registrations in '07 compared with '06: 12% • Share of full-time M.B.A. grads (2000-06) who say they "definitely made the right decision" about the school they chose to attend: 54%

Group study at Chicago's Graduate School of Business

Schools of Business

Rank/School	Overall score	Peer assessment score (5.0=highest)	Recruiter assessment score (5.0=highest)	'07 average undergrad GPA	'07 average GMAT score	'07 acceptance rate	'07 average starting salary and bonus	'07 graduates employed at graduation	Employed 3 months after graduation	'07 out-of-state tuition and fees	'07 total full-time enrollment
1. Harvard University (MA)	100	4.8	4.4	3.63	713	13.8%	$135,630	90.1%	94.3%	$48,738	1,808
Stanford University (CA)	100	4.8	4.4	3.61	721	7.9%	$134,654	86.8%	93.5%	$45,921	741
3. University of Pennsylvania (Wharton)	95	4.8	4.2	3.53	712	17.3%	$132,171	85.6%	92.5%	$49,722	1,620
4. Massachusetts Institute of Technology (Sloan)	93	4.7	4.2	3.50	705	19.7%	$127,839	86.9%	94.6%	$44,792	770
Northwestern University (Kellogg) (IL)	93	4.7	4.3	3.50	704	N/A	$122,932	91.9%	96.9%	$43,935	1,194
University of Chicago	93	4.6	4.3	3.50	709	23.3%	$126,818	89.2%	95.3%	$45,139	1,117
7. Dartmouth College (Tuck) (NH)	89	4.3	4.0	3.46	713	19.2%	$128,182	90.1%	96.4%	$43,240	500
University of California–Berkeley (Haas)	89	4.5	4.0	3.57	710	13.7%	$116,263	82.5%	93.3%	$37,949	504
9. Columbia University (NY)	88	4.4	4.2	3.40	707	16.3%	$129,427	81.6%	92.8%	$45,422	1,226
10. New York University (Stern)	84	4.2	3.9	3.40	700	17.1%	$124,752	88.7%	94.1%	$41,822	839
11. University of California–Los Angeles (Anderson)	83	4.2	3.8	3.60	704	23.4%	$115,318	79.0%	92.9%	$37,286	721
12. University of Michigan–Ann Arbor (Ross)	82	4.4	4.0	3.30	700	20.4%	$120,408	86.1%	89.5%	$43,289	838
13. Yale University (CT)	80	4.2	3.9	3.47	700	14.7%	$118,964	77.4%	87.9%	$47,182	395
14. Cornell University (Johnson) (NY)	79	4.2	3.8	3.31	682	26.7%	$118,888	87.1%	95.4%	$44,260	609
Duke University (Fuqua) (NC)	79	4.3	4.0	3.38	690	31.5%	$117,473	80.5%	85.9%	$45,663	838
University of Virginia (Darden)	79	4.1	3.8	3.33	688	28.9%	$121,279	87.9%	95.0%	$42,602	651
17. Carnegie Mellon University (Tepper) (PA)	77	4.0	3.8	3.32	696	29.8%	$111,996	85.3%	94.9%	$45,644	319
18. University of Texas–Austin (McCombs)	74	3.9	3.8	3.38	673	34.0%	$109,871	85.3%	93.9%	$38,222	517
19. Univ. of North Carolina–Chapel Hill (Kenan-Flagler)	72	4.0	3.8	3.27	681	39.2%	$112,375	80.1%	90.3%	$39,882	568
20. Indiana University–Bloomington (Kelley)	71	3.8	3.7	3.37	656	34.4%	$105,296	86.9%	96.0%	$34,852	444
21. University of Southern California (Marshall)	70	3.9	3.5	3.30	689	29.0%	$103,317	72.3%	94.1%	$81,100 **	458
22. Arizona State University (Carey)	69	3.5	3.4	3.44	675	31.6%	$98,318	89.5%	97.4%	$28,220	168
Georgetown University (McDonough) (DC)	69	3.5	3.7	3.26	677	35.0%	$108,959	82.1%	97.8%	$40,017	591
24. Emory University (Goizueta) (GA)	68	3.7	3.8	3.30	685	36.8%	$107,991	71.6%	88.9%	$37,576	373
25. University of Rochester (Simon) (NY)	66	3.4	3.5	3.52	673	40.9%	$99,436	78.3%	92.4%	$37,791	296
Washington University in St. Louis (Olin)	66	3.6	3.4	3.38	674	32.9%	$96,559	82.4%	94.5%	$38,729	288
27. Ohio State University (Fisher)	65	3.6	3.1	3.41	661	30.2%	$97,622	77.1%	97.9%	$35,337	273
University of Minnesota–Twin Cities (Carlson)	65	3.6	3.5	3.37	661	41.1%	$100,104	76.7%	93.2%	$36,596	218
29. Brigham Young University (Marriott) (UT)	64	3.0	3.5	3.53	661	53.0%	$93,448	93.3%	98.1%	$8,700	305
Georgia Institute of Technology	64	3.3	3.6	3.40	665	39.8%	$88,288	84.9%	98.1%	$30,016	153
Texas A&M University–College Station (Mays)	64	3.3	3.1	3.40	665	29.8%	$97,496	93.8%	100.0%	$25,323	154
University of Wisconsin–Madison	64	3.6	3.3	3.37	656	32.7%	$93,097	83.0%	95.7%	$26,536	224
33. Purdue University–West Lafayette (Krannert) (IN)	63	3.6	3.6	3.32	662	32.8%	$96,196	77.8%	90.1%	$33,462	281
34. Boston College (Carroll)	61	3.4	3.1	3.35	651	37.8%	$94,271	82.8%	98.4%	$1,126 *	191
University of Florida (Hough)	61	3.4	3.5	3.40	680	43.6%	$70,592	80.4%	96.1%	$23,103	142
University of Notre Dame (Mendoza) (IN)	61	3.4	3.4	3.20	673	44.3%	$95,263	71.4%	98.0%	$36,040	330
University of Washington (Foster)	61	3.4	3.4	3.38	679	36.1%	$93,677	67.1%	91.1%	$29,543	218
38. University of Illinois–Urbana-Champaign	60	3.5	3.3	3.40	627	41.5%	$92,239	77.4%	96.8%	$29,610	208
39. University of Maryland–College Park (Smith)	59	3.6	3.0	3.34	650	31.5%	$99,433	69.5%	91.5%	$38,575	237
40. Boston University	58	3.0	3.2	3.38	668	31.3%	$92,634	79.4%	94.8%	$35,370	298
Michigan State University (Broad)	58	3.4	3.2	3.22	633	29.6%	$98,557	90.1%	94.4%	$26,131	202
Pennsylvania State Univ.–University Park (Smeal)	58	3.5	3.5	3.30	650	30.0%	$94,228	70.0%	86.7%	$30,122	171
Rice University (Jones) (TX)	58	3.2	3.4	3.25	642	39.4%	$101,529	81.9%	94.8%	$35,558	229
44. Southern Methodist University (Cox) (TX)	57	3.3	3.4	3.30	640	47.1%	$96,457	78.1%	90.6%	$39,010	164
University of California–Davis	57	3.2	3.3	3.37	674	25.5%	$88,701	68.2%	88.6%	$34,874	120
University of California–Irvine (Merage)	57	3.3	3.2	3.34	667	44.2%	$80,092	80.6%	91.9%	$37,394	199
Vanderbilt University (Owen) (TN)	57	3.5	3.5	3.27	644	46.9%	$104,032	67.7%	83.5%	$38,552	378
48. Babson College (Olin) (MA)	55	3.4	3.5	3.21	631	56.5%	$94,037	70.0%	92.1%	$35,110	383
49. University of Georgia (Terry)	52	3.4	3.1	3.40	653	30.5%	$76,517	71.7%	81.7%	$28,162	123
University of Iowa (Tippie)	52	3.2	3.1	3.34	652	49.8%	$77,952	75.9%	89.7%	$24,920	134

Sources: *U.S. News* and the schools. Assessment data collected by Synovate. Note: N/A means that the data were not provided by the school. *Tuition is per credit. **Tuition is reported for the complete degree program.

PROGRAMS RANKED BEST BY BUSINESS SCHOOL DEANS AND M.B.A. PROGRAM DIRECTORS

ACCOUNTING
1. U. of Texas–Austin (McCombs)
2. University of Pennsylvania (Wharton)
3. University of Illinois–Urbana-Champaign
4. University of Chicago
5. University of Michigan–Ann Arbor (Ross)
6. University of Southern California (Marshall)
7. Stanford University (CA)
8. Brigham Young University (Marriott) (UT)
   New York University (Stern)
10. Northwestern U. (Kellogg) (IL)

ENTREPRENEURSHIP
1. Babson College (Olin) (MA)
2. Stanford University (CA)
3. Harvard University (MA)
4. University of Pennsylvania (Wharton)
5. Massachusetts Institute of Technology (Sloan)
6. University of Southern California (Marshall)
7. Indiana University–Bloomington (Kelley)
8. University of California–Berkeley (Haas)
9. U. of Texas–Austin (McCombs)
10. University of North Carolina–Chapel Hill (Kenan-Flagler)

EXECUTIVE M.B.A.
1. University of Pennsylvania (Wharton)
2. University of Chicago
3. Northwestern U. (Kellogg) (IL)
4. Duke University (Fuqua) (NC)
5. Columbia University (NY)
6. University of California–Los Angeles (Anderson)
7. New York University (Stern)
8. University of California–Berkeley (Haas)
9. University of Michigan–Ann Arbor (Ross)
10. Emory Univ. (Goizueta) (GA)

FINANCE
1. University of Pennsylvania (Wharton)
2. University of Chicago
3. New York University (Stern)
4. Columbia University (NY)
5. Stanford University (CA)
6. Massachusetts Institute of Technology (Sloan)
7. University of California–Los Angeles (Anderson)
8. Harvard University (MA)

9. University of California–Berkeley (Haas)
10. Northwestern U. (Kellogg) (IL)

INFORMATION SYSTEMS
1. Massachusetts Institute of Technology (Sloan)
2. Carnegie Mellon U. (Tepper) (PA)
3. U. of Texas–Austin (McCombs)
4. University of Minnesota–Twin Cities (Carlson)
5. University of Arizona (Eller)
6. University of Maryland–College Park (Smith)
7. Stanford University (CA)
8. New York University (Stern)
9. Georgia State Univ. (Robinson)
10. University of Pennsylvania (Wharton)

INTERNATIONAL
1. Thunderbird School of Global Management (AZ)
2. U. of South Carolina (Moore)
3. University of Pennsylvania (Wharton)
4. University of Michigan–Ann Arbor (Ross)
5. Duke University (Fuqua) (NC)
6. Columbia University (NY)
7. Harvard University (MA)
   New York University (Stern)
9. University of Southern California (Marshall)
10. University of California–Berkeley (Haas)

MANAGEMENT
1. Harvard University (MA)
2. Stanford University (CA)
3. Northwestern U. (Kellogg) (IL)
4. University of Michigan–Ann Arbor (Ross)
   University of Pennsylvania (Wharton)
6. Dartmouth College (Tuck) (NH)
7. University of Virginia (Darden)
8. Duke University (Fuqua) (NC)
9. University of California–Berkeley (Haas)
10. Columbia University (NY)

MARKETING
1. Northwestern U. (Kellogg) (IL)
2. University of Pennsylvania (Wharton)
3. Duke University (Fuqua) (NC)
4. Harvard University (MA)
5. Stanford University (CA)
6. Columbia University (NY)
7. University of Michigan–Ann Arbor (Ross)

8. University of California–Berkeley (Haas)
9. U. of Texas–Austin (McCombs)
10. University of Chicago

NONPROFIT
1. Yale University (CT)
2. Stanford University (CA)
3. Northwestern U. (Kellogg) (IL)
   University of California–Berkeley (Haas)
5. University of Michigan–Ann Arbor (Ross)

PART-TIME M.B.A.
1. New York University (Stern)
2. University of Chicago
3. Northwestern U. (Kellogg) (IL)
4. University of California–Los Angeles (Anderson)
5. Georgia State Univ. (Robinson)
6. DePaul Univ. (Kellstadt) (IL)
   University of California–Berkeley (Haas)
   University of Southern California (Marshall)
9. Southern Methodist University (Cox) (TX)
10. University of Michigan–Ann Arbor (Ross)

PRODUCTION/OPERATIONS
1. Massachusetts Institute of Technology (Sloan)
2. Carnegie Mellon U. (Tepper) (PA)
3. Purdue University–West Lafayette (Krannert) (IN)
4. University of Pennsylvania (Wharton)
5. University of Michigan–Ann Arbor (Ross)
6. Stanford University (CA)
7. Northwestern U. (Kellogg) (IL)
8. Indiana University–Bloomington (Kelley)
9. Harvard University (MA)
10. Columbia University (NY)

SUPPLY CHAIN/LOGISTICS
1. Massachusetts Institute of Technology (Sloan)
2. Michigan State Univ. (Broad)
3. Arizona State Univ. (Carey)
   Carnegie Mellon U. (Tepper) (PA)
5. Pennsylvania State University–University Park (Smeal)
6. University of Pennsylvania (Wharton)
7. Ohio State University (Fisher)
8. Purdue University–West Lafayette (Krannert) (IN)
   Stanford University (CA)
10. University of Tennessee–Knoxville

METHODOLOGY

All 425 master's programs in business accredited by the Association to Advance Collegiate Schools of Business were surveyed. Of those, 383 responded, with 127 providing the data needed to calculate rankings based on a weighted average of the eight quality indicators described below. All 425 schools appear in the directory starting on Page 74. More information about the methodology appears on Page 16.

Quality assessment (weighted by .40): Two separate surveys were conducted in the fall of 2007. Business school deans and directors of accredited M.B.A. programs were asked to rate overall academic quality of the master's programs at each school on a scale from "marginal" (1) to "outstanding" (5); 45 percent responded, and the resulting scores are weighted by .25 in the ranking model. Corporate recruiters and company contacts who hired M.B.A. graduates from previously ranked programs were also asked to rate the programs; 27 percent responded, and their ratings are weighted by .15 in the ranking model.

Placement success (.35): This is measured by mean starting salary and bonus (40 percent) and employment rates for full-time M.B.A. program 2007 graduates, computed at graduation (20 percent) and three months later (40 percent). Those not seeking jobs and those for whom the school has no information are excluded from the placement rates. Salary figures are based on the number of graduates reporting data. The mean signing bonus is weighted by the proportion of graduates reporting their salary who received a bonus, since not everyone who reported a base salary received a signing bonus.

Student selectivity (.25): The strength of full-time students entering in the fall of 2007 was measured by mean GMAT score (65 percent), mean undergraduate GPA (30 percent), and the proportion of applicants accepted by the school (5 percent).

Overall rank: Data were standardized about their means, and standardized scores were weighted, totaled, and rescaled so that the top school received 100; others received their percentage of the top score.

Specialty rankings: These rankings are based solely on ratings by educators at peer schools. Business school deans and M.B.A. program heads were asked to nominate up to 10 programs for excellence in each specialty. Those receiving the most nominations are listed.

Public Affairs

Our ranking, completed in 2008, is based solely on a survey of deans, directors, and department chairs representing 269 master's programs.

Rank/School	Average assessment score (5.0=highest)
1. Syracuse University (NY)	4.5
2. Harvard University (MA)	4.3
Indiana University–Bloomington	4.3
4. Princeton University (NJ)	4.1
University of Georgia	4.1
6. University of California–Berkeley	4.0
7. University of Kansas	3.9
University of Michigan–Ann Arbor	3.9
University of Southern California	3.9
10. Carnegie Mellon University (PA)	3.8
Duke University (NC)	3.8
New York University	3.8
University of Chicago	3.8
14. American University (DC)	3.7
Columbia University (NY)	3.7
Georgetown University (DC)	3.7
George Washington University (DC)	3.7
SUNY–Albany	3.7
University of California–Los Angeles	3.7
University of Minnesota–Twin Cities	3.7
University of North Carolina–Chapel Hill	3.7
University of Texas–Austin	3.7
University of Washington	3.7
University of Wisconsin–Madison	3.7
25. Arizona State University	3.6
University of Maryland–College Park	3.6
27. Florida State University	3.5
Georgia State University	3.5
University of Nebraska–Omaha	3.5
University of Pittsburgh	3.5
Virginia Tech	3.5
32. Johns Hopkins University (MD)	3.4
Rutgers, the State Univ. of New Jersey–Newark	3.4
University of Colorado–Denver	3.4
University of Kentucky	3.4
36. Cornell University (NY)	3.3
Ohio State University	3.3
Texas A&M University–College Station	3.3
University of Arizona	3.3
University of Missouri–Columbia	3.3
41. Northern Illinois University	3.2
University of Delaware	3.2
University of Illinois–Chicago	3.2
University of Pennsylvania	3.2
45. Cleveland State University	3.1
George Mason University (VA)	3.1
Indiana University-Purdue University–Indianapolis	3.1
Naval Postgraduate School (CA)	3.1
49. Portland State University (OR)	3.0
University of Connecticut	3.0

Note: Lists of schools and individuals surveyed were provided by the National Association of Schools of Public Affairs and Administration and the Association for Public Policy Analysis and Management. Respondents were asked to rate the academic quality of programs on a scale of 1 (marginal) to 5 (distinguished). The response rate was 40 percent. Surveys were conducted by Synovate.

The institutions below received the greatest number of nominations from survey respondents for their excellence in a given specialty. Keep in mind that nominees were drawn only from the schools surveyed. So, for example, a university like Yale—which offers a degree in environmental management through its School of Forestry and Environmental Studies but not a degree in public affairs—does not show up here.

CITY MANAGEMENT
1. University of Kansas
2. Cleveland State University
3. Northern Illinois University
4. University of Southern California
5. U. of North Carolina–Chapel Hill
6. Arizona State University
   New York University
8. University of Illinois–Chicago
9. University of North Texas
10. Syracuse University (NY)
    University of Delaware

ENVIRONMENTAL POLICY & MGT.
1. Indiana University–Bloomington
2. Syracuse University (NY)
3. Duke University (NC)
4. University of California–Berkeley
   University of Washington
6. Univ. of Michigan–Ann Arbor
7. Harvard University (MA)
8. U. of North Carolina–Chapel Hill
9. Columbia University (NY)
10. Carnegie Mellon University (PA)
    University of Wisconsin–Madison

HEALTH POLICY & MANAGEMENT
1. Harvard Univ. (MA)
2. Johns Hopkins Univ. (MD)
3. New York University
   Univ. of Michigan–Ann Arbor
5. University of California–Berkeley
6. Duke University (NC)
   George Washington Univ. (DC)
8. Syracuse University (NY)
9. University of Southern California
10. Carnegie Mellon University (PA)

INFORMATION & TECHNOLOGY MGT.
1. Carnegie Mellon University (PA)
2. SUNY–Albany
   Syracuse University (NY)
4. Georgia Institute of Technology
5. Harvard University (MA)
6. Indiana University–Bloomington
   University of Nebraska–Omaha
8. University of California–Berkeley
9. North Carolina State University
   Rutgers, the State Univ. of New Jersey–Newark
   University of Texas–Austin

NONPROFIT MANAGEMENT
1. Indiana University–Bloomington
2. Syracuse University (NY)
3. Indiana University-Purdue University–Indianapolis

4. Harvard University (MA)
5. University of Washington
6. Univ. of Minnesota–Twin Cities
7. University of Southern California
8. Johns Hopkins University (MD)
9. New York University
10. University of Utah

PUBLIC FINANCE & BUDGETING
1. Syracuse University (NY)
2. University of Georgia
3. Indiana University–Bloomington
4. University of Kentucky
5. Georgia State University
6. New York University
7. SUNY–Albany
   University of Connecticut
9. University of Nebraska–Omaha
10. Harvard University (MA)

PUBLIC MANAGEMENT/ADMIN.
1. Syracuse University (NY)
2. University of Georgia
3. Indiana University–Bloomington
4. Harvard University (MA)
5. University of Southern California
6. American University (DC)
7. University of Kansas
8. Arizona State University
   SUNY–Albany
10. Rutgers, the State Univ. of New Jersey–Newark

PUBLIC POLICY ANALYSIS
1. Harvard University (MA)
2. University of California–Berkeley
3. Univ. of Michigan–Ann Arbor
4. Carnegie Mellon University (PA)
5. Duke University (NC)
6. Princeton University (NJ)
7. University of Chicago
8. Syracuse University (NY)
9. Univ. of Maryland–College Park
10. University of Texas–Austin

SOCIAL POLICY
1. Harvard University (MA)
2. Univ. of Michigan–Ann Arbor
3. University of Wisconsin–Madison
4. Syracuse University (NY)
   University of Chicago
6. University of California–Berkeley
7. New York University
8. Duke University (NC)
9. University of Texas–Austin
10. Princeton University (NJ)
    University of Southern California

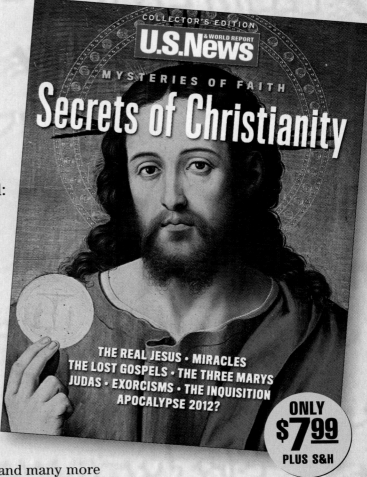

The Lure of Alternative Programs

Salaried training, condensed courses, flexible schedules–but the classroom is still the same

By Lucia Graves

Akilah Robinson, a financial analyst at Goldman Sachs, was at a leadership conference in New York when she realized the financial world wasn't where she belonged. "They spoke about not being afraid to follow your passion," she says. "I remember thinking: It's time for me to follow my passion." And follow it she did—down the street to the New York City Teaching Fellows. Now she teaches elementary special education in Brooklyn, and she took a 55 percent pay cut to do it. Who knew Wall Street's revolving door spun that direction?

Robinson is just one of thousands of teaching fellows who have switched careers to serve some of the most disadvantaged kids in New York. The program, founded in 2000 to get more teachers into the city's struggling schools, currently boasts 8,000 fellows teaching in 1,200 schools. Admission is competitive—this year's acceptance rate is 16 percent—and applicants with outside experience are preferred. "There's a certain maturity that comes from having had a different profession," explains Vicki Bernstein, executive director of teacher recruitment and quality.

Altruism aside, why is the program so popular? Applicants are responding, in part, to the incentives, which are characteristic of alternative teacher certification programs. These typically offer training during atypical times—nights, weekends, and summers. They made their debut in the early 1980s, when a

Akilah Robinson turns over a new leaf at P.S. 150 Christopher School in Brooklyn.

teacher shortage prompted many states to seek out untapped talent by offering salaried training, condensed classes, and flexible schedules. Teaching fellows, for instance, do a seven-week intensive training program on stipend, then go straight into schools, earning $40,000 or more for a school year. Meanwhile, subsidized by the district, they pack in courses at local universities; after two years, they've earned their master's. By contrast, traditional master's students have no opportunity for salaried teaching and often pay more than $40,000 for their degree. It's little wonder alternative routes have become so popular, especially among midcareer professionals,

many of whom have families to support. "There was no other way that I could have obtained my certification," says Paul Perry, who got his through Utica College in New York. "If I had to give up my job and my income to student teach—with no pay—I would not have been able to do it."

No silver bullet. When alternative certification first appeared, it was viewed as a back door or a quick fix for desperate school districts. But today's programs have little in common with "emergency certification," their poor-quality forerunner, which banged out ill-trained teachers in a matter of weeks. "When I have people call me up saying, 'I want an easy way to become a teacher,' I say, 'You're talking to the wrong person,' " says Michael McKibbin, administrator for teacher development at the California Commission on Teacher Credentialing. Alternative programs typically last one to three years, and many offer superior support networks and supervised teaching in partnered school districts.

Today there are over 485 programs, with at least one in every major city and

Smart Choices

Special Ed. The number of teachers in this specialty is forecast to rise almost 15% by 2016. At some schools (e.g., Vanderbilt University's Peabody College), many students are fully funded through U.S. Department of Ed grants. **Foreign Languages.** The student population is increasingly diverse. ¿Hablas español?

all 50 states. In California—where, a decade ago, state legislation that dramatically reduced K–3 class size created an overnight shortage of 18,000 teachers—there are more than 70 programs. In Florida, state legislation mandates that there be 67 programs—one for each of the state's 67 counties. They've even become competition for traditional certification programs. For example, the UCLA School of Education has instituted a well-regarded program in conjunction with school districts in the Los Angeles area, and New York's Pace University has instituted several programs to serve the city's lowest-performing schools.

Caveat teacher. Is alternative certification right for you? That depends. Teachers are often funneled where the need is greatest: into struggling schools that serve families with multiple challenges. How resilient are you? Do you connect with kids? Do you know your subject? Where do you want to live? "Alternative routes are efficient," explains Emily Feistritzer, president of the National Center for Alternative Certification, "because they really have been created to meet demand for specific teachers, in specific subjects, in specific schools where there are specific needs."

If you want to assess an alternative program yourself, McKibbin offers some tips:

● Look at the selection process. Performance evaluations, like asking applicants to present a lesson or organize a classroom, are a sign of quality, as is an emphasis on experience working with kids.

● Seek out schools that blend theory and practice. There's no substitute for spending time in the classroom—the more the better.

● Identify programs with good partnerships. Check what alliances exist between your program, the school district, and local universities: Those are your resources.

● Find out whether there is a strong support system in place. Will you get mentoring in the classroom? How about for your studies? Will you have a chance to talk with your peers about solving classroom problems?

Feistritzer has embarked on a national study looking at which components of alternative routes contribute most to producing effective teachers. Traditional ed schools are looking over their shoulders; if the evidence is there, we may be witnessing a revolution in the way teachers are produced in this country. ●

Insider Tip

Many states offer financial incentives for students willing to work in hard-to-staff subject or geographic areas. The Kansas Teacher Service Scholarship offers $5,000 toward each year of graduate school. Other programs pay up after a year (or more) in the classroom. California's National Board for Professional Teaching Standards Certification Incentive Program pays out $20,000 over a four-year period. The American Federation of Teachers lists teacher scholarship and loan forgiveness programs at *www.aft.org.*

Getting In

Used to a Lab Coat? Between now and 2015, American elementary and secondary schools are expected to need 280,000 new math and science teachers. Expertise in these subject areas is notoriously hard to find—so if you've got it, you have a valuable resource that will make you a widely attractive candidate.

Switch the Scenery. It's much harder to find positions in wealthy or suburban areas than in rural areas or inner cities. A change of scenery could boost your job prospects.

Take the Praxis. The test is required for teacher certification in many states and at an increasing number of ed schools. Check out the ETS website for tips and sample questions: *www.ets.org.*

It's All About Attitude. Looking good on paper isn't enough. Performance is an important aspect of teaching, and many schools are looking for poised candidates with some social seasoning. Cultivate your interpersonal skills.

Reality Check

Average national base salary for full-time teachers: $49,026 · Highest: California, $59,825, and Connecticut, $59,304; lowest: South Dakota, $34,709 · Looking beyond the paycheck, remember that teacher retirement, coupled with increasing public school enrollment, is spurring demand, especially in the South and West. Good bets: Nevada, Texas, Georgia, Arizona · Want some respect? In a national survey of 23 professions, teaching was rated one of the "most prestigious occupations." Only firefighters were held in higher regard

The University of Delaware is in one of several states that offer teacher incentives.

Schools of Education

Rank/School	Overall score	Peer assessment score (5.0=highest)	Superintendent assessment score (5.0=highest)	'07 mean GRE scores (verbal/quantitative)[1]	'07 doctoral acceptance rate	'07 doctoral student/faculty[2]	Doctorals granted/faculty 2006-07	'07 funded research (millions)	'07 funded research/faculty member (thousands)	'07 total graduate education enrollment
1. Stanford University (CA)	100	4.6	4.7	630/706	7.2%	4.9	0.6	$16.3	$387.3	414
2. Vanderbilt University (Peabody) (TN)	99	4.4	4.4	643/716	9.2%	3.3	0.8	$29.3	$361.7	688
3. University of California–Los Angeles	98	4.1	4.3	551/591	35.7%	7.5	1.3	$33.1	$690.2	857
4. Teachers College, Columbia University (NY)	97	4.4	4.7	544/649	22.7%	6.0	1.4	$39.5	$282.3	4,720
5. University of Oregon	96	3.5	4.1	518/617	16.0%	4.8	1.4	$28.6	$1,021.9	846
6. Harvard University (MA)	94	4.4	4.7	636/705	11.8%	6.6	1.1	$16.7	$347.4	908
7. University of California–Berkeley	89	4.3	4.6	578/618	22.4%	8.6	1.1	$14.9	$480.3	431
University of Washington	89	3.9	3.7	585/603	32.2%	3.8	0.5	$29.0	$509.3	1,079
9. University of Michigan–Ann Arbor	88	4.3	4.3	585/693	19.9%	5.4	0.9	$15.3	$300.8	500
10. University of Pennsylvania	86	3.9	4.4	592/668	21.5%	3.7	0.9	$15.0	$374.6	1,040
University of Texas–Austin	86	4.0	4.3	526/599	41.0%	4.6	1.1	$41.6	$340.9	1,288
12. Northwestern University (IL)	85	3.8	4.2	621/719	12.2%	2.7	0.2	$9.8	$410.2	332
University of Wisconsin–Madison	85	4.3	4.5	535/610	42.8%	3.2	0.5	$22.6	$145.1	1,168
14. Michigan State University	80	4.2	4.2	526/599	46.6%	4.4	0.6	$22.8	$191.8	1,658
New York University (Steinhardt)	80	3.8	4.1	589/638	15.7%	2.3	0.4	$24.7	$143.3	3,522
16. Ohio State University	79	4.0	4.1	524/609	43.1%	2.1	0.7	$27.8	$192.9	1,206
17. University of Minnesota–Twin Cities	78	3.9	3.9	547/628	46.5%	4.0	0.7	$28.9	$155.3	2,615
18. Boston College (Lynch)	77	3.7	4.2	568/648	12.1%	4.9	0.9	$12.8	$242.1	858
19. Indiana University–Bloomington	76	4.0	4.2	548/646	41.0%	5.4	0.8	$17.9	$176.8	1,192
20. Johns Hopkins University (MD)	74	3.8	4.5	N/A/N/A	43.5%	0.3	0.1	$11.2	$400.0	2,260
21. University of Connecticut (Neag)	73	3.7	3.9	590/658	23.4%	2.1	0.8	$11.7	$201.1	810
22. University of Kansas	72	3.6	3.8	470/590	65.5%	3.2	0.7	$26.9	$327.6	1,210
University of North Carolina–Chapel Hill	72	3.8	4.1	573/661	30.2%	4.3	0.9	$10.4	$216.0	637
24. Utah State University	71	3.0	3.4	532/583	40.0%	1.3	0.3	$34.4	$299.6	1,073
25. Arizona State University	70	3.7	4.2	540/637	24.7%	4.9	0.9	$11.7	$140.5	1,299
University of Georgia	70	3.8	4.2	544/615	34.0%	2.8	0.5	$15.6	$83.3	2,471
University of Illinois–Urbana-Champaign	70	4.1	4.1	567/705	44.2%	4.1	0.9	$6.9	$70.8	1,148
University of Maryland–College Park	70	3.9	3.9	539/626	32.9%	5.6	0.7	$14.5	$152.7	1,226
29. George Washington University (DC)	69	3.4	4.1	559/576	51.0%	6.1	1.4	$15.1	$369.1	2,045
30. Pennsylvania State University–University Park	68	3.9	4.0	535/642	27.8%	4.5	1.2	$12.0	$115.6	1,124
31. University of Colorado–Boulder	67	3.6	4.0	609/693	29.3%	2.1	0.5	$3.5	$116.8	339
University of Delaware	67	3.2	3.5	658/624	33.0%	3.0	0.7	$12.4	$282.9	583
University of Iowa	67	3.6	3.8	508/614	49.5%	4.3	0.6	$15.0	$180.7	788
University of Virginia (Curry)	67	4.0	4.0	549/598	55.5%	3.8	0.9	$9.4	$107.8	834
35. University of Tennessee–Knoxville	66	3.2	4.0	535/671	56.4%	1.5	0.3	$17.5	$141.4	635
36. Rutgers, the State U. of New Jersey–New Brunswick	65	3.4	4.0	536/609	27.8%	2.3	0.4	$7.0	$142.3	1,014
University of Pittsburgh	65	3.5	4.0	488/556	70.6%	3.1	1.0	$15.3	$247.1	1,282
38. University of Southern California (Rossier)	63	3.8	3.9	513/571	50.7%	15.7	5.3	$12.2	$487.5	1,069
Washington University in St. Louis	63	3.4	3.9	601/674 *	33.3%	0.8	0.4	$1.6	$202.0	22
40. Cornell University (NY)	62	3.4	4.4	612/632	38.1%	2.5	0.3	$.8	$64.3	71
Lehigh University (PA)	62	2.9	3.6	540/620	14.4%	3.1	0.5	$8.3	$319.9	639
Texas A&M University–College Station	62	3.6	3.8	482/545	61.9%	3.2	0.9	$16.0	$134.7	1,294
University of Illinois–Chicago	62	3.4	3.8	486/526	49.4%	2.2	0.4	$11.6	$228.1	635
Virginia Commonwealth University	62	2.9	3.2	503/539	48.1%	1.7	0.3	$16.7	$371.2	1,729
45. Florida State University	61	3.3	3.9	482/617	43.9%	3.0	0.4	$16.1	$156.2	1,249
University of Massachusetts–Amherst	61	3.4	4.1	533/597	47.7%	4.2	0.5	$6.0	$111.4	836
University of Miami (FL)	61	3.1	3.9	542/617	20.8%	2.8	0.3	$8.5	$243.5	310
University of Missouri–Columbia	61	3.5	3.6	501/592	44.1%	3.7	0.7	$13.0	$149.1	2,054
University of South Florida	61	2.9	3.5	481/542	59.8%	2.2	0.4	$28.5	$237.7	2,030
50. Temple University (PA)	60	3.1	3.9	534/563	36.3%	2.2	1.1	$14.4	$265.8	760

[1]GRE scores are for doctoral students only. [2]Student/faculty ratio is for all full-time equivalent doctoral students and full-time faculty. N/A means not available. *The school could not break out GRE scores for doctoral students; average scores for all entering students are shown. Sources: *U.S. News* and the schools. Assessment data collected by Synovate.

PROGRAMS RANKED BEST BY EDUCATION SCHOOL DEANS

ADMINISTRATION/SUPERVISION
1. Vanderbilt University (Peabody) (TN)
2. University of Wisconsin–Madison
3. Harvard University (MA)
4. Pennsylvania State University–University Park
   Stanford University (CA)
6. Ohio State University
   University of Texas–Austin
8. Teachers College, Columbia University (NY)
9. University of Southern California (Rossier)
10. Indiana University–Bloomington

COUNSELING/PERSONNEL SERVICES
1. University of Maryland–College Park
2. University of Wisconsin–Madison
3. University of Florida
4. Ohio State University
   University of North Carolina–Greensboro
6. University of Georgia
7. University of Minnesota–Twin Cities
8. University of Missouri–Columbia
9. Indiana University–Bloomington
10. Pennsylvania State University–University Park

CURRICULUM/INSTRUCTION
1. University of Wisconsin–Madison
2. Michigan State University
3. Stanford University (CA)
4. Teachers College, Columbia University (NY)
5. University of Illinois–Urbana-Champaign
6. Ohio State University
7. University of Michigan–Ann Arbor
8. University of Georgia
9. Indiana University–Bloomington
10. Vanderbilt University (Peabody) (TN)

EDUCATIONAL PSYCHOLOGY
1. University of Wisconsin–Madison
2. Stanford University (CA)
3. University of Michigan–Ann Arbor

4. University of Illinois–Urbana-Champaign
5. Michigan State University
6. University of California–Berkeley
7. University of Maryland–College Park
8. University of Minnesota–Twin Cities
9. University of California–Los Angeles
   Vanderbilt University (Peabody) (TN)

EDUCATION POLICY
1. Stanford University (CA)
2. Harvard University (MA)
3. University of Wisconsin–Madison
4. Vanderbilt University (Peabody) (TN)
5. Teachers College, Columbia University (NY)
6. University of Michigan–Ann Arbor
7. University of Pennsylvania
8. Michigan State University
   Pennsylvania State University–University Park
10. University of California–Los Angeles

ELEMENTARY EDUCATION
1. Michigan State University
2. University of Wisconsin–Madison
3. Teachers College, Columbia University (NY)
   University of Georgia
5. Vanderbilt University (Peabody) (TN)
6. Ohio State University
7. Indiana University–Bloomington
   University of Virginia (Curry)
9. University of Michigan–Ann Arbor
10. University of Illinois–Urbana-Champaign

HIGHER EDUCATION ADMINISTRATION
1. University of Michigan–Ann Arbor
2. Pennsylvania State University–University Park
3. University of California–Los Angeles
4. Michigan State University
5. University of Southern California (Rossier)

6. Indiana University–Bloomington
7. University of Georgia
8. Vanderbilt University (Peabody) (TN)
9. University of Pennsylvania
10. Harvard University (MA)
    University of Maryland–College Park

SECONDARY EDUCATION
1. Michigan State University
2. University of Wisconsin–Madison
3. Stanford University (CA)
4. University of Georgia
5. University of Virginia (Curry)
6. University of Michigan–Ann Arbor
7. Ohio State University
   Teachers College, Columbia University (NY)
9. University of Illinois–Urbana-Champaign
10. University of California–Berkeley
    Vanderbilt University (Peabody) (TN)

SPECIAL EDUCATION
1. University of Kansas
2. Vanderbilt University (Peabody) (TN)
3. University of Oregon
4. University of Florida
   University of Illinois–Urbana-Champaign
   University of Texas–Austin
7. University of Minnesota–Twin Cities
8. University of Virginia (Curry)
9. University of Wisconsin–Madison
10. University of Maryland–College Park

VOCATIONAL/TECHNICAL
1. Ohio State University
2. Pennsylvania State University–University Park
3. University of Georgia
4. University of Minnesota–Twin Cities
5. Virginia Tech

Graduate programs at 278 schools granting doctoral degrees were surveyed. Of those, 245 responded; 242 provided the data needed to calculate rankings based on a weighted average of the 11 quality measures described here.

Quality assessment (weighted by .40): Two surveys were conducted in the fall of 2007. Education school deans and deans of graduate studies were asked to rate program quality from "marginal" (1) to "outstanding" (5). Forty-seven percent responded. The resulting score is weighted by .25. School superintendents nationwide in a sampling of districts were also asked to rate programs. Twenty-four percent responded; their opinions are weighted by .15.

Student selectivity (.18): This combines mean verbal and quantitative GRE scores of doctoral students entering in fall 2007 and the acceptance rate of doctoral applicants for the 2007–2008 academic year (.06 each). Where mean GRE scores are not available for doctoral students, mean GRE scores for all entering students may be substituted, if available.

Faculty resources (.12): Resources include the 2007 ratio of all full-time equivalent doctoral students to full-time faculty (.045); the average percentage of full-time faculty holding awards or editorships among selected education journals in the past two years (.025); and the ratio of doctoral degrees granted to full-time faculty in the past school year (.05).

Research activity (.30): This measure uses average total education school research expenditures (.15) and the average research expenditures per full-time faculty member (.15). Expenditures refer to separately funded research, public and private, conducted by the school, averaged over fiscal years 2006 and 2007.

Overall rank: Data were standardized about their means, and standardized scores were weighted, totaled, and rescaled so that the top school received 100; other schools received their percentage of the top score.

Specialty rankings: These specialty ratings are based solely on nominations by education school deans and deans of graduate studies. They were asked to choose up to 10 top programs noted for excellence in each specialty area. Those with the most votes are listed.

Teacher Preparation at the Top Education Schools

Below, you'll find key information about teacher-prep programs at the top 50 *U.S. News* education schools, listed alphabetically. This table is not a ranking of these programs. Key attributes to consider when choosing a program include how many instructors are engaged in teacher prep, whether students intern in a professional development school that is closely tied to the university, and whether peer working groups are organized for student teachers.

School	Nationally accredited[1]	Type of education school: undergrad/grad	'07 enrollment in graduate teaching programs	Alternative route to licensure program	Students trained in professional development school	Students assigned to peer working groups	'07 full-time faculty engaged in teaching programs	Preparation offered for national certification
Arizona State University	No	U and G	728	Yes	All	All	43	Yes
Boston College (Lynch)	No	U and G	306	No	All	All	20	No
Cornell University (NY)	No	U and G	24	No	No	All	8	No
Florida State University	Yes	U and G	498	No	Some	Some	43	No
George Washington University (DC)	Yes	Grad	490	Yes	Some	Some	15	Yes
Harvard University (MA)	No	Grad	48	No	All	All	9	Yes
Indiana University–Bloomington	Yes	U and G	309	Yes	Some	Some	68	No
Johns Hopkins University (MD)	Yes	Grad	564	Yes	Some	All	6	No
Lehigh University (PA)	No	Grad	149	No	Some	Some	11	No
Michigan State University	No	U and G	765	No	All	All	67	No
New York University (Steinhardt)	Yes	U and G	837	No	All	All	57	No
Northwestern University (IL)	No	U and G	N/A	Yes	All	All	8	No
Ohio State University	Yes	U and G	734	No	Some	All	115	Yes
Pennsylvania State University–University Park	Yes	U and G	89	Yes	All	All	87	No
Rutgers, the State U. of New Jersey–New Brunswick	No	Grad	445	No	No	All	50	No
Stanford University (CA)	Yes	Grad	75	No	All	All	15	Yes
Teachers College, Columbia University (NY)	Yes	Grad	1,589	Yes	Some	All	80	No
Temple University (PA)	No	U and G	N/A	No	Some	Some	N/A	Yes
Texas A&M University–College Station	Yes	U and G	N/A	Yes	All	All	38	No
University of California–Berkeley	No	Grad	103	No	All	All	31	No
University of California–Los Angeles	No	Grad	354	Yes	All	All	10	Yes
University of Colorado–Boulder	Yes	Grad	N/A	No	Some	All	23	No
University of Connecticut (Neag)	Yes	U and G	150	No	All	All	29	No
University of Delaware	Yes	U and G	270	Yes	Some	Some	43	No
University of Georgia	Yes	U and G	927	Yes	All	Some	111	No
University of Illinois–Chicago	No	U and G	243	No	No	All	29	No
University of Illinois–Urbana-Champaign	No	U and G	164	Yes	All	All	57	Yes
University of Iowa	No	Grad	274	No	No	Some	35	Yes
University of Kansas	Yes	U and G	298	Yes	Some	Some	28	No
University of Maryland–College Park	Yes	U and G	173	Yes	All	All	44	Yes
University of Massachusetts–Amherst	Yes	U and G	215	No	Some	Some	21	No
University of Miami (FL)	Yes	U and G	98	Yes	All	Some	15	No
University of Michigan–Ann Arbor	No	U and G	109	No	Some	All	21	No
University of Minnesota–Twin Cities	Yes	U and G	862	Yes	Some	All	191	No
University of Missouri–Columbia	Yes	U and G	N/A	Yes	All	Some	81	No
University of North Carolina–Chapel Hill	Yes	U and G	283	Yes	Some	All	42	No
University of Oregon	No	Grad	246	No	Some	Some	16	No
University of Pennsylvania	No	Grad	455	Yes	Some	All	6	No
University of Pittsburgh	No	Grad	323	Yes	Some	All	24	No
University of South Florida	Yes	U and G	865	No	All	All	N/A	Yes
University of Southern California (Rossier)	No	U and G	N/A	No	All	All	27	No
University of Tennessee–Knoxville	Yes	U and G	N/A	Yes	All	All	112	No
University of Texas–Austin	No	U and G	87	Yes	All	Some	41	No
University of Virginia (Curry)	Yes	U and G	201	No	All	All	26	No
University of Washington	No	Grad	144	No	All	All	40	Yes
University of Wisconsin–Madison	No	U and G	400	No	Some	Some	154	Yes
Utah State University	Yes	U and G	809	Yes	No	All	124	Yes
Vanderbilt University (Peabody) (TN)	Yes	U and G	108	Yes	Some	All	34	No
Virginia Commonwealth University	Yes	U and G	N/A	Yes	Some	Some	34	Yes
Washington University in St. Louis	No	U and G	16	Yes	Some	All	7	No

[1]Denotes schools that are accredited by the National Council for Accreditation of Teacher Education, with the exception of New York University and the University of Virginia, which are accredited by the Teacher Education Accreditation Council. Accreditation status as of February 2008.
N/A means not available. Sources: *U.S. News* and the schools

A Classic Discipline on the Move

From rocket science to nanotechnology, mechanical engineering shows it's still going places

By Thomas K. Grose

A road test for applied engineering: Ewan Pritchard and Advanced Energy's plug-in hybrid school bus

During a childhood visit to the National Air and Space Museum in Washington, D.C., Margaret Anderson caught the space-travel bug. She knew then and there she wanted to work for NASA.

It wasn't just a passing fancy. Now 21, Anderson is a student at the Rochester Institute of Technology, working simultaneously on her master's and bachelor's degrees in mechanical engineering. And she's living her dream. Anderson is employed at the space agency through a student co-op program and is working on hybrid rockets—experimental power plants that combine solid and liquid fuel technologies to find a cheaper, safer way into space.

If it sounds counterintuitive that a fledgling rocket scientist is earning degrees in mechanical engineering, it seemed that way to Anderson at first. She admits she was initially "disappointed" that RIT has made aerospace engineering part of its mechanical engineering program. Now, though, she's "really glad I decided to do it." Mechanical engineering, she says, has given her a wider understanding of engineering, and that has helped her grapple with the myriad issues involved in rocket technology.

Rocket science. Mechanical engineering is all about designing, building, and maintaining machines of all types and sizes. It's an engineering classic, dating to the early days of the industrial revolution, when engineering know-how was needed to harness the potential of the steam engine. But despite its 19th-century pedigree, M.E. is today at the heart of many cutting-edge technologies.

That makes it a hot choice for students. It's by far the most popular undergraduate degree in engineering; according to the American Society for Engineering Education, 16,063 undergrad degrees were awarded in 2006. At the graduate level, it's the third-most-popular discipline among engineering master's and is back in first place among doctorates.

Why the demand? M.E. students have to master key elements of chemical, civil, and electrical engineering, as well as physics and advanced mathematics, particularly calculus. "The breadth of mechanical engineering is unique," explains Larry Silverberg, the associate head of the mechanical and aerospace engineering program at North Carolina State University. "And, no question, that's a selling point."

That's particularly true for M.E. students who go to graduate school, with its focus on a narrow area of study. The broadness of the degree means they have a wide array of possibilities to choose from. Traditionally, many mechanical engineers headed for automotive and aerospace, but energy, robotics, and bioengineering are growth areas, too, as is nanotechnology—which is, after all, the manipulation of particles at the nanolevel to build microsize machines.

Silverberg singles out three sectors critical to America's future: energy, security and defense, and healthcare. "Mechanical engineering plays a big role in all three of those," he says.

Ewan Pritchard, who is completing his Ph.D. in mechanical engineering at North Carolina State, is head of the hybrid program at Advanced Energy, a company that recently unveiled the first commercially available plug-in hybrid

Smart Choices

Agricultural Engineering. Food shortages plague the world, yet more arable land is needed to grow crops for biofuels. Someone has to solve this conundrum. **Nuclear Engineering.** Controversial? You bet. But nuclear's coming back after more than 20 years in the shadow cast by Three Mile Island and Chernobyl.

vehicle, a school bus. He's passionate about developing alternative-fuel vehicles, which is why M.E. was his choice.

"The coming decade is going to be the decade of energy, and when you think energy, you think mechanical engineering," says Pritchard, 35. That's because, as Iowa State University M.E. Prof. Robert C. Brown explains, mechanical engineers are not only experts in thermodynamics—the study and uses of energy—they know how to apply its laws to bring machines to life.

There are four main subdisciplines within M.E.—thermodynamics and fluids, solid mechanics, dynamics and controls, and manufacturing—so students learn early on to work on interdisciplinary teams. And cross-disciplinary research dominates both academia and industry today. "Most of the best research is at the edges of disciplines," where they abut one another, says Joseph Beaman, chairman of the M.E. department at the University of Texas–Austin. Many M.E. departments also encourage students to take biology and business classes to enhance their multidisciplinary capacity.

We're No. 1. The range of skills common to mechanical engineering graduates also goes over well in the job market. At Austin, many M.E. students are top prospects on the wish lists of companies scouting prospective hires. Edward Hensel, head of mechanical engineering at RIT, says "there's a powerful, pent-up demand in industry for mechanical engineers. In more than 20 years as a teacher, I've not seen the like of it before."

Research money is plentiful too, in part because of recent increases in National Science Foundation funding for the physical sciences and engineering. Silverberg says these have particularly favored M.E. "because so many of the critical problems in the forefront now lie in the area of mechanical engineering." His department's research expenditures increased 25 percent over the past five years to $8 million a year. Indeed, North Carolina State recently added two new graduate classes—one in nanomechanics, the other in biofluids—to accommodate M.E.'s increasing involvement in nanotechnology and the life sciences.

Anderson, meanwhile, should have her master's completed by spring 2009 and expects to eventually earn a doctorate, too. She's also adamant she wants to keep working at NASA: "It's better than I had hoped. I've really enjoyed it; I really feel it's the right place for me." Clearly, it's mission accomplished for Anderson's girlhood dream, thanks in large part to her mechanical engineering education. ●

REALITY CHECK SOURCES: AMERICAN SOCIETY FOR ENGINEERING EDUCATION (2007 REPORT); NATIONAL SOCIETY FOR PROFESSIONAL ENGINEERS (2008 DATA)

Insider Tip

Most M.E. grad students have an undergrad degree in the same field. Still, a fair number of non-engineering students, often with degrees in physics and math, opt for mechanical engineering at grad school. It can be a tough transition. Robert C. Brown, an M.E. prof at Iowa State with a B.S. in physics and a B.A. in math, suggests that if you're a science or math major heading into thermal systems research, take classes in fluid dynamics and heat transfer; if you're doing mechanical systems research, look for courses in materials, mechanical design, and controls.

Getting In

Be Open. Joseph Beaman, mechanical engineering department chairman at the University of Texas-Austin, says too many letters of application read as if they were written by formula. As a result, they're uninspiring. Don't be afraid to show some passion, he says: "The ones that stand out seem heartfelt; they're not templates."

Show Innovation. Beaman suggests undergraduates should enter design competitions or work on research. Robert C. Brown at Iowa State agrees and says even freshmen should seek out lab experience: "It's never too early to look into it."

Do Relevant Work. Brown says that grad schools, like industry, value students with work experience—particularly if the work has some relevance to mechanical engineering. That rules out flipping burgers, pouring drafts, or selling trendy clothes at the mall. If you can't find work in a campus lab or an industry co-op, he suggests construction work—where you have to get your fingernails dirty and build things.

Reality Check

Increase in doctoral degrees awarded, past year: 13.8%. Increase in doctoral degrees awarded, past five years: 37% • Top master's engineering discipline: electrical, 5,256 degrees. Second: computer science (within engineering): 5,197. Third: mechanical engineering: 4,637 • Most popular doctoral discipline: mechanical, 1,132 degrees. Second: electrical/computer: 1,112. Third: electrical: 939 • Average starting salary for engineers with master's: $54,208. For engineers with doctorates: $73,752. Average salary with 10 to 14 years' experience: $82,151

Bubbling to the top: Iowa State University's Experimental Multiphase Flow Lab

Schools of Engineering

Rank/School	Overall score	Peer assessment score (5.0=highest)	Recruiter assessment score (5.0=highest)	'07 average quantitative GRE score	'07 accept- ance rate	'07 Ph.D. students/ faculty	'07 faculty membership in National Academy of Engineering	'07 engineering school research expenditures (in millions)	'07 research expenditures per faculty member (in thousands)	Ph.D.'s granted 2006- 2007	'07 total graduate engineering enrollment
1. Massachusetts Institute of Technology	100	4.9	4.8	777	23.5%	4.2	12.7%	$237.7	$642.5	328	2,636
2. Stanford University (CA)	98	4.8	4.7	780	28.0%	6.7	17.5%	$152.3	$735.6	276	3,229
3. University of California–Berkeley	89	4.8	4.6	772	20.4%	5.9	19.8%	$120.3	$507.6	223	1,780
4. Georgia Institute of Technology	86	4.5	4.4	767	36.8%	4.1	4.8%	$219.4	$458.0	366	4,303
5. University of Illinois–Urbana-Champaign	83	4.5	4.4	774	19.2%	4.1	3.9%	$195.2	$482.0	270	2,479
6. California Institute of Technology	81	4.7	4.6	800	13.1%	4.6	9.1%	$84.9	$894.2	112	536
7. Carnegie Mellon University (PA)	79	4.2	4.3	765	21.8%	4.4	9.1%	$161.5	$744.4	137	1,698
8. University of Southern California (Viterbi)	77	3.5	3.6	753	46.6%	5.3	17.1%	$165.0	$993.7	144	3,945
9. Cornell University (NY)	75	4.3	4.2	775	19.8%	4.3	10.9%	$108.0	$562.3	128	1,378
University of Michigan–Ann Arbor	75	4.4	4.1	770	36.4%	3.9	3.8%	$147.8	$473.6	255	2,416
11. University of California–San Diego (Jacobs)	72	3.7	3.9	765	25.0%	4.7	9.7%	$141.0	$834.2	132	1,213
University of Texas–Austin (Cockrell)	72	4.2	4.0	759	22.5%	3.4	8.6%	$135.2	$565.8	191	2,100
13. Texas A&M University–College Station (Look)	69	3.7	3.8	756	37.2%	2.6	2.9%	$205.7	$699.7	173	2,428
University of California–Los Angeles (Samueli)	69	3.8	3.9	768	36.0%	5.2	14.1%	$86.3	$567.7	157	1,388
15. Purdue University–West Lafayette (IN)	68	4.1	4.3	751	32.5%	3.5	3.7%	$133.8	$399.5	228	2,323
University of Wisconsin–Madison	68	4.1	3.9	781	23.5%	3.5	3.9%	$125.6	$570.9	139	1,524
17. University of Maryland–College Park (Clark)	66	3.7	3.6	758	22.5%	3.8	6.4%	$136.1	$594.1	182	1,862
18. Princeton University (NJ)	65	4.1	4.4	783	16.5%	4.0	13.0%	$52.9	$434.0	88	519
19. University of California–Santa Barbara	64	3.5	3.6	773	28.3%	4.2	15.3%	$92.3	$688.8	95	724
20. Northwestern University (McCormick) (IL)	63	3.9	4.0	779	28.1%	3.9	5.0%	$97.1	$542.3	110	1,255
21. Columbia University (Fu Foundation) (NY)	62	3.6	3.5	775	27.6%	4.2	10.9%	$87.2	$636.7	93	1,433
22. Harvard University (MA)	60	3.5	3.7	775	13.0%	5.5	14.3%	$37.9	$642.4	47	355
23. Pennsylvania State University–University Park	58	3.8	3.8	752	31.9%	3.2	0.9%	$111.6	$353.2	167	1,720
24. University of Florida	57	3.4	3.6	758	39.6%	4.4	2.5%	$108.1	$376.8	187	2,474
University of Minnesota–Twin Cities	57	3.7	3.6	766	32.8%	4.0	5.4%	$84.1	$398.6	144	1,790
University of Washington	57	3.7	3.6	736	28.8%	3.8	4.9%	$97.4	$502.0	111	1,423
27. Johns Hopkins University (Whiting) (MD)	56	3.9	3.9	768	24.4%	4.5	2.3%	$56.9	$421.6	69	2,661
28. Virginia Tech	55	3.7	3.8	749	21.6%	2.6	2.3%	$107.3	$310.9	139	1,807
29. Ohio State University	54	3.5	3.5	762	37.4%	2.9	2.4%	$113.4	$448.4	119	1,347
30. North Carolina State University	53	3.4	3.5	756	26.6%	2.9	3.8%	$104.4	$341.3	138	2,125
University of Pennsylvania	53	3.5	3.5	759	35.0%	3.8	7.7%	$51.1	$527.0	69	1,111
32. Rensselaer Polytechnic Institute (NY)	52	3.5	3.8	752	31.1%	3.0	3.7%	$85.2	$535.8	114	1,052
University of California–Davis	52	3.4	3.6	749	35.6%	4.3	5.5%	$68.3	$369.4	111	1,124
University of Rochester (NY)	52	2.7	2.9	769	15.5%	3.8	3.7%	$91.7	$1,104.9	46	451
35. Duke University (NC)	51	3.5	3.5	767	34.1%	3.6	1.8%	$63.6	$558.3	63	648
Rice University (Brown) (TX)	51	3.6	3.7	768	15.2%	4.2	5.5%	$34.8	$328.8	56	521
37. University of California–Irvine (Samueli)	50	3.1	3.5	758	25.8%	4.1	5.5%	$66.2	$427.1	92	984
38. University of Virginia	48	3.3	3.4	749	19.4%	3.4	6.6%	$55.3	$397.6	72	737
39. University of Colorado–Boulder	46	3.2	3.3	757	57.6%	3.5	6.3%	$51.3	$332.9	92	1,298
Yale University (CT)	46	3.3	3.4	772	14.8%	2.8	10.2%	$20.8	$269.6	20	172
41. Iowa State University	45	3.2	3.5	759	21.9%	2.5	1.0%	$65.4	$319.1	82	956
42. Lehigh University (Rossin) (PA)	44	3.0	3.5	767	22.1%	3.2	9.3%	$33.0	$287.0	43	568
Vanderbilt University (TN)	44	3.1	3.3	754	12.5%	3.9	1.2%	$46.4	$566.0	39	406
44. Boston University	43	2.8	3.0	763	26.3%	3.3	4.0%	$70.2	$579.8	68	664
45. Arizona State University (Fulton)	42	3.0	3.2	763	51.2%	3.2	3.1%	$53.4	$279.4	109	2,019
46. University of Delaware	41	2.9	3.3	748	27.4%	3.6	3.3%	$43.9	$369.2	70	629
Washington University in St. Louis (Sever)	41	3.2	3.5	768	14.7%	3.1	2.2%	$19.7	$223.4	42	759
48. University of Pittsburgh	40	2.9	3.3	731	35.8%	2.6	1.6%	$62.1	$517.6	49	641
49. Case Western Reserve University (OH)	39	3.2	3.5	732	34.2%	2.2	1.8%	$36.7	$319.3	48	612
University of Massachusetts–Amherst	39	2.9	3.3	760	22.4%	3.0	N/A	$45.0	$308.0	71	665
University of Notre Dame (IN)	39	3.1	3.5	763	20.8%	3.6	1.0%	$18.4	$187.8	56	401

Sources: *U.S. News*, the schools. Assessment data collected by Synovate.

MORE AT WWW.USNEWS.COM

PROGRAMS RANKED BEST BY ENGINEERING SCHOOL DEPARTMENT HEADS

Rank/School	Average assessment score (5.0=highest)
AEROSPACE/AERONAUTICAL/ASTRONAUTICAL	
1. Massachusetts Institute of Technology	4.7
2. California Institute of Technology	4.6
Stanford University (CA)	4.6
4. Georgia Institute of Technology	4.3
5. Purdue University–West Lafayette (IN)	4.1
University of Michigan–Ann Arbor	4.1
7. University of Illinois–Urbana-Champaign	4.0
8. Cornell University (NY)	3.7
Princeton University (NJ)	3.7
Texas A&M University–College Station (Look)	3.7
University of Maryland–College Park (Clark)	3.7
University of Texas–Austin (Cockrell)	3.7
BIOMEDICAL/BIOENGINEERING	
1. Johns Hopkins University (Whiting) (MD)	4.7
2. Georgia Institute of Technology	4.6
University of California–San Diego (Jacobs)	4.6
4. Duke University (NC)	4.5
5. University of Washington	4.3
6. Massachusetts Institute of Technology	4.2
7. Boston University	4.0
University of Pennsylvania	4.0
9. Case Western Reserve University (OH)	3.9
Rice University (Brown) (TX)	3.9
CHEMICAL	
1. California Institute of Technology	4.8
Massachusetts Institute of Technology	4.8
University of California–Berkeley	4.8
4. University of Minnesota–Twin Cities	4.7
5. Stanford University (CA)	4.5
University of Wisconsin–Madison	4.5
7. Princeton University (NJ)	4.4
8. University of Texas–Austin (Cockrell)	4.3
9. University of California–Santa Barbara	4.2
10. University of Delaware	4.1
University of Illinois–Urbana-Champaign	4.1
CIVIL	
1. University of California–Berkeley	4.7
University of Illinois–Urbana-Champaign	4.7
3. Stanford University (CA)	4.5
4. Massachusetts Institute of Technology	4.4
University of Texas–Austin (Cockrell)	4.4
6. Georgia Institute of Technology	4.3
7. Purdue University–West Lafayette (IN)	4.2
8. California Institute of Technology	4.1
University of Michigan–Ann Arbor	4.1
10. Cornell University (NY)	4.0
Virginia Tech	4.0
COMPUTER	
1. Massachusetts Institute of Technology	4.9
2. Stanford University (CA)	4.8
University of California–Berkeley	4.8
4. Carnegie Mellon University (PA)	4.7
5. University of Illinois–Urbana-Champaign	4.6
6. University of Michigan–Ann Arbor	4.5
7. California Institute of Technology	4.2
Georgia Institute of Technology	4.2
9. University of Texas–Austin (Cockrell)	4.1
10. Cornell University (NY)	4.0
Princeton University (NJ)	4.0
Purdue University–West Lafayette (IN)	4.0
ELECTRICAL/ELECTRONIC/COMMUNICATIONS	
1. Massachusetts Institute of Technology	5.0
2. Stanford University (CA)	4.9
University of California–Berkeley	4.9
4. University of Illinois–Urbana-Champaign	4.7
5. California Institute of Technology	4.6
6. Georgia Institute of Technology	4.5
University of Michigan–Ann Arbor	4.5

Rank/School	Average assessment score (5.0=highest)
8. Carnegie Mellon University (PA)	4.3
9. Cornell University (NY)	4.2
10. Princeton University (NJ)	4.1
Purdue University–West Lafayette (IN)	4.1
ENVIRONMENTAL/ENVIRONMENTAL HEALTH	
1. Stanford University (CA)	4.6
2. University of California–Berkeley	4.5
3. University of Illinois–Urbana-Champaign	4.3
4. University of Texas–Austin (Cockrell)	4.2
5. University of Michigan–Ann Arbor	4.1
6. Georgia Institute of Technology	4.0
Johns Hopkins University (Whiting) (MD)	4.0
8. California Institute of Technology	3.9
Carnegie Mellon University (PA)	3.9
10. Massachusetts Institute of Technology	3.8
University of North Carolina–Chapel Hill	3.8
Virginia Tech	3.8
INDUSTRIAL/MANUFACTURING	
1. Georgia Institute of Technology	4.8
2. University of Michigan–Ann Arbor	4.4
3. University of California–Berkeley	4.3
4. Stanford University (CA)	4.1
5. Northwestern University (McCormick) (IL)	4.0
Pennsylvania State University–University Park	4.0
7. Virginia Tech	3.9
8. Purdue University–West Lafayette (IN)	3.8
9. Cornell University (NY)	3.7
Texas A&M University–College Station (Look)	3.7
University of Wisconsin–Madison	3.7
MATERIALS	
1. Massachusetts Institute of Technology	4.8
2. University of Illinois–Urbana-Champaign	4.6
3. Northwestern University (McCormick) (IL)	4.5
University of California–Berkeley	4.5
5. University of California–Santa Barbara	4.4
6. Stanford University (CA)	4.3
7. University of Michigan–Ann Arbor	4.2
8. Georgia Institute of Technology	4.1
University of Florida	4.1
10. Cornell University (NY)	4.0
Pennsylvania State University–University Park	4.0
MECHANICAL	
1. Massachusetts Institute of Technology	4.9
2. Stanford University (CA)	4.8
3. University of California–Berkeley	4.7
4. California Institute of Technology	4.6
University of Michigan–Ann Arbor	4.6
6. University of Illinois–Urbana-Champaign	4.5
7. Georgia Institute of Technology	4.4
Purdue University–West Lafayette (IN)	4.4
9. Cornell University (NY)	4.2
10. Princeton University (NJ)	4.0
University of Texas–Austin (Cockrell)	4.0
NUCLEAR	
1. University of Michigan–Ann Arbor	4.5
2. Massachusetts Institute of Technology	4.2
University of Wisconsin–Madison	4.2
4. Texas A&M University–College Station (Look)	3.9
5. Pennsylvania State University–University Park	3.8
University of California–Berkeley	3.8
PETROLEUM	
1. University of Texas–Austin (Cockrell)	4.6
2. Stanford University (CA)	4.2
Texas A&M University–College Station (Look)	4.2
4. University of Tulsa (OK)	4.0
5. Colorado School of Mines	3.4
Pennsylvania State University–University Park	3.4
University of Oklahoma	3.4

Programs at the 198 engineering schools that grant doctoral degrees were surveyed; 193 responded; 192 were eligible to be included in the rankings based on a weighted average of the 10 indicators described below. (All schools are listed in the directory, beginning on Page 129.)

Quality assessment (weighted by .40): Two surveys were conducted in fall 2007. Engineering school deans and deans of graduate studies at engineering schools were each asked to rate program quality from marginal (1) to outstanding (5); 59 percent responded. The resulting score is weighted by .25. Corporate recruiters and company contacts who hire engineers with graduate degrees from previously ranked engineering schools were also asked to rate programs; 29 percent responded. Their opinions are weighted by .15.

Student selectivity (.10): The strength of master's and Ph.D. students entering in fall 2007 was measured by mean GRE quantitative score (67.5 percent) and acceptance rate (32.5 percent).

Faculty resources (.25): Based on the 2007 ratio of full-time doctoral students to full-time faculty (30 percent) and full-time master's students to full-time faculty (15 percent); the proportion of full-time faculty who were members of the National Academy of Engineering in 2007 (30 percent); and the number of engineering doctoral degrees granted in the past school year (25 percent).

Research activity (.25): Based on total externally funded engineering research expenditures (60 percent) and research dollars per full-time tenured and tenure-track engineering faculty member (40 percent). Expenditures refer to separately funded research, public and private, conducted by the school, averaged over fiscal years 2006 and 2007.

Overall rank: Data were standardized about their means, and standardized scores were weighted, totaled, and rescaled so that the top-scoring school received 100; others received their percentage of the top score.

Specialty rankings: These rankings are based solely on assessments by department heads in each specialty area. Department heads in their specialty area rated the other schools that offered the specialty on a 5-point scale. Those schools with the highest average scores appear here. Names of the department heads who were surveyed came from the American Society for Engineering Education.

When a Patient's Life Is on the Line

Critical care medicine finds increasingly that intensivists are just what the doctor ordered

By Matthew Shulman

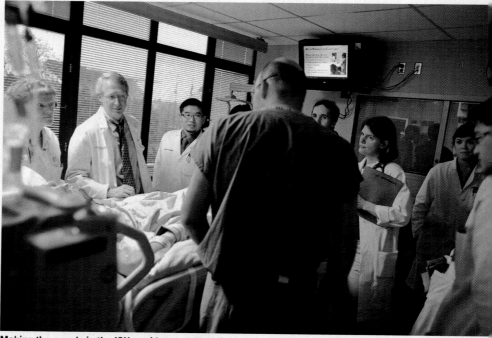

Making the rounds in the ICU: residents at the University of Washington Medical Center in Seattle

Stephen Weston finds everything about the intensive care unit exciting: the life-and-death decisions, the teamwork between specialists, and the head-scratching that goes into treating complex cases. A second-year medical student at the University of California–San Diego, he was introduced to hospital work when he had a job as a respiratory therapist. Now he's found a specialty that will put him squarely in the ICU: critical care medicine.

Physicians with specialized training in critical care, known as intensivists, treat some of the most seriously ill patients in the hospital—those on ventilators or dialysis and those with multiple organ failure. After med school, Weston plans to do a residency in anesthesiology followed by a yearlong fellowship in critical care medicine.

Ever since critical care was recognized as a specialty in the 1980s, hospitals, physicians, and patients have been reaping its benefits. Studies have shown that full-time intensivists, devoted solely to critically ill ICU patients, can trim the length of hospital stays, reduce medical errors, and improve mortality. According to Robb Glenny, a pulmonary critical care specialist at the University of Washington: "That's a win-win situation all around—reducing costs for hospitals and benefiting the patients' survival."

Indeed, the insurance industry has taken notice. The Leapfrog Group, a consortium of large businesses and organizations that includes GE and IBM and promotes healthcare quality and safety, supports the widespread adoption of intensivist-led ICUs. "The intensivist brings an expertise not only to the medical management of acutely ill patients but also [to] the integration of and coordination with other physicians and surgeons," says Peter Pronovost, a professor of anesthesia critical care at Johns Hopkins Medical School and a medical adviser to the Leapfrog Group. The result? A previously "unheard of" 30 percent reduction in mortality, he says.

Single focus. Intensivists have been able to accomplish this by pioneering new standards and protocols in ICU treatment. Specialists point to the dramatic improvement of acute lung illness and injury with advancements in ventilation and lung volume control strategies developed by critical care specialists. Intensivists have more time to devote to ICU patients without the added stress of seeing patients on other floors or off site. This has helped patients with diseases ranging from pulmonary embolism—a blockage of the artery leading from the heart to the lungs—to liver failure and even pneumonia.

With aging baby boomers as its driving force, demand will remain high for more than a decade as hospitals make the switch to intensivist-managed ICUs and as more and more payers insist they have full-time critical care physicians on staff. "Even if we doubled the number of fellowships over the next 10 years, there still wouldn't be enough intensivists to meet the job market's needs," says Gerald Maccioli, president of the American Society of Critical Care Anesthesiologists. If current trends continue, there could be a shortage of intensivists by 2020.

From a lifestyle point of view, part of

Smart Choices

Medical Genetics. Alfred Gilman, dean of University of Texas Southwestern Medical School, says DNA breakthroughs will bring better therapy via personalized and preventive medicine (story, Page 12). That also means more Interdisciplinary Medicine, combining genetics, genomics, and computational biology.

critical care's appeal, says Derek Angus, chairman of the department of critical care medicine at the University of Pittsburgh, is its reinvention as a shift specialty, much like emergency medicine or trauma surgery, with concrete hours—when you're done, you're done. And with a competitive starting salary of around $187,000—and $215,000 for critical care plus pulmonology—the field is likely to attract even more interest.

Critical care medicine is attractive to physicians from a range of medical backgrounds, a feature many experts believe makes for superior patient care and, ultimately, better outcomes in the ICU. While more than 80 percent of intensivists come from internal medicine, those with residency training in general surgery, anesthesiology, pediatrics, and obstetrics and gynecology, can obtain a fellowship or certification in critical care medicine.

Taking charge. Although the ICU is hardly the boardroom, critical care training programs focus increasingly on developing managerial skills. "Intensivists need to be leaders during medical crises, managing a whole cadre of nurses, pharmacists, and respiratory therapists," says Angus. Beyond the medical staff, the intensivist must coordinate with social workers and case managers to help patients' families. "When patients are that sick, it's not only a crisis of the body but a crisis of the family. And intensivists are able to develop deep bonds with them in a relatively short period of time," notes Stephen Frankel, section head of critical care and hospital medicine at National Jewish Medical and Research Center in Denver.

Pittsburgh's program, one of the first and, with about 40 fellows, one of the largest in the country, now runs simulations in a multilevel facility using actors and "robotic" humans. There, future intensivists practice crisis management and learn how to lead an entire ICU team. In one scenario, an actor playing a patient diagnosed with an aggressive cancer becomes unstable, with multiple organ failure. And just as NFL teams review tape to improve performance, "we use video to evaluate how the fellows perform in an end-of-life situation," says Angus.

The football analogy doesn't stop there. Being an intensivist means keeping a lot of people in the loop, says Frankel. "Some liken it to being the captain of a ship, but I think it's more like being a quarterback." ●

REALITY CHECK SOURCES: NATIONAL RESIDENCY MATCHING PROGRAM; ALLIED PHYSICIANS; ASSOCIATION OF AMERICAN MEDICAL COLLEGES

Insider Tip

Sure, bioethics and humanities courses have been staples of medical school curriculums for years. But sculpting, art observation, improvisation, and dance/movement therapy? At Northwestern University's Feinberg School of Medicine they're not only offered; first- and second-year medical students must take at least one each year. Similarly unconventional courses are cropping up at medical schools across the country, part of a national effort to give future physicians tools to bring their whole selves—not just their brains—to patient care. –Lindsay Lyon

Getting In

First Steps. You may not be a medical student yet, but you'll want to visit the website of the American Medical Student Association. Go to amsa.org/premed for loads of premed offerings, including nationwide chapters for doctor wannabes, conferences, and internship and advocacy opportunities. AMSA also provides opportunities for career development and other benefits for its premed members.

Required Reading. You can't take the Medical College Admission Test without signing a form saying you've read about it first, so look for "MCAT Essentials" at aamc.org. About 70,000 students sit for the exam each year; exam dates are chosen to meet most med school application deadlines, and the goal is to have a testing location within 100 miles of every candidate (at least in this country). Already taken the exam? Check with your med school of choice. Schools generally accept scores dating back two or three years. –M.S.

Reality Check

Average in-state tuition at medical school (public): $20,983; out-of-state: $39,428 • Average tuition (private): $37,800 • In '07, more than 15,500 med school seniors bid for their residencies; nearly 84% got one of their top three choices • Average starting salaries: dermatology: $195,000 plus; gastroenterology: $265,000 plus; ophthalmology (retina): $280,000 plus • Ready for a new baby boom? Obstetrics and gynecology filled 99.5% of its residency positions in '07, up 8.3% since '03 • Share of female med school grads in '07: 49% up from 44% in '02

Med students at Northwestern take unconventional courses to improve their skills.

Schools of Medicine

THE TOP SCHOOLS • RESEARCH

Rank/School	Overall score	Peer assessment score (5.0=highest)	Assessment score by residency directors** (5.0=highest)	'07 average undergrad GPA	'07 average MCAT score	'07 acceptance rate	'07 NIH research grants (in millions)	'07 NIH research grants per faculty member (in thousands)	'07 faculty/ student ratio	'07 out-of-state tuition and fees	'07 total medical school enrollment
1. Harvard University (MA)	100	4.8	4.7	3.81	11.9	4.4%	$1,178.5	$153.9	10.1	$41,861	758
2. Johns Hopkins University (MD)	82	4.8	4.7	3.85	11.8	6.4%	$450.8	$192.9	5.1	$40,669	460
3. Washington University in St. Louis	80	4.7	4.5	3.88	12.5	11.1%	$347.0	$229.9	2.6	$43,380	591
4. University of Pennsylvania	79	4.6	4.4	3.79	11.6	4.2%	$486.8	$225.6	3.7	$42,706	585
5. University of California–San Francisco	78	4.7	4.4	3.73	11.4	4.0%	$442.7	$239.5	3.1	$35,683	594
6. Duke University (NC)	77	4.6	4.6	3.74	11.5	3.7%	$369.4	$221.9	4.1	$41,817	404
University of Washington	77	4.4	4.2	3.68	10.5	5.2%	$579.7	$283.2	2.5	$41,904	826
8. Stanford University (CA)	76	4.5	4.6	3.76	11.6	3.3%	$259.0 *	$337.7 *	1.6	$41,760	472
9. University of California–Los Angeles (Geffen)	73	4.1	4.1	3.78	11.9	4.0%	$426.7	$189.9	3.2	$34,796	693
Yale University (CT)	73	4.3	4.3	3.72	11.3	5.8%	$320.2	$301.3	2.7	$40,770	395
11. Columbia U. Col. of Physicians and Surgeons (NY)	72	4.3	4.3	3.78	11.8	4.1%	$362.3	$176.5	3.2	$45,213	645
University of Michigan–Ann Arbor	72	4.3	4.4	3.74	11.7	6.8%	$320.2	$191.9	2.5	$39,119	671
13. Baylor College of Medicine (TX)	71	3.9	3.9	3.82	11.6	6.0%	$413.1	$225.5	2.7	$25,948	681
14. University of California–San Diego	68	4.0	4.0	3.75	11.0	5.5%	$293.0	$327.0	1.7	$35,204	521
University of Pittsburgh	68	4.2	4.1	3.70	11.4	7.9%	$358.3	$180.9	3.4	$39,856	582
16. University of Chicago (Pritzker)	67	4.0	4.1	3.79	11.6	3.9%	$211.7	$243.3	2.0	$38,658	441
Vanderbilt University (TN)	67	4.1	4.2	3.80	11.5	5.9%	$285.8	$155.9	4.4	$39,511	417
18. Cornell University (Weill) (NY)	65	4.1	4.3	3.70	11.5	4.0%	$239.7	$109.8	5.3	$40,890	410
19. University of North Carolina–Chapel Hill	62	4.0	4.1	3.73	11.0	5.7%	$210.1	$159.2	1.8	$35,585	736
20. Emory University (GA)	60	3.8	4.0	3.70	11.5	8.4%	$209.6	$112.2	3.9	$39,976	480
Northwestern University (Feinberg) (IL)	60	3.8	4.0	3.71	11.4	6.0%	$205.9	$107.1	2.7	$43,140	700
22. U. of Texas Southwestern Medical Center–Dallas	59	4.1	4.1	3.68	10.8	12.3%	$182.7	$109.5	1.8	$25,694	909
23. Case Western Reserve University (OH)	58	3.7	3.8	3.62	11.2	7.6%	$246.4	$124.2	2.8	$43,206	711
Mayo Medical School (MN)	58	3.8	3.8	3.81	11.0	1.5%	$188.7	$78.0	15.1	$29,700	160
Mount Sinai School of Medicine (NY)	58	3.6	3.7	3.64	11.3	5.7%	$210.8	$195.7	2.1	$38,528	506
University of Virginia	58	3.7	3.9	3.70	11.1	13.0%	$174.5 *	$188.4 *	1.7	$41,070	558
27. University of Alabama–Birmingham	56	3.9	3.8	3.71	10.0	11.3%	$180.5	$156.7	1.6	$45,238	716
University of Colorado–Denver	56	3.6	3.7	3.71	11.0	9.3%	$188.3	$124.4	2.5	$48,030	607
University of Wisconsin–Madison	56	3.6	3.7	3.76	10.4	7.6%	$184.0	$179.7	1.7	$33,846	614
30. Ohio State University	55	3.4	3.5	3.74	11.2	8.7%	$237.8	$104.3	2.8	$33,322	819
31. Brown University (Alpert) (RI)	54	3.2	3.7	3.66	11.7	3.5%	$118.3	$167.3	1.9	$41,184	372
Dartmouth Medical School (NH)	54	3.4	3.8	3.74	11.1	5.6%	$87.9	$104.4	2.7	$40,675	316
University of Iowa (Carver)	54	3.6	3.8	3.71	10.5	10.3%	$130.9	$166.5	1.4	$41,719	576
34. New York University	53	3.5	3.6	3.76	11.2	5.7%	$143.4	$92.1	2.3	$43,919	670
35. Oregon Health and Science University	52	3.6	3.6	3.61	10.2	4.8%	$201.4	$124.6	3.2	$42,353	512
36. University of Minnesota Medical School	51	3.5	3.6	3.69	10.4	8.7%	$153.2	$98.3	1.7	$40,423	944
University of Rochester (NY)	51	3.5	3.5	3.63	10.6	7.6%	$162.0	$114.1	3.4	$40,384	414
University of Southern California (Keck)	51	3.3	3.5	3.64	11.1	5.6%	$143.7	$119.6	1.8	$44,240	679
Yeshiva University (Einstein) (NY)	51	3.3	3.4	3.73	10.8	7.3%	$178.2	$68.4	3.5	$43,370	753
40. Georgetown University (DC)	50	3.0	3.6	3.68	10.6	3.5%	$190.2	$116.8	2.1	$42,764	779
University of Cincinnati	50	3.0	3.3	3.67	10.6	8.2%	$196.5	$138.8	2.2	$47,639	634
42. Wake Forest University (NC)	49	3.2	3.5	3.64	10.3	3.7%	$129.0 *	$135.6 *	2.1	$37,134	454
43. Boston University	48	3.2	3.5	3.56	10.0	4.3%	$181.8	$129.9	2.1	$43,234	674
University of California–Irvine	48	2.8	3.3	3.65	10.7	6.1%	$98.9	$207.2	1.2	$36,573	408
University of Maryland	48	3.2	3.3	3.67	10.4	7.0%	$149.1 *	$122.2 *	2.0	$41,101	621
46. Indiana University–Indianapolis	47	3.2	3.5	3.73	10.3	13.5%	$97.3 *	$68.7 *	1.2	$42,894	1,175
Tufts University (MA)	47	3.3	3.7	3.60	10.6	7.2%	$86.4	$56.4	2.2	$47,116	705
48. University of California–Davis	46	3.1	3.4	3.62	10.3	4.7%	$75.4	$120.8	1.6	$37,400	393
University of Florida	46	3.1	3.3	3.70	10.6	8.2%	$91.8	$73.6	2.5	$51,018	509
50. University of Utah	45	3.3	3.5	3.64	9.7	11.0%	$98.6	$90.5	2.6	$38,529	411

*The school reported only research grants that the National Institutes of Health made to the medical school. No grants to affiliated hospitals were reported. ** Results from the previous year's residency directors' survey were used for all schools because of a printing error on the survey instrument. Assessment data collected by Synovate. Sources: *U.S. News* and the schools

Rank/School	Overall score	Peer assessment score (5.0=highest)	Assessment score by residency directors (5.0=highest)	Selectivity rank	'07 average undergrad GPA	'07 average MCAT score	'07 acceptance rate	% '05 - '07 graduates entering primary care	'07 faculty/ student ratio	'07 out-of-state tuition and fees	'07 total medical school enrollment
1. University of Washington	100	4.2	4.0	37	3.68	10.5	5.2%	45.0%	2.5	$41,904	826
2. Oregon Health and Science University	92	3.8	3.9	62	3.61	10.2	4.8%	48.0%	3.2	$42,353	512
University of North Carolina–Chapel Hill	92	3.8	3.4	25	3.73	11.0	5.7%	52.0%	1.8	$35,585	736
4. University of Colorado–Denver	89	3.7	3.6	26	3.71	11.0	9.3%	47.6%	2.5	$48,030	607
5. University of Vermont	86	3.3	3.4	46	3.70	10.2	3.3%	58.6%	1.3	$46,243	431
6. University of California–San Francisco	83	3.7	3.6	13	3.73	11.4	4.0%	37.5%	3.1	$35,683	594
7. Baylor College of Medicine (TX)	81	3.2	3.7	5	3.82	11.6	6.0%	43.1%	2.7	$25,948	681
Harvard University (MA)	81	3.3	3.4	3	3.81	11.9	4.4%	44.0%	10.1	$41,861	758
Mich. State U. Coll. of Osteopathic Medicine	81	2.9	2.8	112	3.55	8.7	11.0%	83.3%	0.3	$60,905	787
University of Iowa (Carver)	81	3.6	3.4	37	3.71	10.5	10.3%	45.0%	1.4	$41,719	576
University of Minnesota Medical School	81	3.5	3.5	42	3.69	10.4	8.7%	45.9%	1.7	$40,423	944
12. University of California–Los Angeles (Geffen)	79	3.3	3.3	4	3.78	11.9	4.0%	44.0%	3.2	$34,796	693
13. Dartmouth Medical School (NH)	78	3.4	3.4	23	3.74	11.1	5.6%	43.1%	2.7	$40,675	316
University of Massachusetts–Worcester	78	3.4	3.3	62	3.59	10.5	22.8%	49.5%	2.1	N/A	435
University of Wisconsin–Madison	78	3.4	3.6	32	3.76	10.4	7.6%	41.3%	1.7	$33,846	614
Washington University in St. Louis	78	3.3	3.3	1	3.88	12.5	11.1%	39.8%	2.6	$43,380	591
17. East Carolina University (Brody) (NC)	77	3.2	3.2	110	3.50	9.1	12.9%	60.0%	1.4	$36,075	293
University of Michigan–Ann Arbor	77	3.5	3.5	11	3.74	11.7	6.8%	36.0%	2.5	$39,119	671
19. University of Rochester (NY)	76	3.6	3.6	42	3.63	10.6	7.6%	35.8%	3.4	$40,384	414
20. University of Nebraska College of Medicine	75	3.0	3.0	70	3.73	9.7	12.1%	60.0%	1.2	$53,910	476
University of Pittsburgh	75	3.4	3.4	20	3.70	11.4	7.9%	38.7%	3.4	$39,856	582
22. Michigan State University	74	3.2	3.6	102	3.51	9.5	6.3%	47.8%	1.2	$60,890	494
23. Brown University (Alpert) (RI)	73	3.1	3.3	13	3.66	11.7	3.5%	44.5%	1.9	$41,184	372
Medical University of South Carolina	73	2.9	3.2	96	3.57	9.7	14.4%	58.7%	1.6	$67,243	620
University of Missouri–Columbia	73	3.1	3.4	37	3.77	10.3	13.5%	46.0%	1.3	$47,492	387
26. Indiana University–Indianapolis	72	3.4	3.4	42	3.73	10.3	13.5%	39.5%	1.2	$42,894	1,175
Johns Hopkins University (MD)	72	3.3	3.3	2	3.85	11.8	6.4%	34.9%	5.1	$40,669	460
University of California–Davis	72	3.3	3.4	53	3.62	10.3	4.7%	42.5%	1.6	$37,400	393
U. of Texas Southwestern Medical Center–Dallas	72	3.3	3.3	32	3.68	10.8	12.3%	42.0%	1.8	$25,694	909
Yeshiva University (Einstein) (NY)	72	2.9	2.9	29	3.73	10.8	7.3%	55.0%	3.5	$43,370	753
31. Ohio State University	71	3.0	3.3	20	3.74	11.2	8.7%	44.5%	2.8	$33,322	819
University of New Mexico	71	3.4	3.2	101	3.61	9.2	8.9%	46.0%	2.2	$42,910	315
University of Pennsylvania	71	3.4	3.1	7	3.79	11.6	4.2%	37.0%	3.7	$42,706	585
University of Utah	71	3.3	3.6	89	3.64	9.7	11.0%	39.1%	2.6	$38,529	411
35. Mayo Medical School (MN)	70	3.3	3.3	15	3.81	11.0	1.5%	36.0%	15.1	$29,700	160
University of Arkansas for Medical Sciences	70	3.0	3.1	89	3.62	9.8	16.1%	53.0%	1.7	$31,962	596
University of California–San Diego	70	3.2	3.2	24	3.75	11.0	5.5%	40.7%	1.7	$35,204	521
University of Maryland	70	3.2	3.3	46	3.67	10.4	7.0%	43.0%	2.0	$41,101	621
University of Virginia	70	3.2	3.4	26	3.70	11.1	13.0%	39.0%	1.7	$41,070	558
Wake Forest University (NC)	70	3.1	3.0	50	3.64	10.3	3.7%	50.0%	2.1	$37,134	454
41. Duke University (NC)	69	3.3	2.9	12	3.74	11.5	3.7%	41.2%	4.1	$41,817	404
Tufts University (MA)	69	3.0	3.2	49	3.60	10.6	7.2%	47.0%	2.2	$45,238	705
43. University of Alabama–Birmingham	68	3.3	3.4	53	3.71	10.0	11.3%	38.0%	1.6	$49,463	716
University of Connecticut	68	3.1	3.2	62	3.65	10.0	5.8%	46.0%	1.3	$42,867	320
University of Kansas Medical Center	68	3.0	3.3	82	3.69	9.5	11.5%	48.1%	0.8	$29,700	712
U. of N. Texas Health Sci. Ctr. (Col. of Oste. Med.)	68	2.6	2.4	105	3.56	9.1	20.1%	76.0%	0.5	$29,700	593
West Virginia School of Osteopathic Medicine	68	2.9	2.7	124	3.44	7.8	18.7%	84.5%	0.1	$49,273	598
48. Emory University (GA)	67	3.2	3.1	17	3.70	11.5	8.4%	37.5%	3.9	$39,976	480
49. Medical College of Wisconsin	66	3.1	3.4	50	3.74	9.9	6.8%	39.0%	1.6	$38,055	795
Vanderbilt University (TN)	66	3.3	3.3	9	3.80	11.5	5.9%	30.0%	4.4	$39,511	417

N/A: The school does not accept out-of-state students to its M.D. program.
Sources: *U.S. News* and the schools. Peer assessment data collected by Synovate.

MEDICAL SCHOOL DEANS AND SENIOR FACULTY SELECT THE BEST PROGRAMS

AIDS
1. University of California– San Francisco
2. Johns Hopkins University (MD)
3. Harvard University (MA)
4. University of Washington
5. Univ. of Alabama–Birmingham
6. Univ. of California–San Diego
7. Columbia U. College of Physicians and Surgeons (NY)
8. Duke University (NC)
9. University of California– Los Angeles (Geffen)
10. University of North Carolina– Chapel Hill

DRUG/ALCOHOL ABUSE
1. Yale University (CT)
2. Columbia U. College of Physicians and Surgeons (NY)
3. Johns Hopkins University (MD)
4. Harvard University (MA)
5. University of California– San Francisco
6. University of Pennsylvania
7. New York University
8. University of Washington
9. Medical University of South Carolina
   University of California– Los Angeles (Geffen)

FAMILY MEDICINE
1. University of Washington
2. Oregon Health and Science University
3. Univ. of Missouri–Columbia
   Univ. of Wisconsin–Madison
5. University of North Carolina– Chapel Hill
6. University of Colorado–Denver
7. University of Michigan– Ann Arbor
8. University of California– San Francisco
9. Duke University (NC)
   University of New Mexico

GERIATRICS
1. Johns Hopkins University (MD)
2. Mount Sinai School of Medicine (NY)
3. Duke University (NC)
4. University of California– Los Angeles (Geffen)
5. University of Michigan– Ann Arbor
6. Harvard University (MA)
7. University of Washington
8. Yale University (CT)
9. University of California– San Francisco
10. University of Arkansas for Medical Sciences

INTERNAL MEDICINE
1. Harvard University (MA)
2. Johns Hopkins University (MD)
3. University of California– San Francisco
4. University of Pennsylvania
5. Duke University (NC)
6. University of Washington
7. University of Michigan– Ann Arbor
8. Washington University in St. Louis
9. Yale University (CT)
10. Columbia U. College of Physicians and Surgeons (NY)

PEDIATRICS
1. Harvard University (MA)
2. University of Pennsylvania
3. University of Cincinnati
4. Johns Hopkins University (MD)
5. Baylor Col. of Medicine (TX)
6. Stanford University (CA)
7. University of Washington
   Washington University in St. Louis
9. University of California– San Francisco
10. Columbia U. College of Physicians and Surgeons (NY)

RURAL MEDICINE
1. University of Washington
2. University of New Mexico
3. University of Iowa (Carver)
4. East Tennessee State Univ. (Quillen)
5. University of North Dakota
6. East Carolina University (Brody) (NC)
   University of South Dakota (Sanford)
8. University of North Carolina– Chapel Hill
9. Oregon Health and Science University
   West Virginia University

WOMEN'S HEALTH
1. Harvard University (MA)
2. University of California– San Francisco
3. University of Pennsylvania
4. University of Pittsburgh
5. Johns Hopkins University (MD)
   University of Michigan– Ann Arbor
7. University of Washington
8. University of California– Los Angeles (Geffen)
9. University of North Carolina– Chapel Hill
10. Northwestern University (Feinberg) (IL)

The 125 medical schools fully accredited by the Liaison Committee on Medical Education, plus the 20 schools of osteopathic medicine fully accredited by the American Osteopathic Association, were surveyed for the ranking of research medical schools; 126 schools provided the data needed to calculate the research rankings based on the indicators used in the medical school research model. The same medical and osteopathic schools were surveyed for the primary-care ranking; 126 schools provided the data needed to calculate the medical school primary-care ranking. The medical school research model is based on a weighted average of eight indicators, and the primary-care model is based on seven indicators. Four of the indicators are the same for both models. The research model factors in research activity; the primary-care model adds a measure of the proportion of graduates entering primary-care specialties.

Quality assessment (weighted by .40): Peer assessment surveys were conducted in the fall of 2007, asking medical and osteopathic school deans, deans of academic affairs, and heads of internal medicine or the directors of admissions to rate program quality on a scale of "marginal" (1) to "outstanding" (5). Survey populations were asked to rate program quality for both research and primary-care programs separately on a single survey instrument. The response rate was 48 percent. A research school's average score is weighted by .20; the average score in the primary-care model is weighted by .25. Residency program directors were also asked to rate programs using the same 5-point scale on two separate survey instruments. One survey dealt with research and was sent to a sample of residency program directors in fields outside primary care, including surgery, psychiatry, and radiology. The other survey involved primary care and was sent to residency directors in the fields of family practice, pediatrics, and internal medicine. The response rate for those sent the research survey was 25 percent. The response rate for those sent the primary-care survey was 18 percent. Residency directors' opinions are weighted by .20 in the research model and by .15 in primary care. The source for the names for both of the residency directors' surveys was the Graduate Medical Education Directory 2006–2007 edition, published by the American Medical Association.

Research activity (.30 in research model only): Research was measured as the total dollar amount of National Institutes of Health research grants awarded to the medical school and its affiliated hospitals (.20) and the average amount of those grants calculated per full-time medical school science and clinical faculty member (.10); both factors were averaged for fiscal years 2006 and 2007. An asterisk indicates schools that reported only NIH research grants to their medical school in 2007.

Primary-care rate (.30 in primary-care model only): The percentage of medical or osteopathic school graduates entering primary-care residencies in the fields of family practice, pediatrics, and internal medicine was averaged over the 2005, 2006, and 2007 graduating classes.

Student selectivity (.20 in research model, .15 in primary-care model): This is determined by three components that describe the medical or osteopathic class entering in fall 2007: mean composite Medical College Admission Test score (65 percent), mean undergraduate grade-point average (30 percent), and the acceptance rate, which is the proportion of total applicants accepted (5 percent).

Faculty resources (.10 in research model, .15 in primary-care model): Resources were measured as the ratio of full-time science and clinical faculty to medical or osteopathic students in 2007.

Overall rank: Indicators were standardized about their means, and standardized scores were weighted, totaled, and rescaled so that the top school received 100; other schools received their percentage of the top score.

Specialty rankings: The rankings are based solely on ratings by medical school deans and senior faculty at peer schools. They each identified up to 10 schools offering the best medical school programs in each specialty area. Those programs receiving the most nominations in the top 10 appear here.

Health Disciplines

Schools ranked best by program directors and faculty

AUDIOLOGY

DOCTORATE Ranked in 2008

Rank/School	Average assessment score (5.0=highest)
1. Vanderbilt University (TN)	4.4
2. University of Iowa	4.3
3. University of Washington	4.0
4. University of Texas–Dallas	3.9
5. Washington University in St. Louis	3.7
6. University of Florida	3.6
University of Memphis	3.6
University of North Carolina–Chapel Hill	3.6
9. Northwestern University (IL)	3.5
Purdue University–West Lafayette (IN)	3.5
Rush Univ.-Presbyterian-St. Luke's Medical Center (IL)	3.5
University of Arizona	3.5
University of Kansas	3.5
University of Minnesota–Twin Cities	3.5
University of Texas–Austin	3.5
16. University at Buffalo–SUNY	3.4
University of Pittsburgh	3.4
18. Indiana University–Bloomington	3.3

CLINICAL PSYCHOLOGY

DOCTORATE Ranked in 2008

Rank/School	Average assessment score (5.0=highest)
1. University of California–Los Angeles	4.4
University of Washington	4.4
University of Wisconsin–Madison	4.4
4. University of California–Berkeley	4.3
University of Minnesota–Twin Cities	4.3
6. Indiana University–Bloomington	4.2
University of North Carolina–Chapel Hill	4.2
Yale University (CT)	4.2
9. Duke University (NC)	4.1
Pennsylvania State University–University Park	4.1
SUNY–Stony Brook	4.1
University of Illinois–Urbana-Champaign	4.1
University of Iowa	4.1
University of Pennsylvania	4.1
University of Pittsburgh	4.1
16. University of Kansas (Clinical Child Psych. Program)	4.0
University of Southern California	4.0
University of Texas–Austin	4.0
University of Virginia	4.0
Vanderbilt University (TN)	4.0
Washington University in St. Louis	4.0
22. Arizona State University	3.9
Northwestern University (IL)	3.9
University of Arizona	3.9
25. Emory University (GA)	3.8
San Diego State U./U. of California–San Diego	3.8
University of Florida	3.8

Rank/School	Average assessment score (5.0=highest)
University of Kansas	3.8
University of Miami (FL)	3.8
University of Michigan–Ann Arbor	3.8
University of Missouri–Columbia	3.8
University of Oregon	3.8
33. Boston University	3.7
Ohio State University	3.7
Temple University (PA)	3.7
University of Colorado–Boulder	3.7
University of Georgia	3.7
University of Kentucky	3.7
University of Maryland–College Park	3.7
Virginia Tech	3.7
West Virginia University	3.7
42. Michigan State University	3.6
43. Florida State University	3.5
Purdue University–West Lafayette (IN)	3.5
Rutgers, the State U. of New Jersey–New Brunswick	3.5
SUNY–Albany	3.5
University at Buffalo–SUNY	3.5
University of Nevada–Reno	3.5
University of Rochester (NY)	3.5

HEALTHCARE MANAGEMENT

MASTER'S Ranked in 2007

Rank/School	Average assessment score (5.0=highest)
1. University of Michigan–Ann Arbor	4.5
2. University of Minnesota–Twin Cities	4.2
3. University of North Carolina–Chapel Hill	4.1
4. University of Pennsylvania (Wharton)	4.0
University of Washington	4.0
Virginia Commonwealth University	4.0
7. University of Alabama–Birmingham	3.9
8. Northwestern University (Kellogg) (IL)	3.8
9. U. of California–Berkeley (Sch. of Public Health)	3.7
10. University of California–Berkeley (Haas)	3.6
11. University of California–Los Angeles	3.5
12. Johns Hopkins University (MD)	3.3
New York University	3.3
Ohio State University	3.3
St. Louis University	3.3
University of Missouri–Columbia	3.3
17. Boston University	3.2
University of Iowa	3.2
Washington University in St. Louis	3.2
20. Duke University (Fuqua) (NC)	3.1
Trinity University (TX)	3.1
University of Pittsburgh	3.1
U.S. Army-Baylor University (TX)	3.1

Continued on Page 40

HEALTHCARE MANAGEMENT

MASTER'S Ranked in 2007

Rank/School	Average assessment score (5.0=highest)
Yale University (CT)	3.1
25. Arizona State University	3.0
Cornell University (NY)	3.0
Rush University (IL)	3.0
28. George Washington University (DC)	2.9
Temple University (PA)	2.9

NURSING

MASTER'S Ranked in 2007

Rank/School	Average assessment score (5.0=highest)
1. University of Washington	4.7
2. University of California–San Francisco	4.6
3. University of Pennsylvania	4.5
4. Johns Hopkins University (MD)	4.4
5. University of Michigan–Ann Arbor	4.3
U. of North Carolina–Chapel Hill (Sch. of Nursing)	4.3
7. Oregon Health and Science University	4.2
University of Illinois–Chicago	4.2
University of Maryland–Baltimore	4.2
University of Pittsburgh	4.2
Yale University (CT)	4.2
12. University of California–Los Angeles	4.1
University of Iowa	4.1
U. of North Carolina–Chapel Hill (Sch. of Public Health)	4.1
15. Case Western Reserve University (OH)	4.0
Duke University (NC)	4.0
Indiana Univ.-Purdue Univ.–Indianapolis	4.0
University of Colorado–Denver and Health Sciences Center	4.0
19. Columbia University (NY)	3.9
Rush University (IL)	3.9
University of Texas–Austin	3.9
University of Virginia	3.9
University of Wisconsin–Madison	3.9
Univ. of Texas Health Science Center–Houston	3.9
Vanderbilt University (TN)	3.9
26. Boston College	3.8
Emory University (GA)	3.8
New York University	3.8
University of Alabama–Birmingham	3.8
University of Arizona	3.8
University of Kentucky	3.8
32. Arizona State University	3.7
Georgetown University (DC)	3.7
Ohio State University	3.7
University of Florida	3.7
University of Minnesota–Twin Cities	3.7
University of Nebraska Medical Center	3.7
University of Tennessee Health Science Center	3.7
University of Wisconsin–Milwaukee	3.7
40. Catholic University of America (DC)	3.6
Loyola University Chicago	3.6
University of Arkansas for Medical Sciences	3.6
University of Kansas	3.6
University of Rochester (NY)	3.6
Univ. of Texas Health Science Center–San Antonio	3.6
Wayne State University (MI)	3.6
47. Frontier School of Midwifery and Family Nursing (KY)	3.5
Michigan State University	3.5
University of Missouri–Columbia	3.5

Rank/School	Average assessment score (5.0=highest)
University of San Diego	3.5
University of Utah	3.5
Villanova University (PA)	3.5
Virginia Commonwealth University	3.5
54. Marquette University (WI)	3.4
Medical College of Georgia	3.4
Medical University of South Carolina	3.4
Pennsylvania State University–University Park	3.4
St. Louis University	3.4
Texas Woman's University	3.4
University of Louisville (KY)	3.4
University of Massachusetts–Amherst	3.4
University of San Francisco	3.4
63. George Mason University (VA)	3.3
George Washington University (DC)	3.3
Northeastern University (MA)	3.3
Pace University (NY)	3.3
University of Connecticut	3.3
University of Oklahoma Health Science Center	3.3
Univ. of South Carolina–Columbia	3.3
Univ. of Texas Medical Branch–Galveston	3.3
Washington State University	3.3
72. Baylor University (TX)	3.2
Brigham Young University (UT)	3.2
California State University–Los Angeles	3.2
Creighton University (NE)	3.2
CUNY–Hunter College	3.2
Duquesne University (PA)	3.2
Georgia State University	3.2
Indiana State University	3.2
Mass. General Hospital Inst. of Health Professions	3.2
Rutgers, the State University of New Jersey–Newark	3.2
San Diego State University	3.2
University at Buffalo–SUNY	3.2
University of Cincinnati	3.2
University of Colorado–Colorado Springs	3.2
University of Delaware	3.2
University of Massachusetts–Boston	3.2
University of North Carolina–Charlotte	3.2
University of North Carolina–Greensboro	3.2
University of Portland (OR)	3.2
University of South Florida	3.2
University of Tennessee–Knoxville	3.2
University of Texas–Arlington	3.2
West Virginia University	3.2

NURSING SPECIALTIES

CLINICAL NURSE SPECIALIST
ADULT/MEDICAL-SURGICAL

1. University of California–San Francisco
2. University of Washington
3. Indiana Univ.-Purdue Univ.–Indianapolis
   Yale University (CT)
5. University of Pennsylvania
6. University of Colorado–Denver and Health Sciences Center
   University of Virginia

COMMUNITY/PUBLIC HEALTH

1. University of Washington
2. Johns Hopkins University (MD)
3. U. of North Carolina–Chapel Hill (Sch. of Nursing)
4. U. of North Carolina–Chapel Hill (Sch. of Public Health)
5. Rush University (IL)
6. University of Michigan–Ann Arbor

PSYCHIATRIC/MENTAL HEALTH

1. University of Washington
2. University of California–San Francisco

University of Pennsylvania
4. Yale University (CT)
5. University of Virginia
6. Indiana Univ.-Purdue Univ.–
   Indianapolis
   Rush University (IL)
   University of Pittsburgh
   U. of North Carolina–
   Chapel Hill (Sch. of Nursing)

NURSE PRACTITIONER

ADULT

1. University of Pennsylvania
2. University of California–
   San Francisco
3. Columbia University (NY)
   University of Washington
5. Yale University (CT)
6. Univ. of Maryland–Baltimore
   Univ. of Michigan–Ann Arbor
8. University of Colorado–Denver
   and Health Sciences Center
9. Rush University (IL)
   University of Pittsburgh

FAMILY

1. University of Washington
2. University of California–
   San Francisco
3. University of Pennsylvania
4. Yale University (CT)
5. University of Colorado–Denver
   and Health Sciences Center
   Univ. of Maryland–Baltimore
7. Columbia University (NY)
8. U. of North Carolina–
   Chapel Hill (Sch. of Nursing)
9. Pace University (NY)
10. Rush University (IL)

GERONTOLOGICAL/GERIATRIC

1. University of Pennsylvania
2. University of Iowa
3. New York University

4. Case Western Reserve
   University (OH)
5. Oregon Health and Science
   University
6. University of Michigan–
   Ann Arbor
7. University of California–
   San Francisco
8. Univ. of Texas Health Science
   Center–Houston
9. Rush University (IL)
10. Duke University (NC)
    University of Washington

PEDIATRIC

1. University of Pennsylvania
   Yale University (CT)
3. University of Colorado–Denver
   and Health Sciences Center
4. University of Washington
5. University of California–
   San Francisco
6. University of Pittsburgh
7. Rush University (IL)
8. Columbia University (NY)
   U. of North Carolina–
   Chapel Hill (Sch. of Nursing)
10. Boston College
    Catholic University of
    America (DC)
    University of Rochester (NY)

NURSING SERVICE ADMINISTRATION

1. University of Iowa
2. University of Pennsylvania
3. U. of North Carolina–
   Chapel Hill (Sch. of Nursing)
4. University of Illinois–Chicago
   Univ. of Michigan–Ann Arbor
6. Univ. of Maryland–Baltimore
7. Johns Hopkins University (MD)
   University of California–
   San Francisco

NURSING–ANESTHESIA

MASTER'S Ranked in 2007

Rank/School	Average assessment score (5.0=highest)
1. Virginia Commonwealth University	4.1
2. U.S. Army Graduate Program in Anesthesia Nursing (TX)	4.0
3. Navy Nurse Corps (MD)	3.8
Rush University (IL)	3.8
5. University of Pittsburgh	3.7
6. Albany Medical College (NY)	3.6
Georgetown University (DC)	3.6
Kaiser Permanente Sch. of Anesthesia/Calif. State U.–Fullerton	3.6
Uniformed Services University of the Health Sciences (MD)	3.6
University of Iowa	3.6
11. Baylor College of Medicine (TX)	3.5
Cleveland Clinic Foundation/Case Western Reserve Univ.	3.5
Oakland University–Beaumont (MI)	3.5
University of Cincinnati	3.5
Wake Forest Univ./Univ. of North Carolina–Greensboro	3.5

NURSING–MIDWIFERY

MASTER'S/DOCTORATE Ranked in 2007

Rank/School	Average assessment score (5.0=highest)
1. Oregon Health and Science University	4.2
2. University of Pennsylvania	4.0
3. University of New Mexico	3.9
U. of Calif.–San Francisco/San Francisco General Hospital	3.9
Yale University (CT)	3.9
6. University of Illinois–Chicago	3.7
University of Minnesota–Twin Cities	3.7
8. Emory University (GA)	3.6
University of Michigan–Ann Arbor	3.6
University of Utah	3.6
University of Washington	3.6

Note: All schools listed have master's programs; some may not have doctoral programs.

OCCUPATIONAL THERAPY

MASTER'S/DOCTORATE Ranked in 2008

Rank/School	Average assessment score (5.0=highest)
1. Boston University (Sargent)	4.6
Washington University in St. Louis	4.6
3. University of Southern California	4.5
4. University of Illinois–Chicago	4.4
5. Tufts Univ.-Boston School of Occupational Therapy	4.1
University of Kansas Medical Center	4.1
University of North Carolina–Chapel Hill	4.1
8. Colorado State University	4.0
9. New York University	3.9
University of Pittsburgh	3.9
University of Washington	3.9
12. University of Wisconsin–Madison	3.8
13. Columbia University (NY)	3.7
Thomas Jefferson University (PA)	3.7
University of Florida	3.7
Virginia Commonwealth University	3.7

Note: All schools listed have master's programs; some may not have doctoral programs.

PHARMACY

PHARM.D. Ranked in 2008

Rank/School	Average assessment score (5.0=highest)
1. University of California–San Francisco	4.7
2. University of North Carolina–Chapel Hill	4.4
3. University of Minnesota	4.3
4. University of Texas–Austin	4.2
5. Ohio State University	4.1
University of Kentucky	4.1
University of Michigan–Ann Arbor	4.1
University of Washington	4.1
9. Purdue University (IN)	4.0
University of Arizona	4.0
University of Florida	4.0
University of Illinois–Chicago	4.0
University of Maryland–Baltimore	4.0
University of Wisconsin–Madison	4.0
15. University of Southern California	3.9
16. University of Tennessee Health Science Center	3.8
University of Iowa	3.8
University of Utah	3.8

Continued on Page 42

PHYSICAL THERAPY

MASTER'S/DOCTORATE Ranked in 2008

Rank/School	Average assessment score (5.0=highest)
1. University of Southern California	4.4
2. University of Pittsburgh	4.3
Washington University in St. Louis	4.3
4. University of Delaware	4.2
5. University of Iowa	3.9
U.S. Army-Baylor University (TX)	3.9
7. Arcadia University (PA)	3.8
MGH Institute of Health Professions (MA)	3.8
Northwestern University (IL)	3.8
University of Miami (FL)	3.8
11. Emory University (GA)	3.7
University of North Carolina–Chapel Hill	3.7
13. Duke University (NC)	3.6
U. of Calif.–San Francisco/San Francisco State U.	3.6
15. New York University	3.5
University of Florida	3.5
University of Illinois–Chicago	3.5
University of Maryland–Baltimore	3.5
19. Creighton University (NE)	3.4
Marquette University (WI)	3.4
Ohio State University	3.4
University of Minnesota–Twin Cities	3.4
University of Utah	3.4

Note: All schools listed have master's programs; some may not have doctoral programs.

PHYSICIAN ASSISTANT

MASTER'S/DOCTORATE Ranked in 2007

Rank/School	Average assessment score (5.0=highest)
1. University of Iowa	4.3
2. Duke University (NC)	4.2
3. Emory University (GA)	4.1
4. George Washington University (DC)	4.0
University of Texas Southwestern Medical Center–Dallas	4.0
University of Utah	4.0
7. University of Washington	3.9
8. University of Colorado–Denver and Health Sciences Center	3.8
9. Baylor College of Medicine (TX)	3.7
Oregon Health and Science University	3.7
11. Interservice Physician Assistant Program (TX)	3.6
SUNY–Stony Brook	3.6
University of Texas Medical Branch–Galveston	3.6
14. Quinnipiac University (CT)	3.5
Rosalind Franklin University of Medicine and Science (IL)	3.5
University of Nebraska Medical Center	3.5
17. Northeastern University (MA)	3.4
St. Louis University	3.4
UMDNJ–Newark	3.4
University of Texas Health Science Center–San Antonio	3.4

PUBLIC HEALTH

MASTER'S/DOCTORATE Ranked in 2007

Rank/School	Average assessment score (5.0=highest)
1. Johns Hopkins University (MD)	4.9
2. Harvard University (MA)	4.7
University of North Carolina–Chapel Hill	4.7
4. University of Washington	4.5
5. University of Michigan–Ann Arbor	4.4
6. Columbia University (NY)	4.1
7. Emory University (GA)	4.0
8. University of California–Berkeley	3.9
University of California–Los Angeles	3.9
10. University of Minnesota–Twin Cities	3.8

Note: All schools listed have master's programs; some may not have doctoral programs.

REHABILITATION COUNSELING

MASTER'S/DOCTORATE Ranked in 2007

Rank/School	Average assessment score (5.0=highest)
1. Michigan State University	4.2
University of Wisconsin–Madison	4.2
3. Pennsylvania State University–University Park	4.0
4. University of Iowa	3.9
5. University of Arizona	3.8
6. Boston University	3.7
George Washington University (DC)	3.7
Southern Illinois University–Carbondale	3.7
9. San Diego State University	3.6
University of Florida	3.6
University of Maryland–College Park	3.6
University of Wisconsin–Stout	3.6
13. Illinois Institute of Technology	3.5
Virginia Commonwealth University	3.5
15. University of Arkansas–Fayetteville	3.4
Utah State University	3.4
17. Auburn University–Main Campus (AL)	3.3
California State University–Fresno	3.3

Note: All schools listed have master's programs; some may not have doctoral programs.

SOCIAL WORK

MASTER'S Ranked in 2008

Rank/School	Average assessment score (5.0=highest)
1. Washington University in St. Louis	4.6
2. University of Michigan–Ann Arbor	4.5
3. University of Chicago	4.3
4. Columbia University (NY)	4.2
University of Washington	4.2
6. University of California–Berkeley	4.1
University of Texas–Austin	4.1
8. University of North Carolina–Chapel Hill	3.9
University of Southern California	3.9
10. Case Western Reserve University (OH)	3.8
University of California–Los Angeles	3.8
12. SUNY–Albany	3.7
University of Wisconsin–Madison	3.7
14. Boston College	3.6
University of Pennsylvania	3.6
University of Pittsburgh	3.6
Virginia Commonwealth University	3.6

Rank/School	Average assessment score (5.0=highest)
18. Fordham University (NY)	3.5
University of Illinois–Urbana-Champaign	3.5
University of Kansas	3.5
University of Maryland–Baltimore	3.5
22. Boston University	3.4
New York University	3.4
Smith College (MA)	3.4
University of Illinois–Chicago	3.4
26. CUNY–Hunter College	3.3
Indiana University	3.3
University of Minnesota–Twin Cities	3.3
University of Tennessee–Knoxville	3.3

SPEECH–LANGUAGE PATHOLOGY

MASTER'S Ranked in 2008

Rank/School	Average assessment score (5.0=highest)
1. University of Iowa	4.6
2. Northwestern University (IL)	4.4
Purdue University–West Lafayette	4.4
University of Wisconsin–Madison	4.4
5. University of Arizona	4.3
University of Kansas	4.3
University of Washington	4.3
Vanderbilt University (TN)	4.3
9. University of Illinois–Urbana-Champaign	4.0
University of Minnesota–Twin Cities	4.0
University of Texas–Austin	4.0
12. Indiana University	3.9
University of Florida	3.9
University of Memphis (TN)	3.9
University of Pittsburgh–Main Campus	3.9
University of Texas–Dallas	3.9
17. University of Nebraska–Lincoln	3.8
18. Arizona State University	3.7
Florida State University	3.7
Ohio State University	3.7
Rush Univ.-Presbyterian-St. Luke's Medical Center (IL)	3.7
University of Maryland–College Park	3.7
University of North Carolina–Chapel Hill	3.7
24. MGH Institute of Health Professions (MA)	3.6
25. Boston University	3.5
Pennsylvania State University–University Park	3.5
University at Buffalo–SUNY	3.5
University of Colorado–Boulder	3.5
University of Connecticut	3.5
30. Emerson College (MA)	3.4
Gallaudet University (DC)	3.4
Syracuse University (NY)	3.4
University of Massachusetts–Amherst	3.4
University of North Carolina–Greensboro	3.4
University of Oklahoma Health Sciences Center	3.4
University of Tennessee–Knoxville	3.4
Wichita State University (KS)	3.4
38. George Washington University (DC)	3.3
James Madison University (VA)	3.3
Ohio University	3.3
Teachers College, Columbia University (NY)	3.3
Temple University (PA)	3.3
University of Cincinnati	3.3
University of Vermont	3.3
Western Michigan University	3.3

VETERINARY

DOCTOR OF VETERINARY MEDICINE Ranked in 2007

Rank/School	Average assessment score (5.0=highest)
1. Cornell University (NY)	4.5
2. Colorado State University	4.3
University of California–Davis	4.3
4. University of Pennsylvania	4.1
5. North Carolina State University	3.9
Ohio State University	3.9
Texas A&M University–College Station	3.9
University of Wisconsin–Madison	3.9
9. Michigan State University	3.8
10. University of Minnesota–Twin Cities	3.7

METHODOLOGY

The health rankings are based solely on the results of peer assessment surveys sent to deans, other administrators, and/or faculty at accredited degree programs or schools in each discipline. All schools surveyed in a discipline were sent the same number of surveys. Respondents rated the academic quality of programs on a 5-point scale: outstanding (5 points), strong (4), good (3), adequate (2), or marginal (1). They were instructed to select "don't know" if they did not have enough knowledge to rate a program. Only fully accredited programs in good standing during the survey period are ranked. Those schools with the highest average scores appear.

In the fall of 2007, surveys were conducted for the 2008 rankings of Pharm.D. pharmacy programs accredited by the Accreditation Council for Pharmacy Education (56 percent of those surveyed responded); of doctoral programs in clinical psychology accredited by the American Psychological Association (response rate: 28 percent); graduate programs in occupational therapy accredited by the American Occupational Therapy Association (53 percent); audiology programs and speech-language-pathology programs accredited by the American Speech-Language-Hearing Association (57 percent and 42 percent, respectively); physical therapy programs accredited by the Commission on Accreditation in Physical Therapy Education (33 percent); and master of social work programs accredited by the Commission on Accreditation of the Council on Social Work Education (56 percent).

In the fall of 2006, surveys were conducted for 2007 rankings of schools of public health accredited by the Council on Education for Public Health (response rate: 78 percent); healthcare management programs accredited by the Commission on Accreditation of Healthcare Management Education (72 percent); master's programs in nursing accredited by either the Commission on Collegiate Nursing or the National League for Nursing Accrediting Commission (40 percent); graduate nurse anesthesia programs accredited by the Council on Accreditation of Nurse Anesthesia Educational Programs of the American Association of Nurse Anesthetists (61 percent); graduate nurse-midwifery programs accredited by the American College of Nurse-Midwives Division of Accreditation (74 percent); physician-assistant programs accredited by the Accreditation Review Commission on Education for the Physician Assistant (56 percent); rehabilitation counselor education programs accredited by the Commission on Standards and Accreditation: Council on Rehabilitation Education (53 percent); and veterinary schools accredited by the American Veterinary Medical Association (80 percent). Nursing specialty rankings are based solely on ratings by educators at peer schools. Nursing educators nominated up to 10 schools for excellence in each area. Surveys were conducted by the market research firm Synovate.

These Schools Mean Business

Why accounting and finance are taking their place alongside contracts and torts

By Emma Schwartz

When he graduates from law school this year, Joseph Fowler will come out knowing how to follow a corporate spreadsheet as well as look up case law. Enrolled at the University of Virginia, Fowler is part of a new wave of law students who believe a strong business background is critical to their success as lawyers. "It just helps you hit the ground faster," he says.

Traditionally, law school coursework has focused on the nuts and bolts of law and regulation with little regard for the more practical knowledge students need once they enter the profession. Now students are increasingly able to hone their business acumen during law school, either through joint degrees or, like Fowler, through a special concentration. This focus on business courses is part of a broader shift in the law school curriculum to include more specialized and practical training.

The drive for more practical education comes in part from a recent transformation in the profession of law. Clients are opting more and more for attorneys who know how to meld the law with business goals. That industry-specific knowledge is also critical for lawyers seeking jobs inside corporations, a market that barely existed three decades ago.

The interest in business know-how is also more important inside law firms, where even young lawyers must learn to

Law meets business: Prof. Stephen Presser lectures to a combined class at Northwestern's law school.

woo their own clients to have a shot at making partner. "It's pretty clear that to be a successful lawyer today you need to know more than the content of the law and how to argue about it," says Larry Kramer, dean of the Stanford Law School. But most young lawyers graduate without these skills, something many alums and companies complain about. So law schools across the country are starting to take note, expanding their offerings in accounting, finance, and transactional law.

Doubling up. Major law schools have long offered joint degree programs with their business schools, but the added

year of coursework—and the extra tuition—have kept the pool of applicants small. Northwestern University has been at the forefront of the change by making it easier for students to get a dual degree in business and law. It has consolidated the applications for both schools to one and reduced the program to a jam-packed three years instead of four. Since the consolidation in 1999, enrollment has jumped to nearly 25 students a year. Even regular law students are encouraged to learn the basics of business law. "The resounding theme is really that the students need to be able to work effectively with their clients—and that means understanding what their clients do," says David Van Zandt, law school dean at Northwestern.

The University of Virginia has taken a different tack. Conscious that many students may not want to spend the time—or money—on a double degree, the school now offers a specialized program in business and law. In addition to the basics of law, first-year students in the concentration enroll in basic accounting and finance courses. During the next two years, these students take

Smart Choices

International Law. Cornell University and several other schools offer joint degrees with foreign universities to train students to practice in both countries. **Intellectual Property.** If you have an inclination toward science, look for steady employment in the growing market for intellectual property and patent law.

more specialized classes in securities regulation, bankruptcy, and other electives in specific areas such as high-tech start-ups. "We're trying to get students to a point where they have the vocabulary and analytical skills associated with M.B.A. training," says Paul Mahoney, a University of Virginia law professor overseeing the business concentration.

Stanford has taken a broader approach. In 2006, the law school began revamping its calendar from the semester system to quarters, which every other school on campus uses. It also boosted the number of credits students can take outside the law school and encouraged them to take classes in any specialty they think will complement their legal interest, such as business, engineering, or health. Stanford is also offering classes in which business or engineering students work together with law students on problems such as taking an invention to market or modeling a company merger.

Meeting of the minds. Other campuses run similar classes. Ken Taymor, executive director of the University of California–Berkeley's Boalt Hall School of Law, which also offers joint classes, says they help "bring lawyers and their clients together in a classroom." The school is also considering creating a full certificate program.

Some universities have beefed up courses in business, even if they have yet to offer formal concentration programs like Virginia's. New York University School of Law and the University of Michigan Law School have developed mentoring programs for students with business-oriented law faculty. At Michigan, this effort includes special seminars on business with visiting faculty. And many schools bring in outside lawyers working in the field to teach these courses.

At the University of Texas–Austin, the law school is creating clinics to give students hands-on experience with business before graduation. And others, such as Berkeley and Cornell University, are increasing their research efforts and are supporting new institutes devoted to the study of law and business.

Of course, the increased specialization will hardly mean an end to the basic legal training that has been the hallmark of law schools across the country. "It's not anything close to a vocational training," says Evan Caminker, dean at Michigan's law school. But for students like Fowler it's a way to edge up on the competition. And he would know. He already has a job lined up in the corporate division of a Texas law firm. ●

Insider Tip

Specialization isn't the only way to gain practical know-how in law school. Participating in legal clinics will give you the experience to impress your potential employers. Nearly every school of law now offers its students a chance to gain courtroom experience, and offerings are expanding. The University of Michigan has opened a pediatric advocacy clinic to help with medical rights; in a completely different field, Stanford University has created an international and human rights law clinic that helps foreign countries develop their legal systems.

Getting In

Score High. On your GPA and your LSAT. Not that you can be reduced to just a number, but they're considered two of the best predictors of future success. GPAs that get better by the year can demonstrate maturity and make up for a poor freshman year.

Your Essay. Your personal statement allows you to emotionally connect with the overworked admit dean, but it's less important than you'd imagine. Use it to put some meat on the bare bones of your acronyms (see above). Having something to write about is also critical (see below).

Are You Experienced? Work experience is a great topic for personal statements. Volunteering for a legal aid society or working as a legal intern shows you've invested time in the field—and have an inkling of what you're getting into.

Know Your Audience. Find out where past graduates have landed. If the strengths of the school are aligned with your own ambitions, your application has a better chance.

Reality Check

Average starting salaries are expected to rise 5.4% in '08 • Young associates at big firms will see the greatest gain at 9.1%, to the $102,470–$137,000 range • The biggest firms already top $160,000 for first-years; your colleagues with 10 years' experience could be looking at $234,000 • Base compensation for midlevel paralegals is expected to rise to $48,000–$64,500; for top legal secretaries, to $55,750–$69,500 • Growth areas: legal transactions, healthcare, energy, environment, intellectual property, venture capital, antitrust, elder law

Law students in Hutchins Hall at the University of Michigan Law School in Ann Arbor

Schools of Law

Rank/School	Overall score	Peer assessment score (5.0=highest)	Assessment score by lawyers/judges (5.0=highest)	'07 undergrad GPA 25th-75th percentile	'07 LSAT score 25th-75th percentile	'07 acceptance rate	'07 student/faculty ratio	'06 grads employed at graduation	Employed 9 months after graduation	School's bar passage rate in jurisdiction	Jurisdiction's overall bar passage rate*
1. Yale University (CT)	100	4.8	4.8	3.77-3.97	170-177	7.3%	7.4	96.1%	99.6%	91.2%/NY	77%
2. Harvard University (MA)	91	4.8	4.8	3.75-3.95	170-175	11.8%	10.3	96.4%	98.1%	97.1%/NY	77%
Stanford University (CA)	91	4.7	4.8	3.74-3.95	167-172	9.0%	8.3	98.3%	98.5%	88.7%/CA	65%
4. Columbia University (NY)	88	4.7	4.7	3.56-3.81	169-174	15.9%	9.5	98.9%	98.9%	95.6%/NY	77%
5. New York University	85	4.5	4.5	3.54-3.86	169-173	22.9%	10.4	96.3%	98.5%	95.1%/NY	77%
6. University of California–Berkeley	81	4.5	4.5	3.64-3.90	163-170	12.0%	12.3	99.0%	99.0%	84.9%/CA	65%
7. University of Chicago	80	4.6	4.6	3.49-3.76	169-173	16.2%	10.3	96.4%	99.0%	97.7%/IL	87%
University of Pennsylvania	80	4.3	4.4	3.52-3.86	166-171	16.3%	12.1	95.3%	98.2%	94.4%/NY	77%
9. Northwestern University (IL)	79	4.1	4.3	3.40-3.80	166-172	17.6%	10.4	96.2%	99.2%	95.1%/IL	87%
University of Michigan–Ann Arbor	79	4.5	4.6	3.49-3.79	167-170	20.7%	12.7	97.2%	98.8%	94.8%/NY	77%
University of Virginia	79	4.4	4.6	3.51-3.87	167-171	24.0%	13.3	96.8%	99.6%	91.1%/VA	74%
12. Cornell University (NY)	77	4.2	4.4	3.54-3.78	166-168	21.6%	11.2	96.9%	99.0%	92.1%/NY	77%
Duke University (NC)	77	4.2	4.4	3.61-3.82	167-170	26.6%	13.9	91.8%	98.2%	97.0%/NY	77%
14. Georgetown University (DC)	74	4.2	4.4	3.44-3.82	167-171	23.2%	13.2	94.8%	97.8%	91.0%/NY	77%
15. Vanderbilt University (TN)	72	3.8	4.1	3.54-3.83	164-168	25.0%	12.9	90.5%	98.3%	97.8%/TN	78%
16. University of California–Los Angeles	71	4.0	3.8	3.54-3.85	163-169	17.5%	12.9	94.9%	97.8%	85.7%/CA	65%
University of Texas–Austin	71	4.1	4.2	3.38-3.80	163-168	24.0%	14.2	92.0%	97.4%	89.4%/TX	82%
18. University of Southern California (Gould)	68	3.7	3.6	3.46-3.72	165-167	18.7%	12.7	90.1%	96.0%	85.1%/CA	65%
19. Washington University in St. Louis	67	3.6	3.9	3.30-3.70	163-167	25.7%	11.6	83.9%	98.8%	93.0%/IL	87%
20. George Washington University (DC)	65	3.5	3.8	3.40-3.86	163-168	19.8%	14.9	95.1%	97.1%	93.9%/NY	77%
21. Boston University	64	3.4	3.6	3.51-3.81	164-166	26.8%	12.3	96.3%	98.7%	95.0%/MA	86%
22. Emory University (GA)	63	3.4	3.8	3.28-3.62	162-166	26.2%	10.8	95.9%	98.3%	95.0%/GA	85%
University of Minnesota–Twin Cities	63	3.6	3.6	3.28-3.78	163-167	24.7%	12.1	87.0%	97.5%	96.3%/MN	91%
University of Notre Dame (IN)	63	3.3	3.8	3.40-3.76	164-167	18.6%	14.7	83.8%	97.3%	89.5%/IL	87%
25. Washington and Lee University (VA)	62	3.4	3.9	3.25-3.81	161-167	23.6%	10.6	74.4%	92.4%	79.2%/VA	74%
26. Boston College	61	3.3	3.7	3.44-3.78	162-165	20.2%	12.6	82.5%	97.6%	95.2%/MA	86%
27. Fordham University (NY)	60	3.3	3.5	3.41-3.74	163-167	23.5%	14.6	82.3%	94.7%	89.0%/NY	77%
University of Illinois–Urbana-Champaign	60	3.4	3.7	3.18-3.80	160-167	30.2%	12.4	78.4%	92.6%	88.8%/IL	87%
University of Iowa	60	3.5	3.7	3.41-3.86	159-163	34.6%	13.0	79.9%	92.8%	90.0%/IA	87%
30. College of William and Mary (Marshall-Wythe) (VA)	59	3.2	3.6	3.44-3.82	159-166	27.1%	14.8	82.3%	96.3%	86.8%/VA	74%
University of Washington	59	3.2	3.5	3.47-3.82	159-165	22.7%	10.2	86.7%	97.2%	87.6%/WA	82%
32. Ohio State University (Moritz)	58	3.4	3.4	3.34-3.81	158-164	29.5%	12.6	85.8%	95.4%	84.0%/OH	84%
University of Alabama	58	2.9	3.3	3.31-3.84	160-165	29.2%	9.8	83.7%	96.5%	97.2%/AL	79%
University of Colorado–Boulder	58	3.1	3.1	3.33-3.83	160-165	25.2%	12.2	88.6%	97.0%	91.2%/CO	76%
University of Georgia	58	3.1	3.3	3.42-3.86	159-165	24.9%	14.8	87.9%	98.1%	91.0%/GA	85%
36. Indiana University–Bloomington	57	3.2	3.6	3.03-3.67	158-165	38.9%	11.4	88.1%	97.7%	86.2%/IN	83%
University of Wisconsin–Madison	57	3.4	3.6	3.32-3.74	157-163	29.5%	13.4	72.9%	97.2%	100.0%/WI	89%
38. George Mason University (VA)	56	2.8	3.3	3.11-3.86	159-166	22.3%	16.7	93.2%	98.0%	83.8%/VA	74%
University of Arizona (Rogers)	56	3.2	3.4	3.23-3.73	157-164	30.9%	11.7	78.8%	94.9%	86.5%/AZ	75%
University of California (Hastings)	56	3.4	3.7	3.36-3.74	160-165	26.5%	16.2	67.5%	93.2%	82.4%/CA	65%
University of North Carolina–Chapel Hill	56	3.5	3.8	3.45-3.80	157-164	18.5%	15.7	62.6%	88.8%	86.5%/NC	74%
42. University of Maryland	55	2.9	3.2	3.47-3.84	160-166	15.5%	11.4	79.9%	94.2%	87.5%/MD	77%
Wake Forest University (NC)	55	3.0	3.5	3.17-3.68	159-166	35.4%	10.3	71.3%	95.0%	87.5%/NC	74%
44. Tulane University (LA)	54	3.1	3.5	3.37-3.75	158-163	35.6%	15.4	78.2%	95.8%	82.6%/LA	75%
University of California–Davis	54	3.4	3.5	3.38-3.75	159-165	28.8%	12.4	78.8%	87.1%	75.9%/CA	65%
46. American University (Washington) (DC)	53	3.0	3.2	3.14-3.59	161-163	22.8%	13.8	85.2%	95.8%	81.4%/MD	77%
Brigham Young University (Clark) (UT)	53	2.8	3.3	3.51-3.85	162-167	28.6%	18.9	75.0%	91.2%	96.2%/UT	87%
Southern Methodist University (TX)	53	2.7	3.2	3.28-3.84	157-165	22.9%	14.7	70.1%	94.7%	90.4%/TX	82%
University of Connecticut	53	2.9	3.0	3.24-3.64	160-164	14.1%	11.0	74.4%	95.5%	86.7%/CT	83%
University of Florida (Levin)	53	3.2	3.3	3.44-3.83	156-162	34.3%	15.7	77.7%	96.8%	77.9%/FL	74%
51. University of Utah (Quinney)	52	2.8	3.0	3.31-3.77	156-162	36.9%	9.9	96.2%	98.5%	85.8%/UT	87%
52. Arizona State University (O'Connor)	50	2.9	3.2	3.30-3.81	156-162	23.7%	9.4	N/A	93.3%	78.7%/AZ	75%
University of Cincinnati	50	2.6	2.8	3.39-3.87	157-162	35.1%	9.6	72.8%	96.2%	91.8%/OH	84%
University of Tennessee–Knoxville	50	2.8	3.0	3.35-3.82	157-162	29.2%	13.1	74.0%	95.3%	91.6%/TN	78%
55. Baylor University (Umphrey) (TX)	49	2.5	3.3	3.38-3.78	157-162	30.4%	16.6	68.3%	96.4%	98.5%/TX	82%
Florida State University	49	2.8	2.8	3.30-3.77	158-162	23.8%	13.7	82.0%	95.1%	88.1%/FL	74%
University of Houston	49	2.6	3.0	3.30-3.79	158-163	29.3%	13.9	76.8%	96.3%	88.5%/TX	82%
Yeshiva University (Cardozo) (NY)	49	2.7	2.9	3.30-3.70	162-166	27.5%	16.2	75.1%	95.4%	88.8%/NY	77%
59. Pepperdine University (CA)	48	2.4	3.2	3.42-3.73	158-162	32.5%	16.9	N/A	95.0%	82.8%/CA	65%

Rank/School	Overall score	Peer assessment score (5.0=highest)	Assessment score by lawyers/judges (5.0=highest)	'07 undergrad GPA 25th-75th percentile	'07 LSAT score 25th-75th percentile	'07 acceptance rate	'07 student/faculty ratio	'06 grads employed at graduation	Employed 9 months after graduation	School's bar passage rate in jurisdiction	Jurisdiction's overall bar passage rate*
Temple University (Beasley) (PA)	48	2.7	3.1	3.27-3.65	160-164	41.0%	12.8	66.8%	94.2%	89.7%/PA	83%
University of Kentucky	48	2.5	3.0	3.36-3.79	156-162	36.3%	15.0	77.5%	99.3%	90.0%/KY	83%
University of Missouri–Columbia	48	2.7	3.2	3.26-3.80	156-161	35.8%	17.2	54.9%	98.6%	90.8%/MO	86%
63. Brooklyn Law School (NY)	47	2.7	2.8	3.17-3.63	162-165	29.4%	19.9	66.7%	97.0%	84.5%/NY	77%
Case Western Reserve University (OH)	47	2.7	3.1	3.17-3.60	156-160	34.8%	13.7	70.7%	96.7%	83.3%/OH	84%
Loyola Marymount University (CA)	47	2.6	2.9	3.22-3.65	159-163	29.7%	15.8	66.6%	96.9%	74.9%/CA	65%
66. Illinois Institute of Technology (Chicago-Kent)	46	2.7	2.7	3.20-3.77	157-164	33.3%	11.5	71.8%	90.7%	90.3%/IL	87%
Seton Hall University (NJ)	46	2.5	2.8	3.22-3.65	157-162	42.6%	15.4	89.7%	98.3%	85.4%/NJ	79%
68. Indiana University–Indianapolis	45	2.6	3.1	3.36-3.78	151-158	35.0%	17.0	81.5%	95.9%	84.8%/IN	83%
University of New Mexico	45	2.5	2.7	3.09-3.72	152-159	22.5%	10.0	60.5%	98.5%	92.4%/NM	88%
University of Oklahoma	45	2.5	3.0	3.35-3.78	154-160	38.4%	11.9	81.7%	95.7%	96.2%/OK	92%
University of Richmond (Williams) (VA)	45	2.4	3.1	3.23-3.66	158-162	34.7%	15.6	72.5%	94.6%	84.8%/VA	74%
Villanova University (PA)	45	2.7	3.2	3.14-3.63	160-163	43.4%	16.0	64.2%	94.3%	86.2%/PA	83%
73. Lewis and Clark College (Northwestern) (OR)	44	2.4	2.9	3.15-3.73	157-163	37.0%	10.6	N/A	92.2%	85.8%/OR	82%
University of Kansas	44	2.7	3.1	3.09-3.77	155-160	36.7%	12.1	65.9%	94.7%	91.8%/KS	90%
University of Nebraska–Lincoln	44	2.5	3.0	3.50-3.82	153-159	37.1%	12.5	78.9%	93.9%	87.1%/NE	83%
University of Pittsburgh	44	2.8	2.9	3.11-3.65	158-161	36.9%	15.3	73.5%	94.1%	89.9%/PA	83%
77. Georgia State University	43	2.3	2.6	3.11-3.62	158-162	17.7%	12.8	N/A	97.9%	92.8%/GA	85%
Pennsylvania State University (Dickinson)	43	2.3	2.9	3.02-3.69	156-159	33.3%	11.5	N/A	92.4%	87.4%/PA	83%
Rutgers, the State Univ. of New Jersey–Camden	43	2.6	2.8	3.09-3.65	160-162	22.5%	14.1	71.8%	91.6%	79.4%/NJ	79%
Rutgers, the State Univ. of New Jersey–Newark	43	2.6	2.8	3.08-3.55	155-161	29.8%	14.8	82.4%	95.3%	80.0%/NJ	79%
Santa Clara University (CA)	43	2.6	3.2	3.16-3.59	156-161	51.3%	15.9	72.3%	92.5%	77.3%/CA	65%
82. Loyola University Chicago	42	2.5	3.0	3.35-3.75	159-163	25.8%	14.5	54.2%	89.2%	89.5%/IL	87%
Seattle University	42	2.3	2.8	3.17-3.62	155-161	28.2%	14.4	66.6%	98.5%	81.9%/WA	82%
University of Hawaii (Richardson)	42	2.4	2.7	3.09-3.62	155-160	18.7%	8.5	64.4%	94.3%	82.2%/HI	77%
University of Miami (FL)	42	2.8	2.9	3.21-3.63	155-160	50.9%	19.1	72.4%	90.7%	84.8%/FL	74%
University of Oregon	42	2.9	3.1	3.27-3.68	156-160	40.8%	17.6	63.3%	89.5%	85.4%/OR	82%
University of San Diego	42	2.8	2.9	3.10-3.53	160-164	31.5%	14.0	N/A	87.9%	75.5%/CA	65%
88. Catholic University of America (Columbus) (DC)	41	2.5	2.9	3.08-3.57	156-160	34.3%	13.6	70.1%	93.7%	79.6%/MD	77%
DePaul University (IL)	41	2.4	2.8	3.10-3.66	159-162	35.2%	13.6	82.7%	90.3%	87.2%/IL	87%
Louisiana State University–Baton Rouge	41	2.3	2.9	3.16-3.70	155-159	37.4%	16.2	73.7%	93.8%	88.8%/LA	75%
Northeastern University (MA)	41	2.4	2.8	3.14-3.61	156-162	36.2%	16.9	N/A	93.7%	87.8%/MA	86%
St. John's University (NY)	41	2.4	2.7	3.19-3.74	157-162	34.2%	16.4	65.7%	88.7%	88.8%/NY	77%
University of Denver (Sturm)	41	2.5	2.8	3.15-3.66	155-160	33.4%	18.7	67.4%	95.9%	65.7%/CO	76%
University of Nevada–Las Vegas (Boyd)	41	2.3	2.8	3.20-3.66	156-161	23.0%	14.0	N/A	91.5%	76.6%/NV	72%
95. Marquette University (WI)	40	2.3	3.1	3.20-3.65	155-159	45.6%	17.5	63.4%	95.7%	100.0%/WI	89%
St. Louis University	40	2.4	3.2	3.24-3.74	154-159	52.3%	17.6	70.8%	93.0%	85.6%/MO	86%
University of South Carolina	40	2.3	2.7	3.04-3.69	156-161	30.9%	14.3	63.9%	93.6%	87.9%/SC	81%
University of the Pacific (McGeorge) (CA)	40	2.2	2.5	3.13-3.60	155-159	39.7%	13.5	N/A	94.4%	72.7%/CA	65%
99. Hofstra University (NY)	39	2.4	2.8	3.11-3.69	154-159	42.0%	15.5	N/A	92.9%	73.6%/NY	77%
100. Mercer University (GA)	38	2.2	2.6	3.20-3.69	155-158	31.8%	13.3	62.1%	94.4%	88.0%/GA	85%
Stetson University (FL)	38	2.1	2.4	3.48-3.71	153-157	31.1%	17.9	N/A	97.7%	81.5%/FL	74%
Syracuse University (NY)	38	2.4	2.9	3.09-3.59	152-156	49.6%	12.7	62.6%	92.6%	79.6%/NY	77%
University at Buffalo–SUNY	38	2.4	2.4	3.19-3.65	154-159	38.5%	15.6	73.8%	92.7%	80.6%/NY	77%
University of Louisville (Brandeis) (KY)	38	2.3	2.5	3.17-3.73	155-159	38.0%	14.4	58.9%	93.8%	85.0%/KY	83%

Sources: *U.S. News* and the schools. Assessment data collected by Synovate. N/A means that the data were not provided by the school. Western State University and University of La Verne in California, Florida A&M University, John Marshall Law School–Atlanta, Charleston School of Law in South Carolina, Faulkner University in Alabama, Liberty University in Virginia, and Phoenix School of Law in Arizona are not ranked because as of December 2007 they were only provisionally approved by the American Bar Association. Three law schools in Puerto Rico—Catholic University, Inter-America University, and the University of Puerto Rico—are not ranked. Note: The state bar examination pass rates for first-time test takers in summer 2006 and winter 2007 were provided by the National Conference of Bar Examiners.

METHODOLOGY

The rankings of 184 accredited law schools are based on a weighted average of the 12 measures of quality described below. More on our methods appears on Page 16.

Quality assessment (weighted by .40): Quality was measured by two surveys conducted in fall 2007. The dean and three faculty members at each school were asked to rate schools from "marginal" (1) to "outstanding" (5); 70 percent voted. Their average rating for a school is weighted by .25 in the ranking model. Lawyers and judges also rated schools; 26 percent responded. Their average rating is weighted by .15.

Selectivity (.25): For full-time students entering in 2007, this combines median LSAT scores (50 percent), median undergrad GPA (40 percent), and proportion of applicants accepted (10 percent).

Placement success (.20): Success is determined by employment rates for 2006 graduates at graduation (20 percent) and nine months after (70 percent) as well as their bar passage rate (10 percent). Employment rates include graduates reported as working or pursuing graduate degrees; for the nine-month rate only, 25 percent of those whose status is unknown are also counted as working. All others are counted as unemployed. The bar passage rate indicator is the ratio of a school's rate in the cited jurisdiction to the overall state rate, computed for first-time test takers in summer 2006 and winter 2007. The jurisdiction cited is the state where the largest number of 2006 grads first took the test.

Faculty resources (.15): Resources are based on average 2006 and 2007 expenditures per student for instruction, library, and supporting services (65 percent) and on all other items including financial aid (10 percent); 2007 student/teacher ratio (20 percent); and total number of volumes and titles in library (5 percent).

Overall rank: A school's score on each indicator was standardized. Then scores were weighted, totaled, and rescaled so that the top school received 100 and other schools received a percentage of the top score.

Specialty rankings: Rankings are based solely on votes by law faculty who are listed in the *AALS Directory of Law Teachers 2005–2006* as teaching in the field or by directors of clinical and legal writing programs. They named up to 15 of the best in each field. Schools receiving the most votes are listed.

PROGRAMS RANKED BEST BY FACULTY WHO TEACH IN THE FIELD

CLINICAL TRAINING
1. Georgetown University (DC)
2. American University (Washington) (DC)
3. New York University
4. CUNY–Queens College
5. University of New Mexico
6. Washington Univ. in St. Louis
7. Yale University (CT)
8. University of Maryland
9. University of Michigan–Ann Arbor
10. Fordham University (NY)

DISPUTE RESOLUTION
1. Pepperdine University (CA)
2. Harvard University (MA)
   Univ. of Missouri–Columbia
4. Hamline University (MN)
5. Ohio State University (Moritz)
6. Marquette University (WI)
7. University of Oregon
8. Yeshiva Univ. (Cardozo) (NY)
9. University of Nevada–Las Vegas (Boyd)
10. Fordham University (NY)

ENVIRONMENTAL LAW
1. Lewis and Clark College (Northwestern) (OR)
2. Vermont Law School
3. Pace University (NY)

4. Georgetown University (DC)
5. Duke University (NC)
6. University of Colorado–Boulder
7. Stanford University (CA)
8. University of Maryland
9. University of Oregon
10. Florida State University

HEALTH LAW
1. St. Louis University
2. University of Houston
3. University of Maryland
4. Case Western Reserve University (OH)
   Seton Hall University (NJ)
6. Loyola University Chicago
7. Boston University
8. Georgetown University (DC)
9. Widener University (DE)
10. Georgia State University

INTELLECTUAL PROPERTY LAW
1. University of California–Berkeley
2. Stanford University (CA)
3. George Washington Univ. (DC)
4. Columbia University (NY)
5. Franklin Pierce Law Center (NH)
6. Duke University (NC)
7. University of Houston
8. Santa Clara University (CA)

9. Boston University
10. Illinois Institute of Technology (Chicago-Kent)

INTERNATIONAL LAW
1. New York University
2. Columbia University (NY)
3. Harvard University (MA)
4. Georgetown University (DC)
5. American University (Washington) (DC)
   Yale University (CT)
7. University of Michigan–Ann Arbor
8. George Washington Univ. (DC)
9. University of California–Berkeley
10. University of Virginia

LEGAL WRITING
1. Mercer University (GA)
2. Seattle University
3. University of Nevada–Las Vegas (Boyd)
4. Temple University (Beasley) (PA)
5. John Marshall Law School (IL)
6. Stetson University (FL)
7. Boston College
8. Northwestern University (IL)
9. Brooklyn Law School (NY)
10. University of Oregon

TAX LAW
1. New York University
2. University of Florida (Levin)
3. Georgetown University (DC)
4. Northwestern University (IL)
5. University of California–Los Angeles
6. Harvard University (MA)
   University of Miami (FL)
8. Boston University
9. University of Virginia
10. University of Michigan–Ann Arbor
    University of Texas–Austin
    Yale University (CT)

TRIAL ADVOCACY
1. Stetson University (FL)
2. Temple Univ. (Beasley) (PA)
3. Northwestern University (IL)
4. Washington Univ. in St. Louis
5. Georgetown University (DC)
6. Loyola Marymount University (CA)
   South Texas College of Law
8. Baylor University (Umphrey) (TX)
9. American University (Washington) (DC)
   New York University
   University of Texas–Austin

Other Schools to Consider

The next two quartiles of schools are listed alphabetically in two groups, the Third Tier and Fourth Tier. Law schools within each of these tiers should be considered broadly similar in quality. To be listed, a law school must be accredited and fully approved by the American Bar Association and must draw most of its students from the United States. Remember that in considering a law school, you should look not only at its ranking or tier but also at other characteristics—its location, price, course offerings, and faculty expertise, to name a few. More information on all the schools is available in the directory (Page 73).

THIRD TIER (ranking begins at 105; schools are listed alphabetically)

Rank/School	Peer assessment score (5.0=highest)	Assessment score by lawyers/judges (5.0=highest)	'07 undergrad GPA 25th-75th percentile	'07 LSAT score 25th-75th percentile	'07 acceptance rate	'07 student/ faculty ratio	'06 grads employed at graduation	Employed 9 months after graduation	School's bar passage rate in jurisdiction	Jurisdiction's overall bar passage rate*
Albany Law School-Union University (NY)	2.1	2.4	2.92-3.48	152-157	45.1%	14.7	N/A	97.2%	86.3%/NY	77%
Chapman University (CA)	1.8	1.9	3.10-3.61	154-159	31.5%	12.6	51.1%	95.4%	61.3%/CA	65%
Cleveland State University (Cleveland-Marshall)	2.1	2.3	3.14-3.65	153-157	36.3%	13.0	63.0%	93.3%	82.4%/OH	84%
Creighton University (NE)	2.0	2.9	3.23-3.68	151-156	45.3%	18.1	73.0%	97.3%	75.0%/NE	83%
Drake University (IA)	2.0	2.6	3.11-3.72	153-158	50.7%	12.9	N/A	94.9%	90.6%/IA	87%
Franklin Pierce Law Center (NH)	1.9	2.5	3.00-3.50	150-155	49.8%	14.4	65.8%	95.5%	95.6%/MA	86%
Gonzaga University (WA)	2.1	3.0	3.06-3.54	153-157	45.4%	14.8	N/A	92.6%	84.3%/WA	82%
Hamline University (MN)	1.9	2.3	3.22-3.70	152-158	48.6%	14.6	N/A	91.5%	85.8%/MN	91%
Howard University (DC)	2.3	2.7	2.90-3.50	149-155	22.7%	18.7	87.6%	94.1%	61.5%/NY	77%
Loyola University New Orleans	2.1	3.0	3.09-3.56	149-155	67.2%	17.5	63.4%	95.3%	79.7%/LA	75%
Mercer University (GA)	2.2	2.6	3.20-3.69	155-158	31.8%	13.3	62.1%	94.4%	88.0%/GA	85%
Michigan State University	2.2	2.9	3.21-3.64	155-161	41.8%	19.4	N/A	90.7%	93.7%/MI	89%
New York Law School	2.2	2.8	3.08-3.57	153-157	47.1%	22.9	N/A	90.2%	81.3%/NY	77%
Ohio Northern University (Pettit)	1.7	1.9	3.10-3.70	148-156	29.7%	12.2	N/A	95.5%	81.4%/OH	84%
Pace University (NY)	2.1	2.3	3.13-3.59	153-157	36.9%	14.2	N/A	88.1%	81.0%/NY	77%
Quinnipiac University (CT)	2.0	2.2	3.01-3.62	157-160	27.6%	10.4	N/A	93.8%	82.7%/CT	83%
Samford University (Cumberland) (AL)	1.9	2.3	3.07-3.52	155-159	40.2%	17.6	66.0%	90.1%	89.7%/AL	79%
Stetson University (FL)	2.1	2.4	3.48-3.71	153-157	31.1%	17.9	N/A	97.7%	81.5%/FL	74%

Continued on Page 50

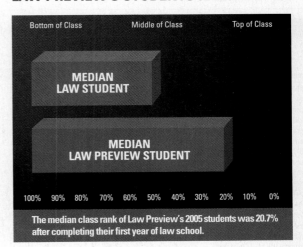

Rank/School	Peer assessment score (5.0=highest)	Assessment score by lawyers/judges (5.0=highest)	'07 undergrad GPA 25th-75th percentile	'07 LSAT score 25th-75th percentile	'07 acceptance rate	'07 student/faculty ratio	'06 grads employed at graduation	Employed 9 months after graduation	School's bar passage rate in jurisdiction	Jurisdiction's overall bar passage rate*
Suffolk University (MA)	2.1	2.4	3.03-3.49	154-158	49.8%	16.5	56.7%	91.4%	81.9%/MA	86%
Syracuse University (NY)	2.4	2.9	3.09-3.59	152-156	49.6%	12.7	62.6%	92.6%	79.6%/NY	77%
Texas Tech University	2.0	2.7	3.34-3.75	151-157	43.4%	15.4	40.7%	92.1%	87.1%/TX	82%
University at Buffalo–SUNY	2.4	2.4	3.19-3.65	154-159	38.5%	15.6	73.8%	92.7%	80.6%/NY	77%
University of Akron (OH)	1.9	2.2	3.16-3.76	156-160	32.1%	13.3	75.2%	91.8%	84.6%/OH	84%
University of Arkansas–Fayetteville	2.4	2.7	3.17-3.70	151-159	30.3%	13.8	N/A	88.6%	83.3%/AR	82%
University of Arkansas–Little Rock (Bowen)	2.2	2.5	2.94-3.68	151-155	26.1%	14.3	N/A	87.8%	85.6%/AR	82%
University of Baltimore	2.0	2.4	3.00-3.57	153-157	40.9%	18.9	93.9%	94.9%	75.3%/MD	77%
University of Idaho	2.1	2.7	3.03-3.64	151-159	43.7%	16.0	N/A	92.7%	87.5%/ID	85%
University of Louisville (Brandeis) (KY)	2.3	2.5	3.17-3.73	155-159	38.0%	14.4	58.9%	93.8%	85.0%/KY	83%
University of Maine	2.3	2.9	3.06-3.69	154-159	46.9%	15.3	N/A	91.8%	85.7%/ME	83%
University of Mississippi	2.2	2.9	3.28-3.79	152-157	30.7%	15.8	59.6%	88.2%	92.2%/MS	88%
University of Missouri–Kansas City	2.3	2.7	3.03-3.64	152-156	50.4%	12.8	N/A	91.2%	88.1%/MO	86%
University of Montana	2.1	2.7	3.12-3.75	151-158	42.3%	14.3	N/A	94.1%	94.9%/MT	92%
University of San Francisco	2.2	2.5	3.02-3.56	156-161	37.7%	19.1	N/A	92.7%	73.3%/CA	65%
University of South Dakota	2.0	2.7	3.21-3.75	150-156	49.3%	16.2	59.3%	93.3%	83.6%/SD	87%
University of St. Thomas (MN)	1.9	2.7	3.16-3.63	154-161	48.6%	16.8	N/A	94.9%	91.2%/MN	91%
University of Toledo (OH)	2.0	2.1	3.10-3.74	156-161	26.9%	15.1	71.5%	92.2%	91.1%/OH	84%
University of Wyoming	2.1	2.9	3.18-3.63	150-159	27.6%	11.4	N/A	87.0%	78.4%/WY	62%
Vermont Law School	2.3	2.7	2.95-3.54	151-158	58.6%	11.6	N/A	90.7%	71.9%/VT	77%
Washburn University (KS)	2.0	2.5	3.06-3.69	150-156	52.3%	13.8	N/A	94.0%	89.3%/KS	90%
Wayne State University (MI)	2.3	2.5	3.29-3.69	152-158	51.8%	14.2	N/A	87.9%	92.2%/MI	89%
West Virginia University	2.1	2.3	3.18-3.75	150-159	37.2%	13.8	67.9%	94.9%	66.3%/WV	66%
Willamette University (Collins) (OR)	2.1	2.6	2.85-3.52	153-158	45.0%	14.1	N/A	87.8%	83.7%/OR	82%

FOURTH TIER (ranking begins at 142; schools are listed alphabetically)

Rank/School	Peer assessment score (5.0=highest)	Assessment score by lawyers/judges (5.0=highest)	'07 undergrad GPA 25th-75th percentile	'07 LSAT score 25th-75th percentile	'07 acceptance rate	'07 student/faculty ratio	'06 grads employed at graduation	Employed 9 months after graduation	School's bar passage rate in jurisdiction	Jurisdiction's overall bar passage rate*
Appalachian School of Law (VA)	1.4	1.5	2.75-3.32	147-153	38.0%	21.0	N/A	69.1%	46.7%/VA	74%
Ave Maria School of Law (MI)	1.3	2.1	2.93-3.47	147-155	51.0%	15.7	N/A	73.3%	96.3%/MI	89%
Barry University (FL)	1.3	1.4	2.70-3.30	148-152	55.3%	20.7	N/A	80.3%	71.1%/FL	74%
California Western School of Law	1.8	2.1	3.00-3.53	150-156	54.9%	17.7	N/A	84.2%	67.6%/CA	65%
Campbell University (Wiggins) (NC)	1.6	2.3	2.94-3.55	151-157	36.2%	16.5	62.6%	93.9%	96.5%/NC	74%
Capital University (OH)	1.8	1.7	2.94-3.54	151-156	51.2%	16.2	N/A	82.1%	84.3%/OH	84%
CUNY–Queens College	2.0	2.2	2.92-3.47	151-156	24.6%	13.0	36.7%	87.7%	76.4%/NY	77%
Duquesne University (PA)	1.9	2.4	3.28-3.65	151-155	52.8%	18.2	N/A	86.1%	87.5%/PA	83%
Florida Coastal School of Law	1.4	1.5	2.81-3.47	149-154	54.9%	19.7	N/A	88.1%	73.7%/FL	74%
Florida International University	1.6	2.1	2.97-3.58	153-157	24.6%	15.0	21.4%	84.2%	82.5%/FL	74%
Golden Gate University (CA)	1.7	2.0	2.82-3.37	150-154	62.9%	18.9	N/A	77.6%	60.4%/CA	65%
John Marshall Law School (IL)	1.8	2.3	2.85-3.42	151-156	49.3%	17.9	N/A	87.5%	87.3%/IL	87%
Mississippi College	1.5	2.5	2.88-3.50	148-153	52.3%	18.9	45.4%	86.7%	83.0%/MS	88%
New England School of Law (MA)	1.8	2.2	3.02-3.52	150-153	57.7%	23.2	30.5%	76.1%	80.0%/MA	86%
North Carolina Central University	1.7	2.1	2.88-3.45	143-151	22.1%	17.6	N/A	81.4%	81.9%/NC	74%
Northern Illinois University	1.7	2.2	3.09-3.66	150-157	37.2%	18.6	55.0%	90.4%	84.4%/IL	87%
Northern Kentucky University (Chase)	1.7	1.6	3.07-3.56	153-156	43.3%	17.1	54.9%	88.6%	81.3%/KY	83%
Nova Southeastern University (Broad) (FL)	1.8	2.0	3.00-3.53	147-151	47.0%	14.1	N/A	85.4%	69.4%/FL	74%
Oklahoma City University	1.7	1.9	2.87-3.40	147-152	57.2%	18.2	N/A	84.4%	89.8%/OK	92%
Regent University (VA)	1.3	1.7	2.95-3.66	150-156	52.8%	20.0	40.6%	82.5%	73.7%/VA	74%
Roger Williams University (RI)	1.8	2.1	2.90-3.50	151-155	57.0%	18.3	N/A	83.8%	84.8%/MA	86%
Southern Illinois University–Carbondale	2.1	2.3	2.90-3.60	151-156	52.0%	11.7	N/A	85.4%	86.2%/IL	87%
Southern University (LA)	1.4	1.9	2.52-3.26	143-149	37.1%	13.0	79.4%	84.0%	62.6%/LA	75%
South Texas College of Law	1.7	2.2	2.99-3.52	150-155	50.5%	20.4	N/A	77.5%	81.6%/TX	82%
Southwestern Law School (CA)	2.0	2.1	3.06-3.58	153-157	33.5%	16.3	76.4%	85.1%	63.5%/CA	65%
St. Mary's University (TX)	1.8	2.3	2.80-3.41	149-156	51.1%	22.1	N/A	81.9%	82.6%/TX	82%
St. Thomas University (FL)	1.5	1.9	2.75-3.43	147-151	45.5%	18.0	N/A	83.0%	64.5%/FL	74%
Texas Southern University (Marshall)	1.4	1.9	2.83-3.29	146-151	35.9%	14.5	N/A	88.1%	56.2%/TX	82%
Texas Wesleyan University	1.7	1.6	2.89-3.40	152-156	45.8%	20.8	54.4%	82.7%	85.8%/TX	82%
Thomas Jefferson School of Law (CA)	1.5	2.1	2.75-3.23	148-151	45.4%	14.9	N/A	80.0%	54.5%/CA	65%
Thomas M. Cooley Law School (MI)	1.4	1.9	2.75-3.35	145-154	73.8%	24.3	N/A	73.3%	79.9%/MI	89%
Touro College (Fuchsberg) (NY)	1.7	1.7	2.81-3.32	150-153	43.4%	15.7	N/A	74.4%	78.4%/NY	77%
University of Dayton (OH)	2.0	2.4	2.96-3.50	149-154	50.7%	14.5	N/A	88.1%	78.0%/OH	84%
University of Detroit Mercy	1.6	2.1	2.95-3.36	146-154	46.6%	16.8	N/A	86.0%	92.0%/MI	89%
University of Memphis (Humphreys)	1.9	2.4	3.03-3.64	154-158	33.8%	17.7	36.0%	89.2%	91.1%/TN	78%
University of North Dakota	2.0	2.5	3.02-3.73	147-154	28.5%	17.7	N/A	92.4%	76.2%/ND	80%
University of the District of Columbia (Clarke)	1.4	1.5	2.70-3.40	148-153	18.7%	10.5	N/A	66.9%	53.8%/MD	77%
University of Tulsa (OK)	2.0	2.4	2.95-3.50	151-155	51.0%	13.5	56.1%	90.5%	88.2%/OK	92%
Valparaiso University (IN)	2.0	2.6	3.23-3.67	150-154	26.6%	15.8	39.4%	88.1%	82.5%/IN	83%
Western New England College (MA)	1.7	1.8	2.80-3.38	150-156	71.0%	13.8	N/A	76.1%	75.3%/MA	86%
Whittier Law School (CA)	1.4	2.0	2.56-3.19	149-153	61.6%	13.9	N/A	92.1%	55.6%/CA	65%
Widener University (DE)	2.0	2.1	2.88-3.46	150-154	51.0%	13.7	52.9%	82.8%	77.3%/PA	83%
William Mitchell College of Law (MN)	1.9	2.1	3.15-3.63	151-157	51.3%	22.5	N/A	90.0%	91.0%/MN	91%

Note: *The state bar examination pass rates for first-time test takers in summer 2006 and winter 2007 were provided by the National Conference of Bar Examiners.

Law School Diversity

To identify law schools where students are most likely to encounter classmates from different racial or ethnic groups, *U.S. News* has created a diversity index based on the total proportion of minority students—not including international students—and the mix of racial and ethnic groups on campus. The index is calculated using demographic data reflecting each law school's student body during the 2007–2008 academic year, including both full- and part-time students. The groups that form the basis for our calculations are African-Americans, Asian-Americans, Hispanics, American Indians, and non-Hispanic whites. Our formula produces a diversity index that ranges from 0.0 to 1.0. The closer a school's number is to 1.0, the more diverse is the student population. Law schools that enroll a large proportion of students from one ethnic group, even if it is a minority group, don't score high in this index. To be included in the table, a law school must be accredited by the American Bar Association. Because student-body ethnic diversity data are not consistently compiled and reported as yet for other types of graduate schools, *U.S. News* has prepared a diversity table for law schools only.

THE MOST DIVERSE SCHOOLS

School	Diversity index (1.0=highest)	Largest minority and its proportion
Texas Southern University (Marshall)	0.67	African-American, 47%
Florida A&M University	0.65	African-American, 47%
University of New Mexico	0.60	Hispanic, 29%
Florida International University	0.59	Hispanic, 42%
University of the District of Columbia (Clarke)	0.59	African-American, 28%
St. Thomas University (FL)	0.58	Hispanic, 32%
North Carolina Central University	0.57	African-American, 42%
Rutgers, the State U. of New Jersey–Newark	0.57	African-American, 14%
Santa Clara University (CA)	0.57	Asian-American, 28%
University of Southern California (Gould)	0.57	Asian-American, 17%
Loyola Marymount University (CA)	0.56	Asian-American, 24%
Northwestern University (IL)	0.56	Asian-American, 19%
University of San Francisco	0.56	Asian-American, 20%
University of Hawaii (Richardson)	0.54	Asian-American, 58%
University of Maryland	0.54	African-American, 14%
Southwestern Law School (CA)	0.53	Asian-American, 16%
Stanford University (CA)	0.53	Asian-American, 14%
Southern University (LA)	0.52	African-American, 54%
University of California–Davis	0.52	Asian-American, 25%
American University (Washington) (DC)	0.51	Hispanic, 12%
St. Mary's University (TX)	0.51	Hispanic, 24%
University of California–Los Angeles	0.51	Asian-American, 20%
Columbia University (NY)	0.50	Asian-American, 15%
CUNY–Queens College	0.50	Asian-American, 16%
Harvard University (MA)	0.50	African-American, 12%
University of California (Hastings)	0.50	Asian-American, 24%
University of California–Berkeley	0.50	Asian-American, 17%
University of La Verne (CA)	0.50	Hispanic, 16%
Whittier Law School (CA)	0.50	Asian-American, 20%
Thomas Jefferson School of Law (CA)	0.49	Hispanic, 13%
Western State University (CA)	0.49	Asian-American, 17%
University of Nevada–Las Vegas (Boyd)	0.47	Asian-American, 12%
University of Texas–Austin	0.47	Hispanic, 16%
Yale University (CT)	0.47	Asian-American, 14%
Emory University (GA)	0.46	Asian-American, 10%
University of Michigan–Ann Arbor	0.46	Asian-American, 14%
University of San Diego	0.46	Asian-American, 17%

School	Diversity index (1.0=highest)	Largest minority and its proportion
Brooklyn Law School (NY)	0.45	Asian-American, 15%
California Western School of Law	0.45	Asian-American, 14%
University of Arizona (Rogers)	0.45	Hispanic, 11%
University of Houston	0.45	Asian-American, 11%
University of Illinois–Urbana-Champaign	0.45	Asian-American, 13%
Arizona State University (O'Connor)	0.44	Hispanic, 14%
Golden Gate University (CA)	0.44	Asian-American, 18%
Northeastern University (MA)	0.44	Asian-American, 10%
University of Chicago	0.43	Asian-American, 12%
University of Pennsylvania	0.43	Asian-American, 9%
University of the Pacific (McGeorge) (CA)	0.43	Asian-American, 13%
George Washington University (DC)	0.42	Asian-American, 10%
Loyola University New Orleans	0.42	African-American, 11%
Nova Southeastern University (Broad) (FL)	0.42	Hispanic, 17%
Seattle University	0.42	Asian-American, 15%
University of Wisconsin–Madison	0.42	Hispanic, 8%
Fordham University (NY)	0.41	Hispanic, 10%
Georgetown University (DC)	0.41	Asian-American, 10%
South Texas College of Law	0.41	Asian-American, 11%
Chapman University (CA)	0.40	Asian-American, 15%
Hofstra University (NY)	0.40	African-American, 9%
John Marshall Law School–Atlanta	0.40	African-American, 16%
Ohio State University (Moritz)	0.40	Asian-American, 9%
Pennsylvania State University (Dickinson)	0.40	African-American, 9%
University of Arkansas–Fayetteville	0.40	African-American, 16%
Boston College	0.39	Asian-American, 11%
New York Law School	0.39	Asian-American, 9%
New York University	0.39	Asian-American, 11%
Southern Methodist University (TX)	0.39	Asian-American, 10%
St. John's University (NY)	0.39	Asian-American, 10%
University of Miami (FL)	0.39	Hispanic, 12%
University of Oklahoma	0.39	Native American, 10%
Cornell University (NY)	0.38	Asian-American, 10%
DePaul University (IL)	0.38	Hispanic, 10%
University of Colorado–Boulder	0.38	Asian-American, 8%
University of Notre Dame (IN)	0.38	Hispanic, 9%

Note: The diversity index is based on ethnicity data collected by *U.S. News* from each law school. The methodology used to compute the index was published in a 1992 article by Philip Meyer and Shawn McIntosh in the *International Journal of Public Opinion Research*. For this index, students classified as ethnicity unknown/unreported were counted as white. A more detailed explanation of the methodology is available at *www.usnews.com*.

Speaking the Global Language

From the sociology of outsourcing in Bangalore to understanding marital therapy in Mexico

By Diane Cole

Prof. Richard Appelbaum (left) and students in UCSB's Orfalea Center for Global and International Studies

Graduate schools are going global—that is, if they haven't done so already. These days, not only do students from around the world come to the United States for grad school (numbers have rebounded since 9/11). American students themselves are increasingly searching out research opportunities abroad—and using the experience to compete for jobs both in and out of academe. Maresi Nerad, director of the Center for Innovation and Research in Graduate Education at the University of Washington, says it's a two-way street: "Our social and environmental problems do not know national boundaries." And more graduate programs reflect that.

Amandeep Sandhu, for instance, who is completing a Ph.D. in sociology with an emphasis on global studies at the University of California–Santa Barbara, is writing his dissertation on the impact on workers in India of outsourcing by U.S. companies. As part of his research, he observed workers at a call center in Bangalore and shared a house with them. Listening to the complaints of the desperate American callers who had maxed out on their credit and then seeing the effect on the stressed-out call-center workers gave Sandhu a double perspective on a social, cultural, and economic phenomenon that cuts across continents. "Exposure to globalization should not be abstract," he says. "Going overseas and living and experiencing another culture makes it reality."

Vive la différence. As at UCSB, graduate programs are increasingly offering majors or minors in global studies, sometimes within individual departments and often through interdisciplinary centers. They include schools both public and private: Rutgers, Arizona State, the University of Minnesota, and the University of North Carolina, for instance, as well as Yale, Washington University, Northwestern, and others.

Twenty-nine percent of U.S. graduate schools have dual or joint degree programs with international universities; additionally, 24 percent plan to establish new programs over the next two years, according to the Council of Graduate Schools. To facilitate international collaboration, the council convened a conference last fall with representatives from the United States, Canada, Europe, China, and Australia. Such programs provide crucial preparation for a world that "requires new ways of sustaining international relationships," says the council's president, Debra Stewart.

Given the interest, perhaps it's no wonder that the Modern Language Association reports that the number of graduate students enrolled in language courses jumped from 36,715 in 2002 to 40,970 in 2006, with Arabic, Middle Eastern languages, and Asian languages showing the greatest increase. UCSB's Sandhu, for instance, spent a year in Cairo learning Arabic. And because individual languages (including English) are spoken in many different countries, the MLA is also encouraging language departments to broaden their scope to incorporate cultural components that go beyond language instruction alone.

Although an awareness of global and

Smart Choices

Think regional, says Scott Jaschik, editor of *InsideHigherEd*. With population spurts in Nevada, parts of California, Texas, Arizona, and Florida, colleges and universities are growing—and looking to hire. Community colleges are also growing, and they're a good fit for those who favor teaching over research.

international issues "was already there pre-9/11, that certainly encouraged interest" in Islamic and Middle Eastern studies as well as religion and politics, says Mark Juergensmeyer, director of the Orfalea Center for Global and International Studies and professor of sociology and global studies at UCSB. At the same time, he says, "students travel and study abroad; they see themselves as living in a global environment; and they see themselves as global citizens, so this kind of graduate work makes sense to them."

Indeed, "whether you're in environmental science or political science or any other field, the feeling is that you have to be aware of the world," says Gary Rhodes, director for the Center for Global Education at Loyola Marymount University in Los Angeles. LMU, for example, offers M.A. candidates in marital and family therapy a summer program in Mexico. Both U.S. and Mexican students participate. As well as earning credit in art therapy courses, they learn about each other's language and culture.

On location. Even English departments and American studies programs have grown increasingly international in focus, and so have history, film, and media studies, says David Marshall, dean of humanities and fine arts at UCSB. In a multicultural country and world, all these fields benefit from international perspectives, he says. In fact, this approach comes naturally to the humanities, he believes, because so much of that discipline "is based on the study of different languages, literatures, and cultures." In the social sciences, says UCSB Social Sciences Dean Melvin Oliver, there is a similar drive to understand how religious, ethnic, racial, political, and national identities transcend borders.

In addition to allowing candidates in individual disciplines to graduate with an emphasis in global studies, UCSB offers a two-year master's that prepares students for careers in the global nonprofit or government sectors. When she receives her degree this spring, Flora Ferati, originally from Kosovo, will look for a position with an organization working toward conflict resolution and human-rights protection. Eddie Saade, also in his second year, is interested in bloggers in the Middle East.

The program, with students with differing concerns from all over the world, is itself a model for cooperation, he finds. "We all support rather than compete with or undercut each other. We ask questions, share information, and help each other," he says. Could there be a better goal for global education? ●

REALITY CHECK SOURCES: AMERICAN ASSOCIATION OF UNIVERSITY PROFESSORS; MODERN LANGUAGE ASSOCIATION; NATIONAL CENTER FOR EDUCATION STATISTICS

Insider Tip

As a single mother in academe in the late '80s, Shirley Tilghman learned firsthand what it meant to juggle work and parenting. As president of Princeton University, Tilghman has set a standard for other institutions with friendlier policies toward graduates and postdocs with families. Benefits include a three-month maternity leave with extended deadlines, need-based child-care grants, and subsidized emergency-backup care. Stanford University, University of California-Berkeley, and Massachusetts Institute of Technology also offer family-friendly packages.

Getting In

Make the Best Match. Before you commit—or even apply—make sure the program profile matches your goals. Meet with faculty, but talk to current students, too. Ask about study projects and job prospects. And remember: It's the reputation of the individual department, not that of the university as a whole, that bestows prestige on your degree—and, by extension, you.

Don't Get Stuck in Limbo. How long do you expect to remain in grad school? Science and engineering students take six to seven years, humanities grads need about 10, and about 19 percent drop out altogether by Year 4, according to the Council of Graduate Schools' Ph.D. Completion Project. Some universities, such as Brown, Harvard, and Princeton, hope to keep students by guaranteeing funding for five years. And a University of Washington study urges better career prep for teaching jobs in academe—and communication and other skills needed for jobs outside the university.

Reality Check

Interested in teaching college? Faculty pay rose 3.8% last year, outpacing inflation for the first time in three years · In keeping with the current interest in all things global, available teaching positions in foreign languages rose from 1,591 to 1,660 while those in English declined from 1,793 to 1,720 · The number of Ph.D.'s awarded continues to grow, with 45,596 granted in '06 compared with 43,385 in '05. Of those, 15,947 went to noncitizens · The number of doctorates awarded by 2016-17 is projected to rise 10% for men and 54% for women over 2004-05 figures

Princeton is reaching out to grad students like Rachel Riedl and her daughter, Adelaide.

The Sciences

Ph.D. programs ranked best by deans and department chairs

BIOLOGICAL SCIENCES

Ranked in 2007

Listed schools may have multiple programs. Methodology is on Page 58.

Rank/School	Average assessment score (5.0=highest)
1. Stanford University (CA)	4.9
2. Massachusetts Institute of Technology	4.8
University of California–Berkeley	4.8
4. California Institute of Technology	4.7
Harvard University (MA)	4.7
6. Johns Hopkins University (MD)	4.6
7. Rockefeller University (NY)	4.5
Scripps Research Institute (CA)	4.5
University of California–San Francisco	4.5
Washington University in St. Louis	4.5
Yale University (CT)	4.5
12. Cornell University (NY)	4.4
Duke University (NC)	4.4
Princeton University (NJ)	4.4
15. Columbia University (NY)	4.3
University of Michigan–Ann Arbor	4.3
University of Wisconsin–Madison	4.3
18. University of California–San Diego	4.2
University of Chicago	4.2
University of Washington	4.2
21. University of Pennsylvania	4.1
University of Texas Southwestern Medical Center–Dallas	4.1
23. University of California–Davis	4.0
University of California–Los Angeles	4.0
University of Texas–Austin	4.0
26. Baylor College of Medicine (TX)	3.9
Cornell University (Weill) (NY)	3.9
University of North Carolina–Chapel Hill	3.9
29. Indiana University–Bloomington	3.8
Mayo Medical School (MN)	3.8
Northwestern University (IL)	3.8
University of Illinois–Urbana-Champaign	3.8
33. University of Colorado–Boulder	3.7
34. Brown University (RI)	3.6
Carnegie Mellon University (PA)	3.6
Dartmouth College (NH)	3.6
Emory University (GA)	3.6
Michigan State University	3.6
University of California–Irvine	3.6
University of Minnesota–Twin Cities	3.6
Vanderbilt University (TN)	3.6
42. Case Western Reserve University (OH)	3.5
Ohio State University	3.5
Pennsylvania State University–University Park	3.5
Purdue University–West Lafayette (IN)	3.5
University of Arizona	3.5
University of Virginia	3.5
48. Brandeis University (MA)	3.4
Rice University (TX)	3.4
Rutgers, the State Univ. of New Jersey–New Brunswick	3.4
SUNY–Stony Brook	3.4
University of Colorado–Denver and Health Sciences Center	3.4
University of Florida	3.4

Rank/School	Average assessment score (5.0=highest)
University of Iowa	3.4
University of Maryland–College Park	3.4
University of Oregon	3.4
Yeshiva University (Einstein) (NY)	3.4
58. Arizona State University	3.3
Mount Sinai School of Medicine (NY)	3.3
New York University	3.3
University of Alabama–Birmingham	3.3
University of California–Santa Barbara	3.3
University of Georgia	3.3
University of Kansas	3.3
University of Massachusetts Medical Center–Worcester	3.3
University of Pittsburgh	3.3
University of Utah	3.3

BIOLOGICAL SCIENCES SPECIALTIES

BIOCHEMISTRY/BIOPHYSICS/ STRUCTURAL BIOLOGY
1. Harvard University (MA)
2. Massachusetts Inst. of Tech.
3. Stanford University (CA)
4. California Inst. of Technology
   Univ. of Calif.–San Francisco
   Yale University (CT)
7. University of California–Berkeley
8. Johns Hopkins University (MD)
9. Rockefeller University (NY)
10. Duke University (NC)
   Univ. of California–San Diego
   Univ. of Texas Southwestern
   Medical Center–Dallas
   Washington Univ. in St. Louis

CELL BIOLOGY
1. Harvard University (MA)
2. Massachusetts Inst. of Tech.
3. Stanford University (CA)
4. Univ. of Calif.–San Francisco
5. University of California–Berkeley
   Yale University (CT)
7. Johns Hopkins University (MD)
   Rockefeller University (NY)
9. Washington Univ. in St. Louis
10. California Inst. of Technology
   Duke University (NC)

ECOLOGY/EVOLUTIONARY BIOLOGY
1. University of Chicago
2. Harvard University (MA)
   University of California–Berkeley
4. University of California–Davis
5. Duke University (NC)
6. Cornell University (NY)
7. Stanford University (CA)
8. Princeton University (NJ)

University of Texas–Austin
10. University of Georgia

GENETICS/GENOMICS/ BIOINFORMATICS
1. Massachusetts Inst. of Tech.
   Stanford University (CA)
3. Harvard University (MA)
4. University of California–Berkeley
   Washington Univ. in St. Louis
6. California Inst. of Technology
   Univ. of Calif.–San Francisco
8. Johns Hopkins University (MD)
9. University of Washington
   Yale University (CT)

IMMUNOLOGY/INFECTIOUS DISEASE
1. Harvard University (MA)
2. Stanford University (CA)
3. Univ. of Calif.–San Francisco
4. Yale University (CT)
5. Johns Hopkins University (MD)
   Washington Univ. in St. Louis
7. Rockefeller University (NY)
   University of Pennsylvania
9. Duke University (NC)
   Univ. of Texas Southwestern
   Medical Center–Dallas

MICROBIOLOGY
1. Harvard University (MA)
2. Stanford University (CA)
3. Univ. of Wisconsin–Madison
   Washington Univ. in St. Louis
5. Univ. of California–Berkeley
6. Massachusetts Inst. of Tech.
7. Univ. of Calif.–San Francisco
8. Johns Hopkins Univ. (MD)
   Univ. of Calif.–Los Angeles
   University of Pennsylvania

MOLECULAR BIOLOGY

1. Harvard University (MA)
2. Massachusetts Inst. of Tech.
3. Stanford University (CA)
4. Univ. of Calif.–San Francisco
5. Univ. of California–Berkeley
6. California Inst. of Technology
   Rockefeller University (NY)
8. Johns Hopkins Univ. (MD)
   Princeton University (NJ)
   Yale University (CT)

NEUROSCIENCE/NEUROBIOLOGY

1. Harvard University (MA)
2. Stanford University (CA)
3. Johns Hopkins University (MD)
4. Massachusetts Inst. of Tech.
5. Univ. of California–San Diego
6. Univ. of Calif.–San Francisco
7. Rockefeller University (NY)
   Yale University (CT)
9. Washington Univ. in St. Louis
10. California Inst. of Technology
    Columbia University (NY)

CHEMISTRY

Ranked in 2007

Rank/School	Average assessment score (5.0=highest)
1. California Institute of Technology	4.9
Massachusetts Institute of Technology	4.9
Stanford University (CA)	4.9
University of California–Berkeley	4.9
5. Harvard University (MA)	4.8
6. Scripps Research Institute (CA)	4.6
7. University of Illinois–Urbana-Champaign	4.5
University of Wisconsin–Madison	4.5
9. Cornell University (NY)	4.4
Northwestern University (IL)	4.4
11. Columbia University (NY)	4.3
12. University of California–Los Angeles	4.2
University of Chicago	4.2
University of Texas–Austin	4.2
15. Yale University (CT)	4.1
16. Pennsylvania State University–University Park	4.0
Princeton University (NJ)	4.0
University of Michigan–Ann Arbor	4.0
University of North Carolina–Chapel Hill	4.0
20. University of California–San Diego	3.9
University of Pennsylvania	3.9
22. Purdue University–West Lafayette (IN)	3.8
Texas A&M University–College Station	3.8
University of California–Irvine	3.8
University of Minnesota–Twin Cities	3.8
26. Georgia Institute of Technology	3.7
University of California–Santa Barbara	3.7
28. Johns Hopkins University (MD)	3.6
Ohio State University	3.6
Rice University (TX)	3.6
University of California–San Francisco	3.6
University of Colorado–Boulder	3.6
University of Washington	3.6
34. Indiana University–Bloomington	3.5
University of California–Davis	3.5
36. Emory University (GA)	3.4
Iowa State University	3.4
Michigan State University	3.4
University of Arizona	3.4
University of Florida	3.4
University of Maryland–College Park	3.4
University of Utah	3.4
43. Colorado State University	3.3
Duke University (NC)	3.3
University of Pittsburgh	3.3
University of Southern California	3.3
Washington University in St. Louis	3.3
48. Florida State University	3.2
University of California–Riverside	3.2

CHEMISTRY SPECIALTIES

ANALYTICAL

1. University of North Carolina–Chapel Hill
2. Purdue U.–West Lafayette (IN)
3. University of Illinois–Urbana-Champaign
4. Indiana University–Bloomington
5. University of Texas–Austin
6. University of Wisconsin–Madison
7. University of Arizona
8. Pennsylvania State University–University Park
9. Univ. of Michigan–Ann Arbor
10. University of Florida
    University of Washington

BIOCHEMISTRY

1. University of California–Berkeley
2. Massachusetts Inst. of Tech.
3. Harvard University (MA)
4. Stanford University (CA)
   Univ. of Calif.–San Francisco
6. Scripps Research Institute (CA)
7. University of Wisconsin–Madison
8. California Inst. of Technology
9. Univ. of California–San Diego
10. Yale University (CT)

INORGANIC

1. Massachusetts Inst. of Tech.
2. California Inst. of Technology
3. Northwestern University (IL)
4. University of California–Berkeley
5. Texas A&M U.–College Station
6. University of Illinois–Urbana-Champaign
7. University of Wisconsin–Madison
8. Stanford University (CA)
9. Cornell University (NY)
10. University of North Carolina–Chapel Hill

ORGANIC

1. Harvard University (MA)
2. University of California–Berkeley
3. Stanford University (CA)
4. Massachusetts Inst. of Tech.
5. California Inst. of Technology
6. Scripps Research Institute (CA)
7. University of Illinois–Urbana-Champaign
8. University of Wisconsin–Madison
9. Columbia University (NY)
10. University of California–Irvine

PHYSICAL

1. University of California–Berkeley
2. California Inst. of Technology
3. Massachusetts Inst. of Tech.
4. Stanford University (CA)
5. Harvard University (MA)
6. University of Illinois–Urbana-Champaign
7. University of Chicago
8. Northwestern University (IL)
   University of Wisconsin–Madison
10. University of Colorado–Boulder

THEORETICAL

1. University of California–Berkeley
2. California Inst. of Technology
3. Massachusetts Inst. of Tech.
   Northwestern University (IL)
5. Harvard University (MA)
   University of Chicago
7. Columbia University (NY)
8. University of Illinois–Urbana-Champaign
9. University of Wisconsin–Madison
10. University of Minnesota–Twin Cities

COMPUTER SCIENCE

Ranked in 2008

Rank/School	Average assessment score (5.0=highest)
1. Massachusetts Institute of Technology	5.0
Stanford University (CA)	5.0
University of California–Berkeley	5.0
4. Carnegie Mellon University (PA)	4.9
5. University of Illinois–Urbana-Champaign	4.6
6. Cornell University (NY)	4.5
Princeton University (NJ)	4.5
University of Washington	4.5
9. Georgia Institute of Technology	4.3
University of Texas–Austin	4.3
11. California Institute of Technology	4.2
University of Wisconsin–Madison	4.2

Continued on Page 56

COMPUTER SCIENCE

Ranked in 2008

Rank/School	Average assessment score (5.0=highest)
13. University of California–Los Angeles	4.0
University of Maryland–College Park	4.0
University of Michigan–Ann Arbor	4.0
16. Columbia University (NY)	3.9
Harvard University (MA)	3.9
University of California–San Diego	3.9
19. Purdue University–West Lafayette (IN)	3.8
20. Brown University (RI)	3.7
Duke University (NC)	3.7
Rice University (TX)	3.7
University of Massachusetts–Amherst	3.7
University of North Carolina–Chapel Hill	3.7
University of Pennsylvania	3.7
University of Southern California	3.7
Yale University (CT)	3.7
28. Johns Hopkins University (MD)	3.6
29. Pennsylvania State University–University Park	3.5
University of Virginia	3.5
31. New York University	3.4
Ohio State University	3.4
Rutgers, the State U. of New Jersey–New Brunswick	3.4
SUNY–Stony Brook	3.4
University of California–Irvine	3.4
University of Minnesota–Twin Cities	3.4
37. University of California–Davis	3.3
University of California–Santa Barbara	3.3

EARTH SCIENCES

Ranked in 2006

Rank/School	Average assessment score (5.0=highest)
1. California Institute of Technology	4.9
2. Massachusetts Institute of Technology	4.8
Stanford University (CA)	4.8
4. University of California–Berkeley	4.6
5. Columbia University (NY)	4.4
University of Michigan–Ann Arbor	4.4
7. Pennsylvania State University–University Park	4.3
8. University of Arizona	4.2
9. Harvard University (MA)	4.1
University of Texas–Austin	4.1
11. Princeton University (NJ)	4.0
University of California–Los Angeles	4.0
University of Washington	4.0
Yale University (CT)	4.0
15. Cornell University (NY)	3.9
University of California–San Diego	3.9
University of Chicago	3.9
University of Wisconsin–Madison	3.9
19. Brown University (RI)	3.8
University of California–Santa Cruz	3.8
21. Johns Hopkins University (MD)	3.7
University of California–Davis	3.7
University of California–Santa Barbara	3.7
University of Minnesota–Twin Cities	3.7
25. Rice University (TX)	3.6
University of Colorado–Boulder	3.6
Washington University in St. Louis	3.6

COMPUTER SCIENCE SPECIALTIES

ARTIFICIAL INTELLIGENCE
1. Massachusetts Inst. of Tech.
2. Carnegie Mellon University (PA)
3. Stanford University (CA)
4. University of California–Berkeley
5. University of Texas–Austin
   University of Washington
7. Georgia Institute of Technology
   University of Illinois–
   Urbana-Champaign
9. Univ. of Maryland–College Park
10. U. of Massachusetts–Amherst

SYSTEMS
1. University of California–Berkeley
2. Massachusetts Inst. of Tech.
3. Stanford University (CA)
4. Carnegie Mellon University (PA)
5. University of Washington
6. University of Illinois–
   Urbana-Champaign
7. Univ. of Wisconsin–Madison
8. University of Texas–Austin
9. Univ. of California–San Diego
10. Georgia Institute of Technology

PROGRAMMING LANGUAGE
1. Carnegie Mellon University (PA)
2. University of California–Berkeley
3. Stanford University (CA)
4. Massachusetts Inst. of Tech.
5. Cornell University (NY)
6. Princeton University (NJ)
   University of Illinois–
   Urbana-Champaign
8. University of Texas–Austin
9. Rice University (TX)
10. Univ. of Wisconsin–Madison

THEORY
1. University of California–Berkeley
2. Massachusetts Inst. of Tech.
3. Stanford University (CA)
4. Cornell University (NY)
   Princeton University (NJ)
6. Carnegie Mellon University (PA)
7. University of Washington
8. Harvard University (MA)
9. Georgia Institute of Technology
10. University of Texas–Austin

EARTH SCIENCES SPECIALTIES

GEOCHEMISTRY
1. California Institute
   of Technology
2. Pennsylvania State University–
   University Park
3. University of California–Berkeley
4. Massachusetts Institute
   of Technology
5. Univ. of Michigan–Ann Arbor
6. Columbia University (NY)
7. Yale University (CT)
8. Harvard University (MA)
9. Stanford University (CA)
10. University of Maryland–
    College Park

GEOLOGY
1. Stanford University (CA)
2. Massachusetts Institute
   of Technology
3. California Institute
   of Technology
   Pennsylvania State University–
   University Park
5. Univ. of Michigan–Ann Arbor
   University of Texas–Austin
7. University of Arizona
8. University of California–Berkeley
9. Univ. of Wisconsin–Madison
10. University of Washington

GEOPHYSICS AND SEISMOLOGY
1. California Institute
   of Technology
2. Massachusetts Institute
   of Technology
3. Stanford University (CA)
4. University of California–Berkeley
5. University of California–
   San Diego
6. Columbia University (NY)
7. Harvard University (MA)
8. University of Texas–Austin
9. Princeton University (NJ)
10. Colorado School of Mines
    Univ. of California–Los Angeles

PALEONTOLOGY
1. University of Chicago
2. Harvard University (MA)
3. Univ. of Michigan–Ann Arbor
   Yale University (CT)
5. University of California–Berkeley
6. University of Kansas
7. University of Cincinnati
8. University of Iowa
9. University of Texas–Austin
10. Ohio State University

MATHEMATICS

Ranked in 2008
Rank/School

Rank/School	Average assessment score (5.0=highest)
1. Princeton University (NJ)	5.0
2. Harvard University (MA)	4.9
Massachusetts Institute of Technology	4.9
Stanford University (CA)	4.9
University of California–Berkeley	4.9
6. University of Chicago	4.8
7. California Institute of Technology	4.6
Yale University (CT)	4.6
9. Columbia University (NY)	4.5
New York University	4.5
University of Michigan–Ann Arbor	4.5
12. University of California–Los Angeles	4.4
13. Cornell University (NY)	4.3
14. Brown University (RI)	4.2
University of Texas–Austin	4.2
University of Wisconsin–Madison	4.2
17. University of Minnesota–Twin Cities	4.1
18. Northwestern University (IL)	4.0
University of Illinois–Urbana-Champaign	4.0
University of Pennsylvania	4.0
21. Duke University (NC)	3.9
Johns Hopkins University (MD)	3.9
University of Maryland–College Park	3.9
24. Rutgers, the State U. of New Jersey–New Brunswick	3.8
SUNY–Stony Brook	3.8
University of California–San Diego	3.8
University of Washington	3.8
28. Indiana University–Bloomington	3.7
Pennsylvania State University–University Park	3.7
Purdue University–West Lafayette (IN)	3.7
Rice University (TX)	3.7
University of North Carolina–Chapel Hill	3.7
33. Carnegie Mellon University (PA)	3.6
Ohio State University	3.6
University of Utah	3.6
36. CUNY Graduate School and University Center	3.5
Georgia Institute of Technology	3.5
University of California–Davis	3.5
University of Illinois–Chicago	3.5
40. Brandeis University (MA)	3.4
University of Arizona	3.4
University of Virginia	3.4
Washington University in St. Louis	3.4

APPLIED MATH
1. New York University
2. Massachusetts Inst. of Tech.
3. California Inst. of Technology
   Univ. of California–Los Angeles
5. University of Minnesota–Twin Cities
6. Brown University (RI)
7. Princeton University (NJ)
   University of California–Berkeley
9. Stanford University (CA)
   University of Texas–Austin

DISCRETE MATHEMATICS AND COMBINATIONS
1. Massachusetts Inst. of Tech.
2. Rutgers, the State U. of New Jersey–New Brunswick
   University of California–Berkeley
4. Univ. of California–San Diego
   University of Michigan–Ann Arbor
6. Princeton University (NJ)
7. Georgia Institute of Technology
8. Univ. of California–Los Angeles
9. University of Illinois–Urbana-Champaign
10. University of Minnesota–Twin Cities

GEOMETRY
1. Harvard University (MA)
2. Princeton University (NJ)
3. Massachusetts Inst. of Tech.
4. Stanford University (CA)
   University of California–Berkeley
6. SUNY–Stony Brook
7. Columbia University (NY)
8. University of Pennsylvania
9. University of Chicago
10. University of Michigan–Ann Arbor
    Yale University (CT)

LOGIC
1. University of California–Berkeley
2. Univ. of California–Los Angeles

3. University of Wisconsin–Madison
4. Cornell University (NY)
   University of Illinois–Urbana-Champaign
6. Carnegie Mellon University (PA)
   Stanford University (CA)
   University of Chicago
9. Massachusetts Inst. of Tech.
   Rutgers, the State U. of New Jersey–New Brunswick
   University of Notre Dame (IN)

STATISTICS
1. Stanford University (CA)
   University of California–Berkeley
3. University of North Carolina–Chapel Hill
4. Harvard University (MA)
5. Iowa State University
6. Duke University (NC)
   University of Chicago
   University of Washington
9. University of Florida
10. Princeton University (NJ)
    Purdue University–West Lafayette (IN)
    University of Michigan–Ann Arbor
    University of Wisconsin–Madison

TOPOLOGY
1. University of California–Berkeley
2. Princeton University (NJ)
3. Harvard University (MA)
4. University of Chicago
5. Massachusetts Inst. of Tech.
6. Columbia University (NY)
7. University of Texas–Austin
8. Stanford University (CA)
9. Yale University (CT)
10. Cornell University (NY)
    University of Michigan–Ann Arbor

MATHEMATICS SPECIALTIES

ALGEBRA/NUMBER THEORY/ ALGEBRAIC GEOMETRY
1. Princeton University (NJ)
2. Harvard University (MA)
3. University of California–Berkeley
4. University of Michigan–Ann Arbor
5. University of Chicago
6. Massachusetts Inst. of Tech.
7. Yale University (CT)
8. Columbia University (NY)
9. Stanford University (CA)
10. Univ. of California–Los Angeles

ANALYSIS
1. Princeton University (NJ)
2. University of California–Berkeley
3. Massachusetts Inst. of Tech.
4. Univ. of California–Los Angeles
5. New York University
6. University of Chicago
7. Harvard University (MA)
   University of Wisconsin–Madison
9. University of Michigan–Ann Arbor
10. University of Texas–Austin

PHYSICS

Ranked in 2008
Rank/School

Rank/School	Average assessment score (5.0=highest)
1. Massachusetts Institute of Technology	5.0
Stanford University (CA)	5.0
3. California Institute of Technology	4.9
Harvard University (MA)	4.9
Princeton University (NJ)	4.9
University of California–Berkeley	4.9
7. Cornell University (NY)	4.7
8. University of Chicago	4.6
University of Illinois–Urbana-Champaign	4.6
10. University of California–Santa Barbara	4.5
11. Columbia University (NY)	4.3

Continued on Page 58

PHYSICS

Ranked in 2008

Rank/School	Average assessment score (5.0=highest)
Yale University (CT)	4.3
13. University of Maryland–College Park	4.2
University of Michigan–Ann Arbor	4.2
University of Pennsylvania	4.2
16. University of California–Los Angeles	4.1
University of California–San Diego	4.1
University of Texas–Austin	4.1
University of Wisconsin–Madison	4.1
20. Johns Hopkins University (MD)	4.0
University of Colorado–Boulder	4.0
University of Washington	4.0
23. Pennsylvania State University–University Park	3.8
SUNY–Stony Brook	3.8
University of Minnesota–Twin Cities	3.8
26. Northwestern University (IL)	3.7
Ohio State University	3.7
Rutgers, the State U. of New Jersey–New Brunswick	3.7
29. Brown University (RI)	3.6
Carnegie Mellon University (PA)	3.6
Duke University (NC)	3.6
Michigan State University	3.6
Rice University (TX)	3.6
University of California–Davis	3.6
University of California–Irvine	3.6
36. Boston University	3.5
Georgia Institute of Technology	3.5
Purdue University–West Lafayette (IN)	3.5
University of Florida	3.5
University of North Carolina–Chapel Hill	3.5
University of Virginia	3.5
42. New York University	3.4
University of Arizona	3.4
University of Rochester (NY)	3.4

PHYSICS SPECIALTIES

ATOMIC/MOLECULAR/OPTICAL

1. University of Colorado–Boulder
2. Massachusetts Institute of Technology
3. Harvard University (MA)
4. Stanford University (CA)
5. Univ. of Maryland–College Park
6. University of Michigan–Ann Arbor
7. California Inst. of Technology
8. University of Rochester (NY)
9. Rice University (TX)
   University of California–Berkeley

CONDENSED MATTER

1. University of Illinois–Urbana-Champaign
2. Massachusetts Institute of Technology
3. Harvard University (MA)
4. University of California–Santa Barbara
5. Cornell University (NY)
6. Stanford University (CA)
7. University of California–Berkeley
8. Princeton University (NJ)
9. University of Chicago
10. California Inst. of Technology
    University of California–San Diego

COSMOLOGY/RELATIVITY/GRAVITY

1. California Inst. of Technology
2. Princeton University (NJ)
3. University of Chicago
4. University of California–Berkeley
5. Stanford University (CA)
6. Massachusetts Institute of Technology
7. Harvard University (MA)
8. University of Texas–Austin
9. Pennsylvania State University–University Park
10. Cornell University (NY)

ELEMENTARY PARTICLES/FIELDS/STRING THEORY

1. California Inst. of Technology
   Massachusetts Institute of Technology

3. Harvard University (MA)
4. Princeton University (NJ)
5. University of California–Berkeley
6. Stanford University (CA)
7. University of California–Santa Barbara
   University of Chicago
9. Cornell University (NY)
10. Columbia University (NY)

NUCLEAR

1. Massachusetts Institute of Technology
2. Michigan State University
3. University of Washington
4. SUNY–Stony Brook
5. Yale University (CT)
6. Columbia University (NY)
   Indiana University–Bloomington
8. California Inst. of Technology
   University of Illinois–Urbana-Champaign
10. Univ. of Maryland–College Park

PLASMA

1. Princeton University (NJ)
2. Massachusetts Institute of Technology

Univ. of Maryland–College Park
University of Wisconsin–Madison
5. University of Texas–Austin
6. University of California–Los Angeles
7. University of California–Berkeley
   University of California–San Diego
9. University of Iowa
10. University of Colorado–Boulder

QUANTUM

1. Massachusetts Institute of Technology
2. Harvard University (MA)
3. California Inst. of Technology
4. Princeton University (NJ)
   Stanford University (CA)
   University of Colorado–Boulder
7. University of California–Berkeley
   University of Illinois–Urbana-Champaign
9. Cornell University (NY)
   Univ. of Maryland–College Park

METHODOLOGY

Rankings of doctoral programs in the sciences are based on the results of surveys sent to academics in computer science, mathematics, and physics during the fall of 2007, in biological sciences and chemistry during fall 2006, and in other fields during fall 2005. The individuals rated the quality of the program at each institution from "marginal" (1) to "outstanding" (5).

Individuals who were unfamiliar with a particular school's programs were asked to select "don't know." The schools with the highest average scores among those who rated them were sorted in descending order and appear here.

Surveys in biological sciences, chemistry, computer science, earth sciences, mathematics, and physics were conducted by Synovate. The universe of schools surveyed in computer science, mathematics, and physics consisted of schools that awarded at least five doctoral degrees according to the National Science Foundation report "Science and Engineering Doctorate Awards" for the years from 2001 through 2006, in bi-

ological sciences and chemistry for the years from 2000 through 2005, and for earth sciences from 1999 through 2004. In biological sciences, graduate programs may be offered in a university's medical school or its college of arts and sciences. If so, the programs were ranked separately.

Questionnaires were sent to the department heads and directors of graduate studies at each program in each discipline. Response rates were as follows: For biological sciences, 21 percent of those surveyed responded; for chemistry, 32 percent; for computer science, 48 percent; for earth sciences, 40 percent; for mathematics, 33 percent; and for physics, 32 percent.

Specialty rankings are based solely on nominations by department heads and directors of graduate studies at peer schools from the list of schools surveyed. These respondents ranked up to 10 programs in each area. Those with the most votes appear here.

Expanded rankings can be found at *www.usnews.com*.

Social Sciences & Humanities

Ph.D. programs ranked best by department chairs and senior faculty

CRIMINOLOGY

Ranked in 2005

Rank/School	Average assessment score (5.0=highest)
1. University of Maryland–College Park	4.9
2. SUNY–Albany	4.7
3. University of Cincinnati	4.1
4. Rutgers, the State Univ. of New Jersey–New Brunswick	4.0
University of California–Irvine	4.0
University of Missouri–St. Louis	4.0
7. Michigan State University	3.6
Pennsylvania State University–University Park	3.6
9. University of Nebraska–Omaha	3.3
University of Pennsylvania	3.3
11. CUNY–John Jay College	3.2
Florida State University	3.2
University of Florida	3.2
14. Northeastern University (MA)	3.1
University of Delaware	3.1

ECONOMICS

Ranked in 2005

Rank/School	Average assessment score (5.0=highest)
1. Massachusetts Institute of Technology	5.0
University of Chicago	5.0
3. Harvard University (MA)	4.9
Princeton University (NJ)	4.9
Stanford University (CA)	4.9
University of California–Berkeley	4.9
7. Yale University (CT)	4.8
8. Northwestern University (IL)	4.6
9. University of Pennsylvania	4.5
10. University of California–San Diego	4.3
11. Columbia University (NY)	4.2
University of California–Los Angeles	4.2
University of Michigan–Ann Arbor	4.2
University of Wisconsin–Madison	4.2
15. New York University	4.1
University of Minnesota–Twin Cities	4.1
17. California Institute of Technology	4.0
Cornell University (NY)	4.0
19. University of Rochester (NY)	3.9
20. Carnegie Mellon University (PA)	3.8
21. Brown University (RI)	3.7
Duke University (NC)	3.7
University of Maryland–College Park	3.7
24. Johns Hopkins University (MD)	3.6
25. Boston University	3.5
University of Texas–Austin	3.5

ECONOMICS SPECIALTIES

DEVELOPMENT ECONOMICS
1. Harvard University (MA)
2. University of California–Berkeley
3. Massachusetts Inst. of Tech.
4. Princeton University (NJ)
   Yale University (CT)
6. University of Chicago
7. Columbia University (NY)

University of Pennsylvania
9. Stanford University (CA)
10. Brown University (RI)
    Cornell University (NY)
    New York University
    Univ. of California–Los Angeles

ECONOMETRICS
1. Massachusetts Inst. of Tech.
2. Univ. of California–San Diego
3. Yale University (CT)
4. University of California–Berkeley
5. Harvard University (MA)
   Princeton University (NJ)
7. University of Chicago
8. Northwestern University (IL)
9. Stanford University (CA)
10. Univ. of Wisconsin–Madison

INDUSTRIAL ORGANIZATION
1. Stanford University (CA)
2. Harvard University (MA)
3. Massachusetts Inst. of Tech.
   Northwestern University (IL)
5. University of California–Berkeley
6. Yale University (CT)
7. University of Chicago
8. Princeton University (NJ)
9. University of Pennsylvania
10. New York University
    Univ. of California–Los Angeles

INTERNATIONAL ECONOMICS
1. Harvard University (MA)
2. Columbia University (NY)
   Princeton University (NJ)
4. Univ. of California–Berkeley
5. Massachusetts Inst. of Tech.
   Univ. of Michigan–Ann Arbor
7. Univ. of Wisconsin–Madison
8. Univ. of California–Los Angeles
   Yale University (CT)
10. University of Chicago

LABOR ECONOMICS
1. University of Chicago

2. Princeton University (NJ)
3. Harvard University (MA)
4. Massachusetts Inst. of Tech.
5. University of California–Berkeley
6. Stanford University (CA)
7. Cornell University (NY)
8. Univ. of Michigan–Ann Arbor
9. Univ. of California–Los Angeles
   University of Pennsylvania
   Yale University (CT)

MACROECONOMICS
1. Massachusetts Inst. of Tech.
2. University of Chicago
3. Harvard University (MA)
4. Stanford University (CA)
5. Univ. of Minnesota–Twin Cities
6. Princeton University (NJ)
7. University of Pennsylvania
8. Northwestern University (IL)
   University of California–Berkeley
10. New York University

MICROECONOMICS
1. Harvard University (MA)
2. Stanford University (CA)
3. Massachusetts Inst. of Tech.
4. Princeton University (NJ)
5. University of California–Berkeley
   University of Chicago
7. University of Pennsylvania
8. Yale University (CT)
9. Northwestern University (IL)
10. California Inst. of Technology

PUBLIC FINANCE
1. Massachusetts Inst. of Tech.
2. Harvard University (MA)
3. University of California–Berkeley
4. Princeton University (NJ)
5. Stanford University (CA)
6. Univ. of Michigan–Ann Arbor
7. University of Chicago
8. Univ. of Wisconsin–Madison
9. University of Pennsylvania
10. Univ. of Maryland–College Park

ENGLISH

Ranked in 2005

Rank/School	Average assessment score (5.0=highest)
1. Harvard University (MA)	4.9
University of California–Berkeley	4.9
Yale University (CT)	4.9
4. Princeton University (NJ)	4.8
Stanford University (CA)	4.8

Continued on Page 60

ENGLISH

Ranked in 2005

Rank/School	Average assessment score (5.0=highest)
6. Cornell University (NY)	4.7
University of Chicago	4.7
8. Columbia University (NY)	4.6
Johns Hopkins University (MD)	4.6
10. University of California–Los Angeles	4.5
University of Pennsylvania	4.5
12. Duke University (NC)	4.4
University of Michigan–Ann Arbor	4.4
University of Virginia	4.4
15. Brown University (RI)	4.3
16. Rutgers, the State Univ. of New Jersey–New Brunswick	4.1
University of California–Irvine	4.1
University of Wisconsin–Madison	4.1
19. Northwestern University (IL)	4.0
University of Illinois–Urbana-Champaign	4.0
University of North Carolina–Chapel Hill	4.0
University of Texas–Austin	4.0
23. CUNY Graduate School and University Center	3.9
Indiana University–Bloomington	3.9
New York University	3.9

ENGLISH SPECIALTIES

AFRICAN-AMERICAN LITERATURE
1. Harvard University (MA)
2. Princeton University (NJ)
3. Duke University (NC)
4. Yale University (CT)
5. U. of North Carolina–Chapel Hill
6. Columbia University (NY)
7. University of California–Berkeley
8. Cornell University (NY)
9. Univ. of Maryland–College Park
   University of Virginia

AMERICAN LITERATURE AFTER 1865
1. University of California–Berkeley
2. Harvard University (MA)
3. Duke University (NC)
   Stanford University (CA)
   Yale University (CT)
6. Univ. of California–Los Angeles
7. University of Virginia
8. Columbia University (NY)
9. University of Chicago
10. University of Pennsylvania

AMERICAN LITERATURE BEFORE 1865
1. Harvard University (MA)
2. Yale University (CT)
3. Stanford University (CA)
   University of California–Berkeley
5. Rutgers, the State Univ. of N.J.–New Brunswick
   Univ. of California–Los Angeles
   University of Virginia
8. Columbia University (NY)
   Duke University (NC)
10. University of Pennsylvania

18TH-THROUGH-20TH-CENTURY BRITISH LITERATURE
1. University of California–Berkeley
2. Yale University (CT)
3. University of Virginia
4. Stanford University (CA)
5. Harvard University (MA)
6. Cornell University (NY)
   Princeton University (NJ)
8. University of Pennsylvania
9. Columbia University (NY)
   University of Chicago

GENDER AND LITERATURE
1. University of California–Berkeley
2. Duke University (NC)
3. Univ. of Michigan–Ann Arbor
4. Rutgers, the State Univ. of N.J.–New Brunswick
5. Princeton University (NJ)
6. Harvard University (MA)
7. Columbia University (NY)
   Univ. of Wisconsin–Madison
9. Brown University (RI)
10. CUNY Graduate School and University Center

LITERARY CRITICISM AND THEORY
1. Duke University (NC)
2. University of California–Irvine
3. Cornell University (NY)
4. Johns Hopkins University (MD)
5. University of California–Berkeley
6. Columbia University (NY)
7. University of Chicago
   Yale University (CT)
9. New York University
10. Stanford University (CA)

MEDIEVAL/RENAISSANCE LITERATURE
1. Harvard University (MA)
   University of California–Berkeley
3. Yale University (CT)
4. Columbia University (NY)
5. University of Pennsylvania
6. Stanford University (CA)
7. Univ. of California–Los Angeles
8. University of Chicago
9. Cornell University (NY)
   Univ. of Michigan–Ann Arbor

HISTORY

Ranked in 2005

Rank/School	Average assessment score (5.0=highest)
1. Yale University (CT)	4.9
2. Princeton University (NJ)	4.8
University of California–Berkeley	4.8
4. Harvard University (MA)	4.7
Stanford University (CA)	4.7
University of Chicago	4.7
7. Columbia University (NY)	4.6
University of Michigan–Ann Arbor	4.6
9. Johns Hopkins University (MD)	4.5
University of California–Los Angeles	4.5
11. Cornell University (NY)	4.4
University of Wisconsin–Madison	4.4
13. University of North Carolina–Chapel Hill	4.3
University of Pennsylvania	4.3
15. Brown University (RI)	4.1
Duke University (NC)	4.1
17. Northwestern University (IL)	4.0
Rutgers, the State Univ. of New Jersey–New Brunswick	4.0
19. Indiana University–Bloomington	3.9
University of Texas–Austin	3.9
University of Virginia	3.9
22. New York University	3.8
University of Illinois–Urbana-Champaign	3.8
University of Minnesota–Twin Cities	3.8
25. University of Maryland–College Park	3.7

HISTORY SPECIALTIES

AFRICAN HISTORY
1. Northwestern University (IL)
2. Univ. of Wisconsin–Madison
3. Univ. of California–Los Angeles
4. Univ. of Michigan–Ann Arbor
5. Yale University (CT)
6. Johns Hopkins University (MD)
   Stanford University (CA)
8. Univ. of Minnesota–Twin Cities
9. Emory University (GA)
   Indiana University–Bloomington

AFRICAN-AMERICAN HISTORY
1. Yale University (CT)
2. Columbia University (NY)
3. University of California–Berkeley
4. Rutgers, the State Univ. of N.J.–New Brunswick
   U. of North Carolina–Chapel Hill
6. Duke University (NC)
7. Harvard University (MA)
   New York University
   Princeton University (NJ)
   Univ. of Michigan–Ann Arbor

ASIAN HISTORY
1. University of California–Berkeley
2. Harvard University (MA)
3. Yale University (CT)
4. Univ. of California–Los Angeles
5. Columbia University (NY)
   University of Chicago
7. Princeton University (NJ)
   Stanford University (CA)
9. Univ. of Michigan–Ann Arbor
10. Univ. of California–San Diego

CULTURAL HISTORY
1. University of California–Berkeley
2. Yale University (CT)
3. University of Chicago
4. Princeton University (NJ)
   Univ. of Michigan–Ann Arbor
6. New York University
7. Rutgers, the State Univ. of N.J.–New Brunswick
   Univ. of Wisconsin–Madison
9. Harvard University (MA)
   Univ. of California–Los Angeles

EUROPEAN HISTORY
1. Princeton University (NJ)
2. Yale University (CT)
3. University of California–Berkeley
4. University of Chicago
5. Harvard University (MA)
6. Univ. of Michigan–Ann Arbor
7. Columbia University (NY)
8. Stanford University (CA)
9. Univ. of California–Los Angeles
10. Johns Hopkins University (MD)
    Univ. of Wisconsin–Madison

LATIN AMERICAN HISTORY
1. University of Texas–Austin
2. Univ. of Wisconsin–Madison
   Yale University (CT)
4. University of California–Berkeley
5. Univ. of California–Los Angeles
6. University of Chicago
7. Univ. of California–San Diego
8. Harvard University (MA)
9. Duke University (NC)
10. Indiana University–Bloomington

MODERN U.S. HISTORY
1. Yale University (CT)
2. Columbia University (NY)
   University of California–Berkeley
4. Harvard University (MA)
5. Princeton University (NJ)

6. Stanford University (CA)
7. University of Pennsylvania
   Univ. of Wisconsin–Madison
9. University of Chicago
10. U. of North Carolina–Chapel Hill

U.S. COLONIAL HISTORY
1. Harvard University (MA)
   Yale University (CT)
3. University of Pennsylvania
4. Col. of William and Mary (VA)
   Johns Hopkins University (MD)
6. Princeton University (NJ)
7. University of Virginia
8. Univ. of Michigan–Ann Arbor
9. University of California–Berkeley
10. Cornell University (NY)
    U. of North Carolina–Chapel Hill

WOMEN'S HISTORY
1. Univ. of Wisconsin–Madison
2. Rutgers, the State Univ. of N.J.–
   New Brunswick
3. Yale University (CT)
4. Univ. of Michigan–Ann Arbor
5. Univ. of California–Los Angeles
   U. of North Carolina–Chapel Hill
7. University of Pennsylvania
8. Univ. of Minnesota–Twin Cities
9. Columbia University (NY)
10. University of California–Berkeley

AMERICAN POLITICS
1. University of Michigan–
   Ann Arbor
2. Harvard University (MA)
3. Stanford University (CA)
4. Princeton University (NJ)
5. Ohio State University
6. Univ. of California–San Diego
7. University of California–Berkeley
8. Yale University (CT)
9. University of North Carolina–
   Chapel Hill
10. Duke University (NC)

COMPARATIVE POLITICS
1. Harvard University (MA)
2. University of California–Berkeley
3. University of California–
   San Diego
4. Princeton University (NJ)
5. Stanford University (CA)
   University of California–
   Los Angeles
7. Columbia University (NY)
   University of Michigan–
   Ann Arbor
9. Yale University (CT)
10. Duke University (NC)

INTERNATIONAL POLITICS
1. Harvard University (MA)
2. Stanford University (CA)
3. Columbia University (NY)
   Princeton University (NJ)
5. University of Michigan–

Ann Arbor
6. University of California–
   San Diego
7. Duke University (NC)
   University of California–Berkeley
9. University of Chicago
10. New York University

POLITICAL METHODOLOGY
1. Harvard University (MA)
2. Stanford University (CA)
   University of Michigan–
   Ann Arbor
4. University of Rochester (NY)
5. Princeton University (NJ)
6. New York University
7. University of California–
   San Diego
8. University of California–Berkeley
9. Washington Univ. in St. Louis
10. Ohio State University

POLITICAL THEORY
1. Harvard University (MA)
2. Princeton University (NJ)
3. University of Chicago
4. Yale University (CT)
5. University of California–Berkeley
6. Duke University (NC)
7. Columbia University (NY)
8. Johns Hopkins University (MD)
   Univ. of Minnesota–Twin Cities
10. New York University
    University of Notre Dame (IN)
    University of Virginia

POLITICAL SCIENCE

Ranked in 2005

Rank/School	Average assessment score (5.0=highest)
1. Harvard University (MA)	5.0
2. Stanford University (CA)	4.9
3. University of Michigan–Ann Arbor	4.8
4. Princeton University (NJ)	4.7
5. University of California–Berkeley	4.6
Yale University (CT)	4.6
7. University of California–San Diego	4.4
8. Duke University (NC)	4.3
University of Chicago	4.3
10. Columbia University (NY)	4.2
Massachusetts Institute of Technology	4.2
University of California–Los Angeles	4.2
13. Ohio State University	4.0
University of North Carolina–Chapel Hill	4.0
University of Rochester (NY)	4.0
16. University of Wisconsin–Madison	3.9
Washington University in St. Louis	3.9
18. Cornell University (NY)	3.8
New York University	3.8
University of Minnesota–Twin Cities	3.8
21. Northwestern University (IL)	3.6
22. Michigan State University	3.4
Texas A&M University–College Station	3.4
University of Illinois–Urbana-Champaign	3.4
25. Indiana University–Bloomington	3.3
University of Iowa	3.3
University of Texas–Austin	3.3
University of Washington	3.3

PSYCHOLOGY

Ranked in 2005
Unless otherwise designated in parentheses, the program is in the department of psychology.

Rank/School	Average assessment score (5.0=highest)
1. Stanford University (CA)	4.8
2. University of California–Berkeley	4.6
University of Michigan–Ann Arbor	4.6
4. Yale University (CT)	4.5
5. Harvard University (MA)	4.4
Princeton University (NJ)	4.4
University of California–Los Angeles	4.4
University of Illinois–Urbana-Champaign	4.4
9. Carnegie Mellon University (PA)	4.2
Harvard U. (Programs in Human Development and Psych.) (MA)	4.2
University of Wisconsin–Madison	4.2
12. Massachusetts Institute of Technology	4.1
Stanford University (Psych. Studies in Education) (CA)	4.1
University of Texas–Austin	4.1
Univ. of Minnesota–Twin Cities (Inst. of Child Development)	4.1
16. Columbia University (NY)	4.0
Cornell University (NY)	4.0
University of California–San Diego	4.0
University of Minnesota–Twin Cities	4.0

Continued on Page 62

PSYCHOLOGY

Ranked in 2005

Rank/School	Average assessment score (5.0=highest)
University of Pennsylvania	4.0
Univ. of California–Irvine (Dept. of Neurobiology & Behavior)	4.0
22. Indiana University–Bloomington	3.9
Johns Hopkins University (MD)	3.9
Northwestern University (IL)	3.9
University of California–Irvine (Cognitive Sci. Dept.)	3.9
University of North Carolina–Chapel Hill	3.9
University of Washington	3.9
28. Cornell University (Dept. of Human Development) (NY)	3.8
Duke University (Dept. of Social and Health Sciences) (NC)	3.8
Indiana University–Bloomington (Cognitive Science Program)	3.8
University of California–Berkeley (School of Education)	3.8
University of Chicago	3.8
University of Colorado–Boulder	3.8
University of Virginia	3.8
U. of Michigan–Ann Arbor (Combined Program in Ed. and Psych.)	3.8
36. Brown University (RI)	3.7
Carnegie Mellon Univ. (Grad. School of Industrial Admin.) (PA)	3.7
Duke University (Dept. of Psychological & Brain Sciences) (NC)	3.7
New York University	3.7
Ohio State University	3.7
Pennsylvania State University–University Park	3.7
Pa. State U.–Univ. Park (Prog. in Human Dev. & Fam. Studies)	3.7
University of Iowa (Psychological and Quantitative Foundations)	3.7
Univ. of Wisconsin–Madison (Dept. of Educational Psychology)	3.7
Vanderbilt University (TN)	3.7
Washington University in St. Louis	3.7
47. Arizona State University	3.6
Emory University (GA)	3.6
University of California–Davis	3.6
University of California–Irvine (Psych. & Social Behavior Dept.)	3.6
University of California–Santa Barbara	3.6
University of Iowa	3.6
University of Oregon	3.6
University of Rochester (Brain & Cognitive Sciences)	3.6
55. Dartmouth College (NH)	3.5
Northwestern University (Dept. of Organization Behavior) (IL)	3.5
University of Arizona	3.5
University of Maryland–College Park	3.5
U. of Mich.–Ann Arbor (Doc. Prog. in Social Work & Social Sci.)	3.5
University of Minnesota–Twin Cities (Educational Psychology)	3.5
University of Pittsburgh	3.5
University of Southern California	3.5
U. of Michigan–Ann Arbor (Org. Behavior & Human Resources)	3.5
U. of Illinois–Urbana-Champaign (Dept. of Ed. Psych.)	3.5
Vanderbilt University (Peabody) (TN)	3.5
66. Michigan State University	3.4
Purdue University–West Lafayette (IN)	3.4
SUNY–Stony Brook	3.4
University of California–San Francisco	3.4
University of Chicago (Educational and Developmental Psych.)	3.4
University of Florida (Dept. of Clinical & Health Psychology)	3.4
University of Florida	3.4
University of Massachusetts–Amherst	3.4
University of Rochester (NY)	3.4
University of Southern California (School of Medicine)	3.4
U. of Texas–Austin (Child Development and Family Relations)	3.4
77. Georgia Institute of Technology	3.3
Northwestern University Medical School (IL)	3.3
Oregon Health and Science University	3.3
Rutgers, the State Univ. of New Jersey–New Brunswick	3.3
Teachers Col. Columbia U. (Dept. of Human Development) (NY)	3.3
Teachers Col. Columbia U. (Dept. of Counsel. & Clin. Psych.) (NY)	3.3
University of Connecticut	3.3
University of Kansas	3.3
University of Missouri–Columbia	3.3
University of Texas–Austin (Dept. of Educational Psych.)	3.3
Univ. of Wisconsin–Madison (Human Dev. & Family Studies)	3.3
Vanderbilt University (Peabody) (Human & Organiz. Dev.) (TN)	3.3

PSYCHOLOGY SPECIALTIES

BEHAVIORAL NEUROSCIENCE
1. University of Michigan–Ann Arbor
2. University of California–Los Angeles
   University of California–San Diego
4. Massachusetts Institute of Technology
5. Univ. of California–Irvine (Dept. of Neurobiology & Behavior)
6. Princeton University (NJ)
7. Johns Hopkins University (MD)
   Stanford University (CA)
   University of California–Berkeley
   University of Wisconsin–Madison

COGNITIVE PSYCHOLOGY
1. Stanford University (CA)
2. Carnegie Mellon University (PA)
3. University of California–San Diego
4. University of Michigan–Ann Arbor
5. Yale University (CT)
6. Harvard University (MA)
   Massachusetts Institute of Technology
   University of Illinois–Urbana-Champaign
9. University of California–Berkeley
   University of California–Los Angeles

DEVELOPMENTAL PSYCHOLOGY
1. Stanford University (CA)
2. University of Michigan–Ann Arbor
3. Univ. of Minnesota–Twin Cities (Inst. of Child Development)
4. University of California–Berkeley
5. Harvard University (MA)
6. Pennsylvania State Univ.–University Park (Program in Human Development & Family Studies)
7. Yale University (CT)
8. University of Illinois–Urbana-Champaign
9. University of Virginia
10. University of North Carolina–Chapel Hill

EXPERIMENTAL PSYCHOLOGY
1. Stanford University (CA)
2. University of Michigan–Ann Arbor
3. Harvard University (MA)
4. University of Illinois–Urbana-Champaign
5. Carnegie Mellon University (PA)
6. Indiana University–Bloomington
   University of California–Los Angeles
   University of California–San Diego
9. Princeton University (NJ)
   University of California–Berkeley
   University of Pennsylvania
   University of Wisconsin–Madison

INDUSTRIAL AND ORGANIZATIONAL PSYCHOLOGY
1. Michigan State University
2. University of Minnesota–Twin Cities
3. Bowling Green State University (OH)
4. Pennsylvania State University–University Park
5. University of Illinois–Urbana-Champaign
6. George Mason University (VA)
   Georgia Institute of Technology
   University of Akron (OH)
9. University of Maryland–College Park
10. University of South Florida

SOCIAL PSYCHOLOGY
1. Stanford University (CA)
2. University of Michigan–Ann Arbor
3. Ohio State University
4. Harvard University (MA)
5. Yale University (CT)
6. University of California–Los Angeles
7. Princeton University (NJ)
8. University of California–Santa Barbara
9. New York University
10. Columbia University (NY)
    University of Illinois–Urbana-Champaign

SOCIOLOGY

Ranked in 2005

Rank/School	Average assessment score (5.0=highest)
1. University of Wisconsin–Madison	4.9
2. University of California–Berkeley	4.8
3. University of Michigan–Ann Arbor	4.7
4. University of Chicago	4.6
University of North Carolina–Chapel Hill	4.6
6. Princeton University (NJ)	4.5
Stanford University (CA)	4.5
8. Harvard University (MA)	4.4
University of California–Los Angeles	4.4
10. University of Pennsylvania	4.2
11. Columbia University (NY)	4.1
Indiana University–Bloomington	4.1
Northwestern University (IL)	4.1
14. Cornell University (NY)	3.9
Duke University (NC)	3.9
University of Texas–Austin	3.9
17. Pennsylvania State University–University Park	3.8
University of Arizona	3.8
University of Washington	3.8
20. Ohio State University	3.7
Yale University (CT)	3.7
22. Johns Hopkins University (MD)	3.6
New York University	3.6
University of Minnesota–Twin Cities	3.6
25. SUNY–Albany	3.5
University of Maryland–College Park	3.5

SOCIOLOGY SPECIALTIES

ECONOMIC SOCIOLOGY
1. University of California–Berkeley
2. Stanford University (CA)
3. Cornell University (NY)
   University of Wisconsin–Madison
5. Princeton University (NJ)
6. Harvard University (MA)
   Northwestern University (IL)
8. Columbia University (NY)
9. University of California–Los Angeles
   University of Michigan–Ann Arbor

HISTORICAL SOCIOLOGY
1. Harvard University (MA)
2. University of California–Berkeley
3. University of Michigan–Ann Arbor
4. University of California–Los Angeles
5. Yale University (CT)
6. Northwestern University (IL)
7. Princeton University (NJ)
   University of Chicago
9. Columbia University (NY)
10. New York University

SEX AND GENDER
1. University of California–Berkeley

2. University of California–Santa Barbara
3. University of Wisconsin–Madison
4. University of Washington
5. University of Michigan–Ann Arbor
6. Stanford University (CA)
   University of Southern California
8. University of Maryland–College Park
9. Indiana University–Bloomington
10. Florida State University
    New York University
    University of California–Los Angeles

SOCIAL PSYCHOLOGY
1. Stanford University (CA)
2. Indiana University–Bloomington
3. University of Iowa
4. University of Michigan–Ann Arbor
5. University of Arizona
   University of Wisconsin–Madison
7. Duke University (NC)
   University of California–Los Angeles
9. University of North Carolina–Chapel Hill

10. Cornell University (NY)
    University of Washington

SOCIAL STRATIFICATION
1. University of Wisconsin–Madison
2. University of California–Berkeley
3. University of Michigan–Ann Arbor
4. Stanford University (CA)
   University of North Carolina–Chapel Hill
6. Harvard University (MA)
7. Ohio State University
   University of California–Los Angeles
9. Cornell University (NY)
   Princeton University (NJ)

SOCIOLOGY OF CULTURE
1. Princeton University (NJ)
2. University of California–Berkeley
3. Northwestern University (IL)
4. Harvard University (MA)
5. Yale University (CT)

6. University of California–San Diego
   University of California–Santa Barbara
   University of Chicago
9. University of California–Los Angeles
10. New York University

SOCIOLOGY OF POPULATION
1. University of Wisconsin–Madison
2. University of California–Berkeley
   University of Michigan–Ann Arbor
4. University of North Carolina–Chapel Hill
5. Pennsylvania State University–University Park
   University of Texas–Austin
7. University of Pennsylvania
8. University of Washington
9. Princeton University (NJ)
10. University of California–Los Angeles

METHODOLOGY

Rankings of doctoral programs in the social sciences and humanities are based solely on the results of peer assessment surveys sent to academics in each discipline. Each school (or, in the case of psychology, each institutional unit) offering a doctoral program was sent two surveys (with the exception of criminology, where each school received four). The questionnaires asked respondents to rate the academic quality of the program at each institution on a 5-point scale: outstanding (5), strong (4), good (3), adequate (2), or marginal (1). Individuals who were unfamiliar with a particular school's programs were asked to select "don't know." Scores for each school were determined by computing a trimmed mean (eliminating the two highest and two lowest responses) of the ratings of all respondents who rated that school; average scores were then sorted in descending order.

Surveys were conducted in the fall of 2004 by Synovate. Questionnaires were sent to department heads and directors of graduate studies (or, alternatively, a senior faculty member who teaches graduate students) at schools that had granted a total of five or more doctorates in each discipline during the five-year period from 1998 through 2002, as indicated by the 2003 Survey of Earned Doctorates. The American Association of Doctoral Programs in Criminology and Criminal Justice provided the list of criminology programs. The surveys asked about Ph.D. programs in criminology (response rate: 88 percent), economics (38 percent), English (39 percent), history (33 percent), political science (40 percent), psychology (23 percent), and sociology (50 percent).

The American Psychological Association supplied the names of the psychology programs. Surveys were sent to the department chair or dean of the school of psychology and the director of graduate studies in each institutional unit that offered a doctoral program. Unless otherwise noted, the psychology program ranked is located in the department of psychology. Programs in clinical psychology are ranked separately in the health professions section (Page 36).

Specialty rankings are based on nominations by department heads and directors of graduate studies at peer schools from the list of schools surveyed. They ranked up to 10 programs in each area. Those with the most votes appear.

Expanded rankings can be found at www.usnews.com.

Library & Information Studies

THE TOP SCHOOLS

Our ranking is based on a 2005 survey of deans, program directors, and senior faculty members at 50 schools with accredited master's programs.

Rank/School	Average assessment score (5.0=highest)
1. University of Illinois–Urbana-Champaign	4.5
University of North Carolina–Chapel Hill	4.5
3. Syracuse University (NY)	4.3
4. University of Washington	4.2
5. University of Michigan–Ann Arbor	4.0
6. Rutgers, the State Univ. of New Jersey–New Brunswick	3.9
7. Indiana University–Bloomington	3.8
University of Pittsburgh	3.8
University of Texas–Austin	3.8
10. Florida State University	3.7
11. Drexel University (PA)	3.6
University of Wisconsin–Madison	3.6

JEFFREY MACMILLAN FOR *USN&WR*

Megan McCarty at U. of Maryland's Human Computer Interaction Lab

SPECIALTIES

The institutions below received the most nominations from survey respondents at peer institutions for their excellence in a given specialty.

ARCHIVES AND PRESERVATION
1. University of Texas–Austin
2. Univ. of Maryland–College Park
   University of Michigan–Ann Arbor
4. University of Pittsburgh
5. Univ. of California–Los Angeles
6. Simmons College (MA)
7. UNC–Chapel Hill
8. University of Wisconsin–Madison
9. SUNY–Albany

DIGITAL LIBRARIANSHIP
1. U. of Illinois–Urbana-Champaign
2. Syracuse University (NY)
3. University of Michigan–Ann Arbor
4. UNC–Chapel Hill
5. University of Washington
6. Drexel University (PA)
   Rutgers, the State Univ. of N.J.–New Brunswick
8. Indiana University–Bloomington
9. Univ. of California–Los Angeles
10. University of Pittsburgh

HEALTH LIBRARIANSHIP
1. University of Pittsburgh
2. UNC–Chapel Hill
3. University of North Texas
   University of Washington
5. Texas Woman's University
   Univ. of Maryland–College Park
7. University of Missouri–Columbia
8. Syracuse University (NY)
   U. of Illinois–Urbana-Champaign
   Univ. of South Carolina–Columbia

INFORMATION SYSTEMS
1. Syracuse University (NY)
2. University of Michigan–Ann Arbor
3. University of Washington
4. U. of Illinois–Urbana-Champaign

5. Drexel University (PA)
   University of Pittsburgh
7. UNC–Chapel Hill
8. Indiana University–Bloomington
   Rutgers, the State Univ. of N.J.–New Brunswick
10. Florida State University

LAW LIBRARIANSHIP
1. University of Washington
2. Catholic Univ. of America (DC)
3. University of Texas–Austin
4. Indiana University–Bloomington
5. U. of Illinois–Urbana-Champaign
   UNC–Chapel Hill

SCHOOL LIBRARY MEDIA
1. Rutgers, the State Univ. of N.J.–New Brunswick
2. Univ. of South Carolina–Columbia
3. Univ. of Maryland–College Park
4. Syracuse University (NY)
5. Florida State University
6. San Jose State University (CA)
   University of Washington
8. Indiana University–Bloomington
9. University of Hawaii–Manoa
   University of Pittsburgh

SERVICES FOR CHILDREN AND YOUTH
1. Florida State University
   U. of Illinois–Urbana-Champaign
3. Rutgers, the State Univ. of N.J.–New Brunswick
4. University of Pittsburgh
5. Univ. of California–Los Angeles
   Univ. of Maryland–College Park
   University of Wisconsin–Madison
8. UNC–Chapel Hill
9. University of Washington
10. Simmons College (MA)

Methodology: The library and information studies program rankings are based solely on the results of a peer assessment survey. Respondents were asked to rate the academic quality of programs on a scale of 1 (marginal) to 5 (outstanding). Scores for each school were totaled and divided by the number of respondents who rated that school. The response rate was 51 percent. Surveys were conducted by Synovate in the fall of 2005.
Note: Lists of schools consist of those master's programs accredited by the American Library Association. The survey was sent to the dean of the program, the program director, and a senior faculty member in each of these programs.

Get over 200 Puzzles!

The Best Sudoku Puzzles Presented by Will Shortz

Inside this special edition you'll find over 200 new sudoku puzzles for every skill level! Whether you're a beginner or expert, there are grids inside that will excite and entertain you.

Plus, you'll also find the latest tips to solving sudoku from Will Shortz, *The New York Times* crossword editor and NPR puzzlemaster. Just pick a grid and start "Sudoku-ing"!

- ✏ **The newest tips for solving sudoku**
- ✏ **Large grids for easy play**
- ✏ **Step-by-step instructions for beginners**
- ✏ **200 easy-to-expert puzzles, plus 20 bonus puzzles**

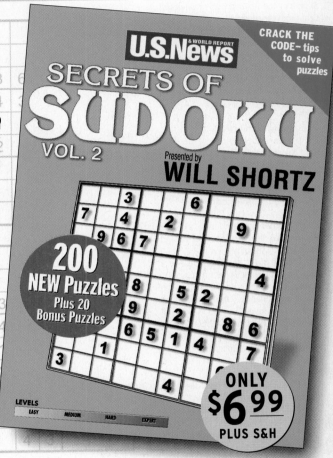

CRACK THE CODE – tips to solve puzzles

U.S.News & WORLD REPORT
SECRETS OF SUDOKU
VOL. 2
Presented by WILL SHORTZ

200 NEW Puzzles Plus 20 Bonus Puzzles

LEVELS
EASY   MEDIUM   HARD   EXPERT

ONLY $6.99 PLUS S&H

ORDER NOW AT
www.usnews.com/sudoku
OR CALL: **1-800-836-6397**

U.S.News & WORLD REPORT

**SCHOOL OF EDUCATION
CURRICULUM LABORATORY
UM-DEARBORN**

Master of Fine Arts

THE TOP SCHOOLS

Our ranking, completed in 2008, is based solely on a survey of art school deans and other top art school academics, two per school, at 220 master of fine arts programs in art and design.

Rank/School	Average assessment score (5.0=highest)
1. Rhode Island School of Design	4.6
2. Yale University (CT)	4.5
3. School of the Art Institute of Chicago	4.4
4. Cranbrook Academy of Art (MI)	4.2
Maryland Institute College of Art	4.2
Virginia Commonwealth University	4.2
7. California Institute of the Arts	4.1
Carnegie Mellon University (PA)	4.1
University of California–Los Angeles	4.1
10. Alfred Univ.–New York State College of Ceramics	4.0
11. Art Center College of Design (CA)	3.9
California College of the Arts	3.9
Columbia University (NY)	3.9
14. Temple University (PA)	3.8
15. Bard College (NY)	3.7
Pratt Institute (NY)	3.7
School of Visual Arts (NY)	3.7
University of California–San Diego	3.7
University of Texas–Austin	3.7
Washington University in St. Louis	3.7
21. CUNY–Hunter College	3.6
New School–Parsons School of Design (NY)	3.6
Ohio State University	3.6
Otis College of Art and Design (CA)	3.6
Rochester Institute of Technology (NY)	3.6
University of California–Davis	3.6
University of Illinois–Urbana-Champaign	3.6
University of Iowa	3.6
University of Wisconsin–Madison	3.6
30. Arizona State University	3.5
Indiana University–Bloomington	3.5
Massachusetts College of Art	3.5
New York University	3.5
Rutgers, the State U. of New Jersey–New Brunswick	3.5
San Francisco Art Institute	3.5
University of California–Berkeley	3.5
37. Minneapolis College of Art and Design	3.4
Tufts U./School of the Museum of Fine Arts–Boston	3.4
University of Georgia	3.4
University of Illinois–Chicago	3.4
University of Michigan	3.4
University of Southern California	3.4
University of the Arts (PA)	3.4
University of Washington	3.4
45. Herron School of Art & Design (IN)	3.3
Stanford University (CA)	3.3
University of Arizona	3.3
University of Cincinnati	3.3
University of Pennsylvania	3.3
50. Claremont Graduate University (CA)	3.2
Cleveland Institute of Art	3.2
Cornell University (NY)	3.2
Syracuse University (NY)	3.2
University of Minnesota–Twin Cities	3.2
University of New Mexico	3.2
University of Tennessee–Knoxville	3.2

SPECIALTIES

The institutions below received the most nominations from survey respondents at peer institutions for their excellence in a given specialty.

CERAMICS
1. Alfred Univ.–New York State College of Ceramics
2. Cranbrook Academy of Art (MI)
3. Rhode Island School of Design
4. California College of the Arts
5. University of Washington
6. Ohio State University

FIBER ARTS
1. Cranbrook Academy of Art (MI)
2. School of the Art Inst. of Chicago
3. California College of the Arts
4. Virginia Commonwealth Univ.
5. Rhode Island School of Design
   University of Washington

GLASS
1. Rhode Island School of Design
2. Alfred Univ.–New York State College of Ceramics
   Rochester Inst. of Tech. (NY)
4. California College of the Arts
5. Virginia Commonwealth Univ.
6. Ohio State University

GRAPHIC DESIGN
1. Rhode Island School of Design
2. Cranbrook Academy of Art (MI)
   Yale University (CT)
4. Virginia Commonwealth Univ.
5. Carnegie Mellon University (PA)
6. Maryland Institute College of Art
   School of Visual Arts (NY)

INDUSTRIAL DESIGN
1. Art Center Col. of Design (CA)
2. Rhode Island School of Design
3. Carnegie Mellon University (PA)
4. Pratt Institute (NY)
5. Ohio State University
6. University of Cincinnati

INTERIOR DESIGN
1. Pratt Institute (NY)
   Rhode Island School of Design
3. University of Cincinnati
4. New York Sch. of Interior Design

METALS/JEWELRY
1. SUNY College of Arts and Sciences–New Paltz
2. Rhode Island School of Design
3. California College of the Arts
   Univ. of Wisconsin–Madison
5. San Diego State University
6. Cranbrook Academy of Art (MI)

MULTIMEDIA/VISUAL COMMUNICATIONS
1. Carnegie Mellon University (PA)
2. California Institute of the Arts
3. Rhode Island School of Design
   School of the Art Inst. of Chicago
5. Univ. of California–Los Angeles
6. Rensselaer Polytechnic Inst. (NY)

PAINTING/DRAWING
1. Yale University (CT)
2. School of the Art Inst. of Chicago
3. Rhode Island School of Design
4. Maryland Institute College of Art
5. Columbia University (NY)
   Univ. of California–Los Angeles

PHOTOGRAPHY
1. Yale University (CT)
2. School of the Art Inst. of Chicago
3. Rhode Island School of Design
   Rochester Inst. of Tech. (NY)
5. University of New Mexico
6. California Institute of the Arts

PRINTMAKING
1. Univ. of Wisconsin–Madison
2. Rhode Island School of Design
   University of Iowa
4. Univ. of Tennessee–Knoxville
5. Indiana University–Bloomington
6. Rutgers, the State U. of New Jersey–New Brunswick

SCULPTURE
1. Virginia Commonwealth Univ.
2. Yale University (CT)
3. Rhode Island School of Design
4. School of the Art Inst. of Chicago
5. Cranbrook Academy of Art (MI)
6. Univ. of California–Los Angeles

Methodology: The master of fine arts program rankings are based solely on the results of a peer assessment survey. Respondents were asked to rate the academic quality of programs on a scale of 1 (marginal) to 5 (outstanding). Scores for each school were totaled and divided by the number of respondents who rated that school. The response rate was 39 percent. Surveys were conducted by Synovate.
Note: Lists of schools, individuals surveyed at each school, and specialty concentrations were developed in cooperation with the Department of Art and Visual Technology at the College of Visual and Performing Arts at George Mason University in Virginia.

DIVERSE GRADUATE PROGRAMS
Radford University
ON THE CUTTING EDGE

- Art, M.F.A.
- Business Administration, M.B.A.
- Communication Sciences and Disorders, M.A., M.S.
- Corporate and Professional Communication, M.S.
- Counseling and Human Development, M.S.*
- Criminal Justice, M.A., M.S.
- Education, M.S.*
- Educational Leadership, M.S.

- English, M.A., M.S.
- Music, M.A., M.S.*
- Nursing, M.S.N.*
- Psychology, M.A., M.S.*
- Reading, M.S.
- School Psychology, Ed.S.
- Social Work, M.S.W.
- Special Education, M.S.*
- New for 2008: Radford's unique Counseling Psychology Psy.D. focusing on mental health in rural areas.

  programs with more than one concentration

RU
RADFORD UNIVERSITY

www.radford.edu/gradcollege
540-831-5724

The University of North Carolina at PEMBROKE

POWERFUL - Get ready to exceed your wildest expectations. You'll be challenged to dig deeply into the critical issues of your profession and lead with confidence.

PERSONAL - We're here for YOU. We design our graduate programs with you in mind. We offer late afternoon and evening classes on campus and at other locations.

PRACTICAL - Not only will you examine theories and concepts in your field of study, but practical professional applications position you to apply knowledge immediately.

The University of North Carolina
UNCP
1887
PEMBROKE

P.O. Box 1510
Pembroke, NC 28372
(910) 521-6271 or 1-866-521-GRAD
www.uncp.edu/grad
EMAIL: grad@uncp.edu

Leading in a **global** environment

Walt Disney World executive Erin Wallace is a testament to what you can do with the essential business skills delivered by a Rollins MBA.

For over 50 years, the MBA program at Rollins' Crummer Graduate School of Business has earned its title as **Florida's Most Prestigious MBA** by giving students the skills to lead the nation's most successful companies with greater vision and integrity.

Find out why the Rollins MBA was recently ranked by *Forbes* Magazine:

- 37th in the nation and 1st in Florida
- in the top 20 of private colleges

ROLLINS
MBA

ROLLINS COLLEGE • CRUMMER GRADUATE SCHOOL OF BUSINESS
Winter Park/Orlando, Florida • 800-866-2405 • www.crummer.rollins.edu

Florida's Most Prestigious MBA™

"The Rollins MBA was the best professional development I could have given myself. I enjoyed the quality of the program, from the faculty through the content of each class."

Erin Wallace '93MBA
Senior Vice President
Walt Disney World Operations

A heartbeat is a universal language.

40 BPM

75 BPM

For three decades, St. George's University has been teaching students how to become doctors and veterinarians with the shared purpose of treating the global community. By taking the best ideas from every continent and applying knowledge from many cultures, we have created a unique approach to education that prepares our students for the challenges of a world without borders.

www.sgu.edu

St. George's University
THINK BEYOND

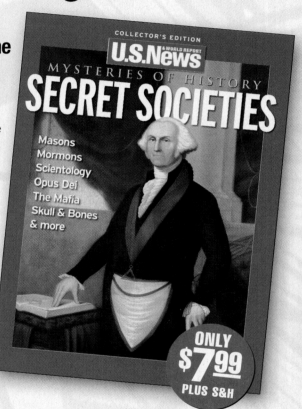

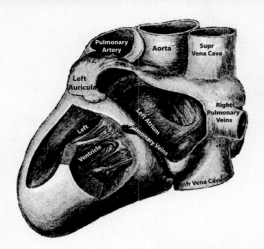

To succeed at Ross University, you must understand both.

When considering candidates for study at Ross, we look at more than your scores. We look at your heart. Because, while Ross trains some of the smartest doctors, we also train the most caring. Here you'll learn in our technologically advanced teaching and laboratory facilities with our enthusiastic faculty that are totally dedicated to teaching.

Ross University School of Medicine in Dominica and School of Veterinary Medicine in St. Kitts are leaders in international medical education. And both Schools are affiliated with top U.S. teaching hospitals and universities where students complete their clinical training. **If you're considering Medical or Veterinary School, you can do no better than Ross University.**

Ross University School of Medicine - A 30 Year History • Awarded over 5,700 M.D. Degrees • Very high USMLE Step 1 first-time pass rate • Graduates licensed to practice in all 50 states, all provinces of Canada and in Puerto Rico

Ross University School of Veterinary Medicine - A 26 Year History • Awarded over 2,000 D.V.M. Degrees • Affiliated with 21 (out of 28 total) AVMA-accredited schools • Graduates are eligible to practice in all 50 states and Canada upon completion of NAVLE

Learn more at www.RossU.edu or call 877-ROSS-EDU

Administrative Offices: Edison, NJ
Admissions@RossU.edu
© 2008 Ross University

ROSS
UNIVERSITY

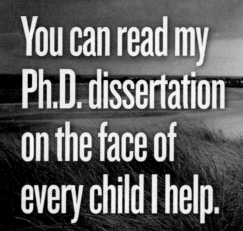

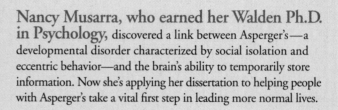

Directory of Graduate Schools

Schools are listed alphabetically by state within each
discipline; data are accurate as of February 2008.
An index to the directory begins on Page 174.
A key to terminology used in the directory can be found
at the beginning of each area of study.

BUSINESS

The business school directory lists all 425 U.S. schools offering master's programs in business accredited by AACSB International, the Association to Advance Collegiate Schools of Business, as of August 2007. Most offer the M.B.A. degree; a few offer the master of business. Three hundred eighty-three schools responded to the *U.S. News* survey conducted in fall 2007 and early 2008, and their data are reported below. Schools that did not respond to the survey have abbreviated entries.

TERMINOLOGY

1 A school whose name is footnoted with the numeral 1 did not return the *U.S. News* statistical survey; limited data appear in its entry.

N/A. Not available from the school or not applicable.

E-mail. The electronic address of the admissions office. If, instead of an E-mail address, a website is given in this field, the website will automatically present an E-mail screen programmed to reach the admissions office.

Application deadline. For fall 2009 enrollment. "Rolling" means there is no application deadline; the school acts on applications as they are received. "Varies" means deadlines vary according to department or whether applicants are U.S. citizens or foreign nationals.

Tuition. For the 2007–2008 academic year, or for the cost of the total graduate business degree program, if specified. Includes required annual student fees.

Credit hour. The cost per credit hour for the 2007–2008 academic year.

Room/board/expenses. For the 2007–2008 academic year.

College-funded aid and international-student aid. A "yes" means the school provides its own financial aid to students.

Average indebtedness. Computed for 2007 graduates who incurred business school debt.

Enrollment. Full- and part-time program totals are for fall 2007.

Minorities. For fall 2007, percentage of students who are Asian-American, African-American, Hispanic, or American Indian. (When the U.S. Department of Education calculates minority enrollment percentages, these are the demographic groupings it uses.)

Acceptance rate. Percentage of full-time program applicants who were accepted for fall 2007.

Average Graduate Management Admission Test (GMAT) score. Calculated separately for full- and part-time students who entered in fall 2007.

Average undergraduate grade-point average (1.0 to 4.0). For full-time program applicants who entered in fall 2007.

Average age of entrants. Calculated for full-time students who entered in fall 2007.

Average months of prior work experience. Calculated only for full-time program students who entered in fall 2007. Refers to post-baccalaureate work experience only.

TOEFL requirement. A "yes" means that students from non-English-speaking countries must submit scores for the Test of English as a Foreign Language.

Minimum TOEFL score. The lowest score on the paper TOEFL accepted for admission. (The computer-administered TOEFL is graded on a different scale.)

Most popular departments. Based on highest student demand for departments or concentrations in the 2007–2008 academic year.

Mean starting base salary for 2007 graduates. Calculated only for graduates who were full-time students, had accepted full-time job offers, and reported salary data. Excludes employer-sponsored students, signing bonuses of any kind, and other forms of guaranteed compensation such as stock options.

Employment locations. For the 2007 graduating class; calculated only for full-time students who had accepted job offers. Abbreviations: **Intl.** international; **N.E.** Northeast (Conn., Maine, Mass., N.H., N.J., N.Y., R.I., Vt.); **M.A.** Middle Atlantic (Del., D.C., Md., Pa., Va., W.Va.); **S.** South (Ala., Ark., Fla., Ga., Ky., La., Miss., N.C., S.C., Tenn.); **M.W.** Midwest (Ill., Ind., Iowa, Kan., Mich., Minn., Mo., Neb., N.D., Ohio, S.D., Wis.); **S.W.** Southwest (Ariz., Colo., N.M., Okla., Texas); **W.** West (Alaska, Calif., Hawaii, Idaho, Mont., Nev., Ore., Utah, Wash., Wyo.).

ALABAMA

Auburn University–Main Campus
415 W. Magnolia, Suite 503
Auburn University, AL 36849
http://www.mba.business.auburn.edu
Public
Admissions: (334) 844-4060
E-mail: mbadmis@auburn.edu
Financial aid: (334) 844-4367
Application deadline: 03/01
In-state tuition: full time: $5,786; part time: $217/credit hour
Out-of-state tuition: full time: $16,286
Room/board/expenses: $10,916
College-funded aid: Yes
International student aid: Yes
Full-time enrollment: 81
men: 59%; women: 41%; minorities: 6%; international: 26%
Part-time enrollment: N/A
men: N/A; women: N/A; minorities: N/A; international: N/A
Acceptance rate (full-time): 42%
Average GMAT (full-time): 635
Average GPA (full-time): 3.32
Average age of entrants to full-time program: 25
Average months of prior work experience (full-time): 28
TOEFL requirement: Yes
Minimum TOEFL score: 550
Most popular departments: finance, marketing, management information systems, operations management, supply chain management
Mean starting base salary for 2007 full-time graduates: $61,648
Employment location for 2007 class: Intl. 4%; N.E. 9%; M.A. 4%; S. 57%; M.W. 4%; S.W. 13%; W. 9%

Auburn University–Montgomery
7300 University Drive
Montgomery, AL 36117
http://www.aum.edu
Public
Admissions: (334) 244-3611
E-mail: sjeffcoa@mail.aum.edu
Financial aid: (334) 244-3571
Application deadline: rolling
In-state tuition: full time: $189/credit hour; part time: N/A
Out-of-state tuition: full time: $540/credit hour
Room/board/expenses: N/A
College-funded aid: Yes
International student aid: No
Full-time enrollment: 81
men: N/A; women: N/A; minorities: N/A; international: N/A
Part-time enrollment: 152
men: N/A; women: N/A; minorities: N/A; international: N/A
Acceptance rate (full-time): 97%
Average GMAT (full-time): 510
Average GPA (full-time): 3.00
Average age of entrants to full-time program: 25
Average months of prior work experience (full-time): 36
TOEFL requirement: Yes
Minimum TOEFL score: 500
Most popular departments: finance, general management, human resources management, marketing, management information systems

Birmingham-Southern College[1]
900 Arkadelphia Road
Birmingham, AL 35254
http://www.bsc.edu/
Private
Admissions: (205) 226-4803
E-mail: graduate@bsc.edu
Financial aid: (205) 226-4688
Tuition: N/A
Room/board/expenses: N/A
Enrollment: N/A

Jacksonville State University
700 Pelham Road N
Jacksonville, AL 36265
http://www.jsu.edu/depart/ccba/
Public
Admissions: (256) 782-5329
E-mail: graduate@jsucc.jsu.edu
Financial aid: (256) 782-5006
Application deadline: N/A
In-state tuition: full time: $225/credit hour; part time: $225/credit hour
Out-of-state tuition: full time: $450/credit hour
Room/board/expenses: $10,000
College-funded aid: Yes
International student aid: Yes
Full-time enrollment: N/A
men: N/A; women: N/A; minorities: N/A; international: N/A
Part-time enrollment: 81
men: 47%; women: 53%; minorities: 11%; international: 14%
Average GMAT (part-time): 477
TOEFL requirement: Yes
Minimum TOEFL score: 500

Samford University
800 Lakeshore Drive
Birmingham, AL 35229
http://www.samford.edu/business
Private
Admissions: (205) 726-2931
E-mail: business.graduate.studies@samford.edu
Financial aid: (205) 726-2860
Application deadline: 06/01
Tuition: full time: N/A; part time: $520/credit hour
Room/board/expenses: N/A
College-funded aid: No
International student aid: No
Full-time enrollment: N/A
men: N/A; women: N/A; minorities: N/A; international: N/A
Part-time enrollment: 143
men: 59%; women: 41%; minorities: 14%; international: 2%
Average GMAT (part-time): 530
TOEFL requirement: No
Minimum TOEFL score: N/A

University of Alabama–Birmingham
1530 Third Avenue S, BEC 219
Birmingham, AL 35294-4460
http://www.business.uab.edu
Public
Admissions: (205) 934-8817
E-mail: mlake@uab.edu
Financial aid: (205) 934-8223
Application deadline: 07/01
In-state tuition: full time: N/A; part time: $182/credit hour
Out-of-state tuition: full time: N/A
Room/board/expenses: N/A
College-funded aid: Yes
International student aid: No

Full-time enrollment: N/A
men: N/A; women: N/A;
minorities: N/A; international: N/A
Part-time enrollment: 383
men: 65%; women: 35%;
minorities: 11%; international: 9%
Average GMAT (part-time): 545
TOEFL requirement: Yes
Minimum TOEFL score: 550

University of Alabama–Huntsville

ASB Room 102
Huntsville, AL 35899
http://www.uah.edu/colleges/
adminsci
Public
Admissions: (256) 824-6681
E-mail: gradbiz@uah.edu
Financial aid: (256) 824-6241
Application deadline: rolling
In-state tuition: full time: $6,548;
part time: $3,716
Out-of-state tuition: full time:
$13,466
Room/board/expenses: $8,961
College-funded aid: Yes
International student aid: Yes
Full-time enrollment: N/A
men: N/A; women: N/A;
minorities: N/A; international: N/A
Part-time enrollment: 97
men: 58%; women: 42%;
minorities: 21%; international: 3%
Average GMAT (part-time): 540
TOEFL requirement: Yes
Minimum TOEFL score: 550
Most popular departments: account-
ing, general management, manu-
facturing and technology manage-
ment, management information
systems, technology

University of Alabama (Manderson)

Box 870223
Tuscaloosa, AL 35487
http://www.cba.ua.edu/~mba
Public
Admissions: (888) 863-2622
E-mail: mba@cba.ua.edu
Financial aid: (205) 348-6517
Application deadline: 04/15
In-state tuition: full time: $7,700;
part time: N/A
Out-of-state tuition: full time:
$18,518
Room/board/expenses: $14,600
College-funded aid: Yes
International student aid: Yes
Full-time enrollment: 118
men: 66%; women: 34%;
minorities: 9%; international: 8%
Part-time enrollment: N/A
men: N/A; women: N/A;
minorities: N/A; international: N/A
Acceptance rate (full-time): 56%
Average GMAT (full-time): 615
Average GPA (full-time): 3.41
Average age of entrants to full-time
program: 24
Average months of prior work
experience (full-time): 12
TOEFL requirement: Yes
Minimum TOEFL score: 550
Most popular departments: consult-
ing, finance, marketing, supply
chain management, statistics and
operations research
Mean starting base salary for 2007
full-time graduates: $60,170
Employment location for 2007 class:
Intl. 0%; N.E. 0%; M.A. 0%; S. 89%;
M.W. 11%; S.W. 0%; W. 0%

University of South Alabama (Mitchell)

307 N. University Boulevard
Mobile, AL 36688
http://mcob.southalabama.edu/
Public
Admissions: (251) 460-6418

E-mail: jgamble@usouthal.edu
Financial aid: (251) 460-6619
Application deadline: 07/01
In-state tuition: full time: N/A; part
time: $176/credit hour
Out-of-state tuition: full time: N/A
Room/board/expenses: $5,522
College-funded aid: Yes
International student aid: Yes
Full-time enrollment: N/A
men: N/A; women: N/A;
minorities: N/A; international: N/A
Part-time enrollment: 85
men: 56%; women: 44%;
minorities: N/A; international: 28%
Average GMAT (part-time): 525
TOEFL requirement: Yes
Minimum TOEFL score: 525

ALASKA

University of Alaska–Anchorage[1]

3211 Providence Drive
Anchorage, AK 99508
http://www.cbpp.alaska.edu
Public
Admissions: (907) 786-1480
E-mail: ayenrol@uaa.alaska.edu
Financial aid: (907) 786-1586
Tuition: N/A
Room/board/expenses: N/A
Enrollment: N/A

University of Alaska–Fairbanks

PO Box 756080
Fairbanks, AK 99775-6080
http://www.uaf.edu/index.html
Public
Admissions: (800) 478-1823
E-mail: admissions@uaf.edu
Financial aid: (888) 474-7256
Application deadline: 06/01
In-state tuition: full time:
$287/credit hour; part
time: $287/credit hour
Out-of-state tuition: full time:
$586/credit hour
Room/board/expenses: $9,380
College-funded aid: Yes
International student aid: Yes
Average student indebtedness at
graduation: $10,954
Full-time enrollment: 12
men: 83%; women: 17%;
minorities: 0%; international: 42%
Part-time enrollment: 16
men: 38%; women: 63%;
minorities: 13%; international: 0%
Acceptance rate (full-time): 47%
Average GMAT (full-time): 530
Average GMAT (part-time): 665
Average age of entrants to full-time
program: 25
TOEFL requirement: Yes
Minimum TOEFL score: 550

ARIZONA

Arizona State University (Carey)

PO Box 874906
Tempe, AZ 85287-4906
http://wpcareymba.asu.edu
Public
Admissions: (480) 965-3332
E-mail: wpcareymba@asu.edu
Financial aid: (480) 965-6890
Application deadline: 05/01
In-state tuition: full time: $16,528;
part time: $20,278
Out-of-state tuition: full time:
$28,220
Room/board/expenses: $18,750
College-funded aid: Yes
International student aid: Yes
Average student indebtedness at
graduation: $39,000
Full-time enrollment: 168
men: 76%; women: 24%;
minorities: 13%; international: 29%

Part-time enrollment: 679
men: 71%; women: 29%;
minorities: 19%; international: 7%
Acceptance rate (full-time): 32%
Average GMAT (full-time): 675
Average GMAT (part-time): 565
Average GPA (full-time): 3.44
Average age of entrants to full-time
program: 27
Average months of prior work
experience (full-time): 53
TOEFL requirement: Yes
Minimum TOEFL score: 600
Most popular departments: finance,
marketing, management informa-
tion systems, sports business,
supply chain management
Mean starting base salary for 2007
full-time graduates: $86,001
Employment location for 2007 class:
Intl. 0%; N.E. 8%; M.A. 7%; S. 1%;
M.W. 11%; S.W. 47%; W. 26%

Arizona State University–West[1]

4701 W. Thunderbird Road
PO Box 37100
Phoenix, AZ 85069-7100
http://www.west.asu.edu/
som/mba
Public
Admissions: (602) 543-6201
E-mail: mbainfo@asu.edu
Financial aid: (602) 543-8178
Tuition: N/A
Room/board/expenses: N/A
Enrollment: N/A

Northern Arizona University (Franke)

PO Box 15066
Flagstaff, AZ 86011-5066
http://www.franke.nau.edu/mba
Public
Admissions: (928) 523-7342
E-mail: mba@nau.edu
Financial aid: (928) 523-4951
Application deadline: 05/31
In-state tuition: full time: $11,040;
part time: $260/credit hour
Out-of-state tuition: full time:
$21,190
Room/board/expenses: $13,277
College-funded aid: Yes
International student aid: Yes
Full-time enrollment: 21
men: 71%; women: 29%;
minorities: 19%; international: 14%
Part-time enrollment: 2
men: 100%; women: 0%;
minorities: 0%; international: 0%
Acceptance rate (full-time): 79%
Average GMAT (full-time): 518
Average GMAT (part-time): 515
Average GPA (full-time): 3.20
Average age of entrants to full-time
program: 26
Average months of prior work
experience (full-time): 24
TOEFL requirement: Yes
Minimum TOEFL score: 600
Most popular departments: account-
ing, finance, general management,
marketing, other

Thunderbird School of Global Management

15249 N. 59th Avenue
Glendale, AZ 85306-6000
http://www.thunderbird.edu
Private
Admissions: (602) 978-7100
E-mail:
admissions@thunderbird.edu
Financial aid: (602) 978-7130
Application deadline: 07/15
Tuition: full time: $37,890; part
time: N/A
Room/board/expenses: $5,265
College-funded aid: Yes
International student aid: Yes

Average student indebtedness at
graduation: $56,044
Full-time enrollment: 548
men: 69%; women: 31%;
minorities: 9%; international: 46%
Part-time enrollment: N/A
men: N/A; women: N/A;
minorities: N/A; international: N/A
Acceptance rate (full-time): 72%
Average GMAT (full-time): 598
Average GPA (full-time): 3.31
Average age of entrants to full-time
program: 28
Average months of prior work
experience (full-time): 51
TOEFL requirement: Yes
Minimum TOEFL score: 600
Mean starting base salary for 2007
full-time graduates: $80,979
Employment location for 2007 class:
Intl. 21%; N.E. 15%; M.A. 5%; S.
6%; M.W. 14%; S.W. 23%; W. 16%

University of Arizona (Eller)

McClelland Hall
Room 210
Tucson, AZ 85721-0108
http://ellermba.arizona.edu
Public
Admissions: (520) 621-6227
E-mail: mba_admissions@
eller.arizona.edu
Financial aid: (520) 621-4717
Application deadline: 04/15
In-state tuition: full time: $15,492;
total program: $35,670 (part-time)
Out-of-state tuition: full time:
$26,299
Room/board/expenses: $13,200
College-funded aid: Yes
International student aid: Yes
Average student indebtedness at
graduation: $30,902
Full-time enrollment: 119
men: 75%; women: 25%;
minorities: 21%; international: 29%
Part-time enrollment: 89
men: 62%; women: 38%;
minorities: 13%; international: 10%
Acceptance rate (full-time): 56%
Average GMAT (full-time): 603
Average GMAT (part-time): 606
Average GPA (full-time): 3.34
Average age of entrants to full-time
program: 26
Average months of prior work
experience (full-time): 42
TOEFL requirement: Yes
Minimum TOEFL score: 600
Most popular departments: account-
ing, entrepreneurship, finance,
marketing, management
information systems
Mean starting base salary for 2007
full-time graduates: $75,003
Employment location for 2007 class:
Intl. 13%; N.E. 0%; M.A. 8%; S.
13%; M.W. 13%; S.W. 28%; W. 28%

ARKANSAS

Arkansas State University

PO Box 970
State University, AR 72467
http://business.astate.edu/
Public
Admissions: (870) 972-3029
E-mail: gradsch@astate.edu
Financial aid: (870) 972-2310
Application deadline: 07/15
In-state tuition: full time: $5,072;
part time: $235/credit hour
Out-of-state tuition: full time:
$10,472
Room/board/expenses: $8,765
College-funded aid: Yes
International student aid: No
Full-time enrollment: 57
men: 47%; women: 53%;
minorities: 16%; international: 28%

Part-time enrollment: 113
men: 56%; women: 44%;
minorities: 16%; international: 7%
Average GMAT (full-time): 500
Average GMAT (part-time): 511
Average GPA (full-time): 3.09
Average age of entrants to full-time
program: 27
TOEFL requirement: Yes
Minimum TOEFL score: 500

Henderson State University[1]

1100 Henderson Street
Box 7801
Arkadelphia, AR 71999-0001
http://www.hsu.edu/dept/
bus/mba.html
Public
Admissions: (870) 230-5126
E-mail: grad@hsu.edu
Financial aid: (870) 230-5148
Tuition: N/A
Room/board/expenses: N/A
Enrollment: N/A

University of Arkansas–Fayetteville (Walton)

475 Business Building
Fayetteville, AR 72701
http://gsb.uark.edu
Public
Admissions: (479) 575-2851
E-mail: gsb@walton.uark.edu
Financial aid: (479) 575-3806
Application deadline: rolling
In-state tuition: full time:
$365/credit hour; part time:
$415/credit hour
Out-of-state tuition: full time:
$864/credit hour
Room/board/expenses: $13,348
College-funded aid: Yes
International student aid: Yes
Average student indebtedness at
graduation: $24,956
Full-time enrollment: 30
men: 67%; women: 33%;
minorities: 0%; international: 33%
Part-time enrollment: 102
men: 75%; women: 25%;
minorities: 3%; international: 5%
Acceptance rate (full-time): 46%
Average GMAT (full-time): 623
Average GMAT (part-time): 585
Average GPA (full-time): 3.50
Average age of entrants to full-time
program: 26
Average months of prior work
experience (full-time): 44
TOEFL requirement: Yes
Minimum TOEFL score: 550
Most popular departments: entre-
preneurship, finance, marketing
Employment location for 2007 class:
Intl. N/A; N.E. 3%; M.A. 6%; S. 76%;
M.W. 3%; S.W. 9%; W. 3%

University of Arkansas–Little Rock[1]

2801 S. University Avenue
Little Rock, AR 72204
http://cba.ualr.edu
Public
Admissions: (501) 569-3356
E-mail: rmmoore@ualr.edu
Financial aid: (501) 569-3035
Tuition: N/A
Room/board/expenses: N/A
Enrollment: N/A

University of Central Arkansas

201 Donaghey
Conway, AR 72035
http://www.uca.edu/divisions/
academic/mba
Public
Admissions: (501) 450-5316

E-mail: davidk@uca.edu
Financial aid: (501) 450-3140
Application deadline: N/A
In-state tuition: full time: $240/credit hour; part time: $240/credit hour
Out-of-state tuition: full time: $441/credit hour
Room/board/expenses: $8,000
College-funded aid: Yes
International student aid: No
Full-time enrollment: N/A
men: N/A; women: N/A; minorities: N/A; international: N/A
Part-time enrollment: 59
men: 66%; women: 34%; minorities: 10%; international: 8%
Average GMAT (part-time): 524
TOEFL requirement: Yes
Minimum TOEFL score: 550

CALIFORNIA

California Polytechnic State University–San Luis Obispo (Orfalea)

1 Grand Avenue
San Luis Obispo, CA 93407
http://www.cob.calpoly.edu/index.html
Public
Admissions: (805) 756-2311
E-mail: admissions@calpoly.edu
Financial aid: (805) 756-2927
Application deadline: 07/01
In-state tuition: full time: $5,331; part time: N/A
Out-of-state tuition: full time: $18,096
Room/board/expenses: $15,586
College-funded aid: Yes
International student aid: No
Full-time enrollment: 88
men: 59%; women: 41%; minorities: 23%; international: 2%
Part-time enrollment: N/A
men: N/A; women: N/A; minorities: N/A; international: N/A
Acceptance rate (full-time): 36%
Average GMAT (full-time): 620
Average GPA (full-time): 3.29
Average age of entrants to full-time program: 27
Average months of prior work experience (full-time): 40
TOEFL requirement: Yes
Minimum TOEFL score: 550

California State Polytechnic University–Pomona[1]

3801 W. Temple Avenue
Pomona, CA 91768
http://www.csupomona.edu/~mba
Public
Admissions: (909) 869-2363
E-mail: mapardington@csupomona.edu
Financial aid: (909) 869-3700
Tuition: N/A
Room/board/expenses: N/A
Enrollment: N/A

California State University–Bakersfield[1]

9001 Stockdale Highway
Bakersfield, CA 93311-1099
http://www.csub.edu/BPA
Public
Admissions: (661) 664-3036
E-mail: hmontalvo@csubak.edu
Financial aid: (661) 664-3016
Tuition: N/A
Room/board/expenses: N/A
Enrollment: N/A

California State University–Chico

W. First and Orange Streets
Chico, CA 95929-0041
http://www.cob.csuchico.edu/
Public
Admissions: (530) 898-6880
E-mail: grin@csuchico.edu
Financial aid: (530) 898-6451
Application deadline: 04/01
In-state tuition: full time: $4,278; part time: $2,900
Out-of-state tuition: full time: $339/credit hour
Room/board/expenses: $17,340
College-funded aid: Yes
International student aid: Yes
Average student indebtedness at graduation: $15,000
Full-time enrollment: 67
men: 57%; women: 43%; minorities: 4%; international: 37%
Part-time enrollment: 24
men: 38%; women: 63%; minorities: 4%; international: 0%
Acceptance rate (full-time): 90%
Average GMAT (full-time): 515
Average GMAT (part-time): 487
Average GPA (full-time): 3.24
Average age of entrants to full-time program: 29
Average months of prior work experience (full-time): 52
TOEFL requirement: Yes
Minimum TOEFL score: 550
Most popular departments: accounting, general management, human resources management, management information systems, supply chain management
Mean starting base salary for 2007 full-time graduates: $60,700
Employment location for 2007 class: Intl. N/A; N.E. N/A; M.A. N/A; S. N/A; M.W. N/A; S.W. N/A; W. 100%

California State University–East Bay

25800 Carlos Bee Boulevard
Hayward, CA 94542
http://www.csueastbay.edu
Public
Admissions: (510) 885-2784
E-mail: admissions@csueastbay.edu
Financial aid: (510) 885-2784
Application deadline: 05/31
In-state tuition: full time: $5,316; part time: $3,404
Out-of-state tuition: full time: $16,164
Room/board/expenses: $15,000
College-funded aid: Yes
International student aid: No
Average student indebtedness at graduation: $5,500
Full-time enrollment: N/A
men: N/A; women: N/A; minorities: N/A; international: N/A
Part-time enrollment: 646
men: 59%; women: 41%; minorities: 75%; international: 20%
Average GMAT (part-time): 543
TOEFL requirement: Yes
Minimum TOEFL score: 550
Most popular departments: accounting, finance, general management, marketing, supply chain management

California State University–Fresno (Craig)

5245 N. Backer Avenue
Fresno, CA 93740-8001
http://www.craig.csufresno.edu/mba
Public
Admissions: (559) 278-2107
E-mail: mbainfo@csufresno.edu
Financial aid: (559) 278-2183
Application deadline: 03/02

In-state tuition: full time: $3,940; part time: N/A
Out-of-state tuition: full time: $10,042
Room/board/expenses: N/A
College-funded aid: Yes
International student aid: Yes
Full-time enrollment: N/A
men: N/A; women: N/A; minorities: N/A; international: N/A
Part-time enrollment: 120
men: 58%; women: 42%; minorities: 21%; international: 33%
Average GMAT (part-time): 600
TOEFL requirement: Yes
Minimum TOEFL score: 550
Most popular departments: entrepreneurship, finance, general management, international business, marketing

California State University–Fullerton

PO Box 6848
Fullerton, CA 92834-6848
http://business.fullerton.edu
Public
Admissions: (714) 278-2300
E-mail: mba@fullerton.edu
Financial aid: (714) 278-3125
Application deadline: 11/17
In-state tuition: full time: $3,984; part time: $2,530
Out-of-state tuition: full time: $10,086
Room/board/expenses: $14,446
College-funded aid: Yes
International student aid: Yes
Full-time enrollment: N/A
men: N/A; women: N/A; minorities: N/A; international: N/A
Part-time enrollment: 383
men: 57%; women: 43%; minorities: 34%; international: 26%
Average GMAT (part-time): 542
TOEFL requirement: Yes
Minimum TOEFL score: 570

California State University–Long Beach

1250 Bellflower Boulevard
Long Beach, CA 90840-8501
http://www.csulb.edu/colleges/cba/mba
Public
Admissions: (562) 985-8627
E-mail: mba@csulb.edu
Financial aid: (562) 985-4141
Application deadline: 03/30
In-state tuition: full time: N/A; part time: N/A
Out-of-state tuition: full time: $339/credit hour
Room/board/expenses: N/A
College-funded aid: Yes
International student aid: Yes
Full-time enrollment: 77
men: 62%; women: 38%; minorities: 48%; international: 30%
Part-time enrollment: 190
men: 57%; women: 43%; minorities: 35%; international: 7%
Acceptance rate (full-time): 43%
Average GMAT (full-time): 547
Average GMAT (part-time): 547
Average GPA (full-time): 3.10
Average age of entrants to full-time program: 28
TOEFL requirement: Yes
Minimum TOEFL score: 550

California State University–Los Angeles

5151 State University Drive
Los Angeles, CA 90032-8120
http://cbe.calstatela.edu/mba/index.htm
Public
Admissions: (323) 343-5156
E-mail: dchrist@calstatela.edu
Financial aid: (323) 343-1784

Application deadline: 06/15
In-state tuition: full time: $5,393; part time: $3,657
Out-of-state tuition: full time: $12,625
Room/board/expenses: N/A
College-funded aid: Yes
International student aid: No
Full-time enrollment: 92
men: 48%; women: 52%; minorities: N/A; international: N/A
Part-time enrollment: N/A
men: N/A; women: N/A; minorities: N/A; international: N/A
Acceptance rate (full-time): 42%
Average GMAT (full-time): 570
TOEFL requirement: Yes
Minimum TOEFL score: 550

California State University–Northridge[1]

18111 Nordhoff Street
Northridge, CA 91330-8380
http://www.csun.edu/mba
Public
Admissions: (818) 677-3625
E-mail: MBA@csun.edu
Financial aid: N/A
Tuition: N/A
Room/board/expenses: N/A
Enrollment: N/A

California State University–Sacramento

6000 J Street
Sacramento, CA 95819-6088
http://www.csus.edu/cbagrad
Public
Admissions: (916) 278-6772
E-mail: cbagrad@csus.edu
Financial aid: (916) 278-6554
Application deadline: 03/01
In-state tuition: total program: $7,150 (full-time); $9,130 (part-time)
Out-of-state tuition: total program: $21,300 (full-time)
Room/board/expenses: $2,700
College-funded aid: Yes
International student aid: Yes
Full-time enrollment: N/A
men: N/A; women: N/A; minorities: N/A; international: N/A
Part-time enrollment: 256
men: 53%; women: 47%; minorities: 35%; international: 14%
Average GMAT (part-time): 567
TOEFL requirement: Yes
Minimum TOEFL score: 550
Most popular departments: accounting, finance, general management, marketing, tax

California State University–San Bernardino

5500 University Parkway
San Bernardino, CA 92407
http://www.cbpa.csusb.edu
Public
Admissions: (909) 537-5703
E-mail: mba@csusb.edu
Financial aid: (909) 880-7800
Application deadline: 08/15
In-state tuition: full time: $4,350; part time: $4,350
Out-of-state tuition: full time: $226/credit hour
Room/board/expenses: $16,000
College-funded aid: Yes
International student aid: No
Average student indebtedness at graduation: $13,000
Full-time enrollment: 220
men: 62%; women: 38%; minorities: 21%; international: 50%
Part-time enrollment: 67
men: 63%; women: 37%; minorities: 42%; international: 0%
Acceptance rate (full-time): 69%

Average GMAT (full-time): 510
Average GMAT (part-time): 510
Average GPA (full-time): 3.10
Average age of entrants to full-time program: 27
Average months of prior work experience (full-time): 36
TOEFL requirement: Yes
Minimum TOEFL score: 550

California State University–Stanislaus

1 University Circle
Turlock, CA 95382
http://www.csustan.edu/Graduate_School/
Public
Admissions: (209) 667-3061
E-mail: grad_applications@csustan.edu
Financial aid: (209) 667-3336
Application deadline: 06/30
In-state tuition: full time: $3,625; part time: $3,625
Out-of-state tuition: full time: $13,795
Room/board/expenses: $12,942
College-funded aid: Yes
International student aid: Yes
Full-time enrollment: 68
men: 57%; women: 43%; minorities: 25%; international: 1%
Part-time enrollment: 68
men: 49%; women: 51%; minorities: 28%; international: 0%
Acceptance rate (full-time): 95%
Average GMAT (full-time): 496
Average GMAT (part-time): 598
Average GPA (full-time): 3.12
Average age of entrants to full-time program: 31
TOEFL requirement: Yes
Minimum TOEFL score: 550

Chapman University (Argyros)

1 University Drive
Orange, CA 92866
http://www.chapman.edu/argyros
Private
Admissions: (714) 997-6596
E-mail: mba@chapman.edu
Financial aid: (714) 997-6741
Application deadline: 05/01
Tuition: full time: $20,020; part time: $770/credit hour
Room/board/expenses: $17,000
College-funded aid: Yes
International student aid: Yes
Average student indebtedness at graduation: $19,600
Full-time enrollment: 80
men: 63%; women: 38%; minorities: 24%; international: 19%
Part-time enrollment: 116
men: 75%; women: 25%; minorities: 23%; international: 3%
Acceptance rate (full-time): 53%
Average GMAT (full-time): 570
Average GMAT (part-time): 530
Average GPA (full-time): 3.30
Average age of entrants to full-time program: 25
Average months of prior work experience (full-time): 26
TOEFL requirement: Yes
Minimum TOEFL score: 550

Claremont Graduate University (Drucker)

1021 N. Dartmouth Avenue
Claremont, CA 91711-6184
http://www.drucker.cgu.edu
Private
Admissions: (800) 944-4312
E-mail: drucker@cgu.edu
Financial aid: (909) 621-8337
Application deadline: 02/01
Tuition: full time: $31,930; part time: $1,376/credit hour
Room/board/expenses: $10,000
College-funded aid: Yes

International student aid: Yes
Average student indebtedness at graduation: $47,180
Full-time enrollment: 117
men: 62%; women: 38%; minorities: 13%; international: 34%
Part-time enrollment: 41
men: 68%; women: 32%; minorities: 34%; international: 7%
Acceptance rate (full-time): 53%
Average GMAT (full-time): 635
Average GPA (full-time): 3.18
Average age of entrants to full-time program: 28
Average months of prior work experience (full-time): 52
TOEFL requirement: Yes
Minimum TOEFL score: 570
Most popular departments: finance, international business, leadership, marketing, other
Mean starting base salary for 2007 full-time graduates: $63,988
Employment location for 2007 class: Intl. 0%; N.E. 0%; M.A. 0%; S. 0%; M.W. 0%; S.W. 0%; W. 100%

Loyola Marymount University

1 LMU Drive, MS 8387
Los Angeles, CA 90045-2659
http://mba.lmu.edu
Private
Admissions: (310) 338-2848
E-mail: mbapc@lmu.edu
Financial aid: (310) 338-2753
Application deadline: rolling
Tuition: full time: $982/credit hour; part time: $982/credit hour
Room/board/expenses: $19,900
College-funded aid: Yes
International student aid: Yes
Average student indebtedness at graduation: $26,768
Full-time enrollment: 72
men: 60%; women: 40%; minorities: 35%; international: 21%
Part-time enrollment: 231
men: 60%; women: 40%; minorities: 34%; international: 0%
Acceptance rate (full-time): 87%
Average GMAT (full-time): 576
Average GMAT (part-time): 571
Average GPA (full-time): 3.20
Average age of entrants to full-time program: 25
Average months of prior work experience (full-time): 36
TOEFL requirement: Yes
Minimum TOEFL score: 600
Most popular departments: entrepreneurship, finance, general management, international business, marketing

Monterey Institute of International Studies (Fisher)

460 Pierce Street
Monterey, CA 93940
http://fisher.miis.edu
Private
Admissions: (831) 647-4123
E-mail: fgsib@miis.edu
Financial aid: (831) 647-4119
Application deadline: rolling
Tuition: full time: $27,950; part time: $1,250/credit hour
Room/board/expenses: $13,610
College-funded aid: Yes
International student aid: Yes
Average student indebtedness at graduation: $32,920
Full-time enrollment: 81
men: 59%; women: 41%; minorities: 6%; international: 46%
Part-time enrollment: N/A
men: N/A; women: N/A; minorities: N/A; international: N/A
Acceptance rate (full-time): 75%
Average GMAT (full-time): 553
Average GPA (full-time): 3.30

Average age of entrants to full-time program: 26
Average months of prior work experience (full-time): 55
TOEFL requirement: Yes
Minimum TOEFL score: 550
Most popular departments: consulting, entrepreneurship, finance, international business, marketing
Mean starting base salary for 2007 full-time graduates: $64,000
Employment location for 2007 class: Intl. 46%; N.E. 7%; M.A. 4%; S. 4%; M.W. 0%; S.W. 0%; W. 39%

Naval Postgraduate School

555 Dyer Road
Monterey, CA 93943
http://www.nps.navy.mil/gsbpp/
Public
Admissions: (831) 656-1062
E-mail: sgdooley@nps.edu
Financial aid: N/A
Application deadline: N/A
In-state tuition: full time: N/A; part time: N/A
Out-of-state tuition: full time: N/A
Room/board/expenses: N/A
Average student indebtedness at graduation: $0
Full-time enrollment: 328
men: N/A; women: N/A; minorities: N/A; international: 13%
Part-time enrollment: 84
men: N/A; women: N/A; minorities: N/A; international: N/A
TOEFL requirement: Yes
Minimum TOEFL score: N/A
Most popular departments: finance, supply chain management, other

Pepperdine University (Graziadio)

24255 Pacific Coast Highway
Malibu, CA 90263-4100
http://www.bschool.pepperdine.edu
Private
Admissions: (310) 568-5535
E-mail: gsbmadm@pepperdine.edu
Financial aid: (310) 568-5530
Application deadline: 05/01
Tuition: full time: $34,544; part time: $31,252
Room/board/expenses: $22,300
College-funded aid: Yes
International student aid: Yes
Average student indebtedness at graduation: $83,245
Full-time enrollment: 98
men: 64%; women: 36%; minorities: 12%; international: 42%
Part-time enrollment: 217
men: 56%; women: 44%; minorities: 33%; international: 8%
Acceptance rate (full-time): 85%
Average GMAT (full-time): 635
Average GMAT (part-time): 550
Average GPA (full-time): 3.23
Average age of entrants to full-time program: 27
Average months of prior work experience (full-time): 49
TOEFL requirement: Yes
Minimum TOEFL score: 600
Most popular departments: entrepreneurship, finance, leadership, marketing, other
Mean starting base salary for 2007 full-time graduates: $74,834
Employment location for 2007 class: Intl. 14%; N.E. 2%; M.A. 0%; S. 0%; M.W. 0%; S.W. 5%; W. 79%

San Diego State University

5500 Campanile Drive
San Diego, CA 92182-8228
http://www.sdsu.edu/business
Public
Admissions: (619) 594-6336

E-mail: sdsumba@mail.sdsu.edu
Financial aid: (619) 594-6323
Application deadline: rolling
In-state tuition: full time: $4,070; part time: $2,636
Out-of-state tuition: full time: $12,206
Room/board/expenses: $14,712
College-funded aid: Yes
International student aid: No
Full-time enrollment: 390
men: 55%; women: 45%; minorities: 17%; international: 36%
Part-time enrollment: 414
men: 59%; women: 41%; minorities: 24%; international: 9%
Acceptance rate (full-time): 52%
Average GMAT (full-time): 591
Average GMAT (part-time): 593
Average GPA (full-time): 3.30
Average age of entrants to full-time program: 26
Average months of prior work experience (full-time): 41
TOEFL requirement: Yes
Minimum TOEFL score: 550
Most popular departments: accounting, entrepreneurship, finance, international business, marketing

San Francisco State University

835 Market Street
Suite 550
San Francisco, CA 94103
http://cob.sfsu.edu/mba
Public
Admissions: (415) 817-4300
E-mail: mba@sfsu.edu
Financial aid: (415) 338-1581
Application deadline: 03/01
In-state tuition: full time: $6,498; part time: $4,064
Out-of-state tuition: full time: $14,634
Room/board/expenses: $20,000
College-funded aid: Yes
International student aid: Yes
Full-time enrollment: 174
men: 48%; women: 52%; minorities: N/A; international: 93%
Part-time enrollment: 415
men: 51%; women: 49%; minorities: N/A; international: 0%
Acceptance rate (full-time): 51%
Average GMAT (full-time): 563
Average GMAT (part-time): 563
Average GPA (full-time): 3.12
Average age of entrants to full-time program: 28
Average months of prior work experience (full-time): 36
TOEFL requirement: Yes
Minimum TOEFL score: 570
Most popular departments: accounting, finance, general management, international business, marketing

San Jose State University (Lucas)

1 Washington Square
San Jose, CA 95192-0162
http://www.cob.sjsu.edu/graduate
Public
Admissions: (408) 924-3420
E-mail: mba@cob.sjsu.edu
Financial aid: (408) 283-7500
Application deadline: 05/01
In-state tuition: total program: $10,000 (full-time); $10,000 (part-time)
Out-of-state tuition: total program: $25,000 (part-time)
Room/board/expenses: $19,192
College-funded aid: Yes
International student aid: No
Full-time enrollment: 30
men: 47%; women: 53%; minorities: 60%; international: 30%
Part-time enrollment: 314
men: 54%; women: 46%; minorities: 65%; international: 13%
Acceptance rate (full-time): 54%

Average GMAT (full-time): 557
Average GMAT (part-time): 561
Average GPA (full-time): 3.25
Average age of entrants to full-time program: 28
TOEFL requirement: Yes
Minimum TOEFL score: 550

Santa Clara University (Leavey)

Kenna Hall
Santa Clara, CA 95053
http://www.scu.edu/business
Private
Admissions: (408) 554-4539
E-mail: mbaadmissions@scu.edu
Financial aid: (408) 554-4505
Application deadline: 06/01
Tuition: full time: $739/credit hour; part time: $739/credit hour
Room/board/expenses: $21,000
College-funded aid: Yes
International student aid: No
Full-time enrollment: 187
men: 62%; women: 38%; minorities: 33%; international: 39%
Part-time enrollment: 875
men: 69%; women: 31%; minorities: 37%; international: 20%
Acceptance rate (full-time): 78%
Average GMAT (full-time): 613
Average GMAT (part-time): 613
Average GPA (full-time): 3.13
Average age of entrants to full-time program: 30
Average months of prior work experience (full-time): 78
TOEFL requirement: Yes
Minimum TOEFL score: 600
Mean starting base salary for 2007 full-time graduates: $93,617
Employment location for 2007 class: Intl. 1%; N.E. 3%; M.A. 1%; S. 0%; M.W. 0%; S.W. 1%; W. 93%

Sonoma State University[1]

1801 East Cotati Avenue
Rohnert Park, CA 94928
N/A
Private
Admissions: (707) 664-2377
Financial aid: N/A
Tuition: N/A
Room/board/expenses: N/A
Enrollment: N/A

Stanford University

518 Memorial Way
Stanford, CA 94305-5015
http://www.gsb.stanford.edu
Private
Admissions: (650) 723-2766
E-mail: mba_2007_08@gsb.stanford.edu
Financial aid: (650) 723-3282
Application deadline: N/A
Tuition: full time: $45,921; part time: N/A
Room/board/expenses: $27,260
College-funded aid: Yes
International student aid: Yes
Average student indebtedness at graduation: $72,500
Full-time enrollment: 741
men: 65%; women: 35%; minorities: 21%; international: 31%
Part-time enrollment: N/A
men: N/A; women: N/A; minorities: N/A; international: N/A
Acceptance rate (full-time): 8%
Average GMAT (full-time): 721
Average GPA (full-time): 3.61
Average months of prior work experience (full-time): 47
TOEFL requirement: Yes
Minimum TOEFL score: 600
Mean starting base salary for 2007 full-time graduates: $117,681
Employment location for 2007 class: Intl. 14%; N.E. 20%; M.A. 3%; S. 3%; M.W. 4%; S.W. 3%; W. 55%

University of California–Berkeley (Haas)

545 Student Services Building
Berkeley, CA 94720-1900
http://www.haas.berkeley.edu
Public
Admissions: (510) 642-1405
Financial aid: (510) 643-0183
Application deadline: 03/12
In-state tuition: full time: $26,880; part time: $32,901
Out-of-state tuition: full time: $37,949
Room/board/expenses: $22,512
College-funded aid: Yes
International student aid: Yes
Average student indebtedness at graduation: $54,254
Full-time enrollment: 504
men: 67%; women: 33%; minorities: 22%; international: 32%
Part-time enrollment: 763
men: 76%; women: 24%; minorities: 45%; international: 15%
Acceptance rate (full-time): 14%
Average GMAT (full-time): 710
Average GMAT (part-time): 697
Average GPA (full-time): 3.57
Average age of entrants to full-time program: 29
Average months of prior work experience (full-time): 65
TOEFL requirement: Yes
Minimum TOEFL score: 570
Most popular departments: entrepreneurship, finance, general management, marketing, other
Mean starting base salary for 2007 full-time graduates: $101,859
Employment location for 2007 class: Intl. 12%; N.E. 4%; M.A. 2%; S. 0%; M.W. 3%; S.W. 1%; W. 77%

University of California–Davis

1 Shields Avenue
Davis, CA 95616-8609
http://www.gsm.ucdavis.edu
Public
Admissions: (530) 752-7658
E-mail: admissions@gsm.ucdavis.edu
Financial aid: (530) 752-7658
Application deadline: 03/11
In-state tuition: full time: $22,629; total program: $61,200 (part-time)
Out-of-state tuition: full time: $34,874
Room/board/expenses: $16,496
College-funded aid: Yes
International student aid: Yes
Average student indebtedness at graduation: $38,740
Full-time enrollment: 120
men: 56%; women: 44%; minorities: 20%; international: 17%
Part-time enrollment: 361
men: 72%; women: 28%; minorities: 40%; international: 7%
Acceptance rate (full-time): 26%
Average GMAT (full-time): 674
Average GMAT (part-time): 614
Average GPA (full-time): 3.37
Average age of entrants to full-time program: 28
Average months of prior work experience (full-time): 57
TOEFL requirement: Yes
Minimum TOEFL score: 600
Most popular departments: entrepreneurship, finance, marketing, organizational behavior, technology
Mean starting base salary for 2007 full-time graduates: $85,555
Employment location for 2007 class: Intl. 5%; N.E. 5%; M.A. 0%; S. 0%; M.W. 0%; S.W. 0%; W. 90%

University of California–Irvine (Merage)

Irvine, CA 92697-3125
http://www.merage.uci.edu
Public
Admissions: (949) 824-4622
E-mail: mba@merage.uci.edu
Financial aid: (949) 824-7967
Application deadline: 04/15
In-state tuition: full time: $26,187; part time: $23,667
Out-of-state tuition: full time: $37,394
Room/board/expenses: $25,340
College-funded aid: Yes
International student aid: Yes
Average student indebtedness at graduation: $35,258
Full-time enrollment: 199
men: 68%; women: 32%; minorities: 18%; international: 33%
Part-time enrollment: 463
men: 70%; women: 30%; minorities: 42%; international: 9%
Acceptance rate (full-time): 44%
Average GMAT (full-time): 667
Average GMAT (part-time): 584
Average GPA (full-time): 3.34
Average age of entrants to full-time program: 28
Average months of prior work experience (full-time): 50
TOEFL requirement: Yes
Minimum TOEFL score: 600
Most popular departments: finance, marketing, management information systems, operations management, real estate
Mean starting base salary for 2007 full-time graduates: $76,407
Employment location for 2007 class: Intl. 5%; N.E. 2%; M.A. 2%; S. 0%; M.W. 0%; S.W. 2%; W. 89%

University of California–Los Angeles (Anderson)

110 Westwood Plaza
Box 951481
Los Angeles, CA 90095-1481
http://www.anderson.ucla.edu
Public
Admissions: (310) 825-6944
E-mail: mba.admissions@anderson.ucla.edu
Financial aid: (310) 825-2746
Application deadline: 04/23
In-state tuition: full time: $28,446; part time: $27,450
Out-of-state tuition: full time: $37,286
Room/board/expenses: $24,983
College-funded aid: Yes
International student aid: Yes
Average student indebtedness at graduation: $70,000
Full-time enrollment: 721
men: 69%; women: 31%; minorities: 19%; international: 31%
Part-time enrollment: 704
men: 70%; women: 30%; minorities: 51%; international: N/A
Acceptance rate (full-time): 23%
Average GMAT (full-time): 704
Average GMAT (part-time): 677
Average GPA (full-time): 3.60
Average age of entrants to full-time program: 28
Average months of prior work experience (full-time): 57
TOEFL requirement: No
Minimum TOEFL score: N/A
Most popular departments: consulting, entrepreneurship, finance, marketing, real estate
Mean starting base salary for 2007 full-time graduates: $99,237
Employment location for 2007 class: Intl. 9%; N.E. 7%; M.A. 1%; S. 0%; M.W. 2%; S.W. 2%; W. 80%

University of California–Riverside (Anderson)

900 University Avenue
Riverside, CA 92521-0203
http://www.agsm.ucr.edu
Public
Admissions: (951) 827-6200
E-mail: mba@ucr.edu
Financial aid: (951) 827-3878
Application deadline: 05/01
In-state tuition: full time: $24,231; part time: $24,231
Out-of-state tuition: full time: $36,477
Room/board/expenses: $14,600
College-funded aid: Yes
International student aid: Yes
Full-time enrollment: 127
men: 46%; women: 54%; minorities: 13%; international: 59%
Part-time enrollment: 12
men: N/A; women: N/A; minorities: N/A; international: N/A
Acceptance rate (full-time): 42%
Average GMAT (full-time): 572
Average GPA (full-time): 3.46
Average age of entrants to full-time program: 27
Average months of prior work experience (full-time): 39
TOEFL requirement: Yes
Minimum TOEFL score: 550

University of San Diego

5998 Alcala Park
San Diego, CA 92110-2492
http://www.sandiego.edu/mba
Private
Admissions: (619) 260-4860
E-mail: mba@sandiego.edu
Financial aid: (619) 260-4514
Application deadline: rolling
Tuition: full time: $1,095/credit hour; part time: $1,095/credit hour
Room/board/expenses: $13,818
College-funded aid: Yes
International student aid: Yes
Full-time enrollment: 37
men: 70%; women: 30%; minorities: 19%; international: 19%
Part-time enrollment: 130
men: 67%; women: 33%; minorities: 20%; international: 16%
Acceptance rate (full-time): 40%
Average GMAT (full-time): 675
Average GMAT (part-time): 581
Average GPA (full-time): 3.10
Average age of entrants to full-time program: 27
Average months of prior work experience (full-time): 50
TOEFL requirement: Yes
Minimum TOEFL score: 580
Most popular departments: entrepreneurship, finance, general management, international business, marketing

University of San Francisco (Masagung)

2130 Fulton Street
San Francisco, CA 94117-1080
http://www.usfca.edu/sobam
Private
Admissions: (415) 422-5714
E-mail: mba@usfca.edu
Financial aid: (415) 422-6303
Application deadline: 03/15
Tuition: full time: N/A; part time: N/A
Room/board/expenses: N/A
College-funded aid: Yes
International student aid: Yes
Full-time enrollment: 202
men: 56%; women: 44%; minorities: 27%; international: 42%
Part-time enrollment: 106
men: 50%; women: 50%; minorities: 46%; international: 5%
Average GPA (full-time): 3.10
Average age of entrants to full-time program: 26
TOEFL requirement: Yes
Minimum TOEFL score: 600
Most popular departments: entrepreneurship, finance, general management, international business, marketing

University of Southern California (Marshall)

University Park
Los Angeles, CA 90089-1421
http://www.marshall.usc.edu
Private
Admissions: (213) 740-7846
E-mail: marshallmba@marshall.usc.edu
Financial aid: (213) 740-1111
Application deadline: 04/01
Tuition: total program: $81,100 (full-time); $82,400 (part-time)
Room/board/expenses: $16,300
College-funded aid: Yes
International student aid: Yes
Full-time enrollment: 458
men: 66%; women: 34%; minorities: 34%; international: 23%
Part-time enrollment: 809
men: 73%; women: 27%; minorities: 45%; international: 4%
Acceptance rate (full-time): 29%
Average GMAT (full-time): 689
Average GMAT (part-time): 624
Average GPA (full-time): 3.30
Average age of entrants to full-time program: 28
Average months of prior work experience (full-time): 61
TOEFL requirement: Yes
Minimum TOEFL score: 600
Most popular departments: entrepreneurship, finance, marketing, portfolio management, real estate
Mean starting base salary for 2007 full-time graduates: $88,841
Employment location for 2007 class: Intl. 6%; N.E. 18%; M.A. 2%; S. 1%; M.W. 2%; S.W. 3%; W. 67%

University of the Pacific (Eberhardt)

3601 Pacific Avenue
Stockton, CA 95211
http://www.business.pacific.edu/mba
Private
Admissions: (209) 946-2629
E-mail: mba@pacific.edu
Financial aid: (209) 946-2421
Application deadline: 03/01
Tuition: total program: $46,450 (full-time); part time: N/A
Room/board/expenses: $10,500
College-funded aid: Yes
International student aid: Yes
Full-time enrollment: 51
men: 71%; women: 29%; minorities: 41%; international: 10%
Part-time enrollment: N/A
men: N/A; women: N/A; minorities: N/A; international: N/A
Acceptance rate (full-time): 56%
Average GMAT (full-time): 552
Average GPA (full-time): 3.39
Average age of entrants to full-time program: 25
Average months of prior work experience (full-time): 16
TOEFL requirement: Yes
Minimum TOEFL score: 550
Most popular departments: entrepreneurship, finance, general management, marketing
Mean starting base salary for 2007 full-time graduates: $53,230

COLORADO

Colorado State University

164 Rockwell Hall
Fort Collins, CO 80523-1270
http://www.csumba.com
Public
Admissions: (970) 491-2461
E-mail: grad@mail.biz.colostate.edu
Financial aid: (970) 491-6321
Application deadline: 12/08
In-state tuition: full time: N/A; total program: $22,950 (part-time)
Out-of-state tuition: full time: N/A
Room/board/expenses: $2,200
College-funded aid: Yes
International student aid: Yes
Full-time enrollment: N/A
men: N/A; women: N/A; minorities: N/A; international: N/A
Part-time enrollment: 648
men: 58%; women: 42%; minorities: 17%; international: 3%
Average GMAT (part-time): 573
TOEFL requirement: Yes
Minimum TOEFL score: 565

Colorado State University–Pueblo

2200 Bonforte Boulevard
Pueblo, CO 81001
http://hsb.colostate-pueblo.edu
Public
Admissions: (719) 549-2461
E-mail: info@colostate-pueblo.edu
Financial aid: N/A
Application deadline: rolling
In-state tuition: full time: $164/credit hour; part time: $164/credit hour
Out-of-state tuition: full time: $605/credit hour
Room/board/expenses: N/A
College-funded aid: Yes
International student aid: Yes
Full-time enrollment: 54
men: 57%; women: 43%; minorities: 7%; international: 48%
Part-time enrollment: 33
men: 55%; women: 45%; minorities: 55%; international: 0%
Acceptance rate (full-time): 95%
Average GMAT (full-time): 435
Average age of entrants to full-time program: 29
TOEFL requirement: Yes
Minimum TOEFL score: 550

University of Colorado–Boulder (Leeds)

995 Regent Drive
419 UCB
Boulder, CO 80309
http://leeds.colorado.edu/mba
Public
Admissions: (303) 492-8397
E-mail: leedsmba@Colorado.edu
Financial aid: (303) 492-8223
Application deadline: 04/01
In-state tuition: full time: $11,662; total program: $42,000 (part-time)
Out-of-state tuition: full time: $25,818
Room/board/expenses: $14,000
College-funded aid: Yes
International student aid: Yes
Average student indebtedness at graduation: $34,256
Full-time enrollment: 128
men: 68%; women: 32%; minorities: 6%; international: 25%
Part-time enrollment: 112
men: 84%; women: 16%; minorities: 9%; international: 6%
Acceptance rate (full-time): 48%
Average GMAT (full-time): 629
Average GMAT (part-time): 622
Average GPA (full-time): 3.36
Average age of entrants to full-time program: 29
Average months of prior work experience (full-time): 57
TOEFL requirement: Yes
Minimum TOEFL score: 600
Most popular departments: entrepreneurship, finance, general management, marketing, operations management, organizational behavior, real estate, other
Mean starting base salary for 2007 full-time graduates: $67,212
Employment location for 2007 class: Intl. 6%; N.E. 0%; M.A. 3%; S. 0%; M.W. 0%; S.W. 85%; W. 6%

University of Colorado–Colorado Springs

1420 Austin Bluffs Parkway
Colorado Springs, CO 80918
http://www.uccs.edu/mba
Public
Admissions: (719) 262-3408
E-mail: mba@uccs.edu
Financial aid: (719) 262-3460
Application deadline: 06/01
In-state tuition: full time: N/A; part time: $607/credit hour
Out-of-state tuition: full time: N/A
Room/board/expenses: N/A
College-funded aid: Yes
International student aid: No
Full-time enrollment: N/A
men: N/A; women: N/A; minorities: N/A; international: N/A
Part-time enrollment: 235
men: 55%; women: 45%; minorities: 9%; international: 3%
Average GMAT (part-time): 550
TOEFL requirement: Yes
Minimum TOEFL score: 550
Most popular departments: accounting, finance, general management, marketing, operations management

University of Colorado–Denver

Campus Box 165
PO Box 173364
Denver, CO 80217-3364
http://www.cudenver.edu/business/
Public
Admissions: (303) 556-5900
E-mail: grad.business@cudenver.edu
Financial aid: (303) 556-2886
Application deadline: 06/01
In-state tuition: full time: $470/credit hour; part time: $470/credit hour
Out-of-state tuition: full time: $1,118/credit hour
Room/board/expenses: $14,270
College-funded aid: Yes
International student aid: Yes
Full-time enrollment: 164
men: 60%; women: 40%; minorities: 13%; international: 17%
Part-time enrollment: 499
men: 65%; women: 35%; minorities: 12%; international: 4%
Acceptance rate (full-time): 67%
Average GMAT (part-time): 544
TOEFL requirement: Yes
Minimum TOEFL score: 525
Most popular departments: accounting, entrepreneurship, finance, general management, health care administration

University of Denver (Daniels)

2101 S. University Boulevard
Denver, CO 80208
http://www.daniels.du.edu/
Private
Admissions: (303) 871-3416
E-mail: daniels@du.edu
Financial aid: (303) 871-3416
Application deadline: 03/15

Tuition: full time: $35,675; part time: $873/credit hour
Room/board/expenses: $10,782
College-funded aid: Yes
International student aid: Yes
Full-time enrollment: 195
men: 64%; women: 36%;
minorities: 7%; international: 16%
Part-time enrollment: 216
men: 64%; women: 36%;
minorities: 10%; international: 2%
Acceptance rate (full-time): 67%
Average GMAT (full-time): 588
Average GMAT (part-time): 597
Average GPA (full-time): 3.09
Average age of entrants to full-time program: 26
Average months of prior work experience (full-time): 51
TOEFL requirement: Yes
Minimum TOEFL score: 570
Most popular departments: finance, general management, international business, leadership, marketing
Mean starting base salary for 2007 full-time graduates: $64,026
Employment location for 2007 class: Intl. 13%; N.E. 2%; M.A. 5%; S. 0%; M.W. 5%; S.W. 58%; W. 17%

CONNECTICUT

Fairfield University (Dolan)

1073 N. Benson Road
Fairfield, CT 06824
http://www.fairfield.edu/dsob.xml
Private
Admissions: (203) 254-4070
E-mail: dwilkie@mail.fairfield.edu
Financial aid: (203) 254-4125
Application deadline: rolling
Tuition: full time: $630/credit hour;
part time: $630/credit hour
Room/board/expenses: N/A
College-funded aid: Yes
International student aid: Yes
Full-time enrollment: N/A
men: N/A; women: N/A;
minorities: N/A; international: N/A
Part-time enrollment: 206
men: 57%; women: 43%;
minorities: N/A; international: N/A
Average GMAT (part-time): 523
TOEFL requirement: Yes
Minimum TOEFL score: 550
Most popular departments: accounting, finance, general management, international business, marketing

Quinnipiac University

275 Mount Carmel Avenue
Hamden, CT 06518
http://www.quinnipiac.edu/x218.xml
Private
Admissions: (800) 462-1944
E-mail: graduate@quinnipiac.edu
Financial aid: (203) 582-8384
Application deadline: rolling
Tuition: full time: $675/credit hour;
part time: $675/credit hour
Room/board/expenses: $16,172
College-funded aid: Yes
International student aid: Yes
Average student indebtedness at graduation: $22
Full-time enrollment: 45
men: 58%; women: 42%;
minorities: 7%; international: 13%
Part-time enrollment: 99
men: 66%; women: 34%;
minorities: 8%; international: 4%
Acceptance rate (full-time): 50%
Average GMAT (full-time): 553
Average GMAT (part-time): 557
Average GPA (full-time): 3.34
Average age of entrants to full-time program: 23
TOEFL requirement: Yes
Minimum TOEFL score: 575

Sacred Heart University (Welch)

5151 Park Avenue
Fairfield, CT 06825
http://www.sacredheart.edu/johnfwelchcob.cfm
Private
Admissions: (203) 365-7619
E-mail: gradstudies@sacredheart.edu
Financial aid: (203) 371-7980
Application deadline: rolling
Tuition: full time: $24,236; part time: $625/credit hour
Room/board/expenses: $11,780
College-funded aid: Yes
International student aid: No
Average student indebtedness at graduation: $41,209
Full-time enrollment: 40
men: 55%; women: 45%;
minorities: 10%; international: 43%
Part-time enrollment: 139
men: 37%; women: 63%;
minorities: 14%; international: 4%
Acceptance rate (full-time): 100%
Average GMAT (full-time): 470
Average GMAT (part-time): 450
Average GPA (full-time): 3.40
Average age of entrants to full-time program: 24
Average months of prior work experience (full-time): 18
TOEFL requirement: Yes
Minimum TOEFL score: 550
Most popular departments: accounting, finance, general management

University of Connecticut

2100 Hillside Road
Unit 1041
Storrs, CT 06269-1041
http://www.business.uconn.edu
Public
Admissions: (860) 486-2872
E-mail: uconnmba@business.uconn.edu
Financial aid: (860) 486-2819
Application deadline: 04/15
In-state tuition: full time: $10,052; part time: $565/credit hour
Out-of-state tuition: full time: $23,534
Room/board/expenses: $18,000
College-funded aid: Yes
International student aid: Yes
Average student indebtedness at graduation: $38,879
Full-time enrollment: 153
men: 60%; women: 40%;
minorities: 16%; international: 41%
Part-time enrollment: 1,151
men: 66%; women: 34%;
minorities: 16%; international: 5%
Acceptance rate (full-time): 54%
Average GMAT (full-time): 634
Average GMAT (part-time): 569
Average GPA (full-time): 3.42
Average age of entrants to full-time program: 29
Average months of prior work experience (full-time): 74
TOEFL requirement: Yes
Minimum TOEFL score: 575
Most popular departments: entrepreneurship, finance, health care administration, marketing, operations management
Mean starting base salary for 2007 full-time graduates: $82,071
Employment location for 2007 class: Intl. 3%; N.E. 92%; M.A. 6%; S. N/A; M.W. N/A; S.W. N/A; W. N/A

University of Hartford (Barney)

200 Bloomfield Avenue
West Hartford, CT 06117
http://barney.hartford.edu
Private
Admissions: (860) 768-4900

E-mail: csilver@hartford.edu
Financial aid: (860) 768-4900
Application deadline: 08/01
Tuition: full time: $595/credit hour; part time: $595/credit hour
Room/board/expenses: N/A
College-funded aid: Yes
International student aid: Yes
Full-time enrollment: 94
men: 66%; women: 34%;
minorities: 14%; international: 37%
Part-time enrollment: 329
men: 57%; women: 43%;
minorities: 20%; international: 2%
Acceptance rate (full-time): 67%
Average GMAT (part-time): 530
Average age of entrants to full-time program: 32
TOEFL requirement: Yes
Minimum TOEFL score: 550

Yale University

Box 208200
New Haven, CT 06520-8200
http://mba.yale.edu
Private
Admissions: (203) 432-5635
E-mail: mba.admissions@yale.edu
Financial aid: (203) 432-5173
Application deadline: 03/12
Tuition: full time: $47,182; part time: N/A
Room/board/expenses: $21,920
College-funded aid: Yes
International student aid: Yes
Average student indebtedness at graduation: $80,234
Full-time enrollment: 395
men: 64%; women: 36%;
minorities: 24%; international: 21%
Part-time enrollment: N/A
men: N/A; women: N/A;
minorities: N/A; international: N/A
Acceptance rate (full-time): 15%
Average GMAT (full-time): 700
Average GPA (full-time): 3.47
Average age of entrants to full-time program: 28
Average months of prior work experience (full-time): 56
TOEFL requirement: Yes
Minimum TOEFL score: 600
Mean starting base salary for 2007 full-time graduates: $99,307
Employment location for 2007 class: Intl. 11%; N.E. 65%; M.A. 5%; S. 3%; M.W. 4%; S.W. 1%; W. 10%

DELAWARE

Delaware State University

1200 DuPont Highway
Dover, DE 19901
http://www.desu.edu/som/mba/index.php
Private
Admissions: (302) 857-6930
E-mail: ksheth@desu.edu
Financial aid: N/A
Application deadline: rolling
Tuition: full time: $344/credit hour; part time: $344/credit hour
Room/board/expenses: $18,500
College-funded aid: No
International student aid: No
Average student indebtedness at graduation: $16,000
Full-time enrollment: 11
men: 55%; women: 45%;
minorities: 27%; international: N/A
Part-time enrollment: 65
men: 60%; women: 40%;
minorities: 51%; international: 3%
Acceptance rate (full-time): 66%
Average age of entrants to full-time program: 30
TOEFL requirement: Yes
Minimum TOEFL score: 450
Most popular departments: finance, other

University of Delaware (Lerner)

103 Alfred Lerner Hall
Newark, DE 19716
http://www.mba.udel.edu
Public
Admissions: (302) 831-2221
E-mail: mbaprogram@udel.edu
Financial aid: (302) 831-8761
Application deadline: rolling
In-state tuition: full time: $9,800; part time: $500/credit hour
Out-of-state tuition: full time: $19,394
Room/board/expenses: $11,000
College-funded aid: Yes
International student aid: Yes
Full-time enrollment: 94
men: 63%; women: 37%;
minorities: 7%; international: 59%
Part-time enrollment: 257
men: 65%; women: 35%;
minorities: 14%; international: 20%
Acceptance rate (full-time): 52%
Average GMAT (full-time): 603
Average GMAT (part-time): 531
Average GPA (full-time): 3.00
Average age of entrants to full-time program: 32
Average months of prior work experience (full-time): 85
TOEFL requirement: Yes
Minimum TOEFL score: 600
Most popular departments: entrepreneurship, finance, general management, international business, marketing
Mean starting base salary for 2007 full-time graduates: $64,000
Employment location for 2007 class: Intl. 24%; N.E. 18%; M.A. 41%; S. 12%; M.W. 6%; S.W. N/A; W. N/A

DISTRICT OF COLUMBIA

American University (Kogod)

4400 Massachusetts Avenue NW
Washington, DC 20016
http://www.kogod.american.edu
Private
Admissions: (202) 885-1913
E-mail: kogodmba@american.edu
Financial aid: (202) 885-1907
Application deadline: 05/01
Tuition: full time: $27,784; part time: $1,048/credit hour
Room/board/expenses: $20,000
College-funded aid: Yes
International student aid: Yes
Average student indebtedness at graduation: $65,000
Full-time enrollment: 130
men: 63%; women: 37%;
minorities: N/A; international: N/A
Part-time enrollment: 122
men: 59%; women: 41%;
minorities: N/A; international: N/A
Acceptance rate (full-time): 48%
Average GMAT (full-time): 570
Average GMAT (part-time): 550
Average GPA (full-time): 3.07
Average age of entrants to full-time program: 27
Average months of prior work experience (full-time): 42
TOEFL requirement: Yes
Minimum TOEFL score: 600
Most popular departments: accounting, consulting, marketing, management information systems, tax
Mean starting base salary for 2007 full-time graduates: $74,884
Employment location for 2007 class: Intl. 2%; N.E. 7%; M.A. 69%; S. 5%; M.W. 5%; S.W. 5%; W. 7%

Georgetown University (McDonough)

206 Old North
Washington, DC 20057-1147
http://msb.georgetown.edu
Private
Admissions: (202) 687-4200
E-mail: mba@georgetown.edu
Financial aid: (202) 687-4547
Application deadline: N/A
Tuition: full time: $40,017; part time: $1,100/credit hour
Room/board/expenses: $22,085
College-funded aid: Yes
International student aid: Yes
Full-time enrollment: 591
men: 68%; women: 32%;
minorities: 21%; international: 28%
Part-time enrollment: 220
men: 66%; women: 34%;
minorities: 23%; international: 9%
Acceptance rate (full-time): 35%
Average GMAT (full-time): 677
Average GMAT (part-time): 662
Average GPA (full-time): 3.26
Average age of entrants to full-time program: 28
Average months of prior work experience (full-time): 62
TOEFL requirement: Yes
Minimum TOEFL score: 600
Most popular departments: consulting, finance, general management, international business, marketing
Mean starting base salary for 2007 full-time graduates: $90,082
Employment location for 2007 class: Intl. 20%; N.E. 41%; M.A. 24%; S. 3%; M.W. 3%; S.W. 4%; W. 6%

George Washington University

710 21st Street NW
Washington, DC 20052
http://www.mba.gwu.edu
Private
Admissions: (202) 994-5536
E-mail: mbaft@gwu.edu
Financial aid: (202) 994-6822
Application deadline: 05/01
Tuition: full time: $1,080/credit hour; part time: $1,080/credit hour
Room/board/expenses: $19,070
College-funded aid: Yes
International student aid: Yes
Average student indebtedness at graduation: $40,655
Full-time enrollment: 210
men: 61%; women: 39%;
minorities: N/A; international: 34%
Part-time enrollment: 615
men: 57%; women: 43%;
minorities: 23%; international: 5%
Acceptance rate (full-time): 45%
Average GMAT (full-time): 618
Average GMAT (part-time): 583
Average GPA (full-time): 3.26
Average age of entrants to full-time program: 28
Average months of prior work experience (full-time): 58
TOEFL requirement: Yes
Minimum TOEFL score: 600
Most popular departments: consulting, entrepreneurship, finance, international business, real estate
Mean starting base salary for 2007 full-time graduates: $74,137
Employment location for 2007 class: Intl. 14%; N.E. 14%; M.A. 64%; S. 2%; M.W. 0%; S.W. 0%; W. 7%

Howard University

2600 Sixth Street NW
Suite 236
Washington, DC 20059
http://www.bschool.howard.edu/programs/progams.html
Private
Admissions: (202) 806-1725
E-mail: MBA_bschool@howard.edu
Financial aid: (202) 806-2820

Application deadline: 05/15
Tuition: full time: $16,980; part time: $899/credit hour
Room/board/expenses: $17,036
College-funded aid: Yes
International student aid: Yes
Average student indebtedness at graduation: $37,833
Full-time enrollment: 101
men: 53%; women: 47%; minorities: 70%; international: 30%
Part-time enrollment: 30
men: 43%; women: 57%; minorities: 83%; international: 13%
Acceptance rate (full-time): 46%
Average GMAT (full-time): 533
Average GPA (full-time): 3.14
Average age of entrants to full-time program: 26
Average months of prior work experience (full-time): 37
TOEFL requirement: Yes
Minimum TOEFL score: 550
Most popular departments: entrepreneurship, finance, general management, marketing, supply chain management
Mean starting base salary for 2007 full-time graduates: $81,475
Employment location for 2007 class: Intl. 0%; N.E. 23%; M.A. 42%; S. 6%; M.W. 10%; S.W. 13%; W. 6%

FLORIDA

Barry University (Andreas)[1]
11300 N.E. Second Avenue
Miami Shores, FL 33161-6695
http://www.barry.edu/business
Private
Admissions: (305) 899-3146
E-mail: dfletcher@mail.barry.edu
Financial aid: (305) 899-3673
Tuition: N/A
Room/board/expenses: N/A
Enrollment: N/A

Florida Atlantic University
777 Glades Road
Boca Raton, FL 33431
http://www.business.fau.edu
Public
Admissions: (561) 297-3624
E-mail: gradadm@fau.edu
Financial aid: (561) 297-3131
Application deadline: 07/01
In-state tuition: full time: $256/credit hour; part time: $256/credit hour
Out-of-state tuition: full time: $915/credit hour
Room/board/expenses: $15,000
College-funded aid: Yes
International student aid: Yes
Full-time enrollment: 232
men: 59%; women: 41%; minorities: 25%; international: 13%
Part-time enrollment: 361
men: 54%; women: 46%; minorities: 28%; international: 5%
Average GMAT (part-time): 525
TOEFL requirement: Yes
Minimum TOEFL score: 600
Most popular departments: accounting, finance, general management, international business, marketing

Florida Gulf Coast University (Lutgert)
10501 FGCU Boulevard S
Fort Myers, FL 33965-6565
http://www.fgcu.edu/cob/
Public
Admissions: (239) 590-7988
E-mail: graduate@fgcu.edu
Financial aid: (239) 590-7920
Application deadline: N/A
In-state tuition: full time: N/A; part time: $243/credit hour
Out-of-state tuition: full time: N/A

Room/board/expenses: N/A
College-funded aid: N/A
men: N/A; women: N/A; minorities: N/A; international: N/A
Part-time enrollment: 151
men: 54%; women: 46%; minorities: 15%; international: 7%
Average GMAT (part-time): 523
TOEFL requirement: Yes
Minimum TOEFL score: 550
Most popular departments: accounting, marketing, management information systems, other

Florida International University
1050 S.W. 112 Avenue
CBC 300
Miami, FL 33199-0001
http://business.fiu.edu
Public
Admissions: (305) 348-7398
E-mail: chapman@fiu.edu
Financial aid: (305) 348-7272
Application deadline: 06/01
In-state tuition: total program: $29,500 (full-time); $20,000 (part-time)
Out-of-state tuition: total program: $34,500 (full-time)
Room/board/expenses: $15,000
College-funded aid: Yes
International student aid: Yes
Average student indebtedness at graduation: $40,000
Full-time enrollment: 65
men: 62%; women: 38%; minorities: 17%; international: 58%
Part-time enrollment: 252
men: 61%; women: 39%; minorities: 52%; international: 30%
Acceptance rate (full-time): 47%
Average GMAT (full-time): 560
Average GMAT (part-time): 552
Average GPA (full-time): 3.22
Average age of entrants to full-time program: 25
Average months of prior work experience (full-time): 36
TOEFL requirement: Yes
Minimum TOEFL score: 550
Most popular departments: entrepreneurship, finance, general management, human resources management, international business
Mean starting base salary for 2007 full-time graduates: $67,722
Employment location for 2007 class: Intl. 0%; N.E. 11%; M.A. 11%; S. 67%; M.W. 11%; S.W. 0%; W. 0%

Florida State University
Graduate Programs
215 Rovetta Building
Tallahassee, FL 32306-1110
http://www.cob.fsu.edu/grad
Public
Admissions: (850) 644-6455
E-mail: lbeverly@cob.fsu.edu
Financial aid: (850) 644-5716
Application deadline: rolling
In-state tuition: full time: $248/credit hour; part time: $248/credit hour
Out-of-state tuition: full time: $880/credit hour
Room/board/expenses: $17,500
College-funded aid: Yes
International student aid: Yes
Full-time enrollment: 61
men: 61%; women: 39%; minorities: 20%; international: 5%
Part-time enrollment: 77
men: 71%; women: 29%; minorities: 31%; international: 14%
Acceptance rate (full-time): 51%
Average GMAT (full-time): 552
Average GMAT (part-time): 541
Average GPA (full-time): 3.39
Average age of entrants to full-time program: 25

Average months of prior work experience (full-time): 42
TOEFL requirement: Yes
Minimum TOEFL score: 600
Most popular departments: accounting, finance, general management, marketing, real estate

Rollins College (Crummer)
1000 Holt Avenue
Winter Park, FL 32789-4499
http://www.crummer.rollins.edu
Private
Admissions: (800) 866-2405
E-mail: jbrito@rollins.edu
Financial aid: (407) 646-2395
Application deadline: rolling
Tuition: full time: $28,350; part time: $928/credit hour
Room/board/expenses: $15,000
College-funded aid: Yes
International student aid: Yes
Average student indebtedness at graduation: $35,902
Full-time enrollment: 151
men: 55%; women: 45%; minorities: 11%; international: 7%
Part-time enrollment: 198
men: 60%; women: 40%; minorities: 20%; international: 4%
Acceptance rate (full-time): 59%
Average GMAT (full-time): 587
Average GMAT (part-time): 548
Average GPA (full-time): 3.30
Average age of entrants to full-time program: 22
Average months of prior work experience (full-time): 9
TOEFL requirement: Yes
Minimum TOEFL score: 560
Most popular departments: entrepreneurship, finance, general management, international business, marketing
Mean starting base salary for 2007 full-time graduates: $55,000
Employment location for 2007 class: Intl. 9%; N.E. 4%; M.A. 4%; S. 77%; M.W. 0%; S.W. 2%; W. 4%

Stetson University[1]
421 N. Woodland Boulevard
Unit 8398
DeLand, FL 32720
http://www.stetson.edu
Private
Admissions: (386) 822-7410
E-mail: fdezoort@stetson.edu
Financial aid: (800) 688-7120
Tuition: N/A
Room/board/expenses: N/A
Enrollment: N/A

University of Central Florida[1]
PO Box 161400
Orlando, FL 32816-1400
http://www.ucfmba.ucf.edu
Public
Admissions: (407) 823-4723
E-mail: graduate@mail.ucf.edu
Financial aid: (407) 823-2827
Tuition: N/A
Room/board/expenses: N/A
Enrollment: N/A

University of Florida (Hough)
134 Bryan Hall
PO Box 117152
Gainesville, FL 32611-7152
http://www.floridamba.ufl.edu
Public
Admissions: (352) 392-7992
E-mail: floridamba@cba.ufl.edu
Financial aid: (352) 392-1275
Application deadline: 03/15
In-state tuition: full time: $7,478; part time: $17,785

Out-of-state tuition: full time: $22,603
Room/board/expenses: $13,760
College-funded aid: Yes
International student aid: Yes
Average student indebtedness at graduation: $18,207
Full-time enrollment: 142
men: 74%; women: 26%; minorities: 18%; international: 14%
Part-time enrollment: 579
men: 75%; women: 25%; minorities: 17%; international: 8%
Acceptance rate (full-time): 44%
Average GMAT (full-time): 680
Average GMAT (part-time): 602
Average GPA (full-time): 3.40
Average age of entrants to full-time program: 27
Average months of prior work experience (full-time): 44
TOEFL requirement: Yes
Minimum TOEFL score: 550
Most popular departments: consulting, finance, marketing, organizational behavior, real estate
Mean starting base salary for 2007 full-time graduates: $66,668
Employment location for 2007 class: Intl. 0%; N.E. 2%; M.A. 4%; S. 76%; M.W. 12%; S.W. 6%; W. 0%

University of Miami
PO Box 248027
Coral Gables, FL 33124-6520
http://www.bus.miami.edu/grad
Private
Admissions: (305) 284-4607
E-mail: mba@miami.edu
Financial aid: (305) 284-5212
Application deadline: rolling
Tuition: full time: $1,350/credit hour; part time: N/A
Room/board/expenses: $15,700
College-funded aid: Yes
International student aid: Yes
Average student indebtedness at graduation: $45,286
Full-time enrollment: 284
men: 66%; women: 34%; minorities: 22%; international: 31%
Part-time enrollment: 27
men: 67%; women: 33%; minorities: 56%; international: 4%
Acceptance rate (full-time): 67%
Average GMAT (full-time): 628
Average GPA (full-time): 3.21
Average age of entrants to full-time program: 25
Average months of prior work experience (full-time): 24
TOEFL requirement: Yes
Minimum TOEFL score: 550
Mean starting base salary for 2007 full-time graduates: $59,272
Employment location for 2007 class: Intl. 2%; N.E. 6%; M.A. 2%; S. 81%; M.W. 3%; S.W. 5%; W. 2%

University of North Florida (Coggin)
4567 St. John's Bluff Road S
Jacksonville, FL 32224-2645
http://www.unf.edu/coggin
Public
Admissions: (904) 620-1360
E-mail: kmartin@unf.edu
Financial aid: (904) 620-5555
Application deadline: 07/15
In-state tuition: full time: $6,390; part time: $266/credit hour
Out-of-state tuition: full time: $20,582
Room/board/expenses: $18,650
College-funded aid: Yes
International student aid: Yes
Average student indebtedness at graduation: $27,795
Full-time enrollment: 129
men: 62%; women: 38%; minorities: 17%; international: 17%
Part-time enrollment: 317
men: 57%; women: 43%; minorities: 19%; international: 1%

Average GMAT (part-time): 527
TOEFL requirement: Yes
Minimum TOEFL score: 550
Most popular departments: accounting, finance, general management, international business, other

University of South Florida
4202 Fowler Avenue
Tampa, FL 33620
http://www.coba.usf.edu/programs/mba/index.html
Public
Admissions: (813) 974-3335
E-mail: mba@coba.usf.edu
Financial aid: (813) 974-4700
Application deadline: 06/01
In-state tuition: full time: $275/credit hour; part time: $275/credit hour
Out-of-state tuition: full time: $919/credit hour
Room/board/expenses: $21,950
College-funded aid: Yes
International student aid: Yes
Full-time enrollment: 147
men: 56%; women: 44%; minorities: 16%; international: 23%
Part-time enrollment: 239
men: 67%; women: 33%; minorities: 20%; international: 7%
Acceptance rate (full-time): 51%
Average GMAT (full-time): 530
Average GMAT (part-time): 526
Average GPA (full-time): 3.23
Average age of entrants to full-time program: 28
Average months of prior work experience (full-time): 60
TOEFL requirement: Yes
Minimum TOEFL score: 550
Most popular departments: entrepreneurship, finance, general management, international business, marketing
Mean starting base salary for 2007 full-time graduates: $53,000
Employment location for 2007 class: Intl. 11%; N.E. 0%; M.A. 0%; S. 89%; M.W. 0%; S.W. 0%; W. 0%

University of South Florida– St. Petersburg
COB 348
140 Seventh Avenue S
St. Petersburg, FL 33701
http://www.stpt.usf.edu/cob/graduate/index.HTM
Public
Admissions: N/A
E-mail: mba@stpt.usf.edu
Financial aid: N/A
Application deadline: 07/01
In-state tuition: full time: N/A; part time: $259/credit hour
Out-of-state tuition: full time: N/A
Room/board/expenses: N/A
College-funded aid: Yes
International student aid: Yes
Average student indebtedness at graduation: $10,100
Full-time enrollment: N/A
men: N/A; women: N/A; minorities: N/A; international: N/A
Part-time enrollment: 127
men: 55%; women: 45%; minorities: 12%; international: 9%
Average GMAT (part-time): 561
TOEFL requirement: Yes
Minimum TOEFL score: 550
Most popular departments: accounting, finance, general management, international business, marketing

University of Tampa (Sykes)
401 W. Kennedy Boulevard
Tampa, FL 33606-1490
http://grad.ut.edu
Public
Admissions: (813) 258-7409
E-mail: utgrad@ut.edu
Financial aid: (813) 253-6219
Application deadline: 07/15
In-state tuition: full time: $450/credit hour; part time: $450/credit hour
Out-of-state tuition: full time: $450/credit hour
Room/board/expenses: $8,142
College-funded aid: Yes
International student aid: Yes
Average student indebtedness at graduation: $21,221
Full-time enrollment: 189
men: 61%; women: 39%; minorities: 11%; international: 38%
Part-time enrollment: 376
men: 61%; women: 39%; minorities: 18%; international: 4%
Acceptance rate (full-time): 70%
Average GMAT (full-time): 535
Average GMAT (part-time): 513
Average GPA (full-time): 3.36
Average age of entrants to full-time program: 24
Average months of prior work experience (full-time): 22
TOEFL requirement: Yes
Minimum TOEFL score: 577
Most popular departments: accounting, finance, general management, international business, marketing
Mean starting base salary for 2007 full-time graduates: $58,030
Employment location for 2007 class: Intl. N/A; N.E. 3%; M.A. 3%; S. 88%; M.W. N/A; S.W. 3%; W. 3%

University of West Florida
11000 University Parkway
Pensacola, FL 32514
http://uwf.edu
Public
Admissions: (850) 474-2230
E-mail: mba@uwf.edu
Financial aid: (850) 474-2400
Application deadline: 06/01
In-state tuition: full time: $252/credit hour; part time: $252/credit hour
Out-of-state tuition: full time: $912/credit hour
Room/board/expenses: $10,450
College-funded aid: Yes
International student aid: Yes
Full-time enrollment: 26
men: 46%; women: 54%; minorities: 15%; international: 38%
Part-time enrollment: 102
men: 64%; women: 36%; minorities: 16%; international: 13%
Average GMAT (full-time): 556
Average GMAT (part-time): 523
Average GPA (full-time): 3.20
Average age of entrants to full-time program: 25
TOEFL requirement: Yes
Minimum TOEFL score: 550

GEORGIA

Augusta State University[1]
2500 Walton Way
Augusta, GA 30904-2200
http://www.aug.edu/coba
Public
Admissions: (706) 737-1565
E-mail: mbainfo@aug.edu
Financial aid: (706) 737-1431
Tuition: N/A
Room/board/expenses: N/A
Enrollment: N/A

Berry College (Campbell)[1]
PO Box 495024
Mount Berry, GA 30149-5024
http://campbell.berry.edu
Private
Admissions: (706) 236-2215
E-mail: admissions@berry.edu
Financial aid: (706) 236-1714
Tuition: N/A
Room/board/expenses: N/A
Enrollment: N/A

Clark Atlanta University
223 James P. Brawley Drive SW
Atlanta, GA 30314
http://www.cau.edu
Private
Admissions: (404) 880-8443
E-mail: pkamas@cau.edu
Financial aid: (404) 880-6265
Application deadline: 04/01
Tuition: full time: $20,638; part time: $648/credit hour
Room/board/expenses: $15,079
College-funded aid: Yes
International student aid: Yes
Average student indebtedness at graduation: $46,985
Full-time enrollment: 65
men: 32%; women: 68%; minorities: 83%; international: 6%
Part-time enrollment: 38
men: 34%; women: 66%; minorities: 95%; international: 0%
Acceptance rate (full-time): 90%
Average GMAT (full-time): 430
Average GMAT (part-time): 450
Average GPA (full-time): 3.04
Average age of entrants to full-time program: 28
Average months of prior work experience (full-time): 48
TOEFL requirement: Yes
Minimum TOEFL score: 500
Most popular departments: finance, marketing
Mean starting base salary for 2007 full-time graduates: $80,000
Employment location for 2007 class: Intl. N/A; N.E. 10%; M.A. N/A; S. 37%; M.W. 47%; S.W. N/A; W. 7%

Columbus State University (Turner)
4225 University Avenue
Columbus, GA 31907
http://datcob.colstate.edu
Public
Admissions: N/A
Financial aid: N/A
Application deadline: 07/13
In-state tuition: full time: $143/credit hour; part time: $143/credit hour
Out-of-state tuition: full time: $569/credit hour
Room/board/expenses: N/A
College-funded aid: Yes
International student aid: Yes
Full-time enrollment: 5
men: 60%; women: 40%; minorities: 40%; international: 40%
Part-time enrollment: 49
men: 49%; women: 51%; minorities: 29%; international: 12%
Acceptance rate (full-time): 100%
Average GMAT (full-time): 530
Average GMAT (part-time): 530
Average GPA (full-time): 3.40
Average age of entrants to full-time program: 23
TOEFL requirement: Yes
Minimum TOEFL score: 550

Emory University (Goizueta)
1300 Clifton Road NE
Atlanta, GA 30322
http://www.goizueta.emory.edu
Private
Admissions: (404) 727-6311
E-mail: admissions@bus.emory.edu
Financial aid: (404) 727-6039
Application deadline: 03/01
Tuition: full time: $37,576; part time: $22,876
Room/board/expenses: $21,562
College-funded aid: Yes
International student aid: Yes
Average student indebtedness at graduation: $61,883
Full-time enrollment: 373
men: 70%; women: 30%; minorities: 17%; international: 41%
Part-time enrollment: 265
men: 69%; women: 31%; minorities: 28%; international: 11%
Acceptance rate (full-time): 37%
Average GMAT (full-time): 685
Average GMAT (part-time): 637
Average GPA (full-time): 3.30
Average age of entrants to full-time program: 28
Average months of prior work experience (full-time): 58
TOEFL requirement: Yes
Minimum TOEFL score: 600
Most popular departments: consulting, finance, general management, leadership, marketing
Mean starting base salary for 2007 full-time graduates: $93,059
Employment location for 2007 class: Intl. 4%; N.E. 19%; M.A. 6%; S. 57%; M.W. 2%; S.W. 4%; W. 7%

Georgia College and State University (Bunting)
Campus Box 019
Milledgeville, GA 31061
http://www.gcsu.edu/business
Public
Admissions: (478) 445-6285
E-mail: mike.augustine@gcsu.edu
Financial aid: (478) 445-5149
Application deadline: 07/01
In-state tuition: full time: $6,876; part time: $207/credit hour
Out-of-state tuition: full time: $23,589
Room/board/expenses: N/A
College-funded aid: Yes
International student aid: Yes
Full-time enrollment: N/A
men: N/A; women: N/A; minorities: N/A; international: N/A
Part-time enrollment: 129
men: 57%; women: 43%; minorities: 19%; international: 7%
Average GMAT (part-time): 486
TOEFL requirement: Yes
Minimum TOEFL score: 500
Most popular departments: accounting, general management, health care administration, management information systems

Georgia Institute of Technology
800 W. Peachtree Street NW
Atlanta, GA 30332-0520
http://www.mgt.gatech.edu
Public
Admissions: (404) 894-8722
E-mail: mba@mgt.gatech.edu
Financial aid: (404) 894-4160
Application deadline: 05/01
In-state tuition: full time: $8,364; part time: $650/credit hour
Out-of-state tuition: full time: $30,016
Room/board/expenses: $12,000
College-funded aid: Yes
International student aid: Yes
Average student indebtedness at graduation: $22,434
Full-time enrollment: 153
men: 71%; women: 29%; minorities: 23%; international: 25%
Part-time enrollment: 45
men: 76%; women: 24%; minorities: 29%; international: 4%
Acceptance rate (full-time): 40%
Average GMAT (full-time): 665
Average GMAT (part-time): 629
Average GPA (full-time): 3.40
Average age of entrants to full-time program: 27
Average months of prior work experience (full-time): 38
TOEFL requirement: Yes
Minimum TOEFL score: 600
Most popular departments: entrepreneurship, finance, management information systems, operations management, supply chain management
Mean starting base salary for 2007 full-time graduates: $81,058
Employment location for 2007 class: Intl. 0%; N.E. 12%; M.A. 12%; S. 67%; M.W. 6%; S.W. 4%; W. 0%

Georgia Southern University
PO Box 8050
Statesboro, GA 30460-8050
http://coba.georgiasouthern.edu/mba
Public
Admissions: (912) 681-5767
E-mail: mba@georgiasouthern.edu
Financial aid: (912) 681-5413
Application deadline: 07/01
In-state tuition: full time: $147/credit hour; part time: $147/credit hour
Out-of-state tuition: full time: $586/credit hour
Room/board/expenses: $13,160
College-funded aid: Yes
International student aid: Yes
Average student indebtedness at graduation: $26,456
Full-time enrollment: 62
men: 65%; women: 35%; minorities: 35%; international: 23%
Part-time enrollment: 117
men: 51%; women: 49%; minorities: 15%; international: 0%
Acceptance rate (full-time): 80%
Average GMAT (full-time): 503
Average GMAT (part-time): 507
Average GPA (full-time): 3.23
Average age of entrants to full-time program: 24
TOEFL requirement: Yes
Minimum TOEFL score: 550

Georgia State University (Robinson)
PO Box 3988
Atlanta, GA 30302-3988
http://robinson.gsu.edu/index_flash.html
Public
Admissions: (404) 413-7140
E-mail: mastersadmissions@gsu.edu
Financial aid: (404) 413-2400
Application deadline: 04/01
In-state tuition: full time: $7,732; part time: $281/credit hour
Out-of-state tuition: full time: $25,444
Room/board/expenses: $15,780
College-funded aid: Yes
International student aid: Yes
Average student indebtedness at graduation: $74,391
Full-time enrollment: 20
men: 40%; women: 60%; minorities: 25%; international: 15%
Part-time enrollment: 871
men: 67%; women: 33%; minorities: 27%; international: 18%
Acceptance rate (full-time): 86%
Average GMAT (full-time): 564
Average GMAT (part-time): 602
Average GPA (full-time): 3.20
Average age of entrants to full-time program: 29
Average months of prior work experience (full-time): 66
TOEFL requirement: Yes
Minimum TOEFL score: 610
Most popular departments: accounting, finance, marketing, management information systems, operations management
Mean starting base salary for 2007 full-time graduates: $76,000

Kennesaw State University (Coles)
1000 Chastain Road
Kennesaw, GA 30144-5591
http://coles.kennesaw.edu
Public
Admissions: (770) 420-4377
E-mail: ksugrad@kennesaw.edu
Financial aid: (770) 423-6525
Application deadline: 06/01
In-state tuition: full time: N/A; part time: $153/credit hour
Out-of-state tuition: full time: N/A
Room/board/expenses: N/A
College-funded aid: Yes
International student aid: Yes
Average student indebtedness at graduation: $20,000
Full-time enrollment: N/A
men: N/A; women: N/A; minorities: N/A; international: N/A
Part-time enrollment: 518
men: 55%; women: 45%; minorities: 30%; international: 24%
Average GMAT (part-time): 539
Average GPA (full-time): N/A
TOEFL requirement: Yes
Minimum TOEFL score: 550
Most popular departments: accounting, general management

Mercer University–Atlanta (Stetson)
3001 Mercer University Drive
Atlanta, GA 30341-4155
http://business.mercer.edu
Private
Admissions: (678) 547-6417
E-mail: atlbusadm@mercer.edu
Financial aid: (678) 547-6400
Application deadline: 08/01
Tuition: full time: N/A; part time: $575/credit hour
Room/board/expenses: N/A
College-funded aid: No
International student aid: No
Full-time enrollment: N/A
men: N/A; women: N/A; minorities: N/A; international: N/A
Part-time enrollment: 427
men: 57%; women: 43%; minorities: 36%; international: 6%
Average GMAT (part-time): 502
TOEFL requirement: Yes
Minimum TOEFL score: 550
Most popular departments: accounting, finance, health care administration, international business, marketing

Savannah State University
PO Box 20359
Savannah, GA 31404
http://coba.savstate.edu/tiki-index.php
Public
Admissions: N/A
Financial aid: N/A
Application deadline: 07/01
In-state tuition: full time: $127/credit hour; part time: N/A
Out-of-state tuition: full time: $508/credit hour
Room/board/expenses: $3,000
College-funded aid: Yes
International student aid: Yes

Average student indebtedness at graduation: $0
Full-time enrollment: N/A
men: N/A; women: N/A;
minorities: N/A; international: N/A
Part-time enrollment: 30
men: 30%; women: 70%;
minorities: 67%; international: 7%
Average GMAT (part-time): 420
TOEFL requirement: Yes
Minimum TOEFL score: 550

University of Georgia (Terry)

335 Brooks Hall
Athens, GA 30602-6251
http://www.terry.uga.edu/mba
Public
Admissions: (706) 542-5671
E-mail: terrymba@terry.uga.edu
Financial aid: (706) 542-6147
Application deadline: 05/11
In-state tuition: full time: $9,308; part time: $650/credit hour
Out-of-state tuition: full time: $28,162
Room/board/expenses: $16,000
College-funded aid: Yes
International student aid: Yes
Full-time enrollment: 123
men: 70%; women: 30%;
minorities: 11%; international: 30%
Part-time enrollment: 272
men: 69%; women: 31%;
minorities: 16%; international: 9%
Acceptance rate (full-time): 30%
Average GMAT (full-time): 653
Average GMAT (part-time): 563
Average GPA (full-time): 3.40
Average age of entrants to full-time program: 28
Average months of prior work experience (full-time): 49
TOEFL requirement: Yes
Minimum TOEFL score: 577
Most popular departments: entrepreneurship, finance, insurance, marketing, real estate
Mean starting base salary for 2007 full-time graduates: $71,908
Employment location for 2007 class: Intl. 2%; N.E. 6%; M.A. 6%; S. 82%; M.W. 4%; S.W. 0%; W. 0%

University of West Georgia (Richards)

1601 Maple Street
Carrollton, GA 30118-3000
http://www.westga.edu/~busn/mba.html
Public
Admissions: (678) 839-6419
E-mail: cthill@westga.edu
Financial aid: (678) 839-6421
Application deadline: rolling
In-state tuition: full time: $3,408; part time: $136/credit hour
Out-of-state tuition: full time: $10,734
Room/board/expenses: $6,776
College-funded aid: Yes
International student aid: Yes
Full-time enrollment: 17
men: 53%; women: 47%;
minorities: 18%; international: 24%
Part-time enrollment: 56
men: 50%; women: 50%;
minorities: 16%; international: 4%
Average GMAT (part-time): 474
Average age of entrants to full-time program: 26
TOEFL requirement: Yes
Minimum TOEFL score: 550

Valdosta State University (Langdale)

1500 N. Patterson Street
Valdosta, GA 31698
http://www.valdosta.edu/coba/grad/
Public
Admissions: (229) 245-2243
E-mail: rcallen@valdosta.edu
Financial aid: (229) 333-5935
Application deadline: 07/15
In-state tuition: full time: $5,676; part time: $147/credit hour
Out-of-state tuition: full time: $16,220
Room/board/expenses: $7,000
College-funded aid: Yes
International student aid: Yes
Full-time enrollment: N/A
men: N/A; women: N/A;
minorities: N/A; international: N/A
Part-time enrollment: 33
men: 52%; women: 48%;
minorities: N/A; international: 9%
Average GMAT (part-time): 524
TOEFL requirement: Yes
Minimum TOEFL score: 550

HAWAII

University of Hawaii-Manoa (Shidler)

2404 Maile Way
Business Administration C-202
Honolulu, HI 96822
http://www.shidler.hawaii.edu
Public
Admissions: (808) 956-8754
E-mail: busgrad@hawaii.edu
Financial aid: (808) 956-7251
Application deadline: 05/01
In-state tuition: full time: $11,096; part time: $454/credit hour
Out-of-state tuition: full time: $16,712
Room/board/expenses: $19,000
College-funded aid: Yes
International student aid: Yes
Full-time enrollment: 46
men: 63%; women: 37%;
minorities: 61%; international: 20%
Part-time enrollment: 113
men: 65%; women: 35%;
minorities: 71%; international: 17%
Acceptance rate (full-time): 41%
Average GMAT (full-time): 632
Average GMAT (part-time): 567
Average GPA (full-time): 3.40
Average age of entrants to full-time program: 28
Average months of prior work experience (full-time): 63
TOEFL requirement: Yes
Minimum TOEFL score: 600
Most popular departments: accounting, finance, general management, international business, marketing

IDAHO

Boise State University

1910 University Drive
B318
Boise, ID 83725-1600
http://cobe.boisestate.edu/graduate
Public
Admissions: (208) 426-3116
E-mail: graduatebusiness@boisestate.edu
Financial aid: (208) 426-1664
Application deadline: 06/01
In-state tuition: full time: $6,470; part time: $272/credit hour
Out-of-state tuition: full time: $14,638
Room/board/expenses: $18,642
College-funded aid: Yes
International student aid: Yes
Average student indebtedness at graduation: $12,349
Full-time enrollment: 130
men: 69%; women: 31%;
minorities: 5%; international: 8%
Part-time enrollment: 107
men: 62%; women: 38%;
minorities: 7%; international: 4%
Acceptance rate (full-time): 67%
Average GMAT (full-time): 561
Average GMAT (part-time): 583
Average GPA (full-time): 3.36
Average age of entrants to full-time program: 28
Average months of prior work experience (full-time): 54
TOEFL requirement: Yes
Minimum TOEFL score: 587
Most popular departments: accounting, finance, general management, management information systems, tax
Employment location for 2007 class: Intl. 21%; N.E. 4%; M.A. 8%; S. N/A; M.W. 4%; S.W. 4%; W. 58%

Idaho State University

PO Box 8020
Pocatello, ID 83209
http://cob.isu.edu
Public
Admissions: (208) 282-2504
E-mail: mba@cob.isu.edu
Financial aid: (208) 282-2756
Application deadline: 07/01
In-state tuition: full time: N/A; part time: N/A
Out-of-state tuition: full time: N/A
Room/board/expenses: N/A
College-funded aid: Yes
International student aid: Yes
Full-time enrollment: 100
men: 76%; women: 24%;
minorities: 14%; international: 9%
Part-time enrollment: 65
men: 83%; women: 17%;
minorities: 9%; international: 0%
Acceptance rate (full-time): 59%
Average GMAT (full-time): 586
Average GMAT (part-time): 597
Average age of entrants to full-time program: 28
Average months of prior work experience (full-time): 18
TOEFL requirement: Yes
Minimum TOEFL score: 550
Most popular departments: accounting, finance, general management, marketing, management information systems

University of Idaho

PO Box 443161
Moscow, ID 83844-3161
http://www.uidaho.edu/cogs
Public
Admissions: (800) 885-4001
E-mail: gadms@uidaho.edu
Financial aid: (208) 885-6326
Application deadline: 05/01
In-state tuition: full time: N/A; part time: $239/credit hour
Out-of-state tuition: full time: $15,030
Room/board/expenses: $13,582
College-funded aid: Yes
International student aid: Yes
Full-time enrollment: 28
men: 25%; women: 75%;
minorities: 0%; international: 36%
Part-time enrollment: N/A
men: N/A; women: N/A;
minorities: N/A; international: N/A
Acceptance rate (full-time): 87%
Average GMAT (full-time): 532
Average GPA (full-time): 3.51
TOEFL requirement: Yes
Minimum TOEFL score: 550
Mean starting base salary for 2007 full-time graduates: $42,000
Employment location for 2007 class: Intl. N/A; N.E. N/A; M.A. N/A; S. N/A; M.W. N/A; S.W. 14%; W. 86%

ILLINOIS

Bradley University (Foster)

1501 W. Bradley Avenue
Peoria, IL 61625
http://www.bradley.edu/fcba/mba
Private
Admissions: (309) 677-2253
E-mail: mba@bradley.edu
Financial aid: (309) 677-3089
Application deadline: rolling
Tuition: full time: $580/credit hour; part time: $580/credit hour
Room/board/expenses: N/A
College-funded aid: Yes
International student aid: Yes
Full-time enrollment: 25
men: N/A; women: N/A;
minorities: N/A; international: N/A
Part-time enrollment: 180
men: N/A; women: N/A;
minorities: N/A; international: N/A
Acceptance rate (full-time): 67%
Average age of entrants to full-time program: 26
TOEFL requirement: Yes
Minimum TOEFL score: 550
Most popular departments: general management, marketing

DePaul University (Kellstadt)

1 E. Jackson Boulevard
Chicago, IL 60604-2287
http://www.kellstadt.depaul.edu/
Private
Admissions: (312) 362-8810
E-mail: kgsb@depaul.edu
Financial aid: (312) 362-8091
Application deadline: 07/01
Tuition: full time: $749/credit hour; part time: $749/credit hour
Room/board/expenses: $1,000
College-funded aid: Yes
International student aid: Yes
Average student indebtedness at graduation: $40,482
Full-time enrollment: 57
men: 68%; women: 32%;
minorities: 21%; international: 14%
Part-time enrollment: 1,829
men: 59%; women: 41%;
minorities: 14%; international: 7%
Acceptance rate (full-time): 40%
Average GMAT (full-time): 645
Average GMAT (part-time): 569
Average GPA (full-time): 3.18
Average age of entrants to full-time program: 28
Average months of prior work experience (full-time): 58
TOEFL requirement: Yes
Minimum TOEFL score: 550
Most popular departments: entrepreneurship, finance, general management, marketing, operations management
Mean starting base salary for 2007 full-time graduates: $66,929
Employment location for 2007 class: Intl. 0%; N.E. 0%; M.A. 0%; S. 0%; M.W. 100%; S.W. 0%; W. 0%

Eastern Illinois University (Lumpkin)

600 Lincoln Avenue
Charleston, IL 61920-3099
http://www.eiu.edu/~mba
Public
Admissions: (217) 581-3028
E-mail: mba@eiu.edu
Financial aid: (217) 581-3714
Application deadline: 08/01
In-state tuition: full time: $190/credit hour; part time: $190/credit hour
Out-of-state tuition: full time: $570/credit hour
Room/board/expenses: $7,500
College-funded aid: Yes
International student aid: Yes
Full-time enrollment: 69
men: 54%; women: 46%;
minorities: 7%; international: 16%
Part-time enrollment: 82
men: 43%; women: 57%;
minorities: 7%; international: 0%
Acceptance rate (full-time): 92%
Average GMAT (full-time): 509
Average GMAT (part-time): 512
Average GPA (full-time): 3.36
Average age of entrants to full-time program: 26
Average months of prior work experience (full-time): 43
TOEFL requirement: Yes
Minimum TOEFL score: 550

Illinois Institute of Technology (Stuart)

565 W. Adams Street
Chicago, IL 60661
http://www.stuart.iit.edu
Private
Admissions: (312) 906-6576
E-mail: admission@stuart.iit.edu
Financial aid: (312) 906-5180
Application deadline: 08/01
Tuition: full time: $804/credit hour; part time: $804/credit hour
Room/board/expenses: $21,772
College-funded aid: Yes
International student aid: Yes
Average student indebtedness at graduation: $65,272
Full-time enrollment: 366
men: 59%; women: 41%;
minorities: 2%; international: 90%
Part-time enrollment: 103
men: 73%; women: 27%;
minorities: 18%; international: 24%
Acceptance rate (full-time): 73%
Average GMAT (full-time): 575
Average GMAT (part-time): 540
Average age of entrants to full-time program: 24
TOEFL requirement: Yes
Minimum TOEFL score: 600
Most popular departments: finance, general management, marketing, statistics and operations research, other

Illinois State University

MBA Program
Campus Box 5570
Normal, IL 61790-5570
http://www.mba.ilstu.edu/
Public
Admissions: (309) 438-8388
E-mail: isumba@exchange.cob.ilstu.edu
Financial aid: (309) 438-2231
Application deadline: 07/01
In-state tuition: full time: $194/credit hour; part time: $194/credit hour
Out-of-state tuition: full time: $404/credit hour
Room/board/expenses: $10,566
College-funded aid: Yes
International student aid: Yes
Full-time enrollment: 54
men: 69%; women: 31%;
minorities: 6%; international: 50%
Part-time enrollment: 125
men: 54%; women: 46%;
minorities: 13%; international: 5%
Average GMAT (part-time): 560
TOEFL requirement: Yes
Minimum TOEFL score: 600

Loyola University Chicago

820 N. Michigan Avenue
Chicago, IL 60611
http://www.gsb.luc.edu
Private
Admissions: (312) 915-6124
E-mail: gsb@luc.edu
Financial aid: (773) 508-3155
Application deadline: 07/15
Tuition: full time: $1,047/credit hour; part time: $1,047/credit hour

Room/board/expenses: $13,965
College-funded aid: Yes
International student aid: Yes
Average student indebtedness at graduation: $34,775
Full-time enrollment: N/A
men: N/A; women: N/A;
minorities: N/A; international: N/A
Part-time enrollment: 744
men: 48%; women: 52%;
minorities: 20%; international: 9%
Average GMAT (part-time): 560
TOEFL requirement: Yes
Minimum TOEFL score: 550
Most popular departments: accounting, finance, human resources management, international business, marketing

Northern Illinois University

Office of MBA Programs
Barsema Hall 203
De Kalb, IL 60115-2897
http://www.cob.niu.edu/mbaprograms
Public
Admissions: (866) 648-6221
E-mail: mba@niu.edu
Financial aid: (815) 753-1395
Application deadline: 07/15
In-state tuition: full time: N/A; part time: $553/credit hour
Out-of-state tuition: full time: N/A
Room/board/expenses: N/A
College-funded aid: Yes
International student aid: Yes
Full-time enrollment: N/A
men: N/A; women: N/A;
minorities: N/A; international: N/A
Part-time enrollment: 588
men: 67%; women: 33%;
minorities: 18%; international: 11%
Average GMAT (part-time): 520
TOEFL requirement: Yes
Minimum TOEFL score: 550
Most popular departments: finance, general management, human resources management, international business, marketing

Northwestern University (Kellogg)

2001 Sheridan Road
Evanston, IL 60208-2001
http://www.kellogg.northwestern.edu
Private
Admissions: (847) 491-3308
E-mail: mbaadmissions@kellogg.northwestern.edu
Financial aid: (847) 491-3308
Application deadline: N/A
Tuition: full time: $43,935; part time: $4,394/credit hour
Room/board/expenses: $15,800
College-funded aid: Yes
International student aid: Yes
Full-time enrollment: 1,194
men: 67%; women: 33%;
minorities: 24%; international: 31%
Part-time enrollment: 1,254
men: 73%; women: 27%;
minorities: 15%; international: 14%
Average GMAT (full-time): 704
Average GMAT (part-time): 690
Average GPA (full-time): 3.50
Average age of entrants to full-time program: 28
Average months of prior work experience (full-time): 64
TOEFL requirement: Yes
Minimum TOEFL score: N/A
Most popular departments: finance, general management, leadership, marketing, other
Mean starting base salary for 2007 full-time graduates: $104,100
Employment location for 2007 class: Intl. 11%; N.E. 22%; M.A. 5%; S. 3%; M.W. 31%; S.W. 7%; W. 20%

Southern Illinois University–Carbondale

133 Rehn Hall
Carbondale, IL 62901-4625
http://www.cba.siu.edu/mba
Public
Admissions: (618) 453-3030
E-mail: mbagp@cba.siu.edu
Financial aid: (618) 453-4334
Application deadline: rolling
In-state tuition: full time: $275/credit hour; part time: N/A
Out-of-state tuition: full time: $688/credit hour
Room/board/expenses: N/A
College-funded aid: Yes
International student aid: Yes
Full-time enrollment: 95
men: N/A; women: N/A;
minorities: N/A; international: N/A
Part-time enrollment: N/A
men: N/A; women: N/A;
minorities: N/A; international: N/A
TOEFL requirement: Yes
Minimum TOEFL score: 550
Most popular departments: finance, general management, marketing, management information systems, organizational behavior

Southern Illinois University–Edwardsville

Box 1051
Edwardsville, IL 62026-1051
http://www.siue.edu/BUSINESS
Public
Admissions: (618) 650-3840
E-mail: mba@siue.edu
Financial aid: (618) 650-3880
Application deadline: 07/15
In-state tuition: full time: $236/credit hour; part time: $236/credit hour
Out-of-state tuition: full time: $591/credit hour
Room/board/expenses: $10,000
College-funded aid: Yes
International student aid: Yes
Full-time enrollment: N/A
men: N/A; women: N/A;
minorities: N/A; international: N/A
Part-time enrollment: 178
men: 56%; women: 44%;
minorities: 7%; international: 5%
Average GMAT (part-time): 512
TOEFL requirement: Yes
Minimum TOEFL score: 550
Most popular departments: accounting, economics, finance, general management, marketing

University of Chicago

5807 S. Woodlawn Avenue
Chicago, IL 60637
http://ChicagoGSB.edu
Private
Admissions: (773) 702-7369
E-mail: admissions@ChicagoGSB.edu
Financial aid: (773) 702-3076
Application deadline: rolling
Tuition: full time: $45,139; part time: N/A
Room/board/expenses: $24,900
College-funded aid: Yes
International student aid: Yes
Average student indebtedness at graduation: $83,600
Full-time enrollment: 1,117
men: 67%; women: 33%;
minorities: 27%; international: 32%
Part-time enrollment: 1,575
men: 78%; women: 22%;
minorities: 27%; international: 16%
Acceptance rate (full-time): 23%
Average GMAT (full-time): 709
Average GPA (full-time): 3.50
Average age of entrants to full-time program: 28
Average months of prior work experience (full-time): 57
TOEFL requirement: Yes

Minimum TOEFL score: 600
Most popular departments: accounting, economics, entrepreneurship, finance, other
Mean starting base salary for 2007 full-time graduates: $103,219
Employment location for 2007 class: Intl. 20%; N.E. 31%; M.A. 2%; S. 2%; M.W. 30%; S.W. 3%; W. 12%

University of Illinois–Chicago (Liautaud)

815 W. Van Buren Street
Suite 220, M/C 077
Chicago, IL 60607
http://www.mba.uic.edu/
Public
Admissions: (312) 996-4573
E-mail: mba@uic.edu
Financial aid: (312) 996-3126
Application deadline: 05/15
In-state tuition: full time: $18,220; part time: $13,188
Out-of-state tuition: full time: $30,218
Room/board/expenses: $12,639
College-funded aid: Yes
International student aid: Yes
Full-time enrollment: 100
men: 54%; women: 46%;
minorities: 18%; international: 32%
Part-time enrollment: 244
men: 69%; women: 31%;
minorities: 19%; international: 5%
Acceptance rate (full-time): 43%
Average GMAT (full-time): 619
Average GMAT (part-time): 603
Average GPA (full-time): 3.26
Average age of entrants to full-time program: 27
Average months of prior work experience (full-time): 48
TOEFL requirement: Yes
Minimum TOEFL score: 570
Mean starting base salary for 2007 full-time graduates: $63,200
Employment location for 2007 class: Intl. N/A; N.E. 8%; M.A. N/A; S. N/A; M.W. 92%; S.W. N/A; W. N/A

University of Illinois–Springfield

1 University Plaza
MS UHB 4000
Springfield , IL 62703
http://www.uis.edu/admissions
Public
Admissions: (888) 977-4847
E-mail: admissions@uis.edu
Financial aid: N/A
Application deadline: rolling
In-state tuition: full time: N/A; part time: $226/credit hour
Out-of-state tuition: full time: N/A
Room/board/expenses: N/A
College-funded aid: Yes
International student aid: Yes
Full-time enrollment: N/A
men: N/A; women: N/A;
minorities: N/A; international: N/A
Part-time enrollment: 113
men: 51%; women: 49%;
minorities: 12%; international: 4%
Average GMAT (part-time): 489
TOEFL requirement: Yes
Minimum TOEFL score: 550

University of Illinois–Urbana-Champaign

1407 W. Gregory Drive
415 DKH, MC-706
Urbana, IL 61801
http://www.mba.uiuc.edu
Public
Admissions: (217) 244-7602
E-mail: mba@uiuc.edu
Financial aid: (217) 333-0100
Application deadline: 03/15
In-state tuition: full time: $20,610; part time: N/A

Out-of-state tuition: full time: $29,610
Room/board/expenses: $19,972
College-funded aid: Yes
International student aid: Yes
Average student indebtedness at graduation: $17,000
Full-time enrollment: 208
men: 70%; women: 30%;
minorities: 15%; international: 51%
Part-time enrollment: N/A
men: N/A; women: N/A;
minorities: N/A; international: N/A
Acceptance rate (full-time): 42%
Average GMAT (full-time): 627
Average GPA (full-time): 3.40
Average age of entrants to full-time program: 27
Average months of prior work experience (full-time): 54
TOEFL requirement: Yes
Minimum TOEFL score: N/A
Mean starting base salary for 2007 full-time graduates: $82,693
Employment location for 2007 class: Intl. 22%; N.E. 7%; M.A. 3%; S. 12%; M.W. 48%; S.W. 5%; W. 3%

Western Illinois University

1 University Circle
Macomb, IL 61455
http://www.wiu.edu/grad/busad.htm
Public
Admissions: (309) 298-2442
E-mail: lc-wall@wiu.edu
Financial aid: (309) 298-2446
Application deadline: 07/01
In-state tuition: full time: $217/credit hour; part time: $217/credit hour
Out-of-state tuition: full time: $433/credit hour
Room/board/expenses: $3,300
College-funded aid: Yes
International student aid: Yes
Full-time enrollment: 49
men: 59%; women: 41%;
minorities: 4%; international: 22%
Part-time enrollment: 56
men: 50%; women: 50%;
minorities: 2%; international: 4%
Acceptance rate (full-time): 82%
Average GMAT (full-time): 515
Average GMAT (part-time): 485
Average GPA (full-time): 3.27
TOEFL requirement: Yes
Minimum TOEFL score: 550
Most popular departments: finance, general management, international business, marketing, supply chain management

Ball State University (Miller)

Whitinger Building, 147
Muncie, IN 47306
http://www.bsu.edu/mba/
Public
Admissions: (765) 285-1931
E-mail: mba@bsu.edu
Financial aid: (765) 285-5600
Application deadline: 07/01
In-state tuition: total program: $10,048 (full-time); $10,225 (part-time)
Out-of-state tuition: total program: $23,670 (full-time)
Room/board/expenses: $23,000
College-funded aid: Yes
International student aid: Yes
Full-time enrollment: 48
men: 73%; women: 27%;
minorities: 6%; international: 17%
Part-time enrollment: 105
men: 72%; women: 28%;
minorities: 7%; international: 2%
Acceptance rate (full-time): 100%
Average GMAT (full-time): 522
Average GMAT (part-time): 535
Average GPA (full-time): 3.37

Average age of entrants to full-time program: 28
Average months of prior work experience (full-time): 36
TOEFL requirement: Yes
Minimum TOEFL score: 550
Most popular departments: entrepreneurship, finance, operations management

Butler University

4600 Sunset Avenue
Indianapolis, IN 46208-3485
http://www.butler.edu/cba/mba
Private
Admissions: (317) 940-9842
E-mail: mba@butler.edu
Financial aid: (317) 940-8200
Application deadline: rolling
Tuition: full time: $500/credit hour; part time: $500/credit hour
Room/board/expenses: $1,500
College-funded aid: Yes
International student aid: Yes
Full-time enrollment: N/A
men: N/A; women: N/A;
minorities: N/A; international: N/A
Part-time enrollment: 198
men: 66%; women: 34%;
minorities: 6%; international: 12%
TOEFL requirement: Yes
Minimum TOEFL score: 550
Most popular departments: finance, general management, international business, leadership, marketing

Indiana State University

MBA Department
800 Sycamore Street
Terre Haute, IN 47809
http://web.indstate.edu/schbus/mba.html
Public
Admissions: (812) 237-2002
E-mail: mba@indstate.edu
Financial aid: (812) 237-2215
Application deadline: rolling
In-state tuition: full time: N/A; part time: N/A
Out-of-state tuition: full time: N/A
Room/board/expenses: N/A
College-funded aid: Yes
International student aid: Yes
Full-time enrollment: 55
men: 78%; women: 22%;
minorities: 0%; international: 60%
Part-time enrollment: N/A
men: N/A; women: N/A;
minorities: N/A; international: N/A
Acceptance rate (full-time): 79%
Average GMAT (full-time): 557
Average age of entrants to full-time program: 27
TOEFL requirement: Yes
Minimum TOEFL score: 550

Indiana University–Bloomington (Kelley)

1275 E. Tenth Street
Suite 2010
Bloomington, IN 47405-1703
http://www.kelley.indiana.edu/mba
Public
Admissions: (812) 855-8006
E-mail: mbaoffice@indiana.edu
Financial aid: (812) 855-8006
Application deadline: 04/15
In-state tuition: full time: $18,234; part time: $500/credit hour
Out-of-state tuition: full time: $34,852
Room/board/expenses: $17,956
College-funded aid: Yes
International student aid: Yes
Average student indebtedness at graduation: $47,500
Full-time enrollment: 444
men: 73%; women: 27%;
minorities: 11%; international: 40%

Part-time enrollment: 339
men: 73%; women: 27%;
minorities: 14%; international: 11%
Acceptance rate (full-time): 34%
Average GMAT (full-time): 656
Average GMAT (part-time): 608
Average GPA (full-time): 3.37
Average age of entrants to full-time program: 28
Average months of prior work experience (full-time): 59
TOEFL requirement: Yes
Minimum TOEFL score: 600
Most popular departments: entrepreneurship, finance, general management, marketing, supply chain management
Mean starting base salary for 2007 full-time graduates: $88,644
Employment location for 2007 class: Intl. 8%; N.E. 10%; M.A. 2%; S. 7%; M.W. 60%; S.W. 5%; W. 8%

Indiana University–Kokomo

2300 S. Washington Street
Kokomo, IN 46904-9003
http://www.iuk.edu/~kobus/
Public
Admissions: (765) 455-9471
E-mail: lficht@iuk.edu
Financial aid: (765) 455-9216
Application deadline: 08/01
In-state tuition: full time: $253/credit hour; part time: $253/credit hour
Out-of-state tuition: full time: $569/credit hour
Room/board/expenses: N/A
College-funded aid: No
International student aid: No
Full-time enrollment: 20
men: 45%; women: 55%;
minorities: 15%; international: 5%
Part-time enrollment: 103
men: 68%; women: 32%;
minorities: 5%; international: 5%
Average GMAT (part-time): 506
TOEFL requirement: Yes
Minimum TOEFL score: 550

Indiana University Northwest[1]

3400 Broadway
Gary, IN 46408-1197
http://www.indiana.edu/~bulletin/iun/grad/busec.html#pro
Public
Admissions: N/A
Financial aid: N/A
Tuition: N/A
Room/board/expenses: N/A
Enrollment: N/A

Indiana University–Purdue University–Fort Wayne (Doermer)

2101 E. Coliseum Boulevard
Fort Wayne, IN 46805-1499
http://www.ipfw.edu/bms/mba/
Public
Admissions: (260) 481-6498
E-mail: mba@ipfw.edu
Financial aid: (260) 481-6820
Application deadline: 07/15
In-state tuition: full time: N/A; part time: $259/credit hour
Out-of-state tuition: full time: N/A
Room/board/expenses: N/A
College-funded aid: Yes
International student aid: Yes
Full-time enrollment: N/A
men: N/A; women: N/A;
minorities: N/A; international: N/A
Part-time enrollment: 162
men: 62%; women: 38%;
minorities: 13%; international: 14%
Average GMAT (part-time): 540
TOEFL requirement: Yes
Minimum TOEFL score: 600

Indiana University–South Bend

1700 Mishawaka Avenue
PO Box 7111
South Bend, IN 46634-7111
http://www.iusb.edu/~buse
Public
Admissions: (574) 520-4138
E-mail: gradbus@iusb.edu
Financial aid: (574) 520-4357
Application deadline: 12/30
In-state tuition: full time: N/A; part time: $223/credit hour
Out-of-state tuition: full time: N/A
Room/board/expenses: N/A
College-funded aid: No
International student aid: No
Full-time enrollment: 59
men: 58%; women: 42%;
minorities: 5%; international: 44%
Part-time enrollment: N/A
men: N/A; women: N/A;
minorities: N/A; international: N/A
Acceptance rate (full-time): 100%
Average GMAT (full-time): 498
TOEFL requirement: Yes
Minimum TOEFL score: 550

Indiana University–Southeast

4201 Grant Line Road
New Albany, IN 47150
http://www.ius.edu/mba
Public
Admissions: (812) 941-2364
E-mail: iusmba@ius.edu
Financial aid: (812) 941-2246
Application deadline: 07/15
In-state tuition: full time: N/A; part time: $270/credit hour
Out-of-state tuition: full time: N/A
Room/board/expenses: N/A
College-funded aid: Yes
International student aid: No
Full-time enrollment: N/A
men: N/A; women: N/A;
minorities: N/A; international: N/A
Part-time enrollment: 210
men: 63%; women: 37%;
minorities: 10%; international: 1%
Average GMAT (part-time): 561
TOEFL requirement: Yes
Minimum TOEFL score: 550

Purdue University–West Lafayette (Krannert)

100 S. Grant Street
Rawls Hall, Room 2020
West Lafayette, IN 47907-2076
http://www.krannert.purdue.edu/programs/masters
Public
Admissions: (765) 494-0773
E-mail: masters@krannert.purdue.edu
Financial aid: (765) 494-0998
Application deadline: rolling
In-state tuition: full time: $18,064; part time: $14,014
Out-of-state tuition: full time: $33,462
Room/board/expenses: $11,604
College-funded aid: Yes
International student aid: Yes
Full-time enrollment: 281
men: 81%; women: 19%;
minorities: 20%; international: 45%
Part-time enrollment: 66
men: 86%; women: 14%;
minorities: 24%; international: 17%
Acceptance rate (full-time): 33%
Average GMAT (full-time): 662
Average GMAT (part-time): 606
Average GPA (full-time): 3.32
Average age of entrants to full-time program: 28
Average months of prior work experience (full-time): 50
TOEFL requirement: Yes
Minimum TOEFL score: 575
Most popular departments: consulting, entrepreneurship, finance, marketing, operations management
Mean starting base salary for 2007 full-time graduates: $84,506
Employment location for 2007 class: Intl. 4%; N.E. 7%; M.A. 3%; S. 10%; M.W. 62%; S.W. 10%; W. 3%

University of Evansville (Schroeder)

1800 Lincoln Avenue
Evansville, IN 47722
http://emba.evansville.edu
Private
Admissions: (812) 488-2455
E-mail: emba@evansville.edu
Financial aid: (812) 488-4428
Application deadline: 05/01
Tuition: total program: $49,500 (full-time); part time: N/A
Room/board/expenses: N/A
College-funded aid: No
International student aid: No
Full-time enrollment: 12
men: 75%; women: 25%;
minorities: 8%; international: 17%
Part-time enrollment: N/A
men: N/A; women: N/A;
minorities: N/A; international: N/A
Acceptance rate (full-time): 93%
Average GPA (full-time): 3.01
Average age of entrants to full-time program: 37
Average months of prior work experience (full-time): 168
TOEFL requirement: Yes
Minimum TOEFL score: 550

University of Notre Dame (Mendoza)

276 Mendoza College of Business
Notre Dame, IN 46556
http://mba.nd.edu
Private
Admissions: (574) 631-8488
E-mail: mba.business@nd.edu
Financial aid: (574) 631-6436
Application deadline: 03/15
Tuition: full time: $36,040; part time: N/A
Room/board/expenses: $15,400
College-funded aid: Yes
International student aid: Yes
Average student indebtedness at graduation: $57,874
Full-time enrollment: 330
men: 79%; women: 21%;
minorities: 12%; international: 20%
Part-time enrollment: N/A
men: N/A; women: N/A;
minorities: N/A; international: N/A
Acceptance rate (full-time): 44%
Average GMAT (full-time): 673
Average GPA (full-time): 3.20
Average age of entrants to full-time program: 27
Average months of prior work experience (full-time): 53
TOEFL requirement: Yes
Minimum TOEFL score: 600
Most popular departments: consulting, entrepreneurship, finance, general management, marketing
Mean starting base salary for 2007 full-time graduates: $85,746
Employment location for 2007 class: Intl. 2%; N.E. 21%; M.A. 5%; S. 10%; M.W. 45%; S.W. 8%; W. 10%

University of Southern Indiana

8600 University Boulevard
Evansville, IN 47712
http://www.usi.edu
Public
Admissions: (812) 465-7015
E-mail: eotto@usi.edu
Financial aid: (812) 464-1767
Application deadline: rolling
In-state tuition: full time: $229/credit hour; part time: $229/credit hour
Out-of-state tuition: full time: $452/credit hour
Room/board/expenses: $8,794
College-funded aid: Yes
International student aid: Yes
Full-time enrollment: N/A
men: N/A; women: N/A;
minorities: N/A; international: N/A
Part-time enrollment: 101
men: 58%; women: 42%;
minorities: 2%; international: 7%
Average GMAT (part-time): 515
TOEFL requirement: Yes
Minimum TOEFL score: 550

Valparaiso University[1]

Urschel Hall
1909 Chapel Drive
Valparaiso, IN 46383
http://www.valpo.edu/cba/mba/
Private
Admissions: (219) 465-7952
E-mail: mba@valpo.edu
Financial aid: (219) 464-5015
Tuition: N/A
Room/board/expenses: N/A
Enrollment: N/A

IOWA

Drake University

2507 University Avenue
Des Moines, IA 50311
http://www.cbpa.drake.edu
Private
Admissions: (515) 271-2188
E-mail: cbpa.gradprograms@drake.edu
Financial aid: (515) 271-2905
Application deadline: rolling
Tuition: full time: $470/credit hour; part time: $470/credit hour
Room/board/expenses: N/A
College-funded aid: No
International student aid: No
Full-time enrollment: N/A
men: N/A; women: N/A;
minorities: N/A; international: N/A
Part-time enrollment: 212
men: 41%; women: 59%;
minorities: 7%; international: 6%
Average GMAT (part-time): 523
TOEFL requirement: Yes
Minimum TOEFL score: 550
Most popular departments: accounting, finance, general management, human resources management, marketing

Iowa State University

1360 Gerdin Business Building
Ames, IA 50011-1350
http://www.bus.iastate.edu/mba
Public
Admissions: (515) 294-8118
E-mail: busgrad@iastate.edu
Financial aid: (515) 294-2223
Application deadline: 06/01
In-state tuition: full time: $7,050; part time: $452/credit hour
Out-of-state tuition: full time: $17,710
Room/board/expenses: $12,820
College-funded aid: Yes
International student aid: Yes
Full-time enrollment: 73
men: 63%; women: 37%;
minorities: 4%; international: 37%
Part-time enrollment: 153
men: 61%; women: 39%;
minorities: 7%; international: 3%
Acceptance rate (full-time): 48%
Average GMAT (full-time): 613
Average GMAT (part-time): 524
Average GPA (full-time): 3.49
Average age of entrants to full-time program: 26
Average months of prior work experience (full-time): 24
TOEFL requirement: Yes
Minimum TOEFL score: 600
Most popular departments: finance, marketing, management information systems, supply chain management
Mean starting base salary for 2007 full-time graduates: $54,152
Employment location for 2007 class: Intl. 0%; N.E. 13%; M.A. 0%; S. 0%; M.W. 73%; S.W. 0%; W. 13%

University of Iowa (Tippie)

108 John Pappajohn Business Building, Suite W160
Iowa City, IA 52242-1000
http://www.biz.uiowa.edu/mba
Public
Admissions: (319) 335-1039
E-mail: tippiemba@uiowa.edu
Financial aid: (319) 335-1039
Application deadline: 07/15
In-state tuition: full time: $13,940; part time: $486/credit hour
Out-of-state tuition: full time: $24,920
Room/board/expenses: $14,600
College-funded aid: Yes
International student aid: Yes
Average student indebtedness at graduation: $27,700
Full-time enrollment: 134
men: 75%; women: 25%;
minorities: 6%; international: 33%
Part-time enrollment: 763
men: 68%; women: 32%;
minorities: 9%; international: 7%
Acceptance rate (full-time): 50%
Average GMAT (full-time): 652
Average GMAT (part-time): 587
Average GPA (full-time): 3.34
Average age of entrants to full-time program: 26
Average months of prior work experience (full-time): 35
TOEFL requirement: Yes
Minimum TOEFL score: 600
Most popular departments: consulting, finance, general management, marketing, portfolio management
Mean starting base salary for 2007 full-time graduates: $73,702
Employment location for 2007 class: Intl. 12%; N.E. 4%; M.A. 4%; S. 0%; M.W. 77%; S.W. 0%; W. 4%

University of Northern Iowa

Curris Business Building 325
Cedar Falls, IA 50614-0123
http://www.cba.uni.edu/mba/
Public
Admissions: (319) 273-6243
E-mail: mba@uni.edu
Financial aid: (319) 273-2700
Application deadline: 05/01
In-state tuition: full time: $7,084; part time: $347/credit hour
Out-of-state tuition: full time: $15,392
Room/board/expenses: $7,980
College-funded aid: Yes
International student aid: No
Average student indebtedness at graduation: $6,381
Full-time enrollment: N/A
men: N/A; women: N/A;
minorities: N/A; international: N/A
Part-time enrollment: 57
men: 61%; women: 39%;
minorities: 2%; international: 40%
Average GMAT (part-time): 580
TOEFL requirement: Yes
Minimum TOEFL score: 550

KANSAS

Emporia State University

1200 Commercial
Campus Box 4059
Emporia, KS 66801-5087
http://www.emporia.edu/business/mbafront.htm
Public
Admissions: (877) 468-6378
E-mail: gradinfo@emporia.edu
Financial aid: (620) 341-5457
Application deadline: rolling
In-state tuition: full time: $5,340; part time: $204/credit hour
Out-of-state tuition: full time: $12,972
Room/board/expenses: $6,600
College-funded aid: Yes
International student aid: Yes
Full-time enrollment: 91
men: 47%; women: 53%; minorities: 1%; international: 37%
Part-time enrollment: 26
men: 58%; women: 42%; minorities: 0%; international: 23%
Acceptance rate (full-time): 80%
Average GMAT (full-time): 510
Average GPA (full-time): 3.29
Average age of entrants to full-time program: 25
TOEFL requirement: Yes
Minimum TOEFL score: 550
Employment location for 2007 class: Intl. N/A; N.E. N/A; M.A. N/A; S. N/A; M.W. 86%; S.W. 14%; W. N/A

Kansas State University

107 Calvin Hall
Manhattan, KS 66506-0501
http://www.cba.ksu.edu/cba/
Public
Admissions: (785) 532-7190
E-mail: flynn@ksu.edu
Financial aid: (785) 532-6420
Application deadline: 05/01
In-state tuition: full time: $9,818; part time: $255/credit hour
Out-of-state tuition: full time: $18,801
Room/board/expenses: $14,000
College-funded aid: Yes
International student aid: Yes
Full-time enrollment: 65
men: 65%; women: 35%; minorities: 11%; international: 23%
Part-time enrollment: 19
men: 47%; women: 53%; minorities: 5%; international: 11%
Acceptance rate (full-time): 57%
Average GMAT (full-time): 565
Average GPA (full-time): 3.39
Average age of entrants to full-time program: 26
Average months of prior work experience (full-time): 36
TOEFL requirement: Yes
Minimum TOEFL score: 550
Most popular departments: entrepreneurship, finance, general management, leadership, management information systems, technology
Mean starting base salary for 2007 full-time graduates: $56,000
Employment location for 2007 class: Intl. N/A; N.E. 10%; M.A. N/A; S. N/A; M.W. 90%; S.W. N/A; W. N/A

Pittsburg State University (Kelce)

1701 S. Broadway
Pittsburg, KS 66762
http://www.pittstate.edu/kelce/graduate.html
Public
Admissions: (620) 235-4222
E-mail: grad@pittstate.edu
Financial aid: (620) 235-4240
Application deadline: rolling
In-state tuition: full time: $5,590; part time: $194/credit hour
Out-of-state tuition: full time: $12,254
Room/board/expenses: $4,590
College-funded aid: Yes
International student aid: Yes
Full-time enrollment: 108
men: 48%; women: 52%; minorities: 6%; international: 52%
Part-time enrollment: 27
men: 63%; women: 37%; minorities: 7%; international: 22%
Acceptance rate (full-time): 60%
Average GMAT (full-time): 510
Average GPA (full-time): 3.20
Average age of entrants to full-time program: 26
Average months of prior work experience (full-time): 24
TOEFL requirement: Yes
Minimum TOEFL score: 550
Most popular departments: accounting, general management, international business

University of Kansas

1300 Sunnyside Avenue
Lawrence, KS 66045-7585
http://www.business.ku.edu
Public
Admissions: (785) 864-7500
E-mail: bschoolgrad@ku.edu
Financial aid: (785) 864-7500
Application deadline: 06/02
In-state tuition: full time: $397/credit hour; part time: $496/credit hour
Out-of-state tuition: full time: $732/credit hour
Room/board/expenses: $11,500
College-funded aid: Yes
International student aid: Yes
Full-time enrollment: 99
men: 80%; women: 20%; minorities: 13%; international: 12%
Part-time enrollment: 222
men: 78%; women: 22%; minorities: 17%; international: 9%
Acceptance rate (full-time): 75%
Average GMAT (full-time): 569
Average GMAT (part-time): 590
Average GPA (full-time): 3.30
Average age of entrants to full-time program: 28
Average months of prior work experience (full-time): 38
TOEFL requirement: Yes
Minimum TOEFL score: 600
Most popular departments: entrepreneurship, finance, international business, marketing, management information systems
Mean starting base salary for 2007 full-time graduates: $60,867
Employment location for 2007 class: Intl. 0%; N.E. 8%; M.A. 8%; S. 0%; M.W. 67%; S.W. 0%; W. 17%

Washburn University

Topeka, KS 66621
http://www.washburn.edu/business
Public
Admissions: (785) 670-1307
E-mail: mba@washburn.edu
Financial aid: N/A
Application deadline: 07/01
In-state tuition: full time: N/A; part time: $320/credit hour
Out-of-state tuition: full time: N/A
Room/board/expenses: N/A
College-funded aid: Yes
International student aid: Yes
Full-time enrollment: N/A
men: N/A; women: N/A; minorities: N/A; international: N/A
Part-time enrollment: 84
men: 43%; women: 57%; minorities: 10%; international: 7%
Average GMAT (part-time): 527
TOEFL requirement: Yes
Minimum TOEFL score: 550

Wichita State University (Barton)

1845 N. Fairmount
Box 48
Wichita, KS 67260-0048
http://www.wichita.edu/mba
Public
Admissions: (316) 978-3230
E-mail: grad.business@wichita.edu
Financial aid: (316) 978-3430
Application deadline: 07/01
In-state tuition: full time: N/A; part time: $206/credit hour
Out-of-state tuition: full time: N/A
Room/board/expenses: N/A
College-funded aid: Yes
International student aid: Yes
Full-time enrollment: N/A
men: N/A; women: N/A; minorities: N/A; international: N/A
Part-time enrollment: 223
men: 59%; women: 41%; minorities: 10%; international: 11%
Average GMAT (part-time): 556
TOEFL requirement: Yes
Minimum TOEFL score: 570
Most popular departments: accounting, economics, entrepreneurship, finance, health care administration, marketing, operations management

KENTUCKY

Bellarmine University (Rubel)

2001 Newburg Road
Louisville, KY 40205-0671
http://www.bellarmine.edu/business/
Private
Admissions: N/A
Financial aid: N/A
Application deadline: rolling
Tuition: full time: N/A; part time: N/A
Room/board/expenses: N/A
College-funded aid: No
International student aid: No
Full-time enrollment: 94
men: 56%; women: 44%; minorities: 7%; international: 3%
Part-time enrollment: 138
men: 62%; women: 38%; minorities: 9%; international: 0%
Acceptance rate (full-time): 96%
Average GMAT (full-time): 499
Average GMAT (part-time): 481
Average GPA (full-time): 3.24
Average age of entrants to full-time program: 26
TOEFL requirement: Yes
Minimum TOEFL score: 550

Eastern Kentucky University

521 Lancaster Avenue
Richmond, KY 40475
http://www.cbt.eku.edu/welcome.php
Public
Admissions: (859) 622-1742
E-mail: graduateschool@eku.edu
Financial aid: (859) 622-2361
Application deadline: 07/09
In-state tuition: full time: $6,140; part time: $341/credit hour
Out-of-state tuition: full time: $16,838
Room/board/expenses: $8,000
College-funded aid: Yes
International student aid: Yes
Full-time enrollment: 13
men: 46%; women: 54%; minorities: 8%; international: 62%
Part-time enrollment: 61
men: 52%; women: 48%; minorities: 3%; international: 7%
Acceptance rate (full-time): 100%
Average GMAT (full-time): 646
Average GMAT (part-time): 514
Average GPA (full-time): 3.28
TOEFL requirement: Yes
Minimum TOEFL score: 550
Most popular departments: accounting, other

Morehead State University

203 Combs Building
Morehead, KY 40351
http://www.moreheadstate.edu/mba
Public
Admissions: (606) 783-2183
E-mail: msu-mba@moreheadstate.edu
Financial aid: (606) 783-2011
Application deadline: 08/01
In-state tuition: full time: $5,730; part time: $320/credit hour
Out-of-state tuition: full time: $5,730
Room/board/expenses: N/A
College-funded aid: Yes
International student aid: Yes
Full-time enrollment: 22
men: 41%; women: 59%; minorities: 18%; international: 9%
Part-time enrollment: 148
men: 46%; women: 54%; minorities: 7%; international: 1%
Average GMAT (full-time): 470
Average GMAT (part-time): 479
Average age of entrants to full-time program: 29
TOEFL requirement: Yes
Minimum TOEFL score: 525

Murray State University[1]

109 Business Building
Murray, KY 42071
http://www.murraystate.edu/cbpa
Public
Admissions: (270) 762-6970
E-mail: admissions@murraystate.edu
Financial aid: (270) 762-2546
Tuition: N/A
Room/board/expenses: N/A
Enrollment: N/A

Northern Kentucky University

Suite 401
BEP Center
Highland Heights, KY 41099
http://www.nku.edu/~mbusiness
Public
Admissions: (859) 572-6336
E-mail: mbusiness@nku.edu
Financial aid: (859) 572-6364
Application deadline: rolling
In-state tuition: full time: $398/credit hour; part time: $398/credit hour
Out-of-state tuition: full time: $457/credit hour
Room/board/expenses: N/A
College-funded aid: Yes
International student aid: Yes
Full-time enrollment: N/A
men: N/A; women: N/A; minorities: N/A; international: N/A
Part-time enrollment: 236
men: 60%; women: 40%; minorities: 16%; international: 3%
Average GMAT (part-time): 530
TOEFL requirement: Yes
Minimum TOEFL score: 550
Most popular departments: finance, general management, human resources management, international business, marketing

University of Kentucky (Gatton)

145 Gatton College of Business and Economics
Lexington, KY 40506-0034
http://gatton.uky.edu
Public
Admissions: (859) 257-1306
E-mail: ukmba@uky.edu
Financial aid: (859) 257-1306
Application deadline: 06/01
In-state tuition: full time: $14,212; part time: $468/credit hour
Out-of-state tuition: full time: $22,700
Room/board/expenses: $12,000
College-funded aid: Yes
International student aid: Yes
Full-time enrollment: 77
men: 75%; women: 25%; minorities: 13%; international: 10%
Part-time enrollment: 104
men: 71%; women: 29%; minorities: 10%; international: 6%
Acceptance rate (full-time): 64%
Average GMAT (full-time): 614
Average GMAT (part-time): 598
Average GPA (full-time): 3.40
Average age of entrants to full-time program: 26
Average months of prior work experience (full-time): 18
TOEFL requirement: Yes
Minimum TOEFL score: 550
Most popular departments: e-commerce, entrepreneurship, finance, general management, international business, marketing, supply chain management, technology
Mean starting base salary for 2007 full-time graduates: $46,991
Employment location for 2007 class: Intl. 0%; N.E. 0%; M.A. 7%; S. 74%; M.W. 0%; S.W. 15%; W. 4%

University of Louisville

Belknap Campus
Louisville, KY 40292
http://business.louisville.edu
Public
Admissions: (502) 852-3969
E-mail: gradadm@louisville.edu
Financial aid: (502) 852-5511
Application deadline: 06/30
In-state tuition: full time: N/A; total program: $28,000 (part-time)
Out-of-state tuition: full time: N/A
Room/board/expenses: $10,000
College-funded aid: Yes
International student aid: Yes
Average student indebtedness at graduation: $30,000
Full-time enrollment: N/A
men: N/A; women: N/A; minorities: N/A; international: N/A
Part-time enrollment: 274
men: 62%; women: 38%; minorities: 17%; international: 5%
Average GMAT (part-time): 570
TOEFL requirement: Yes
Minimum TOEFL score: 530
Most popular departments: entrepreneurship, international business, leadership, operations management, supply chain management

Western Kentucky University (Ford)

434 A. Grise Hall
Bowling Green, KY 42101-1056
http://www.wku.edu/gfcb/
Public
Admissions: (270) 745-2446
E-mail: mba@wku.edu
Financial aid: (270) 745-2755
Application deadline: 06/01
In-state tuition: full time: $7,014; part time: $351/credit hour
Out-of-state tuition: full time: $15,470
Room/board/expenses: N/A
College-funded aid: Yes
International student aid: No
Full-time enrollment: 30
men: 50%; women: 50%; minorities: 3%; international: 57%
Part-time enrollment: 99
men: 60%; women: 40%; minorities: 7%; international: 22%
Average GMAT (full-time): 509

Average GMAT (part-time): 541
Average GPA (full-time): 3.21
TOEFL requirement: Yes
Minimum TOEFL score: 550

LOUISIANA

Louisiana State University–Baton Rouge (Ourso)

3304 Patrick F. Taylor Hall
Baton Rouge, LA 70803
http://mba.lsu.edu
Public
Admissions: (225) 578-8867
E-mail: busmba@lsu.edu
Financial aid: (225) 578-3103
Application deadline: 05/15
In-state tuition: total program: $17,326 (full-time); part time: N/A
Out-of-state tuition: total program: $33,925 (full-time)
Room/board/expenses: $11,020
College-funded aid: Yes
International student aid: Yes
Average student indebtedness at graduation: $29,571
Full-time enrollment: 160
men: 61%; women: 39%;
minorities: 11%; international: 11%
Part-time enrollment: N/A
men: N/A; women: N/A;
minorities: N/A; international: N/A
Acceptance rate (full-time): 56%
Average GMAT (full-time): 637
Average GPA (full-time): 3.43
Average age of entrants to full-time program: 23
Average months of prior work experience (full-time): 19
TOEFL requirement: Yes
Minimum TOEFL score: 550
Most popular departments: consulting, finance, marketing, management information systems, other
Mean starting base salary for 2007 full-time graduates: $61,707
Employment location for 2007 class: Intl. 0%; N.E. 3%; M.A. 0%; S. 63%; M.W. 0%; S.W. 31%; W. 3%

Louisiana State University–Shreveport

1 University Place
Shreveport, LA 71115
http://www.lsus.edu/ba/mba
Public
Admissions: (318) 797-5213
E-mail: swood@pilot.lsus.edu
Financial aid: (318) 797-5363
Application deadline: 06/30
In-state tuition: full time: N/A; part time: N/A
Out-of-state tuition: full time: N/A
Room/board/expenses: N/A
College-funded aid: Yes
International student aid: No
Full-time enrollment: 77
men: 61%; women: 39%;
minorities: 9%; international: 5%
Part-time enrollment: N/A
men: N/A; women: N/A;
minorities: N/A; international: N/A
Average age of entrants to full-time program: 26
TOEFL requirement: Yes
Minimum TOEFL score: 550

Louisiana Tech University

PO Box 10318
Ruston, LA 71272
http://www.cab.latech.edu
Public
Admissions: (318) 257-4528
E-mail: cabgrad@latech.edu
Financial aid: (318) 257-2641
Application deadline: 08/01
In-state tuition: full time: $4,588; part time: $2,062

Out-of-state tuition: full time: $8,168
Room/board/expenses: $10,000
College-funded aid: Yes
International student aid: Yes
Full-time enrollment: 49
men: 57%; women: 43%;
minorities: 0%; international: 24%
Part-time enrollment: 6
men: 67%; women: 33%;
minorities: 0%; international: 0%
Acceptance rate (full-time): 75%
Average GMAT (full-time): 510
Average GPA (full-time): 3.16
TOEFL requirement: Yes
Minimum TOEFL score: 550

Loyola University New Orleans (Butt)

6363 St. Charles Avenue
Campus Box 15
New Orleans, LA 70118
http://www.business.loyno.edu
Private
Admissions: (504) 864-7965
E-mail: mba@loyno.edu
Financial aid: (504) 865-3231
Application deadline: 06/15
Tuition: full time: $761/credit hour; part time: $761/credit hour
Room/board/expenses: $10,528
College-funded aid: Yes
International student aid: Yes
Full-time enrollment: N/A
men: N/A; women: N/A;
minorities: N/A; international: N/A
Part-time enrollment: 71
men: 58%; women: 42%;
minorities: 23%; international: 10%
Average GMAT (part-time): 528
TOEFL requirement: Yes
Minimum TOEFL score: 580

McNeese State University (Burton)

PO Box 91660
Lake Charles, LA 70609
http://www.mcneese.edu/colleges/bus
Public
Admissions: (337) 475-5576
E-mail: mbaprog@mail.mcneese.edu
Financial aid: (337) 475-5065
Application deadline: 08/18
In-state tuition: full time: $3,054; part time: $1,718
Out-of-state tuition: full time: $9,120
Room/board/expenses: N/A
College-funded aid: Yes
International student aid: No
Full-time enrollment: 80
men: 68%; women: 33%;
minorities: 3%; international: 36%
Part-time enrollment: N/A
men: N/A; women: N/A;
minorities: N/A; international: N/A
Acceptance rate (full-time): 78%
Average GMAT (full-time): 480
Average GPA (full-time): 3.10
TOEFL requirement: Yes
Minimum TOEFL score: 500

Nicholls State University

PO Box 2015
Thibodaux, LA 70310
http://www.nicholls.edu/business/
Public
Admissions: (985) 448-4507
E-mail: becky.leblanc-durocher@nicholls.edu
Financial aid: (985) 448-4048
Application deadline: rolling
In-state tuition: full time: $3,595; part time: $469/credit hour
Out-of-state tuition: full time: $9,043
Room/board/expenses: N/A
College-funded aid: Yes
International student aid: Yes

Full-time enrollment: 44
men: 50%; women: 50%;
minorities: N/A; international: N/A
Part-time enrollment: 55
men: 42%; women: 58%;
minorities: N/A; international: N/A
Average GMAT (part-time): 450
TOEFL requirement: Yes
Minimum TOEFL score: 550
Most popular departments: accounting, economics, finance, international business, marketing

Southeastern Louisiana University

SLU 10735
Hammond, LA 70402
http://www.selu.edu/acad_research/programs/grad_bus
Public
Admissions: (985) 549-2066
E-mail: admissions@selu.edu
Financial aid: (985) 549-2244
Application deadline: 07/15
In-state tuition: full time: $3,321; part time: $123/credit hour
Out-of-state tuition: full time: $7,821
Room/board/expenses: $9,856
College-funded aid: Yes
International student aid: Yes
Average student indebtedness at graduation: $7,141
Full-time enrollment: 147
men: 56%; women: 44%;
minorities: 10%; international: 10%
Part-time enrollment: N/A
men: N/A; women: N/A;
minorities: N/A; international: N/A
Acceptance rate (full-time): 98%
Average GMAT (full-time): 481
Average GPA (full-time): 3.21
Average age of entrants to full-time program: 26
TOEFL requirement: Yes
Minimum TOEFL score: 525
Most popular departments: accounting, health care administration, marketing, management information systems

Southern University and A&M College

PO Box 9723
Baton Rouge, LA 70813
http://www.business.subr.edu
Public
Admissions: (225) 771-5390
E-mail: gradschool@subr.edu
Financial aid: (225) 771-2790
Application deadline: 04/15
In-state tuition: full time: $5,922; part time: $5,493
Out-of-state tuition: full time: $12,935
Room/board/expenses: $1,700
College-funded aid: Yes
International student aid: Yes
Full-time enrollment: 52
men: 40%; women: 60%;
minorities: 100%; international: 6%
Part-time enrollment: 39
men: 41%; women: 59%;
minorities: 100%; international: 3%
Acceptance rate (full-time): 83%
Average GMAT (full-time): 400
Average GPA (full-time): 2.85
Average age of entrants to full-time program: 28
TOEFL requirement: Yes
Minimum TOEFL score: 525

Tulane University (Freeman)

7 McAlister Drive
New Orleans, LA 70118-5669
http://freeman.tulane.edu
Private
Admissions: (504) 865-5410
E-mail: freeman.admissions@tulane.edu
Financial aid: (504) 865-5410
Application deadline: 05/02

Tuition: full time: $44,339; part time: $1,294/credit hour
Room/board/expenses: $15,400
College-funded aid: Yes
International student aid: Yes
Full-time enrollment: 74
men: 69%; women: 31%;
minorities: 23%; international: 32%
Part-time enrollment: N/A
men: N/A; women: N/A;
minorities: N/A; international: N/A
Acceptance rate (full-time): 66%
Average GMAT (full-time): 652
Average GPA (full-time): 3.30
Average age of entrants to full-time program: 26
Average months of prior work experience (full-time): 58
TOEFL requirement: Yes
Minimum TOEFL score: 600
Most popular departments: consulting, entrepreneurship, finance, international business, marketing
Mean starting base salary for 2007 full-time graduates: $73,136
Employment location for 2007 class: Intl. 3%; N.E. 15%; M.A. 8%; S. 31%; M.W. 3%; S.W. 31%; W. 10%

University of Louisiana–Lafayette (Moody)

USL Box 44568
Lafayette, LA 70504-4568
http://cobweb.louisiana.edu/
Public
Admissions: (337) 482-6965
E-mail: palmer@louisiana.edu
Financial aid: (337) 482-6497
Application deadline: rolling
In-state tuition: full time: N/A; part time: $1,988
Out-of-state tuition: full time: N/A
Room/board/expenses: $5,000
College-funded aid: Yes
International student aid: Yes
Full-time enrollment: N/A
men: N/A; women: N/A;
minorities: N/A; international: N/A
Part-time enrollment: 184
men: 52%; women: 48%;
minorities: 10%; international: 11%
Average GMAT (part-time): 508
TOEFL requirement: Yes
Minimum TOEFL score: 550
Most popular departments: accounting, health care administration, international business, marketing, management information systems

University of Louisiana–Monroe[1]

700 University Avenue
Monroe, LA 71209
http://ele.ulm.edu
Public
Admissions: (318) 342-1100
E-mail: pena@ulm.edu
Financial aid: (318) 342-5320
Tuition: N/A
Room/board/expenses: N/A
Enrollment: N/A

University of New Orleans

2000 Lakeshore Drive
New Orleans, LA 70148
http://www.uno.edu/
Public
Admissions: (504) 280-6595
E-mail: admissions@uno.edu
Financial aid: (504) 280-6603
Application deadline: rolling
In-state tuition: full time: $6,828; part time: N/A
Out-of-state tuition: full time: $13,872
Room/board/expenses: N/A
College-funded aid: Yes

International student aid: Yes
Full-time enrollment: 499
men: 49%; women: 51%;
minorities: 50%; international: N/A
Part-time enrollment: N/A
men: N/A; women: N/A;
minorities: N/A; international: N/A
Acceptance rate (full-time): 80%
Average GMAT (full-time): 507
Average GPA (full-time): 3.10
Average age of entrants to full-time program: 25
TOEFL requirement: Yes
Minimum TOEFL score: 550
Most popular departments: finance, human resources management, international business, marketing, management information systems

MAINE

University of Maine

Donald P. Corbett Business Building
Orono, ME 04469-5723
http://www.umaine.edu/business
Public
Admissions: (207) 581-1973
E-mail: mba@maine.edu
Financial aid: (207) 581-1324
Application deadline: 01/15
In-state tuition: full time: $325/credit hour; part time: $325/credit hour
Out-of-state tuition: full time: $936/credit hour
Room/board/expenses: $16,000
College-funded aid: Yes
International student aid: Yes
Full-time enrollment: 57
men: 60%; women: 40%;
minorities: 4%; international: 33%
Part-time enrollment: 26
men: 69%; women: 31%;
minorities: 4%; international: 0%
Acceptance rate (full-time): 84%
Average GMAT (full-time): 556
Average GMAT (part-time): 531
Average GPA (full-time): 3.28
Average age of entrants to full-time program: 27
Average months of prior work experience (full-time): 48
TOEFL requirement: Yes
Minimum TOEFL score: 550
Most popular departments: accounting, finance, general management, marketing, statistics and operations research

University of Southern Maine

PO Box 9300
Portland, ME 04104
http://www.usm.maine.edu/sb
Public
Admissions: (207) 780-4184
E-mail: mba@usm.maine.edu
Financial aid: (207) 780-5250
Application deadline: 08/01
In-state tuition: full time: $297/credit hour; part time: $297/credit hour
Out-of-state tuition: full time: $844/credit hour
Room/board/expenses: $19,600
College-funded aid: Yes
International student aid: Yes
Full-time enrollment: N/A
men: N/A; women: N/A;
minorities: N/A; international: N/A
Part-time enrollment: 142
men: 54%; women: 46%;
minorities: 4%; international: 6%
Average GMAT (part-time): 563
TOEFL requirement: Yes
Minimum TOEFL score: 550
Most popular departments: accounting, general management

MARYLAND

Frostburg State University
125 Guild Center
101 Braddock Road
Frostburg, MD 21532-2303
http://www.frostburg.edu/colleges/cob/mba/
Private
Admissions: N/A
E-mail: fsubusiness@frostburg.edu
Financial aid: N/A
Application deadline: rolling
Tuition: full time: $305/credit hour; part time: $305/credit hour
Room/board/expenses: $6,746
College-funded aid: Yes
International student aid: Yes
Full-time enrollment: 33
men: 48%; women: 52%;
minorities: 6%; international: 0%
Part-time enrollment: 73
men: 55%; women: 45%;
minorities: 8%; international: 1%
Acceptance rate (full-time): 85%
Average GMAT (full-time): 536
Average GMAT (part-time): 430
Average GPA (full-time): 3.41
Average age of entrants to full-time program: 27
TOEFL requirement: Yes
Minimum TOEFL score: 550
Most popular departments: finance, general management, marketing, management information systems

Loyola College in Maryland (Sellinger)
4501 N. Charles Street
Baltimore, MD 21210-2699
http://www.loyola.edu/sellinger/
Private
Admissions: (410) 617-5020
E-mail: graduate@loyola.edu
Financial aid: (410) 617-2576
Application deadline: rolling
Tuition: full time: $600/credit hour; part time: $600/credit hour
Room/board/expenses: N/A
College-funded aid: Yes
International student aid: No
Average student indebtedness at graduation: $24,235
Full-time enrollment: N/A
men: N/A; women: N/A;
minorities: N/A; international: N/A
Part-time enrollment: 994
men: 62%; women: 38%;
minorities: 12%; international: 2%
Average GMAT (part-time): 546
TOEFL requirement: Yes
Minimum TOEFL score: 550
Most popular departments: finance, general management, international business, other

Morgan State University (Graves)
1700 E. Cold Spring Lane
Baltimore, MD 21239
http://www.morgan.edu/academics/sbm/academic/sbm.htm
Public
Admissions: (443) 885-3396
E-mail: mba@moac.morgan.edu
Financial aid: (443) 885-3018
Application deadline: rolling
In-state tuition: full time: $283/credit hour; part time: $283/credit hour
Out-of-state tuition: full time: $502/credit hour
Room/board/expenses: $6,800
College-funded aid: Yes
International student aid: Yes
Average student indebtedness at graduation: $15,000
Full-time enrollment: 44
men: 55%; women: 45%;
minorities: 57%; international: 34%
Part-time enrollment: 43

men: 58%; women: 42%;
minorities: 77%; international: 23%
Acceptance rate (full-time): 20%
Average GMAT (full-time): 450
Average GMAT (part-time): 425
Average GPA (full-time): 3.25
Average age of entrants to full-time program: 28
Average months of prior work experience (full-time): 12
TOEFL requirement: Yes
Minimum TOEFL score: N/A

Salisbury University (Perdue)
1101 Camden Avenue
Salisbury, MD 21801-6860
http://www.salisbury.edu/Schools/perdue/welcome.html
Public
Admissions: (410) 543-6161
E-mail: admissions@salisbury.edu
Financial aid: (410) 543-6165
Application deadline: 03/01
In-state tuition: full time: $260/credit hour; part time: $260/credit hour
Out-of-state tuition: full time: $556/credit hour
Room/board/expenses: N/A
College-funded aid: Yes
International student aid: Yes
Full-time enrollment: 43
men: 60%; women: 40%;
minorities: 2%; international: 23%
Part-time enrollment: 50
men: 30%; women: 70%;
minorities: 14%; international: 2%
Acceptance rate (full-time): 93%
Average GMAT (full-time): 500
Average GMAT (part-time): 400
Average GPA (full-time): 3.40
Average age of entrants to full-time program: 23
Average months of prior work experience (full-time): 12
TOEFL requirement: Yes
Minimum TOEFL score: 550

Towson University
8000 York Road
Towson, MD 21252
http://www.towson.edu/cbe/graduate/
Public
Admissions: (410) 704-2501
E-mail: grads@towson.edu
Financial aid: (410) 704-4236
Application deadline: 08/01
In-state tuition: full time: $510/credit hour; part time: $510/credit hour
Out-of-state tuition: full time: $770/credit hour
Room/board/expenses: N/A
College-funded aid: Yes
International student aid: Yes
Full-time enrollment: N/A
men: N/A; women: N/A;
minorities: N/A; international: N/A
Part-time enrollment: 412
men: 52%; women: 48%;
minorities: 21%; international: 15%
Average GMAT (part-time): 523
TOEFL requirement: Yes
Minimum TOEFL score: 550
Most popular departments: finance, international business, leadership, marketing, other

University of Baltimore (Merrick)
1420 N. Charles Street
Baltimore, MD 21201
http://business.ubalt.edu
Public
Admissions: (410) 837-6565
E-mail: gradadmissions@ubalt.edu
Financial aid: (410) 837-4763
Application deadline: 08/01
In-state tuition: full time: $510/credit hour; part time: $510/credit hour

Out-of-state tuition: full time: $770/credit hour
Room/board/expenses: N/A
College-funded aid: Yes
International student aid: Yes
Full-time enrollment: N/A
men: N/A; women: N/A;
minorities: N/A; international: N/A
Part-time enrollment: 759
men: 51%; women: 49%;
minorities: 22%; international: 13%
Average GMAT (part-time): 523
TOEFL requirement: Yes
Minimum TOEFL score: 550
Most popular departments: finance, general management, international business, leadership, marketing

University of Maryland–College Park (Smith)
2308 Van Munching Hall
College Park, MD 20742
http://www.rhsmith.umd.edu
Public
Admissions: (301) 405-2559
E-mail: mba_info@rhsmith.umd.edu
Financial aid: (301) 314-8297
Application deadline: 03/02
In-state tuition: full time: $29,215; part time: $803/credit hour
Out-of-state tuition: full time: $38,575
Room/board/expenses: $15,200
College-funded aid: Yes
International student aid: Yes
Full-time enrollment: 237
men: 67%; women: 33%;
minorities: 24%; international: 36%
Part-time enrollment: 964
men: 70%; women: 30%;
minorities: 30%; international: 10%
Acceptance rate (full-time): 31%
Average GMAT (full-time): 650
Average GMAT (part-time): 608
Average GPA (full-time): 3.34
Average age of entrants to full-time program: 28
Average months of prior work experience (full-time): 61
TOEFL requirement: Yes
Minimum TOEFL score: 600
Most popular departments: consulting, entrepreneurship, finance, marketing, other
Mean starting base salary for 2007 full-time graduates: $88,151
Employment location for 2007 class: Intl. 7%; N.E. 29%; M.A. 48%; S. 3%; M.W. 5%; S.W. 3%; W. 5%

MASSACHUSETTS

Babson College (Olin)
231 Forest Street
Babson Park, MA 02457-0310
http://www.babson.edu/mba
Private
Admissions: (781) 239-5591
E-mail: mbaadmission@babson.edu
Financial aid: (781) 239-4219
Application deadline: 04/15
Tuition: full time: $35,110; part time: $1,041/credit hour
Room/board/expenses: $21,863
College-funded aid: Yes
International student aid: Yes
Average student indebtedness at graduation: $58,813
Full-time enrollment: 383
men: 74%; women: 26%;
minorities: 9%; international: 47%
Part-time enrollment: 1,215
men: 74%; women: 26%;
minorities: 15%; international: 10%
Acceptance rate (full-time): 57%
Average GMAT (full-time): 631
Average GMAT (part-time): 583
Average GPA (full-time): 3.21
Average age of entrants to full-time program: 28
Average months of prior work experience (full-time): 59

TOEFL requirement: Yes
Minimum TOEFL score: 600
Mean starting base salary for 2007 full-time graduates: $89,161
Employment location for 2007 class: Intl. 10%; N.E. 71%; M.A. 1%; S. 4%; M.W. 1%; S.W. 4%; W. 9%

Bentley College (McCallum)
175 Forest Street
Waltham, MA 02452-4705
http://www.bentley.edu/graduate/
Private
Admissions: (781) 891-2108
E-mail: gradadm@bentley.edu
Financial aid: (781) 891-3441
Application deadline: 12/01
Tuition: full time: $29,984; part time: $986/credit hour
Room/board/expenses: $15,065
College-funded aid: Yes
International student aid: Yes
Average student indebtedness at graduation: $16,792
Full-time enrollment: 59
men: 64%; women: 36%;
minorities: 5%; international: 56%
Part-time enrollment: 547
men: 60%; women: 40%;
minorities: 9%; international: 9%
Acceptance rate (full-time): 56%
Average GMAT (full-time): 598
Average GMAT (part-time): 551
Average GPA (full-time): 3.32
Average age of entrants to full-time program: 25
Average months of prior work experience (full-time): 34
TOEFL requirement: Yes
Minimum TOEFL score: 600
Most popular departments: accounting, finance, general management, marketing, operations management
Mean starting base salary for 2007 full-time graduates: $68,273
Employment location for 2007 class: Intl. 7%; N.E. 79%; M.A. 7%; S. 7%; M.W. N/A; S.W. N/A; W. N/A

Boston College (Carroll)
140 Commonwealth Avenue
Fulton Hall 320
Chestnut Hill, MA 02467
http://www.bc.edu/mba
Private
Admissions: (617) 552-3920
E-mail: bcmba@bc.edu
Financial aid: (800) 294-0294
Application deadline: 04/15
Tuition: full time: $1,126/credit hour; part time: $1,126/credit hour
Room/board/expenses: $18,390
College-funded aid: Yes
International student aid: Yes
Average student indebtedness at graduation: $50,059
Full-time enrollment: 191
men: 65%; women: 35%;
minorities: 10%; international: 31%
Part-time enrollment: 569
men: 70%; women: 30%;
minorities: 7%; international: 11%
Acceptance rate (full-time): 38%
Average GMAT (full-time): 651
Average GMAT (part-time): 603
Average GPA (full-time): 3.35
Average age of entrants to full-time program: 28
Average months of prior work experience (full-time): 54
TOEFL requirement: Yes
Minimum TOEFL score: 600
Most popular departments: finance, general management, international business, marketing, portfolio management
Mean starting base salary for 2007 full-time graduates: $87,468
Employment location for 2007 class: Intl. 8%; N.E. 68%; M.A. 5%; S. 3%; M.W. 5%; S.W. 3%; W. 8%

Boston University
595 Commonwealth Avenue
Boston, MA 02215-1704
http://management.bu.edu
Private
Admissions: (617) 353-2670
E-mail: mba@bu.edu
Financial aid: (617) 353-2670
Application deadline: 03/15
Tuition: full time: $35,370; part time: $1,092/credit hour
Room/board/expenses: $17,241
College-funded aid: Yes
International student aid: Yes
Average student indebtedness at graduation: $48,540
Full-time enrollment: 298
men: 62%; women: 38%;
minorities: 16%; international: 32%
Part-time enrollment: 546
men: 62%; women: 38%;
minorities: 14%; international: 7%
Acceptance rate (full-time): 31%
Average GMAT (full-time): 668
Average GMAT (part-time): 590
Average GPA (full-time): 3.38
Average age of entrants to full-time program: 28
Average months of prior work experience (full-time): 57
TOEFL requirement: Yes
Minimum TOEFL score: 600
Most popular departments: finance, general management, marketing, management information systems, other
Mean starting base salary for 2007 full-time graduates: $85,277
Employment location for 2007 class: Intl. 11%; N.E. 77%; M.A. 0%; S. 2%; M.W. 3%; S.W. 0%; W. 6%

Clark University
950 Main Street
Worcester, MA 01610
http://www.clarku.edu/gsom
Private
Admissions: (508) 793-7406
E-mail: clarkmba@clarku.edu
Financial aid: (508) 793-7406
Application deadline: 06/01
Tuition: full time: $21,140; part time: $1,007/credit hour
Room/board/expenses: $11,648
College-funded aid: Yes
International student aid: Yes
Full-time enrollment: 212
men: 49%; women: 51%;
minorities: N/A; international: 85%
Part-time enrollment: 114
men: 61%; women: 39%;
minorities: N/A; international: 2%
Acceptance rate (full-time): 57%
Average GMAT (full-time): 552
Average GMAT (part-time): 538
Average GPA (full-time): 3.28
Average age of entrants to full-time program: 24
Average months of prior work experience (full-time): 24
TOEFL requirement: Yes
Minimum TOEFL score: 550
Most popular departments: accounting, finance, general management, international business, marketing
Mean starting base salary for 2007 full-time graduates: $64,750
Employment location for 2007 class: Intl. 36%; N.E. 64%; M.A. 0%; S. 0%; M.W. 0%; S.W. 0%; W. 0%

Harvard University
Soldiers Field
Boston, MA 02163
http://www.hbs.edu
Private
Admissions: (617) 495-6128
E-mail: admissions@hbs.edu
Financial aid: (617) 495-6640
Application deadline: N/A
Tuition: full time: $48,738; part time: N/A
Room/board/expenses: $24,562
College-funded aid: Yes

International student aid: Yes
Average student indebtedness at graduation: $77,550
Full-time enrollment: 1,808
men: 65%; women: 35%;
minorities: 24%; international: 33%
Part-time enrollment: N/A
men: N/A; women: N/A;
minorities: N/A; international: N/A
Acceptance rate (full-time): 14%
Average GMAT (full-time): 713
Average GPA (full-time): 3.63
Average age of entrants to full-time program: 27
TOEFL requirement: Yes
Minimum TOEFL score: 630
Mean starting base salary for 2007 full-time graduates: $115,665
Employment location for 2007 class: Intl. 19%; N.E. 44%; M.A. 6%; S. 3%; M.W. 8%; S.W. 5%; W. 15%

Massachusetts Institute of Technology (Sloan)

50 Memorial Drive
Cambridge, MA 02142
http://mitsloan.mit.edu/mba
Private
Admissions: (617) 258-5434
E-mail: mbaadmissions@sloan.mit.edu
Financial aid: (617) 253-4971
Application deadline: 01/15
Tuition: full time: $44,792; part time: N/A
Room/board/expenses: $32,490
College-funded aid: Yes
International student aid: Yes
Full-time enrollment: 770
men: 69%; women: 31%;
minorities: 21%; international: 33%
Part-time enrollment: N/A
men: N/A; women: N/A;
minorities: N/A; international: N/A
Acceptance rate (full-time): 20%
Average GMAT (full-time): 705
Average GPA (full-time): 3.50
Average age of entrants to full-time program: 28
Average months of prior work experience (full-time): 60
TOEFL requirement: No
Minimum TOEFL score: N/A
Most popular departments: entrepreneurship, finance, general management, manufacturing and technology management, marketing
Mean starting base salary for 2007 full-time graduates: $107,990
Employment location for 2007 class: Intl. 15%; N.E. 51%; M.A. 3%; S. 3%; M.W. 4%; S.W. 5%; W. 19%

Northeastern University

360 Huntington Avenue
350 Dodge Hall
Boston, MA 02115
http://www.cba.neu.edu/graduate
Private
Admissions: (617) 373-5992
E-mail: gsba@neu.edu
Financial aid: (617) 373-5899
Application deadline: 04/15
Tuition: full time: $1,110/credit hour; part time: $1,110/credit hour
Room/board/expenses: $21,710
College-funded aid: Yes
International student aid: Yes
Average student indebtedness at graduation: $52,605
Full-time enrollment: 200
men: 58%; women: 42%;
minorities: 6%; international: 36%
Part-time enrollment: 468
men: 62%; women: 38%;
minorities: 15%; international: 2%
Acceptance rate (full-time): 52%
Average GMAT (full-time): 589
Average GMAT (part-time): 520
Average GPA (full-time): 3.20

Average age of entrants to full-time program: 26
Average months of prior work experience (full-time): 42
TOEFL requirement: Yes
Minimum TOEFL score: 600
Most popular departments: entrepreneurship, finance, international business, marketing, supply chain management
Mean starting base salary for 2007 full-time graduates: $66,300
Employment location for 2007 class: Intl. 9%; N.E. 88%; M.A. 0%; S. 0%; M.W. 0%; S.W. 3%; W. 0%

Suffolk University (Sawyer)

8 Ashburton Place
Boston, MA 02108
http://www.suffolk.edu/business
Private
Admissions: (617) 573-8302
E-mail: grad.admission@suffolk.edu
Financial aid: (617) 573-8470
Application deadline: 03/15
Tuition: full time: $29,810; part time: $1,303
Room/board/expenses: $15,250
College-funded aid: Yes
International student aid: Yes
Average student indebtedness at graduation: $38,243
Full-time enrollment: 98
men: 58%; women: 42%;
minorities: 5%; international: 58%
Part-time enrollment: 514
men: 54%; women: 46%;
minorities: 7%; international: 3%
Acceptance rate (full-time): 67%
Average GMAT (full-time): 517
Average GMAT (part-time): 493
Average GPA (full-time): 3.29
Average age of entrants to full-time program: 25
Average months of prior work experience (full-time): 33
TOEFL requirement: Yes
Minimum TOEFL score: 550
Most popular departments: accounting, finance, general management, international business, marketing
Mean starting base salary for 2007 full-time graduates: $63,800
Employment location for 2007 class: Intl. 12%; N.E. 88%; M.A. N/A; S. N/A; M.W. N/A; S.W. N/A; W. N/A

University of Massachusetts–Amherst (Isenberg)

121 Presidents Drive
Amherst, MA 01003
http://www.isenberg.umass.edu/mba
Public
Admissions: (413) 545-5608
E-mail: mba@som.umass.edu
Financial aid: (413) 577-0555
Application deadline: 02/01
In-state tuition: full time: $110/credit hour; part time: $670/credit hour
Out-of-state tuition: full time: $414/credit hour
Room/board/expenses: $9,500
College-funded aid: Yes
International student aid: Yes
Average student indebtedness at graduation: $8,500
Full-time enrollment: 69
men: 49%; women: 51%;
minorities: 7%; international: 23%
Part-time enrollment: 804
men: 71%; women: 29%;
minorities: 13%; international: 8%
Acceptance rate (full-time): 28%
Average GMAT (full-time): 642
Average GMAT (part-time): 542
Average GPA (full-time): 3.30
Average age of entrants to full-time program: 28

Average months of prior work experience (full-time): 50
TOEFL requirement: Yes
Minimum TOEFL score: 600
Most popular departments: accounting, finance, general management, operations management, sports business
Mean starting base salary for 2007 full-time graduates: $75,200
Employment location for 2007 class: Intl. 11%; N.E. 79%; M.A. 5%; S. N/A; M.W. N/A; S.W. N/A; W. 5%

University of Massachusetts–Boston

100 Morrissey Boulevard
Boston, MA 02125-3393
http://www.management.umb.edu
Public
Admissions: (617) 287-7720
E-mail: mba@umb.edu
Financial aid: (617) 287-6300
Application deadline: 06/01
In-state tuition: full time: $2,590; part time: $108/credit hour
Out-of-state tuition: full time: $9,758
Room/board/expenses: $9,600
College-funded aid: Yes
International student aid: Yes
Average student indebtedness at graduation: $11,600
Full-time enrollment: 134
men: 52%; women: 48%;
minorities: 13%; international: 46%
Part-time enrollment: 251
men: 46%; women: 54%;
minorities: 27%; international: 4%
Acceptance rate (full-time): 34%
Average GMAT (full-time): 584
Average GMAT (part-time): 579
Average GPA (full-time): 3.42
Average age of entrants to full-time program: 27
Average months of prior work experience (full-time): 44
TOEFL requirement: Yes
Minimum TOEFL score: 600
Most popular departments: accounting, finance, human resources management, international business, management information systems
Mean starting base salary for 2007 full-time graduates: $75,000

University of Massachusetts–Dartmouth (Charlton)

285 Old Westport Road
North Dartmouth, MA 02747-2300
http://www.umassd.edu/charlton/
Public
Admissions: (508) 999-8604
E-mail: graduate@umassd.edu
Financial aid: (508) 999-8632
Application deadline: rolling
In-state tuition: full time: $9,728; part time: $405/credit hour
Out-of-state tuition: full time: $18,174
Room/board/expenses: $11,106
College-funded aid: Yes
International student aid: Yes
Full-time enrollment: 96
men: 50%; women: 50%;
minorities: 5%; international: 38%
Part-time enrollment: 62
men: 52%; women: 48%;
minorities: 3%; international: 3%
Acceptance rate (full-time): 72%
Average GMAT (full-time): 510
Average GMAT (part-time): 485
Average age of entrants to full-time program: 26
TOEFL requirement: Yes
Minimum TOEFL score: 533
Employment location for 2007 class: Intl. 33%; N.E. 67%; M.A. N/A; S. N/A; M.W. N/A; S.W. N/A; W. N/A

University of Massachusetts–Lowell

1 University Avenue
Lowell, MA 01854
http://www.uml.edu/grad
Public
Admissions: (978) 934-2381
E-mail: graduate_school@uml.edu
Financial aid: (978) 934-4220
Application deadline: rolling
In-state tuition: full time: $91/credit hour; part time: $91/credit hour
Out-of-state tuition: full time: $357/credit hour
Room/board/expenses: $8,000
College-funded aid: Yes
International student aid: Yes
Full-time enrollment: 15
men: 53%; women: 47%;
minorities: 20%; international: 47%
Part-time enrollment: 305
men: 62%; women: 38%;
minorities: 21%; international: 13%
Acceptance rate (full-time): 58%
Average GMAT (full-time): 575
Average GMAT (part-time): 525
Average GPA (full-time): 3.40
Average age of entrants to full-time program: 27
Average months of prior work experience (full-time): 42
TOEFL requirement: Yes
Minimum TOEFL score: 600
Most popular departments: accounting, finance, general management, other

Western New England College

1215 Wilbraham Road
Springfield, MA 01119-2684
http://www1.wnec.edu/business/
Private
Admissions: (800) 325-1122
E-mail: ce@wnec.edu
Financial aid: (413) 796-2080
Application deadline: rolling
Tuition: full time: N/A; part time: $599/credit hour
Room/board/expenses: N/A
College-funded aid: Yes
International student aid: No
Full-time enrollment: N/A
men: N/A; women: N/A;
minorities: N/A; international: N/A
Part-time enrollment: 74
men: 45%; women: 55%;
minorities: 4%; international: 0%
TOEFL requirement: Yes
Minimum TOEFL score: 600

Worcester Polytechnic Institute

100 Institute Road
Worcester, MA 01609
http://www.mgt.wpi.edu
Private
Admissions: (508) 831-5957
E-mail: gmp@wpi.edu
Financial aid: (508) 831-5469
Application deadline: 07/01
Tuition: full time: $1,042/credit hour; part time: $1,042/credit hour
Room/board/expenses: $10,500
College-funded aid: Yes
International student aid: Yes
Full-time enrollment: 41
men: 56%; women: 44%;
minorities: 10%; international: 83%
Part-time enrollment: 195
men: 76%; women: 24%;
minorities: 9%; international: 14%
Acceptance rate (full-time): 71%
Average GMAT (full-time): 630
Average GMAT (part-time): 620
Average GPA (full-time): 3.50
Average age of entrants to full-time program: 24
Average months of prior work experience (full-time): 28
TOEFL requirement: Yes

Minimum TOEFL score: 550
Most popular departments: entrepreneurship, manufacturing and technology management, management information systems, operations management, technology
Mean starting base salary for 2007 full-time graduates: $88,571
Employment location for 2007 class: Intl. 0%; N.E. 86%; M.A. 0%; S. 0%; M.W. 0%; S.W. 14%; W. 0%

Central Michigan University

252 ABSC - Grawn Hall
Mount Pleasant, MI 48859
http://www.cba.cmich.edu/mba/
Public
Admissions: (989) 774-3150
E-mail: pamela.stambersky@cmich.edu
Financial aid: (989) 774-3674
Application deadline: rolling
In-state tuition: full time: $388/credit hour; part time: $388/credit hour
Out-of-state tuition: full time: $719/credit hour
Room/board/expenses: N/A
College-funded aid: Yes
International student aid: Yes
Full-time enrollment: 58
men: 52%; women: 48%;
minorities: 2%; international: 57%
Part-time enrollment: 38
men: 45%; women: 55%;
minorities: N/A; international: 3%
Acceptance rate (full-time): 84%
Average GMAT (full-time): 526
TOEFL requirement: Yes
Minimum TOEFL score: 550

Eastern Michigan University

404 Gary M. Owen Building
Ypsilanti, MI 48197
http://www.cob.emich.edu
Public
Admissions: (734) 487-4444
E-mail: cob.graduate@emich.edu
Financial aid: (734) 487-0455
Application deadline: 05/15
In-state tuition: full time: $373/credit hour; part time: $373/credit hour
Out-of-state tuition: full time: $735/credit hour
Room/board/expenses: N/A
College-funded aid: Yes
International student aid: Yes
Full-time enrollment: N/A
men: N/A; women: N/A;
minorities: N/A; international: N/A
Part-time enrollment: 288
men: 57%; women: 43%;
minorities: 18%; international: 27%
Average GMAT (part-time): 454
TOEFL requirement: Yes
Minimum TOEFL score: 550
Most popular departments: finance, general management, human resources management, international business, supply chain management

Grand Valley State University (Seidman)

401 W. Fulton
Grand Rapids, MI 49504-6431
http://www.gvsu.edu
Public
Admissions: (616) 331-7400
E-mail: go2gvmba@gvsu.edu
Financial aid: (616) 331-3234
Application deadline: 08/01
In-state tuition: full time: N/A; part time: $375/credit hour
Out-of-state tuition: full time: N/A
Room/board/expenses: $12,000

College-funded aid: Yes
International student aid: Yes
Full-time enrollment: N/A
men: N/A; women: N/A;
minorities: N/A; international: N/A
Part-time enrollment: 240
men: 70%; women: 30%;
minorities: 4%; international: 5%
Average GMAT (part-time): 569
TOEFL requirement: Yes
Minimum TOEFL score: 550
Most popular departments: accounting, finance

Michigan State University (Broad)

215 Eppley Center
East Lansing, MI 48824-1121
http://www.mba.msu.edu
Public
Admissions: (800) 467-8622
E-mail: mba@msu.edu
Financial aid: (517) 355-7604
Application deadline: 05/11
In-state tuition: full time: $18,681; total program: $48,000 (part-time)
Out-of-state tuition: full time: $26,131
Room/board/expenses: $14,655
College-funded aid: Yes
International student aid: Yes
Average student indebtedness at graduation: $34,802
Full-time enrollment: 202
men: 71%; women: 29%;
minorities: 11%; international: 39%
Part-time enrollment: 203
men: 78%; women: 22%;
minorities: 25%; international: 7%
Acceptance rate (full-time): 30%
Average GMAT (full-time): 633
Average GMAT (part-time): 564
Average GPA (full-time): 3.22
Average age of entrants to full-time program: 28
Average months of prior work experience (full-time): 54
TOEFL requirement: Yes
Minimum TOEFL score: 600
Most popular departments: finance, human resources management, leadership, marketing, supply chain management
Mean starting base salary for 2007 full-time graduates: $85,973
Employment location for 2007 class: Intl. 7%; N.E. 12%; M.A. 1%; S. 12%; M.W. 48%; S.W. 12%; W. 7%

Michigan Technological University

1400 Townsend Drive
Houghton, MI 49931-1295
http://www.mba.mtu.edu
Public
Admissions: (906) 487-3075
E-mail: smgoltz@mtu.edu
Financial aid: N/A
Application deadline: 03/15
In-state tuition: full time: $535/credit hour; part time: $535/credit hour
Out-of-state tuition: full time: $535/credit hour
Room/board/expenses: $11,552
College-funded aid: Yes
International student aid: Yes
Full-time enrollment: 30
men: 53%; women: 47%;
minorities: 10%; international: 13%
Part-time enrollment: N/A
men: N/A; women: N/A;
minorities: N/A; international: N/A
Acceptance rate (full-time): 82%
Average GMAT (full-time): 538
Average GPA (full-time): 3.39
TOEFL requirement: Yes
Minimum TOEFL score: 590
Most popular departments: operations management

Oakland University

432 Elliott Hall
Rochester, MI 48309-4493
http://www.sba.oakland.edu/grad/
Public
Admissions: (248) 370-3287
E-mail: gbp@lists.oakland.edu
Financial aid: (248) 370-2550
Application deadline: 08/01
In-state tuition: full time: N/A; part time: N/A
Out-of-state tuition: full time: N/A
Room/board/expenses: N/A
College-funded aid: Yes
International student aid: Yes
Full-time enrollment: N/A
men: N/A; women: N/A;
minorities: N/A; international: N/A
Part-time enrollment: 470
men: 67%; women: 33%;
minorities: N/A; international: 10%
Average GMAT (part-time): 538
TOEFL requirement: Yes
Minimum TOEFL score: 550

Saginaw Valley State University

7400 Bay Road
University Center, MI 48710
http://www.svsu.edu/cbm/
Public
Admissions: (989) 964-4064
E-mail: cbmdean@svsu.edu
Financial aid: (989) 964-4103
Application deadline: rolling
In-state tuition: full time: $8,264; part time: $344/credit hour
Out-of-state tuition: full time: $15,853
Room/board/expenses: $10,894
College-funded aid: Yes
International student aid: Yes
Full-time enrollment: 39
men: 62%; women: 38%;
minorities: 5%; international: 67%
Part-time enrollment: 57
men: 47%; women: 53%;
minorities: 0%; international: 19%
Acceptance rate (full-time): 93%
Average GMAT (full-time): 350
Average GMAT (part-time): 387
Average GPA (full-time): 3.40
Average age of entrants to full-time program: 27
TOEFL requirement: Yes
Minimum TOEFL score: 525

University of Detroit Mercy

4001 W. McNichols Road
Detroit, MI 48221-3038
http://business.udmercy.edu
Private
Admissions: (313) 993-1202
E-mail: naskibom@udmercy.edu
Financial aid: (313) 993-3350
Application deadline: 08/15
Tuition: full time: $935/credit hour; part time: $935/credit hour
Room/board/expenses: $4,530
College-funded aid: Yes
International student aid: Yes
Full-time enrollment: N/A
men: N/A; women: N/A;
minorities: N/A; international: N/A
Part-time enrollment: 94
men: 67%; women: 33%;
minorities: 13%; international: 54%
Average GMAT (part-time): 570
TOEFL requirement: No
Minimum TOEFL score: N/A
Most popular departments: finance, general management, international business, marketing, organizational behavior

University of Michigan–Ann Arbor (Ross)

701 Tappan Street
Ann Arbor, MI 48109-1234
http://www.bus.umich.edu
Public
Admissions: (734) 763-5796
E-mail: rossmba@umich.edu
Financial aid: (734) 764-5796
Application deadline: 03/01
In-state tuition: full time: $38,289; part time: $1,245/credit hour
Out-of-state tuition: full time: $43,289
Room/board/expenses: $19,054
College-funded aid: Yes
International student aid: Yes
Average student indebtedness at graduation: $66,524
Full-time enrollment: 838
men: 66%; women: 34%;
minorities: 25%; international: 33%
Part-time enrollment: 760
men: 80%; women: 20%;
minorities: 25%; international: 19%
Acceptance rate (full-time): 20%
Average GMAT (full-time): 700
Average GMAT (part-time): 665
Average GPA (full-time): 3.30
Average age of entrants to full-time program: 28
Average months of prior work experience (full-time): 61
TOEFL requirement: Yes
Minimum TOEFL score: 600
Most popular departments: consulting, finance, general management, marketing, technology
Mean starting base salary for 2007 full-time graduates: $99,265
Employment location for 2007 class: Intl. 8%; N.E. 26%; M.A. 5%; S. 3%; M.W. 29%; S.W. 7%; W. 21%

University of Michigan–Dearborn

19000 Hubbard Drive
Dearborn, MI 48126-2638
http://www.som.umd.umich.edu/grad
Public
Admissions: (313) 593-5460
E-mail: gradbusiness@umd.umich.edu
Financial aid: (313) 593-5300
Application deadline: 09/01
In-state tuition: full time: $466/credit hour; part time: $466/credit hour
Out-of-state tuition: full time: $886/credit hour
Room/board/expenses: N/A
College-funded aid: Yes
International student aid: Yes
Full-time enrollment: N/A
men: N/A; women: N/A;
minorities: N/A; international: N/A
Part-time enrollment: 552
men: 66%; women: 34%;
minorities: 25%; international: N/A
Average GMAT (part-time): 571
TOEFL requirement: Yes
Minimum TOEFL score: 560
Most popular departments: accounting, finance, general management, international business, marketing

University of Michigan–Flint

303 E. Kearsley Street
Flint, MI 48502-1950
http://mba.umflint.edu
Public
Admissions: (810) 762-3163
E-mail: umflintmba1@umich.edu
Financial aid: (810) 762-3444
Application deadline: 08/01
In-state tuition: full time: $12,998; part time: $527/credit hour
Out-of-state tuition: full time: $12,998
Room/board/expenses: $6,100
College-funded aid: Yes
International student aid: No
Average student indebtedness at graduation: $31,894
Full-time enrollment: N/A
men: N/A; women: N/A;
minorities: N/A; international: N/A
Part-time enrollment: 180
men: 61%; women: 39%;
minorities: 15%; international: 8%
Average GMAT (part-time): 535
Average age of entrants to full-time program: N/A
TOEFL requirement: Yes
Minimum TOEFL score: 550
Most popular departments: finance, general management, health care administration, international business, leadership

Wayne State University

5201 Cass Avenue
Prentis Building
Detroit, MI 48202
http://www.busadm.wayne.edu
Public
Admissions: (313) 577-4510
E-mail: l.s.zaddach@wayne.edu
Financial aid: (313) 577-3378
Application deadline: 07/01
In-state tuition: full time: $468/credit hour; part time: $468/credit hour
Out-of-state tuition: full time: $955/credit hour
Room/board/expenses: $13,000
College-funded aid: Yes
International student aid: Yes
Average student indebtedness at graduation: $23,000
Full-time enrollment: 215
men: 55%; women: 45%;
minorities: 22%; international: 28%
Part-time enrollment: 1,034
men: 59%; women: 41%;
minorities: 26%; international: 9%
Average GMAT (part-time): 520
TOEFL requirement: Yes
Minimum TOEFL score: 550
Employment location for 2007 class: Intl. N/A; N.E. N/A; M.A. N/A; S. N/A; M.W. 100%; S.W. N/A; W. N/A

Western Michigan University (Haworth)

1903 Oliver Street
Kalamazoo, MI 49008-5457
http://www.hcob.wmich.edu
Public
Admissions: (269) 387-5075
E-mail: business-adv-office@wmich.edu
Financial aid: (269) 387-6000
Application deadline: 06/01
In-state tuition: full time: $345/credit hour; part time: $345/credit hour
Out-of-state tuition: full time: $730/credit hour
Room/board/expenses: $11,807
College-funded aid: Yes
International student aid: Yes
Average student indebtedness at graduation: $20,616
Full-time enrollment: 153
men: 61%; women: 39%;
minorities: 20%; international: 38%
Part-time enrollment: 210
men: 63%; women: 37%;
minorities: 4%; international: 1%
Acceptance rate (full-time): 57%
Average GMAT (full-time): 514
Average GMAT (part-time): 510
Average age of entrants to full-time program: 26
TOEFL requirement: Yes
Minimum TOEFL score: 550
Most popular departments: finance, general management, international business, marketing, management information systems

MINNESOTA

Minnesota State University–Mankato

120 Morris Hall
Mankato, MN 56001
http://cob.mnsu.edu/mba/
Public
Admissions: (507) 389-2967
E-mail: mba@mnsu.edu
Financial aid: (507) 389-1866
Application deadline: 06/01
In-state tuition: full time: $476/credit hour; part time: N/A
Out-of-state tuition: full time: N/A
Room/board/expenses: N/A
College-funded aid: Yes
International student aid: Yes
Full-time enrollment: 62
men: 66%; women: 34%;
minorities: 5%; international: 11%
Part-time enrollment: N/A
men: N/A; women: N/A;
minorities: N/A; international: N/A
Acceptance rate (full-time): 81%
Average GMAT (full-time): 520
Average GPA (full-time): 3.15
Average months of prior work experience (full-time): 60
TOEFL requirement: Yes
Minimum TOEFL score: 550

St. Cloud State University (Herberger)

720 Fourth Avenue S
St. Cloud, MN 56301-4498
http://www.stcloudstate.edu/mba
Public
Admissions: (320) 308-3212
E-mail: mba@stcloudstate.edu
Financial aid: (320) 308-2047
Application deadline: N/A
In-state tuition: full time: N/A; part time: N/A
Out-of-state tuition: full time: N/A
Room/board/expenses: N/A
College-funded aid: Yes
International student aid: Yes
Full-time enrollment: 47
men: 34%; women: 66%;
minorities: 0%; international: 51%
Part-time enrollment: 110
men: 63%; women: 37%;
minorities: 11%; international: 5%
Average GMAT (full-time): 502
Average GMAT (part-time): 537
Average age of entrants to full-time program: 28
TOEFL requirement: Yes
Minimum TOEFL score: 550

University of Minnesota–Duluth (Labovitz)

412 Library Drive
Duluth, MN 55812-2496
http://www.d.umn.edu/sbe/degreeprogs/MBA/
Public
Admissions: (218) 726-8839
E-mail: grad@d.umn.edu
Financial aid: (218) 726-8000
Application deadline: 07/15
In-state tuition: full time: N/A; part time: $773/credit hour
Out-of-state tuition: full time: N/A
Room/board/expenses: $8,000
College-funded aid: Yes
International student aid: No
Average student indebtedness at graduation: $12,000
Full-time enrollment: N/A
men: N/A; women: N/A;
minorities: N/A; international: N/A
Part-time enrollment: 64
men: 61%; women: 39%;
minorities: 2%; international: 5%
Average GMAT (part-time): 547
TOEFL requirement: Yes
Minimum TOEFL score: 550

University of Minnesota–Twin Cities (Carlson)
321 19th Avenue S
Office 4-300
Minneapolis, MN 55455
http://www.carlsonschool.umn.edu/mba
Public
Admissions: (612) 625-5555
E-mail: full-timembainfo@carlsonschool.umn.edu
Financial aid: (612) 624-1111
Application deadline: N/A
In-state tuition: full time: $26,528; part time: $945/credit hour
Out-of-state tuition: full time: $36,596
Room/board/expenses: $15,000
College-funded aid: Yes
International student aid: Yes
Average student indebtedness at graduation: $44,214
Full-time enrollment: 218
men: 68%; women: 32%; minorities: 10%; international: 33%
Part-time enrollment: 1,827
men: 69%; women: 31%; minorities: 12%; international: 5%
Acceptance rate (full-time): 41%
Average GMAT (full-time): 661
Average GMAT (part-time): 616
Average GPA (full-time): 3.37
Average age of entrants to full-time program: 28
Average months of prior work experience (full-time): 54
TOEFL requirement: Yes
Minimum TOEFL score: 580
Most popular departments: consulting, finance, marketing, management information systems, operations management, supply chain management
Mean starting base salary for 2007 full-time graduates: $87,188
Employment location for 2007 class: Intl. 4%; N.E. 3%; M.A. 0%; S. 0%; M.W. 90%; S.W. 0%; W. 3%

MISSISSIPPI

Jackson State University (Moore)[1]
1400 J.R. Lynch Street
Jackson, MS 39217
http://ccaix.jsums.edu/business
Public
Admissions: (601) 432-6315
E-mail: gadmappl@ccaix.jsums.edu
Financial aid: (601) 979-2227
Tuition: N/A
Room/board/expenses: N/A
Enrollment: N/A

Millsaps College (Else)
1701 N. State Street
Jackson, MS 39210
http://millsaps.edu/esom
Private
Admissions: (601) 974-1253
E-mail: mbamacc@millsaps.edu
Financial aid: (601) 974-1220
Application deadline: rolling
Tuition: full time: $864/credit hour; part time: $864/credit hour
Room/board/expenses: N/A
College-funded aid: Yes
International student aid: Yes
Full-time enrollment: 39
men: 56%; women: 44%; minorities: 21%; international: 3%
Part-time enrollment: 50
men: 72%; women: 28%; minorities: 12%; international: N/A
Acceptance rate (full-time): 89%
Average GMAT (full-time): 550
Average GMAT (part-time): 560
Average GPA (full-time): 3.40
Average months of prior work experience (full-time): 12
TOEFL requirement: Yes
Minimum TOEFL score: 550

Mississippi State University
PO Box 5288
Mississippi State, MS 39762
http://www.cbi.msstate.edu/gsb/
Public
Admissions: (662) 325-1891
E-mail: gsb@cobilan.msstate.edu
Financial aid: (662) 325-2450
Application deadline: 07/01
In-state tuition: total program: $7,467 (full-time); part time: $277/credit hour
Out-of-state tuition: total program: $17,204 (full-time)
Room/board/expenses: $19,601
College-funded aid: Yes
International student aid: Yes
Average student indebtedness at graduation: $10,155
Full-time enrollment: 120
men: 53%; women: 47%; minorities: 13%; international: 13%
Part-time enrollment: 176
men: 70%; women: 30%; minorities: 9%; international: 3%
Acceptance rate (full-time): 70%
Average GMAT (full-time): 506
Average GMAT (part-time): 527
Average GPA (full-time): 3.45
Average age of entrants to full-time program: 24
TOEFL requirement: Yes
Minimum TOEFL score: 575
Most popular departments: accounting, economics, finance, general management, management information systems

University of Mississippi
253 Holman Hall
University, MS 33677
http://www.mba.olemiss.edu/
Public
Admissions: (662) 915-5483
E-mail: jholleman@bus.olemiss.edu
Financial aid: (662) 915-7175
Application deadline: 03/01
In-state tuition: total program: $8,472 (full-time); part time: $314/credit hour
Out-of-state tuition: total program: $17,116 (full-time)
Room/board/expenses: $30,000
College-funded aid: Yes
International student aid: Yes
Average student indebtedness at graduation: $17,000
Full-time enrollment: 28
men: 86%; women: 14%; minorities: N/A; international: 7%
Part-time enrollment: 21
men: 67%; women: 33%; minorities: 5%; international: N/A
Acceptance rate (full-time): 42%
Average GMAT (full-time): 560
Average GMAT (part-time): 538
Average GPA (full-time): 3.52
Average age of entrants to full-time program: 25
Average months of prior work experience (full-time): 20
TOEFL requirement: Yes
Minimum TOEFL score: 600
Most popular departments: entrepreneurship, finance, general management, marketing, management information systems
Mean starting base salary for 2007 full-time graduates: $52,150
Employment location for 2007 class: Intl. N/A; N.E. N/A; M.A. N/A; S. 100%; M.W. N/A; S.W. N/A; W. N/A

University of Southern Mississippi
118 College Drive
#5096
Hattiesburg, MS 39406-5096
http://www.usm.edu/mba
Public
Admissions: (601) 266-4653
E-mail: mba@usm.edu
Financial aid: (601) 266-4774
Application deadline: 06/15
In-state tuition: full time: $4,975; part time: $273/credit hour
Out-of-state tuition: full time: $15,652
Room/board/expenses: $6,100
College-funded aid: Yes
International student aid: Yes
Average student indebtedness at graduation: $14,352
Full-time enrollment: 59
men: 56%; women: 44%; minorities: 15%; international: 8%
Part-time enrollment: 49
men: 57%; women: 43%; minorities: 14%; international: 0%
Acceptance rate (full-time): 66%
Average GMAT (full-time): 485
Average GMAT (part-time): 543
Average GPA (full-time): 3.38
Average age of entrants to full-time program: 24
Average months of prior work experience (full-time): 10
TOEFL requirement: Yes
Minimum TOEFL score: 550
Most popular departments: accounting, marketing
Mean starting base salary for 2007 full-time graduates: $42,250
Employment location for 2007 class: Intl. N/A; N.E. N/A; M.A. N/A; S. 100%; M.W. N/A; S.W. N/A; W. N/A

MISSOURI

Missouri State University
901 S. National Avenue
Glass Hall 400
Springfield, MO 65897
http://www.coba.missouristate.edu
Public
Admissions: (417) 836-5335
E-mail: graduatecollege@missouristate.edu
Financial aid: (417) 836-5262
Application deadline: 07/20
In-state tuition: full time: $206/credit hour; part time: $206/credit hour
Out-of-state tuition: full time: $402/credit hour
Room/board/expenses: $9,002
College-funded aid: Yes
International student aid: Yes
Full-time enrollment: 400
men: 54%; women: 46%; minorities: N/A; international: 56%
Part-time enrollment: N/A
men: N/A; women: N/A; minorities: N/A; international: N/A
Average GMAT (full-time): 498
Average age of entrants to full-time program: 27
TOEFL requirement: Yes
Minimum TOEFL score: 550

Rockhurst University (Helzberg)
1100 Rockhurst Road
Kansas City, MO 64110
http://www.rockhurst.edu/hsom/
Private
Admissions: (816) 501-4731
E-mail: mba@rockhurst.edu
Financial aid: N/A
Application deadline: rolling
Tuition: full time: N/A; part time: $575/credit hour
Room/board/expenses: $250
College-funded aid: Yes
International student aid: Yes
Full-time enrollment: N/A
men: N/A; women: N/A; minorities: N/A; international: N/A
Part-time enrollment: 100
men: 66%; women: 34%; minorities: 11%; international: 0%
Average GMAT (part-time): 540
TOEFL requirement: Yes
Minimum TOEFL score: 550
Most popular departments: accounting, finance, general management, international business, marketing

Southeast Missouri State University (Harrison)
1 University Plaza
MS 5890
Cape Girardeau, MO 63701
http://www.semo.edu/hcb/
Public
Admissions: (573) 651-2192
E-mail: mba@semo.edu
Financial aid: (573) 651-2039
Application deadline: 08/01
In-state tuition: full time: $225/credit hour; part time: $225/credit hour
Out-of-state tuition: full time: $396/credit hour
Room/board/expenses: $8,200
College-funded aid: Yes
International student aid: Yes
Full-time enrollment: N/A
men: N/A; women: N/A; minorities: N/A; international: N/A
Part-time enrollment: 106
men: 49%; women: 51%; minorities: 7%; international: 14%
Average GMAT (part-time): 514
TOEFL requirement: Yes
Minimum TOEFL score: 550

St. Louis University (Cook)
3674 Lindell Boulevard
St. Louis, MO 63108
http://gradbiz.slu.edu
Private
Admissions: (314) 977-6221
E-mail: gradbiz@slu.edu
Financial aid: (314) 977-2350
Application deadline: rolling
Tuition: full time: $48,145; part time: $840/credit hour
Room/board/expenses: $12,553
College-funded aid: Yes
International student aid: Yes
Average student indebtedness at graduation: $40,745
Full-time enrollment: 38
men: 68%; women: 32%; minorities: 11%; international: 3%
Part-time enrollment: 385
men: 62%; women: 38%; minorities: 11%; international: 5%
Acceptance rate (full-time): 55%
Average GMAT (full-time): 585
Average GMAT (part-time): 553
Average GPA (full-time): 3.50
Average age of entrants to full-time program: 27
Average months of prior work experience (full-time): 45
TOEFL requirement: Yes
Minimum TOEFL score: 550
Mean starting base salary for 2007 full-time graduates: $59,815
Employment location for 2007 class: Intl. 0%; N.E. 0%; M.A. 0%; S. 7%; M.W. 79%; S.W. 3%; W. 10%

Truman State University
100 E. Normal
Kirksville, MO 63501
http://gradschool.truman.edu
Public
Admissions: (660) 785-4109
E-mail: gradinfo@truman.edu
Financial aid: (660) 785-4130
Application deadline: rolling
In-state tuition: total program: $6,600 (full-time); part time: $288/credit hour
Out-of-state tuition: total program: $11,500 (full-time)
Room/board/expenses: $6,500
College-funded aid: Yes
International student aid: Yes
Full-time enrollment: 31
men: 48%; women: 52%; minorities: 0%; international: 6%
Part-time enrollment: N/A
men: N/A; women: N/A; minorities: N/A; international: N/A
Acceptance rate (full-time): 91%
Average GMAT (full-time): 588
Average GPA (full-time): 3.42
Average age of entrants to full-time program: 22
TOEFL requirement: Yes
Minimum TOEFL score: 550
Most popular departments: accounting
Employment location for 2007 class: Intl. N/A; N.E. N/A; M.A. N/A; S. N/A; M.W. 100%; S.W. N/A; W. N/A

University of Central Missouri (Harmon)
Ward Edwards 1600
Warrensburg, MO 64093
http://www.ucmo.edu/x10656.xml
Public
Admissions: (660) 543-8597
E-mail: engelmann@ucmo.edu
Financial aid: (800) 729-2678
Application deadline: 08/01
In-state tuition: full time: $235/credit hour; part time: $235/credit hour
Out-of-state tuition: full time: $471/credit hour
Room/board/expenses: $8,682
College-funded aid: Yes
International student aid: Yes
Average student indebtedness at graduation: $9,247
Full-time enrollment: 54
men: 56%; women: 44%; minorities: 13%; international: 39%
Part-time enrollment: N/A
men: N/A; women: N/A; minorities: N/A; international: N/A
Acceptance rate (full-time): 67%
Average GMAT (full-time): 490
Average GPA (full-time): 3.34
TOEFL requirement: Yes
Minimum TOEFL score: 550
Most popular departments: accounting, finance, marketing, management information systems

University of Missouri–Columbia
213 Cornell Hall
Columbia, MO 65211
http://mba.missouri.edu
Public
Admissions: (573) 882-2750
E-mail: mba@missouri.edu
Financial aid: (573) 882-7506
Application deadline: 08/01
In-state tuition: full time: $9,928; part time: $320/credit hour
Out-of-state tuition: full time: $22,637
Room/board/expenses: $9,040
College-funded aid: Yes
International student aid: Yes
Full-time enrollment: 207
men: 61%; women: 39%; minorities: 5%; international: 29%
Part-time enrollment: N/A
men: N/A; women: N/A; minorities: N/A; international: N/A
Acceptance rate (full-time): 62%
Average GMAT (full-time): 630
Average GPA (full-time): 3.45
Average age of entrants to full-time program: 25
Average months of prior work experience (full-time): 16
TOEFL requirement: Yes
Minimum TOEFL score: 550
Most popular departments: finance, general management, marketing, management information systems, organizational behavior

Mean starting base salary for 2007 full-time graduates: $56,400
Employment location for 2007 class: Intl. 0%; N.E. 9%; M.A. 0%; S. 3%; M.W. 79%; S.W. 6%; W. 3%

University of Missouri–Kansas City (Bloch)
5100 Rockhill Road
Kansas City, MO 64110
http://www.bsbpa.umkc.edu/
Public
Admissions: (816) 235-1111
E-mail: admit@umkc.edu
Financial aid: (816) 235-1154
Application deadline: 05/01
In-state tuition: full time: $287/credit hour; part time: $287/credit hour
Out-of-state tuition: full time: $741/credit hour
Room/board/expenses: N/A
College-funded aid: Yes
International student aid: Yes
Average student indebtedness at graduation: $28,651
Full-time enrollment: N/A
men: N/A; women: N/A; minorities: N/A; international: N/A
Part-time enrollment: 344
men: 65%; women: 35%; minorities: 9%; international: 6%
Average GMAT (part-time): 540
TOEFL requirement: Yes
Minimum TOEFL score: 550
Most popular departments: entrepreneurship, finance, general management, marketing, management information systems

University of Missouri–St. Louis
1 University Boulevard
St. Louis, MO 63121
http://mba.umsl.edu
Public
Admissions: (314) 516-5885
E-mail: mba@umsl.edu
Financial aid: (314) 516-5526
Application deadline: 07/01
In-state tuition: full time: N/A; part time: $287/credit hour
Out-of-state tuition: full time: N/A
Room/board/expenses: $8,280
College-funded aid: Yes
International student aid: Yes
Average student indebtedness at graduation: $20,142
Full-time enrollment: N/A
men: N/A; women: N/A; minorities: N/A; international: N/A
Part-time enrollment: 419
men: 54%; women: 46%; minorities: 8%; international: 28%
Average GMAT (part-time): 549
TOEFL requirement: Yes
Minimum TOEFL score: 550
Most popular departments: accounting, finance, general management, marketing, management information systems

Washington University in St. Louis (Olin)
1 Brookings Drive
Campus Box 1133
St. Louis, MO 63130-4899
http://www.olin.wustl.edu/mba
Private
Admissions: (314) 935-7301
E-mail: mba@olin.wustl.edu
Financial aid: (314) 935-7301
Application deadline: 05/01
Tuition: full time: $38,729; part time: $1,150/credit hour
Room/board/expenses: $26,676
College-funded aid: Yes
International student aid: Yes
Full-time enrollment: 288
men: 72%; women: 28%; minorities: 12%; international: 36%

Part-time enrollment: 374
men: 76%; women: 24%; minorities: 11%; international: 7%
Acceptance rate (full-time): 33%
Average GMAT (full-time): 674
Average GMAT (part-time): 599
Average GPA (full-time): 3.38
Average age of entrants to full-time program: 27
Average months of prior work experience (full-time): 45
TOEFL requirement: Yes
Minimum TOEFL score: N/A
Most popular departments: consulting, finance, general management, marketing, supply chain management
Mean starting base salary for 2007 full-time graduates: $85,583
Employment location for 2007 class: Intl. 13%; N.E. 12%; M.A. 2%; S. 1%; M.W. 57%; S.W. 6%; W. 9%

MONTANA

Montana State University
PO Box 173040
Bozeman, MT 59717-3040
http://www.montana.edu/wwwdg/
Public
Admissions: (406) 994-4683
E-mail: gradstudy@montana.edu
Financial aid: (406) 994-2845
Application deadline: 06/15
In-state tuition: full time: $5,720; part time: $228/credit hour
Out-of-state tuition: full time: $16,159
Room/board/expenses: $11,000
College-funded aid: Yes
International student aid: Yes
Average student indebtedness at graduation: $12,683
Full-time enrollment: 46
men: 24%; women: 76%; minorities: 0%; international: 4%
Part-time enrollment: 5
men: 20%; women: 80%; minorities: 0%; international: 20%
Acceptance rate (full-time): 89%
Average GMAT (full-time): 511
Average GMAT (part-time): 511
Average GPA (full-time): 3.38
TOEFL requirement: Yes
Minimum TOEFL score: 550
Mean starting base salary for 2007 full-time graduates: $44,143
Employment location for 2007 class: Intl. N/A; N.E. N/A; M.A. N/A; S. N/A; M.W. N/A; S.W. N/A; W. 100%

University of Montana[1]
Missoula, MT 59812-6808
http://www.mba-macct.umt.edu/
Public
Admissions: (406) 243-2361
E-mail: jliston@mso.umt.edu
Financial aid: (406) 243-5373
Tuition: N/A
Room/board/expenses: N/A
Enrollment: N/A

NEBRASKA

Creighton University
2500 California Plaza
Omaha, NE 68178-0130
http://www2.creighton.edu/business/
Private
Admissions: (402) 280-2853
E-mail: cobagrad@creighton.edu
Financial aid: (402) 280-2731
Application deadline: 03/01
Tuition: full time: N/A; part time: $595/credit hour
Room/board/expenses: $24,000
College-funded aid: Yes
International student aid: Yes
Average student indebtedness at graduation: $22,298

Full-time enrollment: N/A
men: N/A; women: N/A; minorities: N/A; international: N/A
Part-time enrollment: 114
men: 71%; women: 29%; minorities: 6%; international: 6%
Average GMAT (part-time): 568
TOEFL requirement: Yes
Minimum TOEFL score: 550
Most popular departments: accounting, finance, leadership, management information systems

University of Nebraska–Kearney[1]
905 West 25th Street
Kearney, NE 68849
http://www.unk.edu/acad/bt/index.php?id=107
Public
Admissions: (800) 717-7881
E-mail: unkbt@unk.edu
Financial aid: N/A
Tuition: N/A
Room/board/expenses: N/A
Enrollment: N/A

University of Nebraska–Lincoln
12th and R Streets
Lincoln, NE 68588-0405
http://www.mba.unl.edu
Public
Admissions: (402) 472-2338
E-mail: cgraduate@unlnotes.unl.edu
Financial aid: (402) 472-2030
Application deadline: 06/15
In-state tuition: full time: N/A; part time: $224/credit hour
Out-of-state tuition: full time: N/A
Room/board/expenses: $11,887
College-funded aid: Yes
International student aid: Yes
Full-time enrollment: N/A
men: N/A; women: N/A; minorities: N/A; international: N/A
Part-time enrollment: 133
men: 70%; women: 30%; minorities: 3%; international: 16%
Average GMAT (part-time): 616
TOEFL requirement: Yes
Minimum TOEFL score: 550
Most popular departments: finance, human resources management, international business, marketing, other

University of Nebraska–Omaha
6001 Dodge Street
Omaha, NE 68182-0048
http://cba.unomaha.edu/mba
Public
Admissions: (402) 554-2303
E-mail: mba@unomaha.edu
Financial aid: (402) 554-2327
Application deadline: 07/01
In-state tuition: full time: N/A; part time: $215/credit hour
Out-of-state tuition: full time: N/A
Room/board/expenses: $19,600
College-funded aid: Yes
International student aid: Yes
Average student indebtedness at graduation: $24,675
Full-time enrollment: N/A
men: N/A; women: N/A; minorities: N/A; international: N/A
Part-time enrollment: 261
men: 65%; women: 35%; minorities: 5%; international: 5%
Average GMAT (part-time): 565
TOEFL requirement: Yes
Minimum TOEFL score: 550
Most popular departments: e-commerce, general management, health care administration, human resources management, international business

NEVADA

University of Nevada–Las Vegas
4505 Maryland Parkway
PO Box 456031
Las Vegas, NV 89154-6031
http://business.unlv.edu
Public
Admissions: (702) 895-3655
E-mail: cobmba@unlv.edu
Financial aid: (702) 895-3682
Application deadline: 01/06
In-state tuition: full time: $172/credit hour; part time: $172/credit hour
Out-of-state tuition: full time: $10,910
Room/board/expenses: $10,000
College-funded aid: Yes
International student aid: Yes
Average student indebtedness at graduation: $34,000
Full-time enrollment: 18
men: 56%; women: 44%; minorities: 11%; international: 33%
Part-time enrollment: 252
men: 64%; women: 36%; minorities: 8%; international: 10%
Acceptance rate (full-time): 81%
Average GMAT (full-time): 602
Average GMAT (part-time): 585
Average GPA (full-time): 3.35
Average age of entrants to full-time program: 26
Average months of prior work experience (full-time): 87
TOEFL requirement: Yes
Minimum TOEFL score: 550

University of Nevada–Reno
1664 N. Virginia Street
Reno, NV 89557
http://www.coba.unr.edu
Public
Admissions: (775) 784-4912
E-mail: vkrentz@unr.edu
Financial aid: (775) 784-4666
Application deadline: 03/15
In-state tuition: full time: N/A; part time: $176/credit hour
Out-of-state tuition: full time: N/A
Room/board/expenses: $2,690
College-funded aid: Yes
International student aid: Yes
Full-time enrollment: N/A
men: N/A; women: N/A; minorities: N/A; international: N/A
Part-time enrollment: 249
men: 58%; women: 42%; minorities: 11%; international: 4%
Average GMAT (part-time): 577
TOEFL requirement: Yes
Minimum TOEFL score: 550
Most popular departments: accounting, finance, general management, marketing, supply chain management

NEW HAMPSHIRE

Dartmouth College (Tuck)
100 Tuck Hall
Hanover, NH 03755-9000
http://www.tuck.dartmouth.edu
Private
Admissions: (603) 646-3162
E-mail: tuck.admissions@dartmouth.edu
Financial aid: (603) 646-0640
Application deadline: 04/01
Tuition: full time: $43,240; part time: N/A
Room/board/expenses: $14,515
College-funded aid: Yes
International student aid: Yes
Average student indebtedness at graduation: $90,078
Full-time enrollment: 500
men: 66%; women: 34%; minorities: 15%; international: 35%

Part-time enrollment: N/A
men: N/A; women: N/A; minorities: N/A; international: N/A
Acceptance rate (full-time): 19%
Average GMAT (full-time): 713
Average GPA (full-time): 3.46
Average age of entrants to full-time program: 28
Average months of prior work experience (full-time): 63
TOEFL requirement: Yes
Minimum TOEFL score: N/A
Most popular departments: accounting, consulting, finance, general management, marketing
Mean starting base salary for 2007 full-time graduates: $107,406
Employment location for 2007 class: Intl. 12%; N.E. 54%; M.A. 4%; S. 4%; M.W. 10%; S.W. 3%; W. 13%

University of New Hampshire (Whittemore)
McConnell Hall
15 College Road
Durham, NH 03824
http://www.mba.unh.edu
Public
Admissions: (603) 862-1367
E-mail: wsbe.grad@unh.edu
Financial aid: (603) 862-3600
Application deadline: 04/01
In-state tuition: total program: $17,000 (full-time); part time: $580/credit hour
Out-of-state tuition: total program: $28,000 (full-time)
Room/board/expenses: $12,600
College-funded aid: Yes
International student aid: Yes
Average student indebtedness at graduation: $30,918
Full-time enrollment: 33
men: 55%; women: 45%; minorities: 6%; international: 27%
Part-time enrollment: 179
men: 66%; women: 34%; minorities: 8%; international: 4%
Acceptance rate (full-time): 77%
Average GMAT (full-time): 551
Average GMAT (part-time): 548
Average GPA (full-time): 3.29
Average age of entrants to full-time program: 25
Average months of prior work experience (full-time): 46
TOEFL requirement: Yes
Minimum TOEFL score: 550
Mean starting base salary for 2007 full-time graduates: $52,704
Employment location for 2007 class: Intl. 5%; N.E. 90%; M.A. N/A; S. N/A; M.W. 5%; S.W. N/A; W. N/A

NEW JERSEY

Fairleigh Dickinson University (Silberman)
1000 River Road
Teaneck, NJ 07666
http://www.fduinfo.com/depts/sctab.php
Private
Admissions: (201) 692-2554
E-mail: grad@fdu.edu
Financial aid: (201) 692-2363
Application deadline: rolling
Tuition: full time: $893/credit hour; part time: $893/credit hour
Room/board/expenses: $10,000
College-funded aid: Yes
International student aid: Yes
Full-time enrollment: 344
men: 57%; women: 43%; minorities: 14%; international: 47%
Part-time enrollment: 482
men: 61%; women: 39%; minorities: 17%; international: 7%
Acceptance rate (full-time): 46%
TOEFL requirement: Yes
Minimum TOEFL score: 550

Most popular departments: accounting, finance, general management, marketing, tax

Monmouth University
400 Cedar Avenue
West Long Branch, NJ 07764-1898
http://www.monmouth.edu
Private
Admissions: (732) 571-3452
E-mail: gradadm@monmouth.edu
Financial aid: (732) 571-3463
Application deadline: 06/01
Tuition: full time: $710/credit hour; part time: $710/credit hour
Room/board/expenses: $15,818
College-funded aid: Yes
International student aid: Yes
Average student indebtedness at graduation: $30,530
Full-time enrollment: 12
men: 67%; women: 33%; minorities: 8%; international: 8%
Part-time enrollment: 213
men: 61%; women: 39%; minorities: 8%; international: 5%
Acceptance rate (full-time): 48%
Average GMAT (full-time): 551
Average GMAT (part-time): 513
Average GPA (full-time): 3.58
Average age of entrants to full-time program: 24
Average months of prior work experience (full-time): 31
TOEFL requirement: Yes
Minimum TOEFL score: 550

Montclair State University
Partridge Hall
1 Normal Avenue
Montclair, NJ 07043
http://www.montclair.edu/mba
Public
Admissions: (973) 655-5147
E-mail: graduate.school@montclair.edu
Financial aid: (973) 655-4461
Application deadline: rolling
In-state tuition: full time: $557/credit hour; part time: $557/credit hour
Out-of-state tuition: full time: $767/credit hour
Room/board/expenses: $16,123
College-funded aid: Yes
International student aid: Yes
Average student indebtedness at graduation: $26,629
Full-time enrollment: 142
men: 51%; women: 49%; minorities: 10%; international: 22%
Part-time enrollment: 259
men: 61%; women: 39%; minorities: 21%; international: 3%
Acceptance rate (full-time): 61%
Average GMAT (full-time): 510
Average GMAT (part-time): 540
Average GPA (full-time): 3.40
Average age of entrants to full-time program: 26
Average months of prior work experience (full-time): 24
TOEFL requirement: Yes
Minimum TOEFL score: 550

New Jersey Institute of Technology
University Heights
Newark, NJ 07102
http://management.njit.edu/
Public
Admissions: (973) 642-7499
E-mail: lipper@njit.edu
Financial aid: (973) 596-3479
Application deadline: N/A
In-state tuition: full time: $14,354; part time: $694/credit hour
Out-of-state tuition: full time: $19,714
Room/board/expenses: $11,600
College-funded aid: Yes
International student aid: Yes
Average student indebtedness at graduation: $9,000
Full-time enrollment: 153
men: 76%; women: 24%; minorities: 18%; international: 37%
Part-time enrollment: 102
men: 78%; women: 22%; minorities: 18%; international: 12%
Acceptance rate (full-time): 52%
Average GMAT (full-time): 519
Average GMAT (part-time): 521
Average age of entrants to full-time program: 31
TOEFL requirement: Yes
Minimum TOEFL score: 550
Most popular departments: e-commerce, finance, manufacturing and technology management, marketing, management information systems
Mean starting base salary for 2007 full-time graduates: $65,000

Rider University
2083 Lawrenceville Road
Lawrenceville, NJ 08648-3099
http://www.rider.edu/mba
Private
Admissions: (609) 896-5036
E-mail: gradadm@rider.edu
Financial aid: (609) 896-5360
Application deadline: rolling
Tuition: full time: N/A; part time: $735/credit hour
Room/board/expenses: $14,030
College-funded aid: Yes
International student aid: Yes
Average student indebtedness at graduation: $28,796
Full-time enrollment: N/A
men: N/A; women: N/A; minorities: N/A; international: N/A
Part-time enrollment: 271
men: 57%; women: 43%; minorities: 21%; international: 12%
Average GMAT (part-time): 500
TOEFL requirement: Yes
Minimum TOEFL score: 550
Most popular departments: finance, general management, international business, marketing, other

Rowan University (Rohrer)
201 Mullica Hill Road
Glassboro, NJ 08028
http://www.rowan.edu/mba
Public
Admissions: (856) 256-4024
E-mail: mba@rowan.edu
Financial aid: (856) 256-4250
Application deadline: rolling
In-state tuition: full time: $10,624; part time: $590/credit hour
Out-of-state tuition: full time: $10,624
Room/board/expenses: N/A
College-funded aid: Yes
International student aid: Yes
Full-time enrollment: 20
men: 50%; women: 50%; minorities: 5%; international: 25%
Part-time enrollment: 64
men: 56%; women: 44%; minorities: 8%; international: 16%
Average GMAT (part-time): 499
TOEFL requirement: Yes
Minimum TOEFL score: 550

Rutgers, the State University of New Jersey–Camden
227 Penn Street
Camden, NJ 08102
http://camden-sbc.rutgers.edu
Public
Admissions: (856) 225-6104
E-mail: camden@camuga.rutgers.edu
Financial aid: (856) 225-6039
Application deadline: rolling
In-state tuition: full time: N/A; part time: N/A
Out-of-state tuition: full time: N/A
Room/board/expenses: N/A
College-funded aid: Yes
International student aid: Yes
Full-time enrollment: N/A
men: N/A; women: N/A; minorities: N/A; international: N/A
Part-time enrollment: 265
men: 65%; women: 35%; minorities: 27%; international: 8%
Average GMAT (part-time): 557
TOEFL requirement: Yes
Minimum TOEFL score: 550

Rutgers, the State University of New Jersey–New Brunswick and Newark
111 Washington Street
Newark, NJ 07102-1895
http://www.business.rutgers.edu
Public
Admissions: (973) 353-1234
E-mail: admit@business.rutgers.edu
Financial aid: (973) 353-1234
Application deadline: 05/01
In-state tuition: full time: $20,820; part time: $780/credit hour
Out-of-state tuition: full time: $32,022
Room/board/expenses: $20,520
College-funded aid: Yes
International student aid: No
Full-time enrollment: 119
men: 56%; women: 44%; minorities: 25%; international: 25%
Part-time enrollment: 979
men: 66%; women: 34%; minorities: 32%; international: 6%
Acceptance rate (full-time): 54%
Average GMAT (full-time): 637
Average GMAT (part-time): 563
Average GPA (full-time): 3.27
Average age of entrants to full-time program: 27
Average months of prior work experience (full-time): 51
TOEFL requirement: Yes
Minimum TOEFL score: 600
Most popular departments: finance, general management, marketing, supply chain management, other
Mean starting base salary for 2007 full-time graduates: $78,921
Employment location for 2007 class: Intl. 3%; N.E. 95%; M.A. 3%; S. N/A; M.W. N/A; S.W. N/A; W. N/A

Seton Hall University (Stillman)[1]
400 S. Orange Avenue
South Orange, NJ 07079
http://www.business.shu.edu
Private
Admissions: (973) 761-9262
E-mail: stillman@shu.edu
Financial aid: (973) 761-9350
Tuition: N/A
Room/board/expenses: N/A
Enrollment: N/A

William Paterson University (Cotsakos)
1600 Valley Road
Wayne, NJ 07474
http://www.wpunj.edu/cob/
Public
Admissions: (973) 720-2237
E-mail: graduate@wpunj.edu
Financial aid: (973) 720-2202
Application deadline: rolling
In-state tuition: full time: $422/credit hour; part time: $422/credit hour
Out-of-state tuition: full time: $721/credit hour
Room/board/expenses: N/A
College-funded aid: Yes
International student aid: Yes
Full-time enrollment: 21
men: 43%; women: 57%; minorities: 33%; international: 19%
Part-time enrollment: 48
men: 65%; women: 35%; minorities: 23%; international: 2%
TOEFL requirement: Yes
Minimum TOEFL score: 550

NEW MEXICO

New Mexico State University
114 Guthrie Hall
MSC 3GSP
Las Cruces, NM 88003
http://www.nmsu.edu/
Public
Admissions: (505) 646-8003
E-mail: mba@nmsu.edu
Financial aid: (505) 646-4490
Application deadline: rolling
In-state tuition: full time: $200/credit hour; part time: $200/credit hour
Out-of-state tuition: full time: $600/credit hour
Room/board/expenses: $3,500
College-funded aid: Yes
International student aid: Yes
Average student indebtedness at graduation: $3,000
Full-time enrollment: 60
men: 67%; women: 33%; minorities: 83%; international: 42%
Part-time enrollment: 270
men: 56%; women: 44%; minorities: 52%; international: 4%
TOEFL requirement: Yes
Minimum TOEFL score: 530
Most popular departments: finance, general management, international business, other

University of New Mexico (Anderson)
1924 Las Lomas NE
Albuquerque, NM 87131
http://www.mgt.unm.edu
Public
Admissions: (505) 277-3147
E-mail: mba@mgt.unm.edu
Financial aid: (505) 277-7045
Application deadline: 06/01
In-state tuition: full time: N/A; part time: $265/credit hour
Out-of-state tuition: full time: N/A
Room/board/expenses: N/A
College-funded aid: Yes
International student aid: Yes
Full-time enrollment: N/A
men: N/A; women: N/A; minorities: N/A; international: N/A
Part-time enrollment: 389
men: 44%; women: 56%; minorities: 35%; international: 10%
Average GMAT (part-time): 545
TOEFL requirement: Yes
Minimum TOEFL score: 550
Most popular departments: accounting, finance, human resources management, marketing, management information systems

NEW YORK

Adelphi University
1 South Avenue
Garden City, NY 11530
http://www.adelphi.edu
Private
Admissions: (516) 877-3050
E-mail: admissions@adelphi.edu
Financial aid: (516) 877-3038
Application deadline: N/A
Tuition: full time: N/A; part time: $755/credit hour
Room/board/expenses: N/A
Full-time enrollment: N/A
men: N/A; women: N/A; minorities: N/A; international: N/A
Part-time enrollment: 250
men: 50%; women: 50%; minorities: 24%; international: 18%
Average GMAT (part-time): 424
Minimum TOEFL score: N/A
Most popular departments: finance, general management, health care administration, human resources management, marketing

Alfred University[1]
Saxon Drive
Alfred, NY 14802
http://business.alfred.edu/mba.html
Private
Admissions: (800) 541-9229
E-mail: gradinquiry@alfred.edu
Financial aid: (607) 871-2159
Tuition: N/A
Room/board/expenses: N/A
Enrollment: N/A

Binghamton University
PO Box 6000
Binghamton, NY 13902-6000
http://som.binghamton.edu/
Public
Admissions: (607) 777-2317
E-mail: somadvis@binghamton.edu
Financial aid: (607) 777-2470
Application deadline: 06/30
In-state tuition: full time: $8,119; part time: $296/credit hour
Out-of-state tuition: full time: $12,359
Room/board/expenses: $8,500
College-funded aid: Yes
International student aid: Yes
Average student indebtedness at graduation: $23,500
Full-time enrollment: 115
men: 65%; women: 35%; minorities: 7%; international: 53%
Part-time enrollment: N/A
men: N/A; women: N/A; minorities: N/A; international: N/A
Acceptance rate (full-time): 72%
Average GMAT (full-time): 617
Average GPA (full-time): 3.46
Average age of entrants to full-time program: 23
Average months of prior work experience (full-time): 19
TOEFL requirement: Yes
Minimum TOEFL score: 590
Most popular departments: finance, marketing
Mean starting base salary for 2007 full-time graduates: $57,273
Employment location for 2007 class: Intl. N/A; N.E. 95%; M.A. N/A; S. N/A; M.W. N/A; S.W. N/A; W. 5%

Canisius College (Wehle)
2001 Main Street
Buffalo, NY 14208
http://www.canisius.edu/mba
Private
Admissions: (800) 543-7906
E-mail: gradubus@canisius.edu
Financial aid: (716) 888-2300
Application deadline: rolling
Tuition: total program: $32,574 (full-time); part time: $651/credit hour
Room/board/expenses: N/A
College-funded aid: Yes
International student aid: Yes
Full-time enrollment: 85
men: 49%; women: 51%; minorities: 11%; international: 15%
Part-time enrollment: 196
men: 58%; women: 42%; minorities: 6%; international: 4%
Acceptance rate (full-time): 61%
Average GMAT (full-time): 517
Average GMAT (part-time): 517
Average GPA (full-time): 3.15

Average age of entrants to full-time program: 24
TOEFL requirement: Yes
Minimum TOEFL score: 500

Clarkson University

Snell Hall 322E, Box 5770
Potsdam, NY 13699-5770
http://www.clarkson.edu/business/graduate
Private
Admissions: (315) 268-6613
E-mail: busgrad@clarkson.edu
Financial aid: (315) 268-7699
Application deadline: rolling
Tuition: full time: $33,215; part time: $949/credit hour
Room/board/expenses: $9,500
College-funded aid: Yes
International student aid: Yes
Average student indebtedness at graduation: $34,930
Full-time enrollment: 44
men: 66%; women: 34%;
minorities: 0%; international: 16%
Part-time enrollment: 6
men: 33%; women: 67%;
minorities: 17%; international: 0%
Acceptance rate (full-time): 79%
Average GMAT (full-time): 550
Average GMAT (part-time): 513
Average GPA (full-time): 3.29
Average age of entrants to full-time program: 24
Average months of prior work experience (full-time): 24
TOEFL requirement: Yes
Minimum TOEFL score: 600
Mean starting base salary for 2007 full-time graduates: $58,365
Employment location for 2007 class: Intl. 3%; N.E. 73%; M.A. 0%; S. 15%; M.W. 6%; S.W. 0%; W. 3%

Columbia University

3022 Broadway
216 Uris Hall
New York, NY 10027
http://www.gsb.columbia.edu
Private
Admissions: (212) 854-1961
E-mail: apply@gsb.columbia.edu
Financial aid: (212) 854-4057
Application deadline: 04/22
Tuition: full time: $45,422; part time: N/A
Room/board/expenses: $25,242
College-funded aid: Yes
International student aid: Yes
Full-time enrollment: 1,226
men: 66%; women: 34%;
minorities: 22%; international: 33%
Part-time enrollment: N/A
men: N/A; women: N/A;
minorities: N/A; international: N/A
Acceptance rate (full-time): 16%
Average GMAT (full-time): 707
Average GPA (full-time): 3.40
Average age of entrants to full-time program: 28
Average months of prior work experience (full-time): 58
TOEFL requirement: Yes
Minimum TOEFL score: N/A
Most popular departments: consulting, entrepreneurship, finance, general management, marketing
Mean starting base salary for 2007 full-time graduates: $107,265

Cornell University (Johnson)

Sage Hall
Ithaca, NY 14853-6201
http://www.johnson.cornell.edu
Private
Admissions: (607) 255-4526
E-mail: mba@cornell.edu
Financial aid: (607) 255-6116
Application deadline: N/A
Tuition: full time: $44,260; part time: N/A
Room/board/expenses: $19,700

College-funded aid: Yes
International student aid: Yes
Average student indebtedness at graduation: $73,800
Full-time enrollment: 609
men: 75%; women: 25%;
minorities: 20%; international: 30%
Part-time enrollment: N/A
men: N/A; women: N/A;
minorities: N/A; international: N/A
Acceptance rate (full-time): 27%
Average GMAT (full-time): 682
Average GPA (full-time): 3.31
Average age of entrants to full-time program: 28
Average months of prior work experience (full-time): 57
TOEFL requirement: Yes
Minimum TOEFL score: 600
Most popular departments: consulting, entrepreneurship, finance, general management, marketing
Mean starting base salary for 2007 full-time graduates: $98,000
Employment location for 2007 class: Intl. 8%; N.E. 56%; M.A. 5%; S. 2%; M.W. 12%; S.W. 3%; W. 14%

CUNY Bernard M. Baruch College (Zicklin)

1 Bernard Baruch Way
New York, NY 10010
http://zicklin.baruch.cuny.edu
Public
Admissions: (646) 312-1300
E-mail: zicklingradadmissions@baruch.cuny.edu
Financial aid: (646) 312-1370
Application deadline: 05/31
In-state tuition: full time: $10,538; part time: $400/credit hour
Out-of-state tuition: full time: $600/credit hour
Room/board/expenses: $17,613
College-funded aid: Yes
International student aid: Yes
Average student indebtedness at graduation: $30,000
Full-time enrollment: 104
men: 53%; women: 47%;
minorities: 21%; international: 44%
Part-time enrollment: 1,462
men: 59%; women: 41%;
minorities: 29%; international: 22%
Acceptance rate (full-time): 36%
Average GMAT (full-time): 633
Average GMAT (part-time): 570
Average GPA (full-time): 3.00
Average age of entrants to full-time program: 29
Average months of prior work experience (full-time): 56
TOEFL requirement: Yes
Minimum TOEFL score: 590
Most popular departments: accounting, finance, general management, international business, marketing
Mean starting base salary for 2007 full-time graduates: $71,299
Employment location for 2007 class: Intl. 4%; N.E. 96%; M.A. 0%; S. 0%; M.W. 0%; S.W. 0%; W. 0%

Fordham University

113 W. 60th Street
Room 624
New York, NY 10023
http://www.bnet.fordham.edu
Private
Admissions: (800) 825-4422
E-mail: admissionsgb@fordham.edu
Financial aid: (212) 636-6700
Application deadline: 06/01
Tuition: full time: $33,115; part time: $22,190
Room/board/expenses: N/A
College-funded aid: Yes
International student aid: No
Full-time enrollment: 365
men: 61%; women: 39%;
minorities: 15%; international: 13%

Part-time enrollment: 1,183
men: 60%; women: 40%;
minorities: 17%; international: 2%
Acceptance rate (full-time): 53%
Average GMAT (full-time): 603
Average GMAT (part-time): 584
Average GPA (full-time): 3.18
Average age of entrants to full-time program: 25
Average months of prior work experience (full-time): 61
TOEFL requirement: Yes
Minimum TOEFL score: 600
Most popular departments: accounting, finance, general management, marketing, management information systems
Mean starting base salary for 2007 full-time graduates: $80,900
Employment location for 2007 class: Intl. 6%; N.E. 89%; M.A. N/A; S. N/A; M.W. 3%; S.W. N/A; W. 3%

Hofstra University (Zarb)

134 Hofstra University
Weller Hall
Hempstead, NY 11549
http://www.hofstra.edu/graduate
Private
Admissions: (800) 463-7872
E-mail: gradstudent@hofstra.edu
Financial aid: (516) 463-6680
Application deadline: rolling
Tuition: full time: $820/credit hour; part time: $820/credit hour
Room/board/expenses: $14,985
College-funded aid: Yes
International student aid: Yes
Full-time enrollment: 167
men: 65%; women: 35%;
minorities: 16%; international: 28%
Part-time enrollment: 386
men: 58%; women: 42%;
minorities: 22%; international: 1%
Acceptance rate (full-time): 78%
Average GMAT (full-time): 528
Average GMAT (part-time): 512
Average GPA (full-time): 2.98
Average age of entrants to full-time program: 26
Average months of prior work experience (full-time): 66
TOEFL requirement: Yes
Minimum TOEFL score: 550
Most popular departments: accounting, finance, health care administration, marketing, management information systems
Mean starting base salary for 2007 full-time graduates: $68,000
Employment location for 2007 class: Intl. 0%; N.E. 96%; M.A. 0%; S. 0%; M.W. 4%; S.W. 0%; W. 0%

Iona College (Hagan)

715 North Avenue
New Rochelle, NY 10801
http://www.iona.edu/hagan
Private
Admissions: (914) 633-2288
E-mail: jfleurismond@iona.edu
Financial aid: (914) 633-2497
Application deadline: rolling
Tuition: full time: $712/credit hour; part time: $712/credit hour
Room/board/expenses: N/A
College-funded aid: Yes
International student aid: Yes
Average student indebtedness at graduation: $17,463
Full-time enrollment: N/A
men: N/A; women: N/A;
minorities: N/A; international: N/A
Part-time enrollment: 311
men: 57%; women: 43%;
minorities: 10%; international: 4%
Average GMAT (part-time): 450
TOEFL requirement: Yes
Minimum TOEFL score: 550

Ithaca College

430 Smiddy Hall
Ithaca, NY 14850-7170
http://www.ithaca.edu/gradstudies
Private
Admissions: (607) 274-3527
E-mail: gps@ithaca.edu
Financial aid: (607) 274-3131
Application deadline: N/A
Tuition: full time: $650/credit hour; part time: $650/credit hour
Room/board/expenses: N/A
College-funded aid: Yes
International student aid: Yes
Full-time enrollment: 21
men: 48%; women: 52%;
minorities: 14%; international: 10%
Part-time enrollment: 3
men: 67%; women: 33%;
minorities: 0%; international: 0%
Acceptance rate (full-time): 83%
Average GMAT (full-time): 531
Average GPA (full-time): 3.19
Average age of entrants to full-time program: 24
Average months of prior work experience (full-time): 24
TOEFL requirement: Yes
Minimum TOEFL score: 550

Long Island University– C.W. Post Campus

720 Northern Boulevard
Brookville, NY 11548-1300
http://www.liu.edu/postmba
Private
Admissions: (516) 299-2900
E-mail: enroll@cwpost.liu.edu
Financial aid: (516) 299-2338
Application deadline: 08/15
Tuition: full time: $835/credit hour; part time: $835/credit hour
Room/board/expenses: $6,000
College-funded aid: Yes
International student aid: Yes
Full-time enrollment: 119
men: 58%; women: 42%;
minorities: 13%; international: 50%
Part-time enrollment: 191
men: 62%; women: 38%;
minorities: 25%; international: 1%
Acceptance rate (full-time): 76%
Average GMAT (full-time): 460
Average GMAT (part-time): 440
Average GPA (full-time): 3.05
Average age of entrants to full-time program: 26
Average months of prior work experience (full-time): 42
TOEFL requirement: Yes
Minimum TOEFL score: 527
Most popular departments: accounting, general management, tax

Marist College

149 Dyson Center
Poughkeepsie, NY 12601
http://www.marist.edu/mba
Private
Admissions: (845) 575-3800
E-mail: graduate@marist.edu
Financial aid: (845) 575-3230
Application deadline: 07/01
Tuition: full time: $665/credit hour; part time: $665/credit hour
Room/board/expenses: $1,398
College-funded aid: Yes
International student aid: No
Full-time enrollment: N/A
men: N/A; women: N/A;
minorities: N/A; international: N/A
Part-time enrollment: 210
men: 63%; women: 37%;
minorities: 10%; international: 0%
Average GMAT (part-time): 532
TOEFL requirement: Yes
Minimum TOEFL score: 550
Most popular departments: accounting, finance, leadership, marketing, operations management

New York University (Stern)

44 W. Fourth Street
New York, NY 10012-1126
http://www.stern.nyu.edu
Private
Admissions: (212) 998-0600
E-mail: sternmba@stern.nyu.edu
Financial aid: (212) 998-0790
Application deadline: 03/15
Tuition: full time: $41,822; part time: $1,440/credit hour
Room/board/expenses: $28,222
College-funded aid: Yes
International student aid: Yes
Average student indebtedness at graduation: $64,141
Full-time enrollment: 839
men: 64%; women: 36%;
minorities: 24%; international: 36%
Part-time enrollment: 2,022
men: 66%; women: 34%;
minorities: 22%; international: 16%
Acceptance rate (full-time): 17%
Average GMAT (full-time): 700
Average GMAT (part-time): 676
Average GPA (full-time): 3.40
Average age of entrants to full-time program: 27
Average months of prior work experience (full-time): 60
TOEFL requirement: Yes
Minimum TOEFL score: N/A
Mean starting base salary for 2007 full-time graduates: $96,738
Employment location for 2007 class: Intl. 11%; N.E. 80%; M.A. 2%; S. 1%; M.W. 1%; S.W. 1%; W. 5%

Niagara University[1]

Second Floor, Library
Niagara University, NY 14109
http://www.niagara.edu/mba
Private
Admissions: (716) 286-8051
E-mail: wkh@niagara.edu
Financial aid: (716) 286-8686
Tuition: N/A
Room/board/expenses: N/A
Enrollment: N/A

Pace University (Lubin)

1 Pace Plaza
New York, NY 10038
http://www.pace.edu/lubin/
Private
Admissions: (212) 346-1531
E-mail: gradnyc@pace.edu
Financial aid: (914) 773-3751
Application deadline: rolling
Tuition: full time: $857/credit hour; part time: $857/credit hour
Room/board/expenses: $14,460
College-funded aid: Yes
International student aid: Yes
Average student indebtedness at graduation: $39,001
Full-time enrollment: 208
men: 50%; women: 50%;
minorities: 16%; international: 51%
Part-time enrollment: 565
men: 60%; women: 40%;
minorities: 23%; international: 20%
Acceptance rate (full-time): 52%
Average GMAT (full-time): 545
Average GMAT (part-time): 536
Average GPA (full-time): 3.17
Average age of entrants to full-time program: 27
TOEFL requirement: Yes
Minimum TOEFL score: 573
Most popular departments: accounting, finance, international business, marketing, management information systems
Employment location for 2007 class: Intl. 1%; N.E. 96%; M.A. N/A; S. N/A; M.W. 1%; S.W. N/A; W. 1%

Rensselaer Polytechnic Institute (Lally)

110 Eighth Street
Pittsburgh Bldg. 3218
Troy, NY 12180-3590
http://lallyschool.rpi.edu
Private
Admissions: (518) 276-6565
E-mail: lallymba@rpi.edu
Financial aid: (518) 276-6586
Application deadline: rolling
Tuition: full time: $36,702; part time: $1,454/credit hour
Room/board/expenses: $13,604
College-funded aid: Yes
International student aid: Yes
Full-time enrollment: 32
men: 69%; women: 31%; minorities: 16%; international: 28%
Part-time enrollment: 175
men: 63%; women: 37%; minorities: 25%; international: 1%
Acceptance rate (full-time): 73%
Average GMAT (full-time): 619
Average GMAT (part-time): 610
Average GPA (full-time): 3.20
Average age of entrants to full-time program: 27
Average months of prior work experience (full-time): 40
TOEFL requirement: Yes
Minimum TOEFL score: 600
Most popular departments: entrepreneurship, finance, manufacturing and technology management, technology, other
Mean starting base salary for 2007 full-time graduates: $68,441
Employment location for 2007 class: Intl. 6%; N.E. 72%; M.A. 11%; S. 6%; M.W. 0%; S.W. 0%; W. 6%

Rochester Institute of Technology (Saunders)

105 Lomb Memorial Drive
Rochester, NY 14623-5608
http://www.cob.rit.edu
Private
Admissions: (585) 475-7284
E-mail: gradinfo@rit.edu
Financial aid: (585) 475-2186
Application deadline: rolling
Tuition: full time: $28,974; part time: $800/credit hour
Room/board/expenses: $10,000
College-funded aid: Yes
International student aid: Yes
Full-time enrollment: 77
men: 61%; women: 39%; minorities: 0%; international: 51%
Part-time enrollment: 38
men: 68%; women: 32%; minorities: 0%; international: 5%
Acceptance rate (full-time): 97%
Average GMAT (full-time): 545
Average GMAT (part-time): 520
Average GPA (full-time): 3.22
Average age of entrants to full-time program: 27
TOEFL requirement: Yes
Minimum TOEFL score: 580
Employment location for 2007 class: Intl. N/A; N.E. 93%; M.A. 2%; S. N/A; M.W. N/A; S.W. 2%; W. 2%

St. Bonaventure University[1]

St. Bonaventure, NY 14778
http://www.sbu.edu/go/academics/business/graduate/index.htm
Private
Admissions: (716) 375-2021
E-mail: gradsch@sbu.edu
Financial aid: (716) 375-2528
Tuition: N/A
Room/board/expenses: N/A
Enrollment: N/A

St. John Fisher University (Bittner)

3690 East Avenue
Rochester, NY 14618
http://www.sjfc.edu/bittner/
Private
Admissions: (585) 385-8068
E-mail: grad@sjfc.edu
Financial aid: N/A
Application deadline: rolling
Tuition: full time: $46,050; part time: $803/credit hour
Room/board/expenses: N/A
College-funded aid: No
International student aid: No
Average student indebtedness at graduation: $33,253
Full-time enrollment: 23
men: 48%; women: 52%; minorities: 26%; international: 0%
Part-time enrollment: 70
men: 57%; women: 43%; minorities: 10%; international: 0%
Acceptance rate (full-time): 86%
Average GMAT (full-time): 428
Average GMAT (part-time): 422
Average GPA (full-time): 3.11
Average age of entrants to full-time program: 35
TOEFL requirement: Yes
Minimum TOEFL score: 575

St. John's University (Tobin)

8000 Utopia Parkway
Queens, NY 11439
http://www.stjohns.edu/tobincollege
Private
Admissions: (718) 990-1345
E-mail: mbaadmissions@stjohns.edu
Financial aid: (718) 990-2000
Application deadline: 07/02
Tuition: full time: $835/credit hour; part time: $835/credit hour
Room/board/expenses: $16,000
College-funded aid: Yes
International student aid: Yes
Full-time enrollment: 276
men: 50%; women: 50%; minorities: 13%; international: 46%
Part-time enrollment: 446
men: 54%; women: 46%; minorities: 13%; international: 22%
Acceptance rate (full-time): 71%
Average GMAT (full-time): 530
Average GMAT (part-time): 530
Average GPA (full-time): 3.25
Average age of entrants to full-time program: 26
Average months of prior work experience (full-time): 24
TOEFL requirement: Yes
Minimum TOEFL score: 600
Most popular departments: accounting, finance, insurance, organizational behavior, tax
Mean starting base salary for 2007 full-time graduates: $65,000

SUNY–Albany

1400 Washington Avenue
Albany, NY 12222
http://www.albany.edu/business
Public
Admissions: (518) 442-4961
E-mail: busweb@uamail.albany.edu
Financial aid: (518) 442-5757
Application deadline: 03/15
In-state tuition: full time: $8,320; part time: $296/credit hour
Out-of-state tuition: full time: $12,560
Room/board/expenses: $13,000
College-funded aid: Yes
International student aid: No
Full-time enrollment: 70
men: 50%; women: 50%; minorities: 7%; international: 40%
Part-time enrollment: 215
men: N/A; women: N/A; minorities: N/A; international: N/A
Acceptance rate (full-time): 44%
Average GMAT (full-time): 566
Average GMAT (part-time): 581
Average GPA (full-time): 3.40
Average age of entrants to full-time program: 24
TOEFL requirement: Yes
Minimum TOEFL score: 580
Most popular departments: entrepreneurship, finance, general management, human resources management, management information systems
Mean starting base salary for 2007 full-time graduates: $54,000
Employment location for 2007 class: Intl. N/A; N.E. 92%; M.A. N/A; S. N/A; M.W. 3%; S.W. 3%; W. 3%

SUNY–Oswego

238 Rich Hall
Oswego, NY 13126
http://www.oswego.edu/academics/colleges_and_departments/business/index.html
Public
Admissions: (315) 312-3152
E-mail: gradoff@oswego.edu
Financial aid: (315) 312-2248
Application deadline: rolling
In-state tuition: full time: $7,875; part time: $296/credit hour
Out-of-state tuition: full time: $12,115
Room/board/expenses: $11,470
College-funded aid: Yes
International student aid: Yes
Average student indebtedness at graduation: $29,993
Full-time enrollment: 43
men: 44%; women: 56%; minorities: 7%; international: 35%
Part-time enrollment: 23
men: 52%; women: 48%; minorities: 4%; international: 17%
Acceptance rate (full-time): 87%
Average GMAT (full-time): 516
Average GMAT (part-time): 500
Average GPA (full-time): 3.29
Average age of entrants to full-time program: 28
TOEFL requirement: Yes
Minimum TOEFL score: 560

Syracuse University (Whitman)

721 University Avenue
Suite 315
Syracuse, NY 13244-2450
http://whitman.syr.edu
Private
Admissions: (315) 443-9214
E-mail: mbainfo@syr.edu
Financial aid: (315) 443-9214
Application deadline: 05/01
Tuition: full time: $31,234; part time: $1,012/credit hour
Room/board/expenses: $17,021
College-funded aid: Yes
International student aid: Yes
Average student indebtedness at graduation: $36,482
Full-time enrollment: 76
men: 64%; women: 36%; minorities: 7%; international: 51%
Part-time enrollment: 229
men: 69%; women: 31%; minorities: 22%; international: 7%
Acceptance rate (full-time): 50%
Average GMAT (full-time): 615
Average GPA (full-time): 3.36
Average age of entrants to full-time program: 25
Average months of prior work experience (full-time): 26
TOEFL requirement: Yes
Minimum TOEFL score: 600
Most popular departments: accounting, entrepreneurship, finance, marketing, supply chain management
Mean starting base salary for 2007 full-time graduates: $58,059
Employment location for 2007 class: Intl. 12%; N.E. 82%; M.A. N/A; S. N/A; M.W. N/A; S.W. N/A; W. 6%

Union Graduate College

807 Union Street
Schenectady, NY 12308-3107
http://www.uniongraduatecollege.edu
Private
Admissions: (518) 388-6238
E-mail: sheehanr@union.edu
Financial aid: (518) 388-6123
Application deadline: rolling
Tuition: full time: $690/credit hour; part time: $690/credit hour
Room/board/expenses: $15,000
College-funded aid: Yes
International student aid: Yes
Average student indebtedness at graduation: $21,200
Full-time enrollment: 106
men: 54%; women: 46%; minorities: 6%; international: 8%
Part-time enrollment: 172
men: 53%; women: 47%; minorities: 8%; international: 4%
Acceptance rate (full-time): 94%
Average GMAT (full-time): 550
Average GMAT (part-time): 550
Average GPA (full-time): 3.25
Average age of entrants to full-time program: 23
Average months of prior work experience (full-time): 17
TOEFL requirement: Yes
Minimum TOEFL score: 550
Most popular departments: finance, general management, health care administration, human resources management, marketing
Mean starting base salary for 2007 full-time graduates: $54,000
Employment location for 2007 class: Intl. N/A; N.E. 90%; M.A. N/A; S. 5%; M.W. 5%; S.W. N/A; W. N/A

University at Buffalo–SUNY

203 Alfiero Center
Buffalo, NY 14260-4010
http://www.mgt.buffalo.edu
Public
Admissions: (716) 645-3204
E-mail: som-apps@buffalo.edu
Financial aid: (716) 645-2450
Application deadline: 05/01
In-state tuition: full time: $9,007; part time: $600/credit hour
Out-of-state tuition: full time: $13,247
Room/board/expenses: $12,940
College-funded aid: Yes
International student aid: Yes
Full-time enrollment: 202
men: 52%; women: 48%; minorities: 5%; international: 40%
Part-time enrollment: 206
men: 69%; women: 31%; minorities: 7%; international: 12%
Acceptance rate (full-time): 45%
Average GMAT (full-time): 619
Average GMAT (part-time): 580
Average GPA (full-time): 3.30
Average age of entrants to full-time program: 25
Average months of prior work experience (full-time): 29
TOEFL requirement: Yes
Minimum TOEFL score: 570
Most popular departments: accounting, consulting, finance, international business, marketing
Mean starting base salary for 2007 full-time graduates: $54,282
Employment location for 2007 class: Intl. 7%; N.E. 82%; M.A. 1%; S. 6%; M.W. 1%; S.W. 3%; W. 0%

University of Rochester (Simon)

Schlegel Hall
Rochester, NY 14627
http://www.simon.rochester.edu
Private
Admissions: (585) 275-3533
E-mail: admissions@simon.rochester.edu
Financial aid: (585) 275-3533
Application deadline: 06/01
Tuition: full time: $37,791; part time: $1,228/credit hour
Room/board/expenses: $14,835
College-funded aid: Yes
International student aid: Yes
Average student indebtedness at graduation: $27,903
Full-time enrollment: 296
men: 70%; women: 30%; minorities: 11%; international: 54%
Part-time enrollment: 170
men: 76%; women: 24%; minorities: 11%; international: 12%
Acceptance rate (full-time): 41%
Average GMAT (full-time): 673
Average GMAT (part-time): 585
Average GPA (full-time): 3.52
Average age of entrants to full-time program: 26
Average months of prior work experience (full-time): 53
TOEFL requirement: Yes
Minimum TOEFL score: N/A
Most popular departments: entrepreneurship, finance, international business, marketing, operations management
Mean starting base salary for 2007 full-time graduates: $84,137
Employment location for 2007 class: Intl. 16%; N.E. 64%; M.A. N/A; S. 1%; M.W. 13%; S.W. 3%; W. 3%

NORTH CAROLINA

Appalachian State University (Walker)

Box 32037
Boone, NC 28608-2037
http://www.business.appstate.edu/grad/mba.asp
Public
Admissions: (828) 262-2130
E-mail: mba@appstate.edu
Financial aid: (828) 262-2190
Application deadline: 03/01
In-state tuition: full time: $7,623; part time: $144/credit hour
Out-of-state tuition: full time: $18,624
Room/board/expenses: $6,500
College-funded aid: Yes
International student aid: Yes
Full-time enrollment: 8
men: 50%; women: 50%; minorities: 0%; international: 0%
Part-time enrollment: 14
men: 64%; women: 36%; minorities: 0%; international: 0%
Acceptance rate (full-time): 59%
Average GMAT (full-time): 540
Average GPA (full-time): 3.10
Average age of entrants to full-time program: 25
TOEFL requirement: Yes
Minimum TOEFL score: 550

Duke University (Fuqua)

Box 90104
Durham, NC 27708-0104
http://www.fuqua.duke.edu
Private
Admissions: (919) 660-7705
E-mail: admissions-info@fuqua.duke.edu
Financial aid: (919) 660-7687
Application deadline: N/A
Tuition: full time: $45,663; part time: N/A
Room/board/expenses: $17,540
College-funded aid: Yes

International student aid: Yes
Average student indebtedness at graduation: $82,154
Full-time enrollment: 838
men: 67%; women: 33%; minorities: 20%; international: 38%
Part-time enrollment: N/A
men: N/A; women: N/A; minorities: N/A; international: N/A
Acceptance rate (full-time): 31%
Average GMAT (full-time): 690
Average GPA (full-time): 3.38
Average age of entrants to full-time program: 29
Average months of prior work experience (full-time): 66
TOEFL requirement: Yes
Minimum TOEFL score: N/A
Most popular departments: accounting, economics, finance, health care administration, marketing
Mean starting base salary for 2007 full-time graduates: $98,510
Employment location for 2007 class: Intl. 11%; N.E. 28%; M.A. 7%; S. 21%; M.W. 15%; S.W. 4%; W. 13%

East Carolina University
Greenville, NC 27858-4353
http://www.business.ecu.edu/grad/
Public
Admissions: (252) 328-6970
E-mail: gradbus@ecu.edu
Financial aid: (252) 328-6610
Application deadline: rolling
In-state tuition: full time: $5,779; part time: $218/credit hour
Out-of-state tuition: full time: $16,094
Room/board/expenses: N/A
College-funded aid: Yes
International student aid: Yes
Full-time enrollment: 247
men: N/A; women: N/A; minorities: N/A; international: N/A
Part-time enrollment: 358
men: N/A; women: N/A; minorities: N/A; international: N/A
TOEFL requirement: Yes
Minimum TOEFL score: 550

Elon University (Love)
100 Campus Drive
Elon, NC 27244-2010
http://www.elon.edu/mba
Private
Admissions: (800) 334-8448
E-mail: elonmba@elon.edu
Financial aid: (800) 334-8448
Application deadline: rolling
Tuition: full time: N/A; part time: N/A
Room/board/expenses: N/A
College-funded aid: Yes
International student aid: No
Average student indebtedness at graduation: $19,111
Full-time enrollment: N/A
men: N/A; women: N/A; minorities: N/A; international: N/A
Part-time enrollment: 131
men: 67%; women: 33%; minorities: 14%; international: 5%
Average GMAT (part-time): 550
TOEFL requirement: Yes
Minimum TOEFL score: 550

Fayetteville State University
1200 Murchison Road
Newbold Station
Fayetteville, NC 28301-1033
http://www.uncfsu.edu/sbe/academics/graduate.asp
Private
Admissions: (910) 672-1197
E-mail: mbaprogram@uncfsu.edu
Financial aid: N/A
Application deadline: 12/10
Tuition: full time: $3,336; part time: $278/credit hour

Room/board/expenses: $6,500
College-funded aid: Yes
International student aid: No
Average student indebtedness at graduation: $3,336
Full-time enrollment: N/A
men: N/A; women: N/A; minorities: N/A; international: N/A
Part-time enrollment: 100
men: 41%; women: 59%; minorities: 45%; international: 11%
Average GMAT (part-time): 500
TOEFL requirement: Yes
Minimum TOEFL score: 500
Most popular departments: accounting, entrepreneurship, general management, health care administration, marketing

North Carolina A&T State University[1]
1601 E. Market Street
Greensboro, NC 27411
http://www.ncat.edu/~business/
Public
Admissions: N/A
Financial aid: N/A
Tuition: N/A
Room/board/expenses: N/A
Enrollment: N/A

North Carolina Central University[1]
School of Business
Durham, NC 27707
http://ariel.acc.nccu.edu/business/
Private
Admissions: (919) 530-6100
E-mail: mba@nccu.edu
Financial aid: N/A
Tuition: N/A
Room/board/expenses: N/A
Enrollment: N/A

North Carolina State University (Jenkins)
2130 Nelson Hall
Campus Box 8114
Raleigh, NC 27695-8114
http://www.mba.ncsu.edu
Public
Admissions: (919) 515-5584
E-mail: mba@ncsu.edu
Financial aid: (919) 515-2421
Application deadline: 03/02
In-state tuition: full time: $12,261; part time: $8,131
Out-of-state tuition: full time: $24,184
Room/board/expenses: $15,000
College-funded aid: Yes
International student aid: Yes
Average student indebtedness at graduation: $28,723
Full-time enrollment: 76
men: 67%; women: 33%; minorities: 12%; international: 33%
Part-time enrollment: 297
men: 73%; women: 27%; minorities: 14%; international: 13%
Acceptance rate (full-time): 47%
Average GMAT (full-time): 608
Average GMAT (part-time): 573
Average GPA (full-time): 3.33
Average age of entrants to full-time program: 28
Average months of prior work experience (full-time): 44
TOEFL requirement: Yes
Minimum TOEFL score: 600
Most popular departments: consulting, entrepreneurship, finance, supply chain management, technology
Mean starting base salary for 2007 full-time graduates: $72,568
Employment location for 2007 class: Intl. 0%; N.E. 3%; M.A. 9%; S. 69%; M.W. 0%; S.W. 16%; W. 3%

Queens University of Charlotte (McColl)[1]
McColl School of Business
1900 Selwyn Avenue
Charlotte, NC 28274
http://mccoll.queens.edu
Private
Admissions: (704) 337-2352
Financial aid: N/A
Tuition: N/A
Room/board/expenses: N/A
Enrollment: N/A

University of North Carolina–Chapel Hill (Kenan-Flagler)
CB 3490
McColl Building
Chapel Hill, NC 27599-3490
http://www.kenan-flagler.unc.edu
Public
Admissions: (919) 962-3236
E-mail: mba_info@unc.edu
Financial aid: (919) 962-9096
Application deadline: 03/07
In-state tuition: full time: $21,508; part time: N/A
Out-of-state tuition: full time: $39,882
Room/board/expenses: $20,840
College-funded aid: Yes
International student aid: Yes
Average student indebtedness at graduation: $70,366
Full-time enrollment: 568
men: 72%; women: 28%; minorities: 14%; international: 28%
Part-time enrollment: N/A
men: N/A; women: N/A; minorities: N/A; international: N/A
Acceptance rate (full-time): 39%
Average GMAT (full-time): 681
Average GPA (full-time): 3.27
Average age of entrants to full-time program: 29
Average months of prior work experience (full-time): 67
TOEFL requirement: Yes
Minimum TOEFL score: 600
Most popular departments: consulting, finance, general management, marketing, supply chain management
Mean starting base salary for 2007 full-time graduates: $92,505
Employment location for 2007 class: Intl. 3%; N.E. 26%; M.A. 8%; S. 40%; M.W. 11%; S.W. 4%; W. 8%

University of North Carolina–Charlotte (Belk)
9201 University City Boulevard
Charlotte, NC 28223
http://www.belkcollege.uncc.edu
Public
Admissions: (704) 687-7566
E-mail: mba@uncc.edu
Financial aid: (704) 687-2461
Application deadline: rolling
In-state tuition: total program: $15,000 (full-time); $21,000 (part-time)
Out-of-state tuition: total program: $30,000 (full-time)
Room/board/expenses: N/A
College-funded aid: Yes
International student aid: Yes
Full-time enrollment: 14
men: 64%; women: 36%; minorities: 14%; international: 7%
Part-time enrollment: 291
men: 65%; women: 35%; minorities: 9%; international: 15%
Acceptance rate (full-time): 45%
Average GMAT (full-time): 572
Average GMAT (part-time): 590
Average GPA (full-time): 3.03
Average age of entrants to full-time program: 25

Average months of prior work experience (full-time): 36
TOEFL requirement: Yes
Minimum TOEFL score: 550
Most popular departments: finance, general management, international business, real estate, sports business

University of North Carolina–Greensboro (Bryan)
PO Box 26165
Greensboro, NC 27402-6165
http://www.mybryanmba.com
Public
Admissions: (336) 334-5390
E-mail: mybryanmba@uncg.edu
Financial aid: (336) 334-5702
Application deadline: 07/01
In-state tuition: full time: $6,093; part time: $304/credit hour
Out-of-state tuition: full time: $17,143
Room/board/expenses: $13,634
College-funded aid: Yes
International student aid: Yes
Full-time enrollment: 39
men: 51%; women: 49%; minorities: 5%; international: 31%
Part-time enrollment: 156
men: 63%; women: 37%; minorities: 13%; international: 21%
Acceptance rate (full-time): 70%
Average GMAT (full-time): 550
Average GMAT (part-time): 571
Average GPA (full-time): 3.20
Average age of entrants to full-time program: 23
Average months of prior work experience (full-time): 12
TOEFL requirement: Yes
Minimum TOEFL score: 550
Most popular departments: finance, human resources management, marketing, operations management, organizational behavior

University of North Carolina–Wilmington (Cameron)
601 S. College Road
Wilmington, NC 28403-5920
http://www.csb.uncw.edu/mba/index.stm
Public
Admissions: (910) 962-3903
E-mail: ericksonk@uncw.edu
Financial aid: (910) 962-3177
Application deadline: 03/01
In-state tuition: full time: N/A; total program: $11,000 (part-time)
Out-of-state tuition: full time: N/A
Room/board/expenses: N/A
College-funded aid: Yes
International student aid: Yes
Average student indebtedness at graduation: $12,000
Full-time enrollment: N/A
men: N/A; women: N/A; minorities: N/A; international: N/A
Part-time enrollment: 84
men: 52%; women: 48%; minorities: 2%; international: 4%
Average GMAT (part-time): 559
TOEFL requirement: Yes
Minimum TOEFL score: 550
Most popular departments: entrepreneurship, finance, human resources management

Wake Forest University (Babcock)
PO Box 7659
Winston-Salem, NC 27109-7659
http://www.mba.wfu.edu
Private
Admissions: (336) 758-5422
E-mail: admissions@mba.wfu.edu
Financial aid: (336) 758-4424

Application deadline: 05/01
Tuition: full time: $33,550; part time: $30,315
Room/board/expenses: $15,280
College-funded aid: Yes
International student aid: Yes
Average student indebtedness at graduation: $39,443
Full-time enrollment: 153
men: 67%; women: 33%; minorities: 10%; international: 25%
Part-time enrollment: 236
men: 74%; women: 26%; minorities: 22%; international: 1%
Acceptance rate (full-time): 50%
Average GMAT (full-time): 632
Average GMAT (part-time): 568
Average GPA (full-time): 3.10
Average age of entrants to full-time program: 28
Average months of prior work experience (full-time): 54
TOEFL requirement: Yes
Minimum TOEFL score: 600
Most popular departments: consulting, finance, general management, marketing, operations management
Mean starting base salary for 2007 full-time graduates: $81,013
Employment location for 2007 class: Intl. N/A; N.E. 14%; M.A. 19%; S. 51%; M.W. 5%; S.W. 9%; W. 2%

Wake Forest University (Calloway)[1]
PO Box 7285 Reynolds Station
Winston-Salem, NC 27109-7285
http://www.wfu.edu/calloway
Private
Admissions: (336) 758-5304
E-mail: calloway@wfu.edu
Financial aid: N/A
Tuition: N/A
Room/board/expenses: N/A
Enrollment: N/A

Western Carolina University
Belk Building
Cullowhee, NC 28723
http://www.wcu.edu/cob/mba/
Public
Admissions: (828) 227-3227
E-mail: shenson@email.wcu.edu
Financial aid: (828) 227-7290
Application deadline: rolling
In-state tuition: full time: $4,943; part time: $5,173
Out-of-state tuition: full time: $14,528
Room/board/expenses: $11,500
College-funded aid: Yes
International student aid: Yes
Full-time enrollment: 34
men: 47%; women: 53%; minorities: 6%; international: 18%
Part-time enrollment: 60
men: 60%; women: 40%; minorities: 7%; international: 2%
Acceptance rate (full-time): 80%
Average GMAT (full-time): 535
Average GMAT (part-time): 547
Average GPA (full-time): 3.41
Average age of entrants to full-time program: 25
Average months of prior work experience (full-time): 62
TOEFL requirement: Yes
Minimum TOEFL score: 550
Most popular departments: entrepreneurship, health care administration, human resources management, other

Winston-Salem State University[1]

RJR Center Suite 109
Winston-Salem, NC 27110
http://www.wssu.edu/WSSU/GraduateStudies/Graduate+Programs/MBA/
Public
Admissions: (336) 750-3045
E-mail: graduate@wssu.edu
Financial aid: (336) 750-3280
Tuition: N/A
Room/board/expenses: N/A
Enrollment: N/A

NORTH DAKOTA

North Dakota State University

PO Box 5137
Fargo, ND 58105
http://www.ndsu.nodak.edu/cba/mba
Public
Admissions: (701) 231-7681
E-mail: paul.brown@ndsu.edu
Financial aid: (800) 726-3188
Application deadline: rolling
In-state tuition: full time: N/A; part time: N/A
Out-of-state tuition: full time: N/A
Room/board/expenses: N/A
College-funded aid: Yes
International student aid: Yes
Full-time enrollment: 21
men: 62%; women: 38%; minorities: 14%; international: 71%
Part-time enrollment: 101
men: 50%; women: 50%; minorities: 8%; international: 5%
Acceptance rate (full-time): 56%
Average GMAT (full-time): 550
Average GMAT (part-time): 550
Average GPA (full-time): 3.40
Average age of entrants to full-time program: 25
Average months of prior work experience (full-time): 36
TOEFL requirement: Yes
Minimum TOEFL score: 550
Most popular departments: accounting, finance, general management, human resources management, marketing

University of North Dakota

PO Box 8098
Grand Forks, ND 58202-8098
http://www.und.nodak.edu/dept/grad/mbahome.htm
Public
Admissions: (701) 777-2784
E-mail: gradschool@mail.und.nodak.edu
Financial aid: (701) 777-3121
Application deadline: rolling
In-state tuition: full time: $225/credit hour; part time: $225/credit hour
Out-of-state tuition: full time: $601/credit hour
Room/board/expenses: $13,600
College-funded aid: Yes
International student aid: Yes
Full-time enrollment: 58
men: 64%; women: 36%; minorities: 19%; international: 29%
Part-time enrollment: 85
men: 55%; women: 45%; minorities: 13%; international: 9%
Acceptance rate (full-time): 55%
Average GMAT (full-time): 510
Average GPA (full-time): 3.17
Average age of entrants to full-time program: 25
TOEFL requirement: Yes
Minimum TOEFL score: 550

OHIO

Bowling Green State University

Bowling Green, OH 43403
http://www.cba.bgsu.edu/cba/welcomegradprogrm.html
Public
Admissions: (800) 247-8622
E-mail: mba-info@bgsu.edu
Financial aid: (419) 372-2651
Application deadline: 02/15
In-state tuition: total program: $22,398 (full-time); part time: $543/credit hour
Out-of-state tuition: total program: $37,014 (full-time)
Room/board/expenses: $10,918
College-funded aid: Yes
International student aid: Yes
Full-time enrollment: 48
men: 58%; women: 42%; minorities: 4%; international: 63%
Part-time enrollment: N/A
men: N/A; women: N/A; minorities: N/A; international: N/A
Average GMAT (full-time): 542
Average GPA (full-time): 3.20
TOEFL requirement: Yes
Minimum TOEFL score: 550

Case Western Reserve University (Weatherhead)

Peter B. Lewis Building
10900 Euclid Avenue
Cleveland, OH 44106-7235
http://www.weatherhead.case.edu
Private
Admissions: (216) 368-2030
E-mail: mbainfo@case.edu
Financial aid: (216) 368-8907
Application deadline: rolling
Tuition: full time: $33,650; part time: $1,366/credit hour
Room/board/expenses: $18,621
College-funded aid: Yes
International student aid: Yes
Average student indebtedness at graduation: $51,674
Full-time enrollment: 162
men: 69%; women: 31%; minorities: 9%; international: 48%
Part-time enrollment: 403
men: 61%; women: 39%; minorities: 15%; international: 8%
Acceptance rate (full-time): 67%
Average GMAT (full-time): 611
Average GMAT (part-time): 543
Average GPA (full-time): 3.20
Average age of entrants to full-time program: 27
Average months of prior work experience (full-time): 41
TOEFL requirement: Yes
Minimum TOEFL score: 600
Most popular departments: consulting, finance, general management, health care administration, organizational behavior
Mean starting base salary for 2007 full-time graduates: $72,949
Employment location for 2007 class: Intl. N/A; N.E. N/A; M.A. 4%; S. N/A; M.W. 92%; S.W. N/A; W. 4%

Cleveland State University (Nance)

1860 E. 18th Street
BU420
Cleveland, OH 44114
http://www.csuohio.edu/mba
Public
Admissions: (216) 687-5599
E-mail: cbacsu@csuohio.edu
Financial aid: (216) 687-3764
Application deadline: 07/07
In-state tuition: full time: $10,536; part time: $439/credit hour
Out-of-state tuition: full time: $20,016
Room/board/expenses: $9,500
College-funded aid: Yes
International student aid: Yes
Average student indebtedness at graduation: N/A
Full-time enrollment: 147
men: 59%; women: 41%; minorities: 18%; international: 29%
Part-time enrollment: 494
men: 60%; women: 40%; minorities: 14%; international: 4%
Acceptance rate (full-time): 72%
Average GMAT (full-time): 500
Average GMAT (part-time): 500
Average GPA (full-time): 3.15
Average age of entrants to full-time program: 25
Average months of prior work experience (full-time): 34
TOEFL requirement: Yes
Minimum TOEFL score: 550
Mean starting base salary for 2007 full-time graduates: $60,900
Employment location for 2007 class: Intl. 13%; N.E. 6%; M.A. 3%; S. 2%; M.W. 70%; S.W. 2%; W. 5%

John Carroll University

20700 N. Park Boulevard
University Heights, OH 44118
http://bsob.jcu.edu/graduatebusiness
Private
Admissions: (216) 397-1970
E-mail: ggannon@jcu.edu
Financial aid: (216) 397-4248
Application deadline: 07/14
Tuition: full time: N/A; part time: $793/credit hour
Room/board/expenses: N/A
College-funded aid: Yes
International student aid: Yes
Average student indebtedness at graduation: $11,097
Full-time enrollment: N/A
men: N/A; women: N/A; minorities: N/A; international: N/A
Part-time enrollment: 214
men: 57%; women: 43%; minorities: 4%; international: 2%
Average GMAT (part-time): 550
TOEFL requirement: Yes
Minimum TOEFL score: 550
Most popular departments: accounting, finance, general management, international business, marketing

Kent State University

PO Box 5190
Kent, OH 44242-0001
http://business.kent.edu/grad
Public
Admissions: (330) 672-2282
E-mail: gradbus@kent.edu
Financial aid: (330) 672-2972
Application deadline: 04/01
In-state tuition: full time: $8,968; part time: $408/credit hour
Out-of-state tuition: full time: $15,980
Room/board/expenses: $9,500
College-funded aid: Yes
International student aid: Yes
Full-time enrollment: 81
men: 47%; women: 53%; minorities: 11%; international: 25%
Part-time enrollment: 134
men: 58%; women: 42%; minorities: 4%; international: 1%
Acceptance rate (full-time): 83%
Average GMAT (full-time): 520
Average GMAT (part-time): 516
Average GPA (full-time): 3.36
Average age of entrants to full-time program: 23
TOEFL requirement: Yes
Minimum TOEFL score: 550
Most popular departments: accounting, finance, human resources management, marketing, management information systems
Mean starting base salary for 2007 full-time graduates: $48,371
Employment location for 2007 class: Intl. N/A; N.E. N/A; M.A. N/A; S. N/A; M.W. 100%; S.W. N/A; W. N/A

Miami University (Farmer)

104 Laws Hall
Oxford, OH 45056
http://mba.muohio.edu
Public
Admissions: (513) 529-6643
E-mail: miamimba@muohio.edu
Financial aid: (513) 529-8555
Application deadline: 03/17
In-state tuition: total program: $21,159 (full-time); part time: N/A
Out-of-state tuition: total program: $45,631 (full-time)
Room/board/expenses: $20,786
College-funded aid: Yes
International student aid: Yes
Average student indebtedness at graduation: $10,000
Full-time enrollment: 27
men: 52%; women: 48%; minorities: 19%; international: 19%
Part-time enrollment: N/A
men: N/A; women: N/A; minorities: N/A; international: N/A
Acceptance rate (full-time): 56%
Average GMAT (full-time): 558
Average GPA (full-time): 3.20
Average age of entrants to full-time program: 29
Average months of prior work experience (full-time): 67
TOEFL requirement: Yes
Minimum TOEFL score: 550
Mean starting base salary for 2007 full-time graduates: $67,643
Employment location for 2007 class: Intl. N/A; N.E. 7%; M.A. N/A; S. 7%; M.W. 79%; S.W. 7%; W. N/A

Ohio State University (Fisher)

100 Gerlach Hall
2108 Neil Avenue
Columbus, OH 43210-1144
http://fishermba.osu.edu
Public
Admissions: (614) 292-8511
E-mail: mba@fisher.osu.edu
Financial aid: (614) 292-8511
Application deadline: 05/30
In-state tuition: full time: $21,183; part time: $678/credit hour
Out-of-state tuition: full time: $35,337
Room/board/expenses: $21,306
College-funded aid: Yes
International student aid: Yes
Average student indebtedness at graduation: $28,574
Full-time enrollment: 273
men: 71%; women: 29%; minorities: 11%; international: 33%
Part-time enrollment: 324
men: 73%; women: 27%; minorities: 23%; international: 10%
Acceptance rate (full-time): 30%
Average GMAT (full-time): 661
Average GMAT (part-time): 614
Average GPA (full-time): 3.41
Average age of entrants to full-time program: 27
Average months of prior work experience (full-time): 51
TOEFL requirement: Yes
Minimum TOEFL score: 600
Most popular departments: consulting, finance, marketing, operations management, supply chain management
Mean starting base salary for 2007 full-time graduates: $87,446
Employment location for 2007 class: Intl. 9%; N.E. 9%; M.A. 1%; S. 3%; M.W. 70%; S.W. 4%; W. 4%

Ohio University

514 Copeland Hall
Athens, OH 45701
http://www.cob.ohiou.edu
Public
Admissions: (740) 593-2053
E-mail: rossj@ohio.edu
Financial aid: (740) 593-4141
Application deadline: 02/01
In-state tuition: full time: $12,675; part time: $387/credit hour
Out-of-state tuition: full time: $25,995
Room/board/expenses: $15,000
College-funded aid: Yes
International student aid: Yes
Full-time enrollment: 54
men: 70%; women: 30%; minorities: 17%; international: 19%
Part-time enrollment: 58
men: 59%; women: 41%; minorities: 2%; international: 16%
Acceptance rate (full-time): 46%
Average GMAT (full-time): 533
Average GPA (full-time): 3.30
Average age of entrants to full-time program: 25
Average months of prior work experience (full-time): 15
TOEFL requirement: Yes
Minimum TOEFL score: 600
Most popular departments: consulting, health care administration, sports business

University of Akron

CBA 412
Akron, OH 44325-4805
http://www.uakron.edu/cba/grad/
Public
Admissions: (330) 972-7043
E-mail: gradcba@uakron.edu
Financial aid: (330) 972-7032
Application deadline: 08/01
In-state tuition: full time: $402/credit hour; part time: $402/credit hour
Out-of-state tuition: full time: $647/credit hour
Room/board/expenses: $12,000
College-funded aid: Yes
International student aid: Yes
Full-time enrollment: 160
men: 55%; women: 45%; minorities: 5%; international: 50%
Part-time enrollment: 163
men: 66%; women: 34%; minorities: 2%; international: 5%
Acceptance rate (full-time): 89%
Average GMAT (full-time): 546
Average GMAT (part-time): 545
Average GPA (full-time): 3.23
Average age of entrants to full-time program: 27
Average months of prior work experience (full-time): 48
TOEFL requirement: Yes
Minimum TOEFL score: 550
Most popular departments: finance, general management, international business, marketing, supply chain management
Mean starting base salary for 2007 full-time graduates: $50,450
Employment location for 2007 class: Intl. 17%; N.E. 6%; M.A. 0%; S. 0%; M.W. 61%; S.W. 6%; W. 11%

University of Cincinnati

606 Lindner Hall
Cincinnati, OH 45221-0020
http://www.business.uc.edu/mba
Public
Admissions: (513) 556-7024
E-mail: graduate@uc.edu
Financial aid: (513) 556-6982
Application deadline: 04/01
In-state tuition: total program: $23,404 (full-time); part time: $497/credit hour
Out-of-state tuition: total program: $28,808 (full-time)
Room/board/expenses: $19,000
College-funded aid: Yes

International student aid: Yes
Average student indebtedness at graduation: $16,503
Full-time enrollment: 80
men: 69%; women: 31%;
minorities: 8%; international: 40%
Part-time enrollment: 284
men: 63%; women: 37%;
minorities: 16%; international: 5%
Acceptance rate (full-time): 75%
Average GMAT (full-time): 567
Average GMAT (part-time): 563
Average GPA (full-time): 3.20
Average age of entrants to full-time program: 27
Average months of prior work experience (full-time): 41
TOEFL requirement: Yes
Minimum TOEFL score: 600
Most popular departments: finance, general management, international business, marketing, other
Mean starting base salary for 2007 full-time graduates: $62,350
Employment location for 2007 class: Intl. 0%; N.E. 0%; M.A. 0%; S. 5%; M.W. 95%; S.W. 0%; W. 0%

University of Dayton

300 College Park Avenue
Dayton, OH 45469-2234
http://www.sba.udayton.edu/mba
Private
Admissions: (937) 229-3733
E-mail: mba@udayton.edu
Financial aid: (937) 229-4311
Application deadline: rolling
Tuition: full time: N/A; part time: $694/credit hour
Room/board/expenses: N/A
College-funded aid: Yes
International student aid: Yes
Full-time enrollment: N/A
men: N/A; women: N/A;
minorities: N/A; international: N/A
Part-time enrollment: 460
men: 65%; women: 35%;
minorities: N/A; international: N/A
Average GMAT (part-time): 560
TOEFL requirement: Yes
Minimum TOEFL score: 550

University of Toledo

Room 1033
Stranahan Hall
Toledo, OH 43606-3390
http://utoledo.edu/business/gradprograms/
Public
Admissions: (419) 530-2775
E-mail: mba@utoledo.edu
Financial aid: (419) 530-5800
Application deadline: 08/01
In-state tuition: full time: $448/credit hour; part time: $448/credit hour
Out-of-state tuition: full time: $815/credit hour
Room/board/expenses: $8,500
College-funded aid: Yes
International student aid: Yes
Full-time enrollment: 165
men: 59%; women: 41%;
minorities: 5%; international: 30%
Part-time enrollment: 143
men: 72%; women: 28%;
minorities: 9%; international: 5%
Acceptance rate (full-time): 60%
Average GMAT (part-time): 550
Average age of entrants to full-time program: 25
TOEFL requirement: Yes
Minimum TOEFL score: 550
Most popular departments: finance, general management, international business, marketing, management information systems
Mean starting base salary for 2007 full-time graduates: $61,545

Wright State University (Soin)

3640 Colonel Glenn Highway
Dayton, OH 45435
http://www.wright.edu/business
Public
Admissions: (937) 775-2437
E-mail: mba_director@wright.edu
Financial aid: (937) 775-5721
Application deadline: 07/01
In-state tuition: full time: N/A; part time: $310/credit hour
Out-of-state tuition: full time: N/A
Room/board/expenses: $9,000
College-funded aid: Yes
International student aid: Yes
Average student indebtedness at graduation: $6,000
Full-time enrollment: N/A
men: N/A; women: N/A;
minorities: N/A; international: N/A
Part-time enrollment: 494
men: 58%; women: 42%;
minorities: 13%; international: 19%
Average GMAT (part-time): 530
TOEFL requirement: Yes
Minimum TOEFL score: 550
Most popular departments: finance, general management, international business, marketing, management information systems

Xavier University (Williams)

3800 Victory Parkway
Cincinnati, OH 45207-3221
http://www.xavier.edu/MBA
Private
Admissions: (513) 745-3525
E-mail: xumba@xu.edu
Financial aid: (513) 745-3142
Application deadline: 08/01
Tuition: full time: $655/credit hour; part time: $655/credit hour
Room/board/expenses: $2,000
College-funded aid: Yes
International student aid: Yes
Average student indebtedness at graduation: $30,130
Full-time enrollment: N/A
men: N/A; women: N/A;
minorities: N/A; international: N/A
Part-time enrollment: 994
men: 66%; women: 34%;
minorities: 18%; international: 3%
Average GMAT (part-time): 550
TOEFL requirement: Yes
Minimum TOEFL score: 550
Most popular departments: finance, general management, international business, marketing, other

Youngstown State University (Williamson)[1]

1 University Plaza
Youngstown, OH 44555
http://www.wcba.ysu.edu
Public
Admissions: (330) 941-3091
E-mail: graduateschool@cc.ysu.edu
Financial aid: (330) 941-3505
Tuition: N/A
Room/board/expenses: N/A
Enrollment: N/A

Oklahoma State University (Spears)

102 Gundersen
Stillwater, OK 74078-4011
http://spears.okstate.edu/mba
Public
Admissions: (405) 744-2951
E-mail: mba-osu@okstate.edu
Financial aid: (405) 744-6604
Application deadline: 07/01
In-state tuition: full time: $148/credit hour; part time: $148/credit hour

Out-of-state tuition: full time: $555/credit hour
Room/board/expenses: $10,440
College-funded aid: Yes
International student aid: Yes
Full-time enrollment: 111
men: 62%; women: 38%;
minorities: 8%; international: 21%
Part-time enrollment: 296
men: 60%; women: 40%;
minorities: 11%; international: 1%
Acceptance rate (full-time): 73%
Average GMAT (full-time): 538
Average GMAT (part-time): 536
Average GPA (full-time): 3.34
Average age of entrants to full-time program: 24
TOEFL requirement: Yes
Minimum TOEFL score: 575
Mean starting base salary for 2007 full-time graduates: $54,163
Employment location for 2007 class: Intl. 0%; N.E. 7%; M.A. 4%; S. 0%; M.W. 7%; S.W. 81%; W. 0%

University of Oklahoma (Price)

Price Hall
1003 Asp Avenue
Suite 1040
Norman, OK 73019-4302
http://price.ou.edu/mba
Public
Admissions: (405) 325-4107
E-mail: gamundson@ou.edu
Financial aid: (405) 325-4521
Application deadline: 07/01
In-state tuition: full time: $144/credit hour; part time: $144/credit hour
Out-of-state tuition: full time: $518/credit hour
Room/board/expenses: $11,700
College-funded aid: Yes
International student aid: Yes
Full-time enrollment: 95
men: 71%; women: 29%;
minorities: 21%; international: 16%
Part-time enrollment: 149
men: 77%; women: 23%;
minorities: 21%; international: 6%
Acceptance rate (full-time): 72%
Average GMAT (full-time): 619
Average GMAT (part-time): 573
Average GPA (full-time): 3.50
Average age of entrants to full-time program: 25
Average months of prior work experience (full-time): 18
TOEFL requirement: Yes
Minimum TOEFL score: 600
Most popular departments: entrepreneurship, finance, management information systems, supply chain management, other
Mean starting base salary for 2007 full-time graduates: $71,833
Employment location for 2007 class: Intl. 0%; N.E. 13%; M.A. N/A; S. N/A; M.W. 9%; S.W. 70%; W. 9%

University of Tulsa

800 S. Tucker Drive
Tulsa, OK 74104-3189
http://www.cba.utulsa.edu
Private
Admissions: (918) 631-2242
E-mail: graduate-business@utulsa.edu
Financial aid: (918) 631-2526
Application deadline: 08/01
Tuition: full time: $778/credit hour; part time: $778/credit hour
Room/board/expenses: $9,604
College-funded aid: Yes
International student aid: Yes
Full-time enrollment: 75
men: 61%; women: 39%;
minorities: 7%; international: 25%
Part-time enrollment: 63
men: 75%; women: 25%;
minorities: 14%; international: 8%
Acceptance rate (full-time): 73%
Average GMAT (full-time): 564
Average GMAT (part-time): 572

Average GPA (full-time): 3.33
Average age of entrants to full-time program: 24
Average months of prior work experience (full-time): 24
TOEFL requirement: Yes
Minimum TOEFL score: 575
Most popular departments: accounting, finance, general management, marketing, management information systems
Mean starting base salary for 2007 full-time graduates: $59,340

Oregon State University

Bexell Hall 200
Corvallis, OR 97331
http://www.bus.oregonstate.edu
Public
Admissions: (541) 737-4411
E-mail: osuadmit@oregonstate.edu
Financial aid: (541) 737-2241
Application deadline: 06/01
In-state tuition: full time: $11,622; part time: $338/credit hour
Out-of-state tuition: full time: $17,292
Room/board/expenses: $11,454
College-funded aid: Yes
International student aid: Yes
Average student indebtedness at graduation: $21,350
Full-time enrollment: 80
men: 63%; women: 38%;
minorities: 10%; international: 19%
Part-time enrollment: N/A
men: N/A; women: N/A;
minorities: N/A; international: N/A
Average GMAT (full-time): 576
Average GPA (full-time): 3.27
Average age of entrants to full-time program: 27
TOEFL requirement: Yes
Minimum TOEFL score: 575
Most popular departments: entrepreneurship
Mean starting base salary for 2007 full-time graduates: $55,000
Employment location for 2007 class: Intl. 0%; N.E. 0%; M.A. 0%; S. 0%; M.W. 0%; S.W. 0%; W. 100%

Portland State University

PO Box 751
Portland, OR 97207-0751
http://www.mba.pdx.edu
Public
Admissions: (503) 725-4733
E-mail: pamm@sba.pdx.edu
Financial aid: (503) 725-5442
Application deadline: 06/01
In-state tuition: full time: $13,336; part time: $9,724
Out-of-state tuition: full time: $18,844
Room/board/expenses: $17,600
College-funded aid: Yes
International student aid: Yes
Full-time enrollment: 59
men: 63%; women: 37%;
minorities: 24%; international: 31%
Part-time enrollment: 235
men: 69%; women: 31%;
minorities: 15%; international: 8%
Acceptance rate (full-time): 60%
Average GMAT (full-time): 623
Average GMAT (part-time): 608
Average GPA (full-time): 3.18
Average age of entrants to full-time program: 29
Average months of prior work experience (full-time): 19
TOEFL requirement: Yes
Minimum TOEFL score: 550
Mean starting base salary for 2007 full-time graduates: $58,028
Employment location for 2007 class: Intl. 11%; N.E. 0%; M.A. 0%; S. 0%; M.W. 0%; S.W. 11%; W. 79%

University of Oregon (Lundquist)

1208 University of Oregon
Eugene, OR 97403-1208
http://oregonmba.com
Public
Admissions: (541) 346-3306
E-mail: info@oregonmba.com
Financial aid: (541) 346-3221
Application deadline: 03/15
In-state tuition: full time: $13,242; part time: $768/credit hour
Out-of-state tuition: full time: $17,994
Room/board/expenses: $11,394
College-funded aid: Yes
International student aid: Yes
Average student indebtedness at graduation: $39,500
Full-time enrollment: 101
men: 61%; women: 39%;
minorities: 5%; international: 26%
Part-time enrollment: N/A
men: N/A; women: N/A;
minorities: N/A; international: N/A
Acceptance rate (full-time): 63%
Average GMAT (full-time): 626
Average GPA (full-time): 3.32
Average age of entrants to full-time program: 28
Average months of prior work experience (full-time): 56
TOEFL requirement: Yes
Minimum TOEFL score: 600
Most popular departments: entrepreneurship, finance, marketing, sports business, supply chain management
Mean starting base salary for 2007 full-time graduates: $55,718
Employment location for 2007 class: Intl. N/A; N.E. 6%; M.A. N/A; S. 12%; M.W. N/A; S.W. 6%; W. 76%

University of Portland (Pamplin)

5000 N. Willamette Boulevard
Portland, OR 97203-5798
http://business.up.edu
Private
Admissions: (503) 943-7225
E-mail: mba-up@up.edu
Financial aid: (503) 943-7311
Application deadline: 07/01
Tuition: full time: $775/credit hour; part time: $775/credit hour
Room/board/expenses: N/A
College-funded aid: Yes
International student aid: Yes
Full-time enrollment: 57
men: 58%; women: 42%;
minorities: 21%; international: 68%
Part-time enrollment: 81
men: 62%; women: 38%;
minorities: 12%; international: 6%
Acceptance rate (full-time): 76%
Average GMAT (full-time): 540
Average GMAT (part-time): 540
Average GPA (full-time): 3.30
Average age of entrants to full-time program: 24
Average months of prior work experience (full-time): 18
TOEFL requirement: Yes
Minimum TOEFL score: 570
Most popular departments: entrepreneurship, finance, general management, health care administration, marketing

Willamette University (Atkinson)

900 State Street
Salem, OR 97301-3922
http://www.willamette.edu/mba
Private
Admissions: (503) 370-6167
E-mail: mba-admission@willamette.edu
Financial aid: (503) 370-6273
Application deadline: 05/01
Tuition: full time: $25,280; total program: $42,000 (part-time)

Room/board/expenses: $12,000
College-funded aid: Yes
International student aid: Yes
Average student indebtedness at graduation: $35,523
Full-time enrollment: 131
men: 63%; women: 37%;
minorities: 12%; international: 25%
Part-time enrollment: 98
men: 60%; women: 40%;
minorities: 14%; international: 1%
Acceptance rate (full-time): 86%
Average GMAT (full-time): 598
Average GMAT (part-time): 545
Average GPA (full-time): 3.32
Average age of entrants to full-time program: 25
Average months of prior work experience (full-time): 22
TOEFL requirement: Yes
Minimum TOEFL score: 570
Most popular departments: accounting, finance, general management, human resources management, marketing
Mean starting base salary for 2007 full-time graduates: $58,697
Employment location for 2007 class: Intl. 3%; N.E. 3%; M.A. 0%; S. 0%; M.W. 3%; S.W. 3%; W. 90%

PENNSYLVANIA

Bloomsburg University
Sutliff Hall
Room 212
400 Second Street
Bloomsburg, PA 17815-1301
http://cob.bloomu.edu/
Public
Admissions: N/A
Financial aid: N/A
Application deadline: rolling
In-state tuition: full time: $6,214;
part time: $345/credit hour
Out-of-state tuition: full time: $9,944
Room/board/expenses: N/A
College-funded aid: Yes
International student aid: Yes
Full-time enrollment: N/A
men: N/A; women: N/A;
minorities: N/A; international: N/A
Part-time enrollment: 61
men: N/A; women: N/A;
minorities: N/A; international: N/A
Average GMAT (full-time): 500
Average GPA (full-time): 3.00
TOEFL requirement: Yes
Minimum TOEFL score: 550

Carnegie Mellon University (Tepper)
5000 Forbes Avenue
Pittsburgh, PA 15213
http://www.tepper.cmu.edu
Private
Admissions: (412) 268-2272
E-mail: mba-admissions@andrew.cmu.edu
Financial aid: (412) 268-7581
Application deadline: 04/27
Tuition: full time: $45,644; part time: $495/credit hour
Room/board/expenses: $20,356
College-funded aid: Yes
International student aid: Yes
Full-time enrollment: 319
men: 76%; women: 24%;
minorities: 28%; international: 30%
Part-time enrollment: 366
men: 78%; women: 22%;
minorities: 23%; international: 14%
Acceptance rate (full-time): 30%
Average GMAT (full-time): 696
Average GMAT (part-time): 629
Average GPA (full-time): 3.32
Average age of entrants to full-time program: 28
Average months of prior work experience (full-time): 50
TOEFL requirement: Yes
Minimum TOEFL score: 600

Most popular departments: entrepreneurship, finance, marketing, operations management, other
Mean starting base salary for 2007 full-time graduates: $97,394
Employment location for 2007 class: Intl. 10%; N.E. 24%; M.A. 32%; S. 1%; M.W. 13%; S.W. 2%; W. 18%

Clarion University of Pennsylvania
Still Hall
Clarion, PA 16214
http://www.clarion.edu/mba
Public
Admissions: (814) 393-2605
E-mail: mba@clarion.edu
Financial aid: (814) 393-2315
Application deadline: rolling
In-state tuition: full time: $8,044;
part time: $345/credit hour
Out-of-state tuition: full time: $11,774
Room/board/expenses: $13,360
College-funded aid: Yes
International student aid: Yes
Full-time enrollment: 21
men: 76%; women: 24%;
minorities: 5%; international: 33%
Part-time enrollment: 30
men: 47%; women: 53%;
minorities: 3%; international: 0%
Average GMAT (full-time): 488
Average GMAT (part-time): 498
Average GPA (full-time): 3.21
TOEFL requirement: Yes
Minimum TOEFL score: 550

Drexel University (LeBow)
3141 Chestnut Street
Philadelphia, PA 19104
http://www.lebow.drexel.edu/
Private
Admissions: (215) 895-0562
E-mail: mba@drexel.edu
Financial aid: (215) 895-6395
Application deadline: 08/25
Tuition: total program: $50,100 (full-time); part time: $835/credit hour
Room/board/expenses: $15,000
College-funded aid: Yes
International student aid: Yes
Full-time enrollment: 201
men: 54%; women: 46%;
minorities: 15%; international: 52%
Part-time enrollment: 754
men: 63%; women: 37%;
minorities: 22%; international: 5%
Acceptance rate (full-time): 21%
Average GMAT (full-time): 600
Average GMAT (part-time): 605
Average GPA (full-time): 3.20
Average age of entrants to full-time program: 29
Average months of prior work experience (full-time): 80
TOEFL requirement: Yes
Minimum TOEFL score: 600
Most popular departments: accounting, entrepreneurship, finance, international business, marketing
Mean starting base salary for 2007 full-time graduates: $61,021
Employment location for 2007 class: Intl. 5%; N.E. 16%; M.A. 71%; S. 0%; M.W. 0%; S.W. 3%; W. 5%

Duquesne University (Donahue)
704 Rockwell Hall
Pittsburgh, PA 15282
http://www.bus.duq.edu/GRAD
Private
Admissions: (412) 396-6276
E-mail: grad-bus@duq.edu
Financial aid: (412) 396-6607
Application deadline: 05/01

Tuition: total program: $37,364 (full-time); part time: $774/credit hour
Room/board/expenses: $9,000
College-funded aid: Yes
International student aid: Yes
Full-time enrollment: 15
men: 60%; women: 40%;
minorities: 7%; international: 7%
Part-time enrollment: 318
men: 58%; women: 42%;
minorities: 5%; international: 8%
Average GMAT (full-time): 550
Average GMAT (part-time): 520
TOEFL requirement: Yes
Minimum TOEFL score: 550
Mean starting base salary for 2007 full-time graduates: $59,290
Employment location for 2007 class: Intl. N/A; N.E. N/A; M.A. N/A; S. N/A; M.W. N/A; S.W. N/A; W. N/A

Indiana University of Pennsylvania (Eberly)
664 Pratt Drive
Room 402
Indiana, PA 15705
http://www.eberly.iup.edu/mba
Public
Admissions: (724) 357-2522
E-mail: kjdavis@iup.edu
Financial aid: (724) 357-2218
Application deadline: N/A
In-state tuition: full time: $7,544;
part time: $345/credit hour
Out-of-state tuition: full time: $11,274
Room/board/expenses: $9,396
College-funded aid: Yes
International student aid: Yes
Full-time enrollment: 177
men: 68%; women: 32%;
minorities: 5%; international: 70%
Part-time enrollment: 128
men: 55%; women: 45%;
minorities: 1%; international: 70%
Acceptance rate (full-time): 71%
Average GMAT (full-time): 508
Average GMAT (part-time): 529
Average age of entrants to full-time program: 23
TOEFL requirement: Yes
Minimum TOEFL score: 550

King's College (McGowan)[1]
133 N. River Street
Wilkes-Barre, PA 18711
http://www.kings.edu/academics/mcgowan.htm
Private
Admissions: (570) 208-5991
E-mail: elizabethlott@kings.edu
Financial aid: N/A
Tuition: N/A
Room/board/expenses: N/A
Enrollment: N/A

La Salle University
1900 W. Olney Avenue
Philadelphia, PA 19141
http://www.lasalle.edu/mba
Private
Admissions: (215) 951-1057
E-mail: mba@lasalle.edu
Financial aid: (215) 951-1070
Application deadline: 08/15
Tuition: full time: $16,470; part time: $675/credit hour
Room/board/expenses: N/A
College-funded aid: Yes
International student aid: Yes
Full-time enrollment: 60
men: 50%; women: 50%;
minorities: 23%; international: 23%
Part-time enrollment: 470
men: 60%; women: 40%;
minorities: 15%; international: 0%
Acceptance rate (full-time): 42%
Average GPA (full-time): 3.30

Average age of entrants to full-time program: 24
TOEFL requirement: Yes
Minimum TOEFL score: 573
Most popular departments: accounting, finance, general management, marketing, other

Lehigh University
621 Taylor Street
Bethlehem, PA 18015
http://www.lehigh.edu/mba
Private
Admissions: (610) 758-5280
E-mail: mba.admissions@lehigh.edu
Financial aid: (610) 758-4450
Application deadline: 05/01
Tuition: full time: $630/credit hour;
part time: $630/credit hour
Room/board/expenses: $16,100
College-funded aid: Yes
International student aid: Yes
Average student indebtedness at graduation: $19,283
Full-time enrollment: 50
men: 66%; women: 34%;
minorities: 6%; international: 36%
Part-time enrollment: 228
men: 70%; women: 30%;
minorities: 13%; international: 7%
Acceptance rate (full-time): 58%
Average GMAT (full-time): 619
Average GMAT (part-time): 637
Average GPA (full-time): 3.09
Average age of entrants to full-time program: 29
Average months of prior work experience (full-time): 62
TOEFL requirement: Yes
Minimum TOEFL score: 600
Most popular departments: entrepreneurship, finance, manufacturing and technology management, marketing, supply chain management
Mean starting base salary for 2007 full-time graduates: $75,800
Employment location for 2007 class: Intl. 8%; N.E. 58%; M.A. 0%; S. 17%; M.W. 8%; S.W. 8%; W. 0%

Pennsylvania State University-Erie, The Behrend College (Black)
5101 Jordan Road
Erie, PA 16563
http://www.pennstatebehrend.psu.edu
Public
Admissions: (814) 898-7255
E-mail: behrend.admissions@psu.edu
Financial aid: (814) 898-6162
Application deadline: 07/22
In-state tuition: full time: $648/credit hour; part time: $648/credit hour
Out-of-state tuition: full time: $1,006/credit hour
Room/board/expenses: $9,970
College-funded aid: Yes
International student aid: Yes
Average student indebtedness at graduation: $24,817
Full-time enrollment: 42
men: 55%; women: 45%;
minorities: 10%; international: 2%
Part-time enrollment: 95
men: 63%; women: 37%;
minorities: 13%; international: 8%
Acceptance rate (full-time): 84%
Average GMAT (full-time): 519
Average GMAT (part-time): 534
Average GPA (full-time): 3.30
Average age of entrants to full-time program: 23
TOEFL requirement: Yes
Minimum TOEFL score: 550
Most popular departments: finance, international business, leadership, marketing, other

Pennsylvania State University-Great Valley
30 E. Swedesford Road
Malvern, PA 19335
http://www.gv.psu.edu
Public
Admissions: (610) 648-3242
E-mail: gvadmiss@psu.edu
Financial aid: (610) 648-3311
Application deadline: rolling
In-state tuition: full time: $736/credit hour; part time: $736/credit hour
Out-of-state tuition: full time: $1,195/credit hour
Room/board/expenses: $5,000
College-funded aid: Yes
International student aid: Yes
Full-time enrollment: N/A
men: N/A; women: N/A;
minorities: N/A; international: N/A
Part-time enrollment: 360
men: 61%; women: 39%;
minorities: 23%; international: 4%
Average GMAT (part-time): 525
TOEFL requirement: Yes
Minimum TOEFL score: 550
Most popular departments: entrepreneurship, finance, general management, health care administration, marketing

Pennsylvania State University-Harrisburg
777 W. Harrisburg Pike
Middletown, PA 17057-4898
http://www.hbg.psu.edu/hbg/programs/gradprog/badm.html
Public
Admissions: (717) 948-6250
E-mail: mbahbg@psu.edu
Financial aid: (717) 948-6307
Application deadline: 07/18
In-state tuition: full time: $648/credit hour; part time: $648/credit hour
Out-of-state tuition: full time: $1,006/credit hour
Room/board/expenses: N/A
College-funded aid: Yes
International student aid: Yes
Full-time enrollment: 22
men: 55%; women: 45%;
minorities: 18%; international: 23%
Part-time enrollment: 168
men: 67%; women: 33%;
minorities: 10%; international: 2%
Average GMAT (part-time): 547
TOEFL requirement: Yes
Minimum TOEFL score: 550

Pennsylvania State University-University Park (Smeal)
220 Business Building
University Park, PA 16802-3000
http://www.smeal.psu.edu/mba
Public
Admissions: (814) 863-0474
E-mail: smealmba@psu.edu
Financial aid: (814) 865-6301
Application deadline: 04/15
In-state tuition: full time: $18,520;
part time: N/A
Out-of-state tuition: full time: $30,122
Room/board/expenses: $16,428
College-funded aid: Yes
International student aid: Yes
Average student indebtedness at graduation: $11,058

Full-time enrollment: 171
men: 70%; women: 30%;
minorities: 19%; international: 35%
Part-time enrollment: N/A
men: N/A; women: N/A;
minorities: N/A; international: N/A
Acceptance rate (full-time): 30%
Average GMAT (full-time): 650
Average GPA (full-time): 3.30
Average age of entrants to full-time program: 28
Average months of prior work experience (full-time): 57
TOEFL requirement: Yes
Minimum TOEFL score: 600
Most popular departments: consulting, entrepreneurship, finance, marketing, supply chain management
Mean starting base salary for 2007 full-time graduates: $83,098
Employment location for 2007 class: Intl. 2%; N.E. 32%; M.A. 30%; S. 4%; M.W. 8%; S.W. 15%; W. 9%

Shippensburg University of Pennsylvania (Grove)

1871 Old Main Drive
Shippensburg, PA 17257
http://www.ship.edu/~business
Public
Admissions: (717) 477-1231
Financial aid: (717) 477-1131
Application deadline: rolling
In-state tuition: full time: N/A; part time: N/A
Out-of-state tuition: full time: N/A
Room/board/expenses: N/A
College-funded aid: Yes
International student aid: No
Full-time enrollment: 12
men: N/A; women: N/A;
minorities: N/A; international: N/A
Part-time enrollment: 158
men: N/A; women: N/A;
minorities: N/A; international: N/A
Acceptance rate (full-time): 44%
Average GMAT (part-time): 565
TOEFL requirement: No
Minimum TOEFL score: N/A

St. Joseph's University (Haub)

5600 City Avenue
Philadelphia, PA 19131
http://www.sju.edu
Private
Admissions: (610) 660-1101
E-mail: admit@sju.edu
Financial aid: (610) 660-1555
Application deadline: 07/15
Tuition: full time: $765/credit hour; part time: $765/credit hour
Room/board/expenses: N/A
College-funded aid: Yes
International student aid: Yes
Average student indebtedness at graduation: $16,250
Full-time enrollment: N/A
men: N/A; women: N/A;
minorities: N/A; international: N/A
Part-time enrollment: 974
men: 60%; women: 40%;
minorities: 13%; international: 6%
Average GMAT (part-time): 525
TOEFL requirement: Yes
Minimum TOEFL score: 550
Most popular departments: finance, general management, marketing, other

Temple University (Fox)

1810 N. 13th Street
Philadelphia, PA 19122-6083
http://www.sbm.temple.edu/mbams
Public
Admissions: (215) 204-7678
E-mail: foxgrad.info@temple.edu
Financial aid: (215) 204-8449
Application deadline: 06/01
In-state tuition: full time: $18,010; part time: $574/credit hour
Out-of-state tuition: full time: $26,245
Room/board/expenses: $15,000
College-funded aid: Yes
International student aid: Yes
Average student indebtedness at graduation: $19,000
Full-time enrollment: 100
men: 63%; women: 37%;
minorities: 6%; international: 36%
Part-time enrollment: 325
men: 67%; women: 33%;
minorities: 12%; international: 4%
Acceptance rate (full-time): 56%
Average GMAT (full-time): 645
Average GMAT (part-time): 608
Average GPA (full-time): 3.28
Average age of entrants to full-time program: 27
Average months of prior work experience (full-time): 43
TOEFL requirement: Yes
Minimum TOEFL score: 575
Most popular departments: finance, general management, health care administration, international business, marketing
Mean starting base salary for 2007 full-time graduates: $80,964
Employment location for 2007 class: Intl. 14%; N.E. 25%; M.A. 61%; S. N/A; M.W. N/A; S.W. N/A; W. N/A

University of Pennsylvania (Wharton)

420 Jon M. Huntsman Hall
3730 Walnut Street
Philadelphia, PA 19104
http://mba.wharton.upenn.edu/
Private
Admissions: (215) 898-6183
E-mail: mba.admissions@wharton.upenn.edu
Financial aid: (215) 898-6183
Application deadline: 02/28
Tuition: full time: $49,722; part time: N/A
Room/board/expenses: $22,226
College-funded aid: Yes
International student aid: Yes
Average student indebtedness at graduation: $93,500
Full-time enrollment: 1,620
men: 64%; women: 36%;
minorities: N/A; international: 45%
Part-time enrollment: N/A
men: N/A; women: N/A;
minorities: N/A; international: N/A
Acceptance rate (full-time): 17%
Average GMAT (full-time): 712
Average GPA (full-time): 3.53
Average age of entrants to full-time program: 28
TOEFL requirement: Yes
Minimum TOEFL score: N/A
Most popular departments: entrepreneurship, finance, health care administration, marketing, other
Mean starting base salary for 2007 full-time graduates: $110,551
Employment location for 2007 class: Intl. 18%; N.E. 47%; M.A. 8%; S. 4%; M.W. 4%; S.W. 3%; W. 16%

University of Pittsburgh (Katz)

372 Mervis Hall
Pittsburgh, PA 15260
http://www.katz.pitt.edu
Public
Admissions: (412) 648-1700
E-mail: mba@katz.pitt.edu
Financial aid: (412) 648-1700
Application deadline: 03/01
In-state tuition: total program: $29,676 (full-time); part time: $853/credit hour
Out-of-state tuition: total program: $44,416 (full-time)
Room/board/expenses: $13,200
College-funded aid: Yes
International student aid: Yes
Full-time enrollment: 228
men: 64%; women: 36%;
minorities: 5%; international: 50%
Part-time enrollment: 497
men: 65%; women: 35%;
minorities: 4%; international: 3%
Acceptance rate (full-time): 52%
Average GMAT (full-time): 615
Average GMAT (part-time): 566
Average GPA (full-time): 3.31
Average age of entrants to full-time program: 26
Average months of prior work experience (full-time): 37
TOEFL requirement: Yes
Minimum TOEFL score: 600
Most popular departments: finance, marketing, management information systems, organizational behavior, statistics and operations research
Mean starting base salary for 2007 full-time graduates: $72,000
Employment location for 2007 class: Intl. 6%; N.E. 12%; M.A. 54%; S. 8%; M.W. 10%; S.W. 4%; W. 8%

University of Scranton

800 Linden Street
Scranton, PA 18510-4632
http://matrix.scranton.edu/
Private
Admissions: (570) 941-7600
E-mail: goonanj1@scranton.edu
Financial aid: (570) 941-7700
Application deadline: rolling
Tuition: full time: N/A; part time: $728/credit hour
Room/board/expenses: $15,150
College-funded aid: Yes
International student aid: Yes
Average student indebtedness at graduation: $17,768
Full-time enrollment: N/A
men: N/A; women: N/A;
minorities: N/A; international: N/A
Part-time enrollment: 99
men: 74%; women: 26%;
minorities: 3%; international: 20%
Average GMAT (part-time): 521
TOEFL requirement: Yes
Minimum TOEFL score: 500
Most popular departments: accounting, finance, general management, management information systems, operations management

Villanova University[1]

Bartley Hall
800 Lancaster Avenue
Villanova, PA 19085
http://www.gradbusiness.villanova.edu
Private
Admissions: (610) 519-4336
E-mail: gradbusiness@villanova.edu
Financial aid: (610) 519-6456
Tuition: N/A
Room/board/expenses: N/A
Enrollment: N/A

West Chester University of Pennsylvania

1160 McDermott Drive
West Chester, PA 19383
http://www.wcupa.edu/_ADMISSIONS/SCH_DGR/
Public
Admissions: (610) 436-2943
E-mail: gradstudy@wcupa.edu
Financial aid: (610) 436-2627
Application deadline: rolling
In-state tuition: full time: $6,214; part time: $345/credit hour
Out-of-state tuition: full time: $9,944
Room/board/expenses: N/A
College-funded aid: Yes
International student aid: Yes
Full-time enrollment: N/A
men: N/A; women: N/A;
minorities: N/A; international: N/A
Part-time enrollment: 106
men: 60%; women: 40%;
minorities: 21%; international: 3%
Average GMAT (part-time): 516
TOEFL requirement: Yes
Minimum TOEFL score: 550
Most popular departments: accounting, general management

Widener University

1 University Place
Chester, PA 19013
http://www.widener.edu/sba
Private
Admissions: (610) 499-4305
E-mail: gradbus.advise@widener.edu
Financial aid: (610) 499-4174
Application deadline: rolling
Tuition: full time: $720/credit hour; part time: $720/credit hour
Room/board/expenses: N/A
College-funded aid: Yes
International student aid: Yes
Full-time enrollment: 10
men: 40%; women: 60%;
minorities: 20%; international: 10%
Part-time enrollment: 90
men: N/A; women: N/A;
minorities: N/A; international: N/A
Average GMAT (full-time): 573
Average GMAT (part-time): 530
TOEFL requirement: Yes
Minimum TOEFL score: 550

RHODE ISLAND

Bryant University

1150 Douglas Pike
Smithfield, RI 02917
http://www.bryant.edu/
Private
Admissions: (401) 232-6230
E-mail: gradprog@bryant.edu
Financial aid: (401) 232-6020
Application deadline: rolling
Tuition: full time: N/A; part time: $699/credit hour
Room/board/expenses: $2,800
College-funded aid: Yes
International student aid: Yes
Average student indebtedness at graduation: $23,823
Full-time enrollment: N/A
men: N/A; women: N/A;
minorities: N/A; international: N/A
Part-time enrollment: 267
men: 65%; women: 35%;
minorities: 6%; international: 4%
Average GMAT (part-time): 567
TOEFL requirement: Yes
Minimum TOEFL score: 580

University of Rhode Island

7 Lippitt Road
Kingston, RI 02881
http://www.cba.uri.edu/mba
Public
Admissions: (401) 874-5000
E-mail: hadz@uri.edu
Financial aid: (401) 874-9500
Application deadline: 04/15
In-state tuition: total program: $12,711 (full-time); part time: $385/credit hour
Out-of-state tuition: total program: $34,914 (full-time)
Room/board/expenses: $13,000
College-funded aid: Yes
International student aid: Yes
Full-time enrollment: 17
men: 71%; women: 29%;
minorities: N/A; international: N/A
Part-time enrollment: 153
men: 68%; women: 32%;
minorities: N/A; international: N/A
Acceptance rate (full-time): 78%
Average GMAT (full-time): 550
Average GMAT (part-time): 558
Average GPA (full-time): 3.34
Average age of entrants to full-time program: 26
TOEFL requirement: Yes
Minimum TOEFL score: 575
Most popular departments: accounting, finance, general management, marketing, supply chain management

SOUTH CAROLINA

The Citadel

171 Moultrie Street
Charleston, SC 29409
http://www.citadel.edu/csba/
Public
Admissions: (843) 953-5089
E-mail: cgc@citadel.edu
Financial aid: (843) 953-5187
Application deadline: 07/18
In-state tuition: full time: $280/credit hour; part time: $280/credit hour
Out-of-state tuition: full time: $503/credit hour
Room/board/expenses: N/A
College-funded aid: Yes
International student aid: Yes
Full-time enrollment: 31
men: 74%; women: 26%;
minorities: 3%; international: 0%
Part-time enrollment: 220
men: 61%; women: 39%;
minorities: 11%; international: 3%
Average GMAT (full-time): 493
Average GMAT (part-time): 501
Average age of entrants to full-time program: 25
TOEFL requirement: Yes
Minimum TOEFL score: 550
Most popular departments: health care administration, sports business, other

Clemson University

124 Sirrine Hall
PO Box 341315
Clemson, SC 29634-1315
http://business.clemson.edu/mba
Public
Admissions: (864) 656-3975
E-mail: mba@clemson.edu
Financial aid: (864) 656-2280
Application deadline: 06/15
In-state tuition: full time: $7,768; part time: $535/credit hour
Out-of-state tuition: full time: $15,056
Room/board/expenses: $26,360
College-funded aid: Yes
International student aid: Yes
Average student indebtedness at graduation: $7,776
Full-time enrollment: 56
men: 63%; women: 38%;
minorities: 7%; international: 30%
Part-time enrollment: 115
men: 71%; women: 29%;
minorities: 9%; international: 4%
Acceptance rate (full-time): 64%
Average GMAT (full-time): 595
Average GMAT (part-time): 557
Average GPA (full-time): 3.30
Average age of entrants to full-time program: 26
Average months of prior work experience (full-time): 43
TOEFL requirement: Yes
Minimum TOEFL score: 600
Most popular departments: entrepreneurship, health care administration, marketing, real estate, supply chain management
Mean starting base salary for 2007 full-time graduates: $69,333
Employment location for 2007 class: Intl. 7%; N.E. 0%; M.A. 7%; S. 79%; M.W. 7%; S.W. N/A; W. N/A

Coastal Carolina University (Wall)
PO Box 261954
Conway, SC 29528-6054
http://www.coastal.edu/admissions
Public
Admissions: (843) 349-2026
E-mail: admissions@coastal.edu
Financial aid: (843) 349-2313
Application deadline: 08/15
In-state tuition: full time: $9,704; part time: $401/credit hour
Out-of-state tuition: full time: $10,568
Room/board/expenses: $5,232
College-funded aid: Yes
International student aid: Yes
Full-time enrollment: 23
men: 61%; women: 39%; minorities: 17%; international: 13%
Part-time enrollment: 29
men: 52%; women: 48%; minorities: 7%; international: 3%
Acceptance rate (full-time): 100%
Average GMAT (full-time): 556
Average GMAT (part-time): 540
Average GPA (full-time): 3.52
Average age of entrants to full-time program: 26
TOEFL requirement: Yes
Minimum TOEFL score: 500

College of Charleston
Randolph Hall 310
Charleston, SC 29424
http://www.cofc.edu/sobe/
Public
Admissions: (843) 953-5614
E-mail: gradsch@cofc.edu
Financial aid: (843) 953-5540
Application deadline: 04/01
In-state tuition: full time: $324/credit hour; part time: $324/credit hour
Out-of-state tuition: full time: $781/credit hour
Room/board/expenses: N/A
College-funded aid: Yes
International student aid: Yes
Full-time enrollment: 57
men: 42%; women: 58%; minorities: 2%; international: 9%
Part-time enrollment: N/A
men: N/A; women: N/A; minorities: N/A; international: N/A
Acceptance rate (full-time): 71%
Average GMAT (full-time): 573
Average GPA (full-time): 3.47
Average age of entrants to full-time program: 25
TOEFL requirement: Yes
Minimum TOEFL score: 600
Mean starting base salary for 2007 full-time graduates: $47,142
Employment location for 2007 class: Intl. N/A; N.E. 3%; M.A. 3%; S. 94%; M.W. N/A; S.W. N/A; W. N/A

Francis Marion University
Box 100547
Florence, SC 29501
http://alpha1.fmarion.edu/~gradmba/
Public
Admissions: (843) 661-1419
E-mail: bkyer@fmarion.edu
Financial aid: (843) 661-1190
Application deadline: rolling
In-state tuition: full time: N/A; part time: N/A
Out-of-state tuition: full time: N/A
Room/board/expenses: N/A
College-funded aid: Yes
International student aid: Yes
Full-time enrollment: N/A
men: N/A; women: N/A; minorities: N/A; international: N/A
Part-time enrollment: 60
men: 50%; women: 50%; minorities: N/A; international: N/A
Average GMAT (part-time): 450
TOEFL requirement: Yes
Minimum TOEFL score: 550

South Carolina State University
300 College Street NE
Orangeburg, SC 29117
http://belcher.scsu.edu
Public
Admissions: (803) 536-8558
E-mail: admissions@scsu.edu
Financial aid: (803) 536-7067
Application deadline: 04/15
In-state tuition: full time: $7,278; part time: $404/credit hour
Out-of-state tuition: full time: $14,322
Room/board/expenses: N/A
College-funded aid: Yes
International student aid: Yes
Full-time enrollment: 10
men: 70%; women: 30%; minorities: 70%; international: 30%
Part-time enrollment: 1
men: 0%; women: 100%; minorities: 100%; international: 0%
Acceptance rate (full-time): 100%
Average GMAT (part-time): 500
Average age of entrants to full-time program: 24
Average months of prior work experience (full-time): 12
TOEFL requirement: Yes
Minimum TOEFL score: 550

University of South Carolina (Moore)
1705 College Street
Columbia, SC 29208
http://mooreschool.sc.edu/
Public
Admissions: (803) 777-4346
E-mail: gradadmit@moore.sc.edu
Financial aid: (803) 777-8134
Application deadline: 05/15
In-state tuition: total program: $35,000 (full-time); part time: $450/credit hour
Out-of-state tuition: total program: $52,000 (full-time)
Room/board/expenses: $18,000
College-funded aid: Yes
International student aid: Yes
Average student indebtedness at graduation: $21,500
Full-time enrollment: 214
men: 69%; women: 31%; minorities: 10%; international: 22%
Part-time enrollment: 353
men: 73%; women: 27%; minorities: 5%; international: 5%
Acceptance rate (full-time): 58%
Average GMAT (full-time): 638
Average GMAT (part-time): 604
Average GPA (full-time): 3.30
Average age of entrants to full-time program: 27
Average months of prior work experience (full-time): 41
TOEFL requirement: Yes
Minimum TOEFL score: 600
Most popular departments: entrepreneurship, finance, international business, marketing, supply chain management
Mean starting base salary for 2007 full-time graduates: $75,402
Employment location for 2007 class: Intl. 13%; N.E. 8%; M.A. 6%; S. 42%; M.W. 11%; S.W. 13%; W. 6%

Winthrop University[1]
Room 213
Thurmond Building
Rock Hill, SC 29733
http://cba.winthrop.edu
Public
Admissions: (803) 323-2409
E-mail: hagerp@winthrop.edu
Financial aid: (803) 323-2189
Tuition: N/A
Room/board/expenses: N/A
Enrollment: N/A

SOUTH DAKOTA

University of South Dakota
414 E. Clark Street
Vermillion, SD 57069
http://www.usd.edu/business/mba
Public
Admissions: (605) 677-5232
E-mail: mba@usd.edu
Financial aid: (605) 677-5446
Application deadline: 06/01
In-state tuition: full time: $125/credit hour; part time: $125/credit hour
Out-of-state tuition: full time: $369/credit hour
Room/board/expenses: N/A
College-funded aid: Yes
International student aid: Yes
Full-time enrollment: 92
men: 58%; women: 42%; minorities: 2%; international: 28%
Part-time enrollment: 107
men: 62%; women: 38%; minorities: 0%; international: 5%
Acceptance rate (full-time): 93%
Average GMAT (full-time): 555
Average GMAT (part-time): 520
Average GPA (full-time): 3.38
Average age of entrants to full-time program: 25
TOEFL requirement: Yes
Minimum TOEFL score: 550
Most popular departments: general management, health care administration

TENNESSEE

Belmont University (Massey)
1900 Belmont Boulevard
Nashville, TN 37212
http://www.belmont.edu/business/graduatebusiness
Private
Admissions: (615) 460-6480
E-mail: masseyadmissions@mail.belmont.edu
Financial aid: (615) 460-6403
Application deadline: 07/01
Tuition: full time: N/A; total program: $39,400 (part-time)
Room/board/expenses: N/A
College-funded aid: Yes
International student aid: Yes
Full-time enrollment: N/A
men: N/A; women: N/A; minorities: N/A; international: N/A
Part-time enrollment: 223
men: 57%; women: 43%; minorities: 11%; international: 3%
Average GMAT (part-time): 553
TOEFL requirement: Yes
Minimum TOEFL score: 550
Most popular departments: accounting, entrepreneurship, finance, general management, marketing

East Tennessee State University
PO Box 70699
Johnson City, TN 37614
http://www.etsu.edu/cbat
Public
Admissions: (423) 439-5314
E-mail: business@etsu.edu
Financial aid: (423) 439-4300
Application deadline: 06/01
In-state tuition: full time: $288/credit hour; part time: $288/credit hour
Out-of-state tuition: full time: $446/credit hour
Room/board/expenses: $5,000
College-funded aid: Yes
International student aid: Yes
Average student indebtedness at graduation: $2,000
Full-time enrollment: 25
men: 60%; women: 40%; minorities: 28%; international: 36%
Part-time enrollment: 52
men: 62%; women: 38%; minorities: 19%; international: 0%
Acceptance rate (full-time): 67%
Average GMAT (full-time): 535
Average GMAT (part-time): 535
Average GPA (full-time): 3.50
Average age of entrants to full-time program: 23
Average months of prior work experience (full-time): 36
TOEFL requirement: Yes
Minimum TOEFL score: 550
Most popular departments: accounting, entrepreneurship, finance, general management, health care administration

Middle Tennessee State University
PO Box 290
Murfreesboro, TN 37132
http://www.mtsu.edu
Public
Admissions: (615) 898-2964
E-mail: fester@mtsu.edu
Financial aid: (615) 898-2830
Application deadline: 07/01
In-state tuition: total program: $16,000 (full-time); $14,000 (part-time)
Out-of-state tuition: total program: $28,000 (full-time)
Room/board/expenses: $10,000
College-funded aid: Yes
International student aid: Yes
Full-time enrollment: 152
men: N/A; women: N/A; minorities: N/A; international: N/A
Part-time enrollment: 325
men: N/A; women: N/A; minorities: N/A; international: N/A
Average GMAT (part-time): 490
TOEFL requirement: Yes
Minimum TOEFL score: 525
Most popular departments: finance, health care administration, human resources management, industrial management, marketing

Tennessee State University
330 N. 10th Avenue
Nashville, TN 37203
http://www.cob.tnstate.edu/grad/gprograms.htm
Public
Admissions: (615) 963-7170
E-mail: rrussell3@tnstate.edu
Financial aid: (615) 963-7544
Application deadline: N/A
In-state tuition: full time: $6,714; part time: $4,520
Out-of-state tuition: full time: $16,990
Room/board/expenses: N/A
College-funded aid: Yes
International student aid: Yes
Full-time enrollment: 50
men: 50%; women: 50%; minorities: 60%; international: 20%
Part-time enrollment: 50
men: 50%; women: 50%; minorities: 60%; international: 0%
TOEFL requirement: Yes
Minimum TOEFL score: 500

Tennessee Technological University
Box 5023
Cookeville, TN 38505
http://www.tntech.edu/mba
Public
Admissions: (931) 372-3600
E-mail: mbastudies@tntech.edu
Financial aid: (931) 372-3073
Application deadline: 08/03
In-state tuition: full time: $347/credit hour; part time: $347/credit hour
Out-of-state tuition: full time: $793/credit hour
Room/board/expenses: $6,500
College-funded aid: Yes
International student aid: Yes
Average student indebtedness at graduation: $15,000
Full-time enrollment: 61
men: 56%; women: 44%; minorities: 2%; international: 8%
Part-time enrollment: 177
men: 60%; women: 40%; minorities: 5%; international: 3%
Acceptance rate (full-time): 79%
Average GMAT (full-time): 523
Average GMAT (part-time): 544
Average GPA (full-time): 3.31
Average age of entrants to full-time program: 25
Average months of prior work experience (full-time): 12
TOEFL requirement: Yes
Minimum TOEFL score: 550
Most popular departments: accounting, general management, human resources management, international business, management information systems

University of Memphis (Fogelman)
Memphis, TN 38152
http://fcbe.memphis.edu/
Public
Admissions: (901) 678-2911
E-mail: kweddle@memphis.edu
Financial aid: (901) 678-4825
Application deadline: 07/01
In-state tuition: full time: $349/credit hour; part time: $349/credit hour
Out-of-state tuition: full time: $797/credit hour
Room/board/expenses: $6,626
College-funded aid: Yes
International student aid: No
Average student indebtedness at graduation: $45,000
Full-time enrollment: 15
men: 53%; women: 47%; minorities: 13%; international: 0%
Part-time enrollment: 212
men: 55%; women: 45%; minorities: 16%; international: 35%
Acceptance rate (full-time): 89%
Average GMAT (full-time): 521
Average GMAT (part-time): 518
Average GPA (full-time): 3.16
Average age of entrants to full-time program: 37
Average months of prior work experience (full-time): 180
TOEFL requirement: Yes
Minimum TOEFL score: 550

University of Tennessee–Chattanooga
615 McCallie Avenue
Chattanooga, TN 37403
http://www.utc.edu/Academic/Business/
Public
Admissions: (423) 425-4210
E-mail: kim-turner@utc.edu
Financial aid: (423) 425-4677
Application deadline: rolling
In-state tuition: full time: N/A; part time: $393/credit hour
Out-of-state tuition: full time: N/A
Room/board/expenses: N/A
College-funded aid: Yes
International student aid: Yes
Full-time enrollment: N/A
men: N/A; women: N/A; minorities: N/A; international: N/A
Part-time enrollment: 237
men: 61%; women: 39%; minorities: 6%; international: 2%

Average GMAT (part-time): 511
TOEFL requirement: Yes
Minimum TOEFL score: 550

University of Tennessee–Knoxville

527 Stokely Management Center
Knoxville, TN 37996-0552
http://mba.utk.edu
Public
Admissions: (865) 974-5033
E-mail: mba@utk.edu
Financial aid: (865) 974-3131
Application deadline: 02/01
In-state tuition: total program: $20,081 (full-time); part time: N/A
Out-of-state tuition: total program: $38,444 (full-time)
Room/board/expenses: $13,000
College-funded aid: Yes
International student aid: Yes
Average student indebtedness at graduation: $8,000
Full-time enrollment: 151
men: 70%; women: 30%;
minorities: 7%; international: 18%
Part-time enrollment: N/A
men: N/A; women: N/A;
minorities: N/A; international: N/A
Acceptance rate (full-time): 59%
Average GMAT (full-time): 600
Average GPA (full-time): 3.35
Average age of entrants to full-time program: 27
Average months of prior work experience (full-time): 39
TOEFL requirement: Yes
Minimum TOEFL score: 600
Most popular departments: entrepreneurship, finance, marketing, operations management, supply chain management
Mean starting base salary for 2007 full-time graduates: $66,190
Employment location for 2007 class: Intl. 0%; N.E. 3%; M.A. 3%; S. 69%; M.W. 15%; S.W. 5%; W. 5%

University of Tennessee–Martin

103 Business Administration Building
Martin, TN 38238
http://www.utm.edu/departments/cbpa/mba
Public
Admissions: (731) 881-7012
E-mail: larant@utm.edu
Financial aid: (731) 881-7040
Application deadline: 08/10
In-state tuition: full time: $275/credit hour; part time: $275/credit hour
Out-of-state tuition: full time: $833/credit hour
Room/board/expenses: N/A
College-funded aid: Yes
International student aid: Yes
Full-time enrollment: 17
men: 53%; women: 47%;
minorities: 0%; international: 18%
Part-time enrollment: 56
men: 55%; women: 45%;
minorities: 11%; international: 5%
Acceptance rate (full-time): 86%
Average GMAT (full-time): 518
Average GMAT (part-time): 548
Average GPA (full-time): 3.10
Average age of entrants to full-time program: 25
Average months of prior work experience (full-time): 35
TOEFL requirement: Yes
Minimum TOEFL score: 525
Most popular departments: general management

Vanderbilt University (Owen)

401 21st Avenue S
Nashville, TN 37203
http://www.owen.vanderbilt.edu
Private
Admissions: (615) 322-6469
E-mail: admissions@owen.vanderbilt.edu
Financial aid: (615) 322-3591
Application deadline: 05/15
Tuition: full time: $38,552; part time: N/A
Room/board/expenses: $20,568
College-funded aid: Yes
International student aid: Yes
Average student indebtedness at graduation: $78,346
Full-time enrollment: 378
men: 73%; women: 27%;
minorities: 8%; international: 25%
Part-time enrollment: N/A
men: N/A; women: N/A;
minorities: N/A; international: N/A
Acceptance rate (full-time): 47%
Average GMAT (full-time): 644
Average GPA (full-time): 3.27
Average age of entrants to full-time program: 28
Average months of prior work experience (full-time): 56
TOEFL requirement: Yes
Minimum TOEFL score: 600
Most popular departments: finance, general management, health care administration, marketing, other
Mean starting base salary for 2007 full-time graduates: $89,268
Employment location for 2007 class: Intl. 11%; N.E. 18%; M.A. 5%; S. 47%; M.W. 8%; S.W. 5%; W. 6%

TEXAS

Abilene Christian University

ACU Box 29300
Abilene, TX 79699-9300
http://www.acu.edu/academics/coba.html
Private
Admissions: (325) 674-2245
E-mail: coba@acu.edu
Financial aid: N/A
Application deadline: rolling
Tuition: full time: $17,410; part time: $557/credit hour
Room/board/expenses: $10,540
College-funded aid: Yes
International student aid: Yes
Full-time enrollment: 36
men: 67%; women: 33%;
minorities: 8%; international: 14%
Part-time enrollment: 5
men: 40%; women: 60%;
minorities: 20%; international: 20%
Acceptance rate (full-time): 88%
Average GPA (full-time): 3.46
Average age of entrants to full-time program: 24
TOEFL requirement: Yes
Minimum TOEFL score: 525
Mean starting base salary for 2007 full-time graduates: $44,700
Employment location for 2007 class: Intl. N/A; N.E. N/A; M.A. N/A; S. N/A; M.W. N/A; S.W. 95%; W. 5%

Baylor University (Hankamer)

1 Bear Place #98013
Waco, TX 76798-8013
http://www.baylor.edu/mba
Private
Admissions: (254) 710-3718
E-mail: mba_info@baylor.edu
Financial aid: (254) 710-2611
Application deadline: 06/15
Tuition: full time: $24,940; part time: N/A
Room/board/expenses: $12,480
College-funded aid: Yes

International student aid: Yes
Average student indebtedness at graduation: $15,326
Full-time enrollment: 83
men: 75%; women: 25%;
minorities: 17%; international: 29%
Part-time enrollment: N/A
men: N/A; women: N/A;
minorities: N/A; international: N/A
Acceptance rate (full-time): 53%
Average GMAT (full-time): 595
Average GPA (full-time): 3.20
Average age of entrants to full-time program: 25
Average months of prior work experience (full-time): 23
TOEFL requirement: Yes
Minimum TOEFL score: 600
Mean starting base salary for 2007 full-time graduates: $59,425
Employment location for 2007 class: Intl. 13%; N.E. 3%; M.A. 5%; S. 3%; M.W. 3%; S.W. 75%; W. 0%

Lamar University–Beaumont

4400 Martin Luther King Parkway
Beaumont, TX 77710
http://mba.lamar.edu
Public
Admissions: (409) 880-8356
E-mail: gradmissions@lamar.edu
Financial aid: (409) 880-8450
Application deadline: 01/30
In-state tuition: full time: $5,663; part time: N/A
Out-of-state tuition: full time: $12,335
Room/board/expenses: $11,232
College-funded aid: Yes
International student aid: Yes
Full-time enrollment: 93
men: 57%; women: 43%;
minorities: 18%; international: 14%
Part-time enrollment: N/A
men: N/A; women: N/A;
minorities: N/A; international: N/A
Acceptance rate (full-time): 67%
Average GMAT (full-time): 484
Average GPA (full-time): 3.28
Average age of entrants to full-time program: 26
TOEFL requirement: Yes
Minimum TOEFL score: 525
Most popular departments: accounting, entrepreneurship, finance, marketing, other
Mean starting base salary for 2007 full-time graduates: $53,750
Employment location for 2007 class: Intl. 10%; N.E. N/A; M.A. N/A; S. N/A; M.W. N/A; S.W. 90%; W. N/A

Prairie View A&M University[1]

PO Box 519
MS 2300
Prarie View, TX 77446
http://www.pvamu.edu/pages/129.asp
Public
Admissions: (936) 261-9200
Financial aid: N/A
Tuition: N/A
Room/board/expenses: N/A
Enrollment: N/A

Rice University (Jones)

PO Box 2932
Houston, TX 77252-2932
http://www.jonesgsm.rice.edu
Private
Admissions: (713) 348-4918
E-mail: ricemba@rice.edu
Financial aid: (713) 348-4958
Application deadline: 04/01
Tuition: full time: $35,558; total program: $79,000 (part-time)
Room/board/expenses: $16,440
College-funded aid: Yes
International student aid: Yes

Average student indebtedness at graduation: $70,308
Full-time enrollment: 229
men: 68%; women: 32%;
minorities: 24%; international: 31%
Part-time enrollment: 181
men: 71%; women: 29%;
minorities: 28%; international: 13%
Acceptance rate (full-time): 39%
Average GMAT (full-time): 642
Average GMAT (part-time): 609
Average GPA (full-time): 3.25
Average age of entrants to full-time program: 27
Average months of prior work experience (full-time): 45
TOEFL requirement: Yes
Minimum TOEFL score: 600
Most popular departments: consulting, entrepreneurship, finance, marketing, other
Mean starting base salary for 2007 full-time graduates: $89,006
Employment location for 2007 class: Intl. 3%; N.E. 5%; M.A. 0%; S. 4%; M.W. 3%; S.W. 78%; W. 7%

Sam Houston State University

PO Box 2056
Huntsville, TX 77341
http://coba.shsu.edu/
Public
Admissions: (936) 294-1246
E-mail: eco_mjm@shsu.edu
Financial aid: (936) 294-1724
Application deadline: 08/01
In-state tuition: full time: $8,299; part time: N/A
Out-of-state tuition: full time: $18,271
Room/board/expenses: $12,000
College-funded aid: Yes
International student aid: Yes
Full-time enrollment: 20
men: 45%; women: 55%;
minorities: N/A; international: 100%
Part-time enrollment: 272
men: 57%; women: 43%;
minorities: 19%; international: N/A
Average GMAT (part-time): 520
TOEFL requirement: Yes
Minimum TOEFL score: 550

Southern Methodist University (Cox)

PO Box 750333
Dallas, TX 75275-0333
http://www.mba.cox.smu.edu/
Private
Admissions: (800) 472-3622
E-mail: mbainfo@cox.smu.edu
Financial aid: (214) 768-2371
Application deadline: 04/15
Tuition: full time: $39,010; part time: $41,364
Room/board/expenses: $16,950
College-funded aid: Yes
International student aid: Yes
Full-time enrollment: 164
men: 72%; women: 28%;
minorities: 17%; international: 23%
Part-time enrollment: 427
men: 30%; women: 70%;
minorities: 12%; international: 13%
Acceptance rate (full-time): 47%
Average GMAT (full-time): 640
Average GMAT (part-time): 596
Average GPA (full-time): 3.30
Average age of entrants to full-time program: 27
Average months of prior work experience (full-time): 40
TOEFL requirement: Yes
Minimum TOEFL score: 600
Most popular departments: consulting, entrepreneurship, finance, marketing, other
Mean starting base salary for 2007 full-time graduates: $83,978
Employment location for 2007 class: Intl. 0%; N.E. 11%; M.A. 2%; S. 4%; M.W. 4%; S.W. 76%; W. 4%

Stephen F. Austin State University

PO Box 13004
SFA Station
Nacogdoches, TX 75962-3004
http://www.cob.sfasu.edu
Public
Admissions: (936) 468-2807
E-mail: gschool@titan.sfasu.edu
Financial aid: (936) 468-2807
Application deadline: 07/31
In-state tuition: full time: $130/credit hour; part time: $130/credit hour
Out-of-state tuition: full time: $450/credit hour
Room/board/expenses: N/A
College-funded aid: Yes
International student aid: Yes
Full-time enrollment: 38
men: 55%; women: 45%;
minorities: N/A; international: N/A
Part-time enrollment: 20
men: 60%; women: 40%;
minorities: N/A; international: N/A
Acceptance rate (full-time): 88%
Average GMAT (full-time): 485
Average GMAT (part-time): 485
Average GPA (full-time): 2.95
TOEFL requirement: Yes
Minimum TOEFL score: 550

St. Mary's University (Greehey)[1]

1 Camino Santa Maria
San Antonio, TX 78228-8607
http://www.stmarytx.edu/business
Private
Admissions: (210) 436-3708
E-mail: rmenger@stmarytx.edu
Financial aid: (210) 436-3141
Tuition: N/A
Room/board/expenses: N/A
Enrollment: N/A

Texas A&M International University

5201 University Boulevard
Western Hemispheric
Trade Center, Suite 203
Laredo, TX 78041-1900
http://www.tamiu.edu
Public
Admissions: (956) 326-2200
E-mail: adms@tamiu.edu
Financial aid: (956) 326-2225
Application deadline: 04/30
In-state tuition: total program: $5,734 (full-time); part time: $780
Out-of-state tuition: total program: $14,074 (full-time)
Room/board/expenses: $7,781
College-funded aid: Yes
International student aid: Yes
Full-time enrollment: 106
men: 62%; women: 38%;
minorities: 16%; international: 82%
Part-time enrollment: 157
men: 59%; women: 41%;
minorities: 46%; international: 49%
Acceptance rate (full-time): 99%
Average GMAT (full-time): 463
Average GPA (full-time): 3.24
Average age of entrants to full-time program: 22
Average months of prior work experience (full-time): 32
TOEFL requirement: Yes
Minimum TOEFL score: 550
Most popular departments: accounting, finance, general management, international business, management information systems

Texas A&M University–College Station (Mays)

4117 TAMU
390 Wehner Building
College Station, TX 77843-4117
http://mba.tamu.edu
Public
Admissions: (979) 845-4714
E-mail: maysmba@tamu.edu
Financial aid: (979) 845-3236
Application deadline: 04/15
In-state tuition: full time: $15,315;
part time: N/A
Out-of-state tuition: full time:
$25,323
Room/board/expenses: $13,925
College-funded aid: Yes
International student aid: Yes
Average student indebtedness at
graduation: $26,000
Full-time enrollment: 154
men: 73%; women: 27%;
minorities: 13%; international: 27%
Part-time enrollment: N/A
men: N/A; women: N/A;
minorities: N/A; international: N/A
Acceptance rate (full-time): 30%
Average GMAT (full-time): 665
Average GPA (full-time): 3.40
Average age of entrants to full-time
program: 27
Average months of prior work
experience (full-time): 53
TOEFL requirement: Yes
Minimum TOEFL score: 600
Mean starting base salary for 2007
full-time graduates: $87,475
Employment location for 2007 class:
Intl. 2%; N.E. 6%; M.A. 3%; S. 3%;
M.W. 5%; S.W. 68%; W. 14%

Texas A&M University–Commerce

PO Box 3011
Commerce, TX 75429-3011
http://www.tamu-commerce.edu/
graduateprograms
Public
Admissions: (903) 886-5163
E-mail: graduate_school@
tamu-commerce.edu
Financial aid: (903) 886-5096
Application deadline: rolling
In-state tuition: full time:
$342/credit hour; part time:
$342/credit hour
Out-of-state tuition: full time:
$620/credit hour
Room/board/expenses: $7,700
College-funded aid: Yes
International student aid: Yes
Full-time enrollment: 354
men: 56%; women: 44%;
minorities: 13%; international: 40%
Part-time enrollment: 540
men: 54%; women: 46%;
minorities: 33%; international: 4%
Acceptance rate (full-time): 82%
TOEFL requirement: Yes
Minimum TOEFL score: 500

Texas A&M University–Corpus Christi

6300 Ocean Drive
Corpus Christi, TX 78412-5808
http://www.cob.tamucc.edu/
graduate/
Public
Admissions: (361) 825-2177
E-mail:
maria.martinez@tamucc.edu
Financial aid: (361) 825-2338
Application deadline: 07/15
In-state tuition: full time: $143/credit
hour; part time: $143/credit hour
Out-of-state tuition: full time:
$421/credit hour
Room/board/expenses: N/A
College-funded aid: Yes
International student aid: Yes

Full-time enrollment: N/A
men: N/A; women: N/A;
minorities: N/A; international: N/A
Part-time enrollment: 187
men: 52%; women: 48%;
minorities: 22%; international: 48%
Average GMAT (part-time): 459
TOEFL requirement: Yes
Minimum TOEFL score: 550
Most popular departments: health
care administration, international
business

Texas Christian University (Neeley)

PO Box 298540
Fort Worth, TX 76129
http://www.mba.tcu.edu
Private
Admissions: (817) 257-7531
E-mail: mbainfo@tcu.edu
Financial aid: (817) 257-7531
Application deadline: 04/30
Tuition: full time: $29,300; part
time: $18,920
Room/board/expenses: $12,000
College-funded aid: Yes
International student aid: Yes
Average student indebtedness at
graduation: $30,500
Full-time enrollment: 92
men: 72%; women: 28%;
minorities: 8%; international: 25%
Part-time enrollment: 191
men: 73%; women: 27%;
minorities: 13%; international: 2%
Acceptance rate (full-time): 71%
Average GMAT (full-time): 608
Average GMAT (part-time): 590
Average GPA (full-time): 3.29
Average age of entrants to full-time
program: 27
Average months of prior work
experience (full-time): 46
TOEFL requirement: Yes
Minimum TOEFL score: 550
Most popular departments:
consulting, finance, marketing,
portfolio management, supply
chain management
Mean starting base salary for 2007
full-time graduates: $70,477
Employment location for 2007 class:
Intl. 3%; N.E. 3%; M.A. 0%; S. 0%;
M.W. 0%; S.W. 90%; W. 3%

Texas Southern University (Jones)

3100 Cleburne Avenue
Houston, TX 77004
http://www.tsu.edu/business
Public
Admissions: (713) 313-7590
E-mail: richardson_bj@tsu.edu
Financial aid: (713) 313-7530
Application deadline: 07/01
In-state tuition: full time:
$100/credit hour; part time:
$100/credit hour
Out-of-state tuition: full time:
$343/credit hour
Room/board/expenses: $6,500
College-funded aid: Yes
International student aid: Yes
Average student indebtedness at
graduation: $3,600
Full-time enrollment: N/A
men: N/A; women: N/A;
minorities: N/A; international: N/A
Part-time enrollment: 173
men: 40%; women: 60%;
minorities: 62%; international: 20%
Average GMAT (part-time): 428
TOEFL requirement: Yes
Minimum TOEFL score: 550
Most popular departments: account-
ing, finance, general management,
marketing, organizational behavior

Texas State University–San Marcos (McCoy)

601 University Drive
San Marcos, TX 78666-4616
http://www.txstate.edu
Public
Admissions: (512) 245-3591
E-mail: nw04@txstate.edu
Financial aid: (512) 245-2315
Application deadline: 06/02
In-state tuition: full time: N/A; total
program: $10,518 (part-time)
Out-of-state tuition: full time: N/A
Room/board/expenses: N/A
College-funded aid: Yes
International student aid: Yes
Full-time enrollment: N/A
men: N/A; women: N/A;
minorities: N/A; international: N/A
Part-time enrollment: 220
men: 60%; women: 40%;
minorities: 24%; international: 7%
Average GMAT (part-time): 520
TOEFL requirement: Yes
Minimum TOEFL score: 550
Most popular departments: general
management, health care adminis-
tration, international business,
manufacturing and technology
management

Texas Tech University (Rawls)

PO Box 42101
Lubbock, TX 79409-2101
http://mba.ba.ttu.edu/
MBAhome.asp
Public
Admissions: (806) 742-2787
E-mail: fred.hartmeister@ttu.edu
Financial aid: (806) 742-0454
Application deadline: 07/01
In-state tuition: full time: $194/credit
hour; part time: $194/credit hour
Out-of-state tuition: full time:
$194/credit hour
Room/board/expenses: $11,500
College-funded aid: Yes
International student aid: Yes
Average student indebtedness at
graduation: $15,192
Full-time enrollment: 68
men: 71%; women: 29%;
minorities: 10%; international: 12%
Part-time enrollment: 367
men: 65%; women: 35%;
minorities: 18%; international: 8%
Acceptance rate (full-time): 23%
Average GMAT (full-time): 616
Average GMAT (part-time): 496
Average GPA (full-time): 3.58
Average age of entrants to full-time
program: 24
Average months of prior work
experience (full-time): 24
TOEFL requirement: Yes
Minimum TOEFL score: 550
Most popular departments:
entrepreneurship, finance,
general management, health
care administration, marketing
Mean starting base salary for 2007
full-time graduates: $53,072
Employment location for 2007 class:
Intl. 0%; N.E. 0%; M.A. 0%; S. 11%;
M.W. 0%; S.W. 89%; W. 0%

Trinity University

1 Trinity Place
San Antonio, TX 78212-7200
http://www.trinity.edu/
departments/business_admin/
grad_program.htm
Private
Admissions: (210) 999-7238
Financial aid: N/A
Application deadline: 05/01
Tuition: total program: $24,869
(full-time); part time: N/A
Room/board/expenses: N/A
College-funded aid: Yes

International student aid: Yes
Full-time enrollment: 16
men: 38%; women: 63%;
minorities: 13%; international: N/A
Part-time enrollment: N/A
men: N/A; women: N/A;
minorities: N/A; international: N/A
Acceptance rate (full-time): 84%
Average GMAT (full-time): 584
Average GPA (full-time): 3.33
Average age of entrants to full-time
program: 22
Average months of prior work
experience (full-time): 36
TOEFL requirement: Yes
Minimum TOEFL score: N/A
Most popular departments:
accounting

University of Houston–Clear Lake

2700 Bay Area Boulevard
Box 71
Houston, TX 77058
http://www.uhcl.edu
Public
Admissions: (281) 283-2500
E-mail: admissions@uhcl.edu
Financial aid: (281) 283-2480
Application deadline: 08/01
In-state tuition: full time: N/A; part
time: $100/credit hour
Out-of-state tuition: full time: N/A
Room/board/expenses: $13,486
College-funded aid: Yes
International student aid: Yes
Full-time enrollment: N/A
men: N/A; women: N/A;
minorities: N/A; international: N/A
Part-time enrollment: 364
men: 61%; women: 39%;
minorities: 25%; international: 23%
Average GMAT (part-time): 524
TOEFL requirement: Yes
Minimum TOEFL score: 550
Most popular departments: finance,
general management, human re-
sources management, marketing,
management information systems

University of Houston–Main Campus (Bauer)

334 Melcher Hall
Suite 330
Houston, TX 77204-6021
http://www.bauer.uh.edu/mba
Public
Admissions: (713) 743-4638
E-mail: houstonmba@uh.edu
Financial aid: (713) 743-5158
Application deadline: 05/01
In-state tuition: full time: $12,864;
part time: $10,752
Out-of-state tuition: full time:
$19,536
Room/board/expenses: $12,400
College-funded aid: Yes
International student aid: Yes
Average student indebtedness at
graduation: $28,650
Full-time enrollment: 62
men: 55%; women: 45%;
minorities: 27%; international: 23%
Part-time enrollment: 515
men: 67%; women: 33%;
minorities: 34%; international: 11%
Acceptance rate (full-time): 72%
Average GMAT (full-time): 591
Average GMAT (part-time): 535
Average GPA (full-time): 3.31
Average age of entrants to full-time
program: 28
Average months of prior work
experience (full-time): 56
TOEFL requirement: Yes
Minimum TOEFL score: 600

University of Houston–Victoria

University West Room 214
3007 N. Ben Wilson
Victoria, TX 77901
http://www.uhv.edu/bus/
default.asp
Public
Admissions: (361) 570-4110
E-mail: worthamt@uhv.edu
Financial aid: (361) 570-4131
Application deadline: rolling
In-state tuition: full time: $4,656;
part time: $3,492
Out-of-state tuition: full time:
$10,128
Room/board/expenses: $15,058
College-funded aid: Yes
International student aid: Yes
Full-time enrollment: 140
men: 47%; women: 53%;
minorities: 57%; international: 8%
Part-time enrollment: 560
men: 52%; women: 48%;
minorities: 49%; international: 9%
Acceptance rate (full-time): 72%
Average GMAT (full-time): 436
Average GMAT (part-time): 460
Average GPA (full-time): 3.20
Average age of entrants to full-time
program: 29
TOEFL requirement: Yes
Minimum TOEFL score: 550
Most popular departments: account-
ing, entrepreneurship, finance,
general management, international
business

University of North Texas

PO Box 311160
Denton, TX 76203
http://www.coba.unt.edu
Public
Admissions: (940) 369-8977
E-mail: mbarecep@cobaf.unt.edu
Financial aid: (940) 565-2302
Application deadline: 07/15
In-state tuition: full time: $195/credit
hour; part time: $195/credit hour
Out-of-state tuition: full time:
$473/credit hour
Room/board/expenses: $6,830
College-funded aid: Yes
International student aid: Yes
Full-time enrollment: N/A
men: N/A; women: N/A;
minorities: N/A; international: N/A
Part-time enrollment: 503
men: 55%; women: 45%;
minorities: 21%; international: 22%
Average GMAT (part-time): 540
TOEFL requirement: Yes
Minimum TOEFL score: 550
Most popular departments: account-
ing, finance, general management,
supply chain management, tax

University of Texas–Arlington

UTA Box 19376
Arlington, TX 76019-0376
http://www2.uta.edu/gradbiz/
Public
Admissions: (817) 272-3005
E-mail: admit@uta.edu
Financial aid: (817) 272-3561
Application deadline: rolling
In-state tuition: full time: $21,396;
part time: $16,214
Out-of-state tuition: full time:
$29,736
Room/board/expenses: $10,696
College-funded aid: Yes
International student aid: Yes
Full-time enrollment: 228
men: 66%; women: 34%;
minorities: 8%; international: 68%
Part-time enrollment: 206
men: 67%; women: 33%;
minorities: 12%; international: 51%
TOEFL requirement: Yes
Minimum TOEFL score: 550

University of Texas–Austin (McCombs)

MBA Program
1 University Station, B6004
Austin, TX 78712
http://mba.mccombs.utexas.edu
Public
Admissions: (512) 471-7698
E-mail: mccombsmba@mccombs.utexas.edu
Financial aid: (512) 471-7605
Application deadline: 04/01
In-state tuition: full time: $21,418; part time: $28,426
Out-of-state tuition: full time: $38,222
Room/board/expenses: $14,500
College-funded aid: Yes
International student aid: Yes
Average student indebtedness at graduation: $62,808
Full-time enrollment: 517
men: 72%; women: 28%;
minorities: 21%; international: 25%
Part-time enrollment: 217
men: 77%; women: 23%;
minorities: 27%; international: 17%
Acceptance rate (full-time): 34%
Average GMAT (full-time): 673
Average GMAT (part-time): 659
Average GPA (full-time): 3.38
Average age of entrants to full-time program: 28
Average months of prior work experience (full-time): 62
TOEFL requirement: Yes
Minimum TOEFL score: 620
Most popular departments: consulting, finance, general management, marketing, portfolio management
Mean starting base salary for 2007 full-time graduates: $93,649
Employment location for 2007 class: Intl. 6%; N.E. 11%; M.A. 3%; S. 4%; M.W. 8%; S.W. 60%; W. 8%

University of Texas–Dallas

800 W. Campbell Road
Richardson, TX 75080-3021
http://www.som.utdallas.edu/
Public
Admissions: (972) 883-6822
E-mail: cmba@utdallas.edu
Financial aid: (972) 883-2941
Application deadline: 05/01
In-state tuition: full time: $9,000; part time: $7,590
Out-of-state tuition: full time: $18,000
Room/board/expenses: $12,000
College-funded aid: Yes
International student aid: Yes
Full-time enrollment: 94
men: 54%; women: 46%;
minorities: 10%; international: 47%
Part-time enrollment: 1,033
men: 64%; women: 36%;
minorities: 32%; international: 21%
Acceptance rate (full-time): 40%
Average GMAT (full-time): 650
Average GMAT (part-time): 577
Average GPA (full-time): 3.64
Average age of entrants to full-time program: 28
Average months of prior work experience (full-time): 60
TOEFL requirement: Yes
Minimum TOEFL score: 550
Most popular departments: accounting, finance, marketing, operations management, supply chain management
Mean starting base salary for 2007 full-time graduates: $61,429
Employment location for 2007 class: Intl. N/A; N.E. 7%; M.A. N/A; S. 7%; M.W. N/A; S.W. 87%; W. N/A

University of Texas–El Paso

500 W. University Avenue
El Paso, TX 79968
http://www.utep.edu
Public
Admissions: (915) 747-5491
E-mail: gradschool@utep.edu
Financial aid: (915) 747-5204
Application deadline: rolling
In-state tuition: full time: N/A; part time: N/A
Out-of-state tuition: full time: N/A
Room/board/expenses: N/A
College-funded aid: Yes
International student aid: Yes
Full-time enrollment: N/A
men: N/A; women: N/A;
minorities: N/A; international: N/A
Part-time enrollment: 300
men: 50%; women: 50%;
minorities: 58%; international: 24%
Average GMAT (part-time): 427
TOEFL requirement: Yes
Minimum TOEFL score: 600

University of Texas of the Permian Basin

4901 E. University
Odessa, TX 79762
http://www.utpb.edu/utpb_adm/academicaffairs/schoolofbusiness/index.html
Private
Admissions: (432) 552-210
Financial aid: N/A
Application deadline: rolling
Tuition: full time: $150/credit hour; part time: $150/credit hour
Room/board/expenses: $5,700
College-funded aid: Yes
International student aid: No
Full-time enrollment: 83
men: N/A; women: N/A;
minorities: N/A; international: N/A
Part-time enrollment: 10
men: N/A; women: N/A;
minorities: N/A; international: N/A
TOEFL requirement: Yes
Minimum TOEFL score: 550
Most popular departments: accounting, general management

University of Texas–Pan American

1201 W. University Drive
Edinburg, TX 78539
http://www.coba.panam.edu/mba
Public
Admissions: (956) 381-3313
E-mail: mbaprog@panam.edu
Financial aid: (956) 381-5372
Application deadline: rolling
In-state tuition: full time: $159/credit hour; part time: $159/credit hour
Out-of-state tuition: full time: $437/credit hour
Room/board/expenses: N/A
College-funded aid: Yes
International student aid: Yes
Full-time enrollment: 42
men: 43%; women: 57%;
minorities: 64%; international: 29%
Part-time enrollment: 109
men: 53%; women: 47%;
minorities: 77%; international: 6%
TOEFL requirement: Yes
Minimum TOEFL score: 500

University of Texas–San Antonio

1 UTSA Circle
San Antonio, TX 78249
http://business.utsa.edu
Public
Admissions: (210) 458-4330
E-mail: graduatestudies@utsa.edu
Financial aid: (210) 458-8000
Application deadline: 07/01
In-state tuition: full time: $6,378; part time: $4,389

Out-of-state tuition: full time: $16,386
Room/board/expenses: N/A
College-funded aid: Yes
International student aid: Yes
Full-time enrollment: 101
men: 50%; women: 50%;
minorities: 26%; international: 33%
Part-time enrollment: 259
men: 64%; women: 36%;
minorities: 40%; international: 2%
Acceptance rate (full-time): 52%
Average GMAT (full-time): 581
Average GMAT (part-time): 560
Average GPA (full-time): 3.28
Average age of entrants to full-time program: 28
Average months of prior work experience (full-time): 59
TOEFL requirement: Yes
Minimum TOEFL score: 500
Most popular departments: accounting, finance, general management, international business, other
Mean starting base salary for 2007 full-time graduates: $54,129
Employment location for 2007 class: Intl. N/A; N.E. 15%; M.A. 8%; S. 8%; M.W. N/A; S.W. 69%; W. N/A

University of Texas–Tyler[1]

3900 University Boulevard
Tyler, TX 75799
http://www.uttyl.edu/cbt/mba.htm
Public
Admissions: (903) 566-7142
E-mail: gsmith@mail.uttyler.edu
Financial aid: (903) 566-7180
Tuition: N/A
Room/board/expenses: N/A
Enrollment: N/A

Brigham Young University (Marriott)

640 TNRB
Provo, UT 84602
http://marriottschool.byu.edu/mba
Private
Admissions: (801) 422-3500
E-mail: mba@byu.edu
Financial aid: (801) 422-6824
Application deadline: 05/01
Tuition: full time: $8,700; part time: N/A
Room/board/expenses: $12,108
College-funded aid: Yes
International student aid: Yes
Average student indebtedness at graduation: $21,888
Full-time enrollment: 305
men: 83%; women: 17%;
minorities: 9%; international: 17%
Part-time enrollment: N/A
men: N/A; women: N/A;
minorities: N/A; international: N/A
Acceptance rate (full-time): 53%
Average GMAT (full-time): 661
Average GPA (full-time): 3.53
Average age of entrants to full-time program: 29
Average months of prior work experience (full-time): 43
TOEFL requirement: Yes
Minimum TOEFL score: 590
Most popular departments: finance, human resources management, manufacturing and technology management, marketing, supply chain management
Mean starting base salary for 2007 full-time graduates: $81,934
Employment location for 2007 class: Intl. 11%; N.E. 10%; M.A. 0%; S. 5%; M.W. 16%; S.W. 21%; W. 37%

Southern Utah University

351 W. University Boulevard
Cedar City, UT 84720
http://www.suu.edu/business
Public
Admissions: (435) 586-5462
Financial aid: N/A
Application deadline: 03/31
In-state tuition: full time: $297/credit hour; part time: $297/credit hour
Out-of-state tuition: full time: $980/credit hour
Room/board/expenses: $17,626
College-funded aid: Yes
International student aid: Yes
Average student indebtedness at graduation: $12,146
Full-time enrollment: 27
men: 74%; women: 26%;
minorities: 4%; international: 0%
Part-time enrollment: 7
men: 86%; women: 14%;
minorities: 0%; international: 0%
Acceptance rate (full-time): 72%
Average GMAT (full-time): 565
Average GMAT (part-time): 520
Average GPA (full-time): 3.40
TOEFL requirement: Yes
Minimum TOEFL score: 500

University of Utah (Eccles)

1645 E. Campus Center Drive
Room 101
Salt Lake City, UT 84112-9301
http://www.business.utah.edu/go/masters
Public
Admissions: (801) 581-7785
E-mail: information@business.utah.edu
Financial aid: (801) 581-7785
Application deadline: 02/15
In-state tuition: full time: $11,420; part time: $12,220
Out-of-state tuition: full time: $24,420
Room/board/expenses: $16,000
College-funded aid: Yes
International student aid: Yes
Full-time enrollment: 98
men: 78%; women: 22%;
minorities: 11%; international: 19%
Part-time enrollment: 319
men: 83%; women: 17%;
minorities: 6%; international: 0%
Acceptance rate (full-time): 56%
Average GMAT (full-time): 600
Average GMAT (part-time): 592
Average GPA (full-time): 3.46
Average age of entrants to full-time program: 27
Average months of prior work experience (full-time): 35
TOEFL requirement: Yes
Minimum TOEFL score: 600
Most popular departments: accounting, entrepreneurship, finance, international business, marketing
Mean starting base salary for 2007 full-time graduates: $58,000
Employment location for 2007 class: Intl. 0%; N.E. 4%; M.A. 7%; S. 0%; M.W. 4%; S.W. 4%; W. 82%

Utah State University (Huntsman)

3500 Old Main Hill
Logan, UT 84322-3500
http://www.huntsman.usu.edu/mba/
Public
Admissions: (435) 797-2360
E-mail: katherine.mcconkie@usu.edu
Financial aid: (435) 797-0173
Application deadline: 02/15

In-state tuition: total program: $9,732 (full-time); $12,375 (part-time)
Out-of-state tuition: total program: $20,396 (part-time)
Room/board/expenses: $10,800
College-funded aid: Yes
International student aid: Yes
Full-time enrollment: 39
men: 69%; women: 31%;
minorities: 0%; international: 18%
Part-time enrollment: 153
men: 85%; women: 15%;
minorities: 3%; international: 1%
Acceptance rate (full-time): 61%
Average GMAT (full-time): 540
Average GMAT (part-time): 553
Average GPA (full-time): 3.43
Average age of entrants to full-time program: 26
Average months of prior work experience (full-time): 24
TOEFL requirement: Yes
Minimum TOEFL score: 550
Most popular departments: accounting, general management, human resources management, manufacturing and technology management

Weber State University (Goddard)

2750 N. University Park Boulevard
MC102
Layton, UT 84041-9099
http://weber.edu/mba
Public
Admissions: (801) 395-3528
E-mail: mba@weber.edu
Financial aid: (801) 626-7569
Application deadline: 06/12
In-state tuition: full time: N/A; total program: $11,217 (part-time)
Out-of-state tuition: full time: N/A
Room/board/expenses: $8,000
College-funded aid: Yes
International student aid: Yes
Full-time enrollment: N/A
men: N/A; women: N/A;
minorities: N/A; international: N/A
Part-time enrollment: 207
men: 77%; women: 23%;
minorities: N/A; international: 2%
Average GMAT (part-time): 573
TOEFL requirement: Yes
Minimum TOEFL score: 550
Most popular departments: accounting, e-commerce, health care administration, management information systems, supply chain management

University of Vermont

55 Colchester Avenue
Burlington, VT 05405
http://www.bsad.uvm.edu/mba
Public
Admissions: (802) 656-2699
E-mail: studentservices@bsad.uvm.edu
Financial aid: (802) 656-1340
Application deadline: rolling
In-state tuition: full time: $11,880; part time: $434/credit hour
Out-of-state tuition: full time: $27,764
Room/board/expenses: $20,892
College-funded aid: Yes
International student aid: Yes
Average student indebtedness at graduation: $3,818
Full-time enrollment: 20
men: 60%; women: 40%;
minorities: 0%; international: 10%
Part-time enrollment: 37
men: 51%; women: 49%;
minorities: 11%; international: 3%
Acceptance rate (full-time): 68%
Average GMAT (full-time): 619
Average GMAT (part-time): 593
Average GPA (full-time): 3.18

Average age of entrants to full-time program: 25
Average months of prior work experience (full-time): 36
TOEFL requirement: Yes
Minimum TOEFL score: 550

VIRGINIA

College of William and Mary (Mason)

PO Box 8795
Williamsburg, VA 23187-8795
http://mason.wm.edu/mba
Public
Admissions: (757) 221-2900
E-mail: admissions@mason.wm.edu
Financial aid: (757) 221-2900
Application deadline: 04/01
In-state tuition: full time: $18,124; part time: $465/credit hour
Out-of-state tuition: full time: $31,924
Room/board/expenses: $16,330
College-funded aid: Yes
International student aid: Yes
Average student indebtedness at graduation: $37,743
Full-time enrollment: 137
men: 73%; women: 27%;
minorities: 4%; international: 32%
Part-time enrollment: 151
men: 75%; women: 25%;
minorities: 7%; international: 4%
Acceptance rate (full-time): 59%
Average GMAT (full-time): 613
Average GMAT (part-time): 589
Average GPA (full-time): 3.40
Average age of entrants to full-time program: 26
Average months of prior work experience (full-time): 41
TOEFL requirement: Yes
Minimum TOEFL score: 600
Most popular departments: entrepreneurship, finance, marketing, management information systems, supply chain management
Mean starting base salary for 2007 full-time graduates: $76,297
Employment location for 2007 class: Intl. 11%; N.E. 26%; M.A. 45%; S. 5%; M.W. 5%; S.W. 3%; W. 5%

George Mason University

4400 University Drive
Fairfax, VA 22030
http://www.som.gmu.edu
Public
Admissions: (703) 993-2136
E-mail: somgrad@gmu.edu
Financial aid: (703) 993-2353
Application deadline: 04/01
In-state tuition: full time: $555/credit hour; part time: $555/credit hour
Out-of-state tuition: full time: $985/credit hour
Room/board/expenses: N/A
College-funded aid: Yes
International student aid: Yes
Full-time enrollment: 47
men: 66%; women: 34%;
minorities: 9%; international: 32%
Part-time enrollment: 301
men: 62%; women: 38%;
minorities: 22%; international: 0%
Acceptance rate (full-time): 46%
Average GMAT (full-time): 551
Average GMAT (part-time): 570
Average GPA (full-time): 3.00
Average age of entrants to full-time program: 29
Average months of prior work experience (full-time): 99
TOEFL requirement: Yes
Minimum TOEFL score: 650
Most popular departments: accounting, entrepreneurship, finance

James Madison University

Showker Hall
Harrisonburg, VA 22807
http://www.jmu.edu/mba/
Public
Admissions: (540) 568-3009
E-mail: bahnkb@jmu.edu
Financial aid: (540) 568-8059
Application deadline: 06/01
In-state tuition: full time: $280/credit hour; part time: $280/credit hour
Out-of-state tuition: full time: $796/credit hour
Room/board/expenses: $14,500
College-funded aid: Yes
International student aid: Yes
Full-time enrollment: N/A
men: N/A; women: N/A;
minorities: N/A; international: N/A
Part-time enrollment: 102
men: 59%; women: 41%;
minorities: 12%; international: 2%
Average GMAT (part-time): 585
TOEFL requirement: Yes
Minimum TOEFL score: 570
Most popular departments: accounting, other

Longwood University[1]

201 High Street
Farmville, VA 23909
http://www.longwood.edu/business/
Private
Admissions: (877) 267-7883
E-mail: graduate@longwood.edu
Financial aid: N/A
Tuition: N/A
Room/board/expenses: N/A
Enrollment: N/A

Old Dominion University

1026 Constant Hall
Norfolk, VA 23529
http://bpa.odu.edu/
Public
Admissions: (757) 683-3585
E-mail: mbainfo@odu.edu
Financial aid: (757) 683-3683
Application deadline: 06/01
In-state tuition: full time: $304/credit hour; part time: $304/credit hour
Out-of-state tuition: full time: $761/credit hour
Room/board/expenses: N/A
College-funded aid: Yes
International student aid: Yes
Full-time enrollment: 107
men: 50%; women: 50%;
minorities: 15%; international: 38%
Part-time enrollment: 227
men: 59%; women: 41%;
minorities: 18%; international: 4%
Average GMAT (part-time): 545
Average GPA (full-time): 3.25
TOEFL requirement: Yes
Minimum TOEFL score: 550

Radford University

PO Box 6956
Radford, VA 24142
http://www.radford.edu
Public
Admissions: (540) 831-5431
E-mail: gradcoll@radford.edu
Financial aid: (540) 831-5408
Application deadline: rolling
In-state tuition: full time: $279/credit hour; part time: $279/credit hour
Out-of-state tuition: full time: $519/credit hour
Room/board/expenses: N/A
College-funded aid: Yes
International student aid: Yes
Full-time enrollment: 42
men: 76%; women: 24%;
minorities: 17%; international: 19%

Part-time enrollment: 37
men: 65%; women: 35%;
minorities: 5%; international: 0%
Acceptance rate (full-time): 80%
Average GMAT (full-time): 499
Average GMAT (part-time): 463
Average GPA (full-time): 3.20
Average age of entrants to full-time program: 23
TOEFL requirement: Yes
Minimum TOEFL score: 550

Shenandoah University (Byrd)[1]

Henkel Hall
Room 218
Winchester, VA 22601
http://www.su.edu/bsb/default.asp
Private
Admissions: (540) 665-4526
Financial aid: N/A
Tuition: N/A
Room/board/expenses: N/A
Enrollment: N/A

University of Richmond (Robins)

1 Gateway Road
Richmond, VA 23173
http://business.richmond.edu/mba
Private
Admissions: (804) 289-8553
E-mail: mba@richmond.edu
Financial aid: (804) 289-8438
Application deadline: 05/01
Tuition: full time: N/A; part time: $770/credit hour
Room/board/expenses: N/A
College-funded aid: Yes
International student aid: Yes
Full-time enrollment: N/A
men: N/A; women: N/A;
minorities: N/A; international: N/A
Part-time enrollment: 148
men: 55%; women: 45%;
minorities: 12%; international: 8%
Average GMAT (part-time): 592
TOEFL requirement: Yes
Minimum TOEFL score: 600
Most popular departments: entrepreneurship, finance, international business, leadership, marketing

University of Virginia (Darden)

PO Box 6550
Charlottesville, VA 22906-6550
http://www.darden.virginia.edu
Public
Admissions: (434) 924-7281
E-mail: darden@virginia.edu
Financial aid: (434) 924-7739
Application deadline: 11/01
In-state tuition: full time: $37,602; part time: N/A
Out-of-state tuition: full time: $42,602
Room/board/expenses: $19,500
College-funded aid: Yes
International student aid: Yes
Average student indebtedness at graduation: $69,458
Full-time enrollment: 651
men: 74%; women: 26%;
minorities: 13%; international: 30%
Part-time enrollment: N/A
men: N/A; women: N/A;
minorities: N/A; international: N/A
Acceptance rate (full-time): 29%
Average GMAT (full-time): 688
Average GPA (full-time): 3.33
Average age of entrants to full-time program: 28
Average months of prior work experience (full-time): 53
TOEFL requirement: Yes
Minimum TOEFL score: N/A
Mean starting base salary for 2007 full-time graduates: $100,575
Employment location for 2007 class: Intl. 7%; N.E. 31%; M.A. 24%; S. 12%; M.W. 10%; S.W. 9%; W. 7%

University of Virginia (McIntire)[1]

Monroe Hall
248 McCormick Road
Charlottesville, VA 22903
http://www.commerce.virginia.edu
Public
Admissions: (877) 349-2620
E-mail: mcintiregrad@virginia.edu
Financial aid: N/A
Tuition: N/A
Room/board/expenses: N/A
Enrollment: N/A

Virginia Commonwealth University

1015 Floyd Avenue
PO Box 844000
Richmond, VA 23284-4000
http://www.gsib.bus.vcu.edu
Public
Admissions: (804) 828-4622
E-mail: gsib@vcu.edu
Financial aid: (804) 828-6669
Application deadline: 07/15
In-state tuition: full time: $8,884; part time: $468/credit hour
Out-of-state tuition: full time: $19,392
Room/board/expenses: $12,000
College-funded aid: Yes
International student aid: Yes
Full-time enrollment: N/A
men: N/A; women: N/A;
minorities: N/A; international: N/A
Part-time enrollment: 308
men: 65%; women: 35%;
minorities: 17%; international: 12%
Average GMAT (part-time): 564
TOEFL requirement: Yes
Minimum TOEFL score: 600
Most popular departments: finance, general management, human resources management, marketing, real estate

Virginia Tech (Pamplin)

1044 Pamplin Hall (0209)
Blacksburg, VA 24061
http://www.mba.vt.edu
Public
Admissions: (540) 231-6152
E-mail: mba_info@vt.edu
Financial aid: (540) 231-5179
Application deadline: 07/01
In-state tuition: full time: $9,156; part time: $409/credit hour
Out-of-state tuition: full time: $15,351
Room/board/expenses: $8,200
College-funded aid: Yes
International student aid: Yes
Average student indebtedness at graduation: $28,404
Full-time enrollment: 79
men: 80%; women: 20%;
minorities: 6%; international: 52%
Part-time enrollment: 123
men: 60%; women: 40%;
minorities: 23%; international: 15%
Acceptance rate (full-time): 58%
Average GMAT (full-time): 629
Average GMAT (part-time): 614
Average GPA (full-time): 3.42
Average age of entrants to full-time program: 26
Average months of prior work experience (full-time): 37
TOEFL requirement: Yes
Minimum TOEFL score: 550
Most popular departments: accounting, finance, general management, leadership
Mean starting base salary for 2007 full-time graduates: $64,921
Employment location for 2007 class: Intl. N/A; N.E. 19%; M.A. 67%; S. 5%; M.W. 5%; S.W. N/A; W. 5%

WASHINGTON

Eastern Washington University

668 N. Riverpoint Boulevard
Suite A
Spokane, WA 99202-1677
http://www.ewu.edu/mba
Public
Admissions: (509) 358-2270
E-mail: mbaprogram@ewu.edu
Financial aid: (509) 359-2314
Application deadline: 09/10
In-state tuition: total program: $8,635 (full-time); part time: $216/credit hour
Out-of-state tuition: total program: $14,005 (full-time)
Room/board/expenses: $11,150
College-funded aid: Yes
International student aid: Yes
Full-time enrollment: N/A
men: N/A; women: N/A;
minorities: N/A; international: N/A
Part-time enrollment: 86
men: 57%; women: 43%;
minorities: 7%; international: 27%
Average GMAT (part-time): 519
TOEFL requirement: Yes
Minimum TOEFL score: 580
Most popular departments: accounting, finance, health care administration, marketing, public administration

Gonzaga University

502 E. Boone Avenue
Spokane, WA 99258-0009
http://www.jepson.gonzaga.edu/graduate
Private
Admissions: (509) 323-3414
E-mail: piskel@jepson.gonzaga.edu
Financial aid: (509) 323-6581
Application deadline: rolling
Tuition: full time: N/A; part time: $670/credit hour
Room/board/expenses: $5,000
College-funded aid: Yes
International student aid: Yes
Average student indebtedness at graduation: $12,115
Full-time enrollment: N/A
men: N/A; women: N/A;
minorities: N/A; international: N/A
Part-time enrollment: 221
men: 63%; women: 37%;
minorities: 12%; international: 10%
Average GMAT (part-time): 568
TOEFL requirement: Yes
Minimum TOEFL score: 570
Most popular departments: accounting, entrepreneurship, finance, health care administration, marketing

Pacific Lutheran University

Tacoma, WA 98447
http://www.plu.edu/~busa/mba
Private
Admissions: (253) 535-7151
E-mail: business@plu.edu
Financial aid: (253) 535-7161
Application deadline: rolling
Tuition: full time: N/A; part time: N/A
Room/board/expenses: N/A
College-funded aid: Yes
International student aid: Yes
Full-time enrollment: N/A
men: N/A; women: N/A;
minorities: N/A; international: N/A
Part-time enrollment: 84
men: 52%; women: 48%;
minorities: 8%; international: 18%
Average GMAT (part-time): 523
TOEFL requirement: Yes
Minimum TOEFL score: 570

Seattle Pacific University

3307 Third Avenue W
Suite 201
Seattle, WA 98119-1950
http://www.spu.edu/sbe
Private
Admissions: (206) 281-2753
E-mail: djwysom@spu.edu
Financial aid: (206) 281-2469
Application deadline: 08/01
Tuition: full time: N/A; part time:
$625/credit hour
Room/board/expenses: $12,901
College-funded aid: No
International student aid: No
Full-time enrollment: N/A
men: N/A; women: N/A;
minorities: N/A; international: N/A
Part-time enrollment: 134
men: 56%; women: 44%;
minorities: 16%; international: 6%
Average GMAT (part-time): 530
TOEFL requirement: Yes
Minimum TOEFL score: 565
Most popular departments:
e-commerce, finance, general
management, human resources
management, management
information systems

Seattle University (Albers)

901 12th Avenue
PO Box 222000
Seattle, WA 98122-1090
http://www.seattleu.edu/asbe
Private
Admissions: (206) 296-5708
E-mail: carpms@seattleu.edu
Financial aid: (206) 296-2000
Application deadline: 08/20
Tuition: full time: $645/credit hour;
part time: $645/credit hour
Room/board/expenses: $11,518
College-funded aid: Yes
International student aid: No
**Average student indebtedness at
graduation:** $28,047
Full-time enrollment: N/A
men: N/A; women: N/A;
minorities: N/A; international: N/A
Part-time enrollment: 698
men: 62%; women: 38%;
minorities: 21%; international: 11%
Average GMAT (part-time): 573
TOEFL requirement: Yes
Minimum TOEFL score: 580
Most popular departments: account-
ing, finance, general management,
international business, leadership

University of Washington (Foster)

PO Box 353200
Seattle, WA 98195-3200
http://foster.washington.edu/mba/
Public
Admissions: (206) 543-4661
E-mail: mba@u.washington.edu
Financial aid: (206) 543-4661
Application deadline: 03/15
In-state tuition: full time: $19,843;
part time: $16,536
Out-of-state tuition: full time:
$29,543
Room/board/expenses: $24,191
College-funded aid: Yes
International student aid: Yes
**Average student indebtedness at
graduation:** $30,800
Full-time enrollment: 218
men: 61%; women: 39%;
minorities: 13%; international: 33%
Part-time enrollment: 206
men: 70%; women: 30%;
minorities: 20%; international: 11%
Acceptance rate (full-time): 36%
Average GMAT (full-time): 679
Average GMAT (part-time): 663
Average GPA (full-time): 3.38
**Average age of entrants to full-time
program:** 29

**Average months of prior work
experience (full-time):** 68
TOEFL requirement: Yes
Minimum TOEFL score: 600
**Mean starting base salary for 2007
full-time graduates:** $84,992
Employment location for 2007 class:
Intl. 5%; N.E. 2%; M.A. 0%; S. 0%;
M.W. 2%; S.W. 0%; W. 92%

Washington State University

PO Box 644744
Pullman, WA 99164-4744
http://www.cbe.wsu.edu/graduate
Public
Admissions: (509) 335-7617
E-mail: mba@wsu.edu
Financial aid: (509) 335-9711
Application deadline: 01/10
In-state tuition: full time: $11,126;
part time: $354/credit hour
Out-of-state tuition: full time:
$22,118
Room/board/expenses: $14,058
College-funded aid: Yes
International student aid: Yes
Full-time enrollment: 56
men: 64%; women: 36%;
minorities: 14%; international: 38%
Part-time enrollment: N/A
men: N/A; women: N/A;
minorities: N/A; international: N/A
Acceptance rate (full-time): 48%
Average GMAT (full-time): 570
Average GPA (full-time): 3.39
**Average age of entrants to full-time
program:** 25
**Average months of prior work
experience (full-time):** 39
TOEFL requirement: Yes
Minimum TOEFL score: 580
**Mean starting base salary for 2007
full-time graduates:** $43,021
Employment location for 2007 class:
Intl. 33%; N.E. N/A; M.A. N/A; S.
N/A; M.W. N/A; S.W. N/A; W. 67%

Western Washington University

516 High Street, MS 9072
Bellingham, WA 98225-9072
http://www.cbe.wwu.edu/mba/
Public
Admissions: (360) 650-3898
E-mail: mba@wwu.edu
Financial aid: (360) 650-3470
Application deadline: 05/01
In-state tuition: full time: $7,948;
part time: $208/credit hour
Out-of-state tuition: full time:
$17,911
Room/board/expenses: $6,900
College-funded aid: Yes
International student aid: Yes
**Average student indebtedness at
graduation:** $10,000
Full-time enrollment: 41
men: 49%; women: 51%;
minorities: 7%; international: 12%
Part-time enrollment: 27
men: 48%; women: 52%;
minorities: 26%; international: 4%
Acceptance rate (full-time): 75%
Average GMAT (full-time): 551
Average GPA (full-time): 3.15
**Average age of entrants to full-time
program:** 27
**Average months of prior work
experience (full-time):** 38
TOEFL requirement: Yes
Minimum TOEFL score: 567

Marshall University (Lewis)

1 John Marshall Drive
Huntington, WV 25755-2020
http://lcob.marshall.edu
Public
Admissions: (800) 642-9842
E-mail: johnson73@marshall.edu
Financial aid: (800) 438-5390
Application deadline: rolling
In-state tuition: full time: $4,606;
part time: $240/credit hour
Out-of-state tuition: full time:
$12,548
Room/board/expenses: $800
College-funded aid: Yes
International student aid: Yes
Full-time enrollment: 214
men: 40%; women: 60%;
minorities: 17%; international: 20%
Part-time enrollment: 132
men: 39%; women: 61%;
minorities: 13%; international: 2%
Acceptance rate (full-time): 70%
Average GMAT (full-time): 540
Average GPA (full-time): 3.32
**Average age of entrants to full-time
program:** 23
TOEFL requirement: Yes
Minimum TOEFL score: 550
Most popular departments:
accounting, general management,
health care administration, human
resources management

West Virginia University

PO Box 6027
Morgantown, WV 26506
http://www.be.wvu.edu
Public
Admissions: (304) 293-5408
E-mail: mba@wvu.edu
Financial aid: (304) 293-5242
Application deadline: 03/01
In-state tuition: total program:
$11,738 (full-time); part time:
$595/credit hour
Out-of-state tuition: total program:
$31,868 (full-time)
Room/board/expenses: $12,490
College-funded aid: Yes
International student aid: Yes
Full-time enrollment: 50
men: 62%; women: 38%;
minorities: 6%; international: 10%
Part-time enrollment: 153
men: 63%; women: 37%;
minorities: 3%; international: 3%
Acceptance rate (full-time): 46%
Average GMAT (full-time): 540
Average GMAT (part-time): 536
Average GPA (full-time): 3.44
**Average age of entrants to full-time
program:** 24
**Average months of prior work
experience (full-time):** 32
TOEFL requirement: Yes
Minimum TOEFL score: 580

Marquette University

PO Box 1881
Milwaukee, WI 53201-1881
http://www.marquette.edu/gsm
Private
Admissions: (414) 288-7145
E-mail: mba@Marquette.edu
Financial aid: (414) 288-7137
Application deadline: rolling
Tuition: full time: $800/credit hour;
part time: $800/credit hour
Room/board/expenses: $14,210
College-funded aid: Yes
International student aid: Yes
Full-time enrollment: N/A
men: N/A; women: N/A;
minorities: N/A; international: N/A

Part-time enrollment: 586
men: 67%; women: 33%;
minorities: 8%; international: 9%
Average GMAT (part-time): 569
TOEFL requirement: Yes
Minimum TOEFL score: 550
Most popular departments: finance,
general management, international
business, marketing, management
information systems

University of Wisconsin–Eau Claire

Schneider Hall 309
Eau Claire, WI 54702-4004
http://www.uwec.edu/cob/
academics/mba/index.htm
Public
Admissions: (715) 836-5415
E-mail: uwecmba@uwec.edu
Financial aid: (715) 836-3373
Application deadline: 07/01
In-state tuition: full time: $412/credit
hour; part time: $412/credit hour
Out-of-state tuition: full time:
$1,003/credit hour
Room/board/expenses: $4,620
College-funded aid: Yes
International student aid: Yes
Full-time enrollment: N/A
men: N/A; women: N/A;
minorities: N/A; international: N/A
Part-time enrollment: 100
men: 60%; women: 40%;
minorities: N/A; international: N/A
Average GMAT (part-time): 570
TOEFL requirement: Yes
Minimum TOEFL score: 550
Most popular departments:
accounting, general manage-
ment, human resources manage-
ment, marketing, operations
management

University of Wisconsin–La Crosse

1725 State Street
La Crosse, WI 54601
http://www.uwlax.edu
Public
Admissions: (608) 785-8939
E-mail: admissions@uwlax.edu
Financial aid: (608) 785-8604
Application deadline: rolling
In-state tuition: full time: $7,588;
part time: $664/credit hour
Out-of-state tuition: full time:
$18,200
Room/board/expenses: $7,000
College-funded aid: Yes
International student aid: Yes
Full-time enrollment: N/A
men: N/A; women: N/A;
minorities: N/A; international: N/A
Part-time enrollment: 55
men: N/A; women: N/A;
minorities: N/A; international: N/A
Average GMAT (part-time): 533
TOEFL requirement: Yes
Minimum TOEFL score: 550

University of Wisconsin–Madison

3150 Grainger Hall
975 University Avenue
Madison, WI 53706-1323
http://www.bus.wisc.edu/mba
Public
Admissions: (608) 262-4000
E-mail: mba@bus.wisc.edu
Financial aid: (608) 262-4000
Application deadline: rolling
In-state tuition: full time: $11,098;
part time: $15,796
Out-of-state tuition: full time:
$26,536
Room/board/expenses: $14,943
College-funded aid: Yes
International student aid: Yes

Full-time enrollment: 224
men: 71%; women: 29%;
minorities: 12%; international: 25%
Part-time enrollment: 146
men: 71%; women: 29%;
minorities: 11%; international: 16%
Acceptance rate (full-time): 33%
Average GMAT (full-time): 656
Average GMAT (part-time): 593
Average GPA (full-time): 3.37
**Average age of entrants to full-time
program:** 28
**Average months of prior work
experience (full-time):** 48
TOEFL requirement: Yes
Minimum TOEFL score: 600
Most popular departments:
finance, marketing, portfolio
management, real estate, supply
chain management
**Mean starting base salary for 2007
full-time graduates:** $82,000
Employment location for 2007 class:
Intl. 1%; N.E. 19%; M.A. 6%; S. 6%;
M.W. 57%; S.W. 2%; W. 10%

University of Wisconsin– Milwaukee (Lubar)

PO Box 742
Milwaukee, WI 53201-9863
http://www.uwm.edu/Business
Public
Admissions: (414) 229-5403
E-mail: mba-ms@uwm.edu
Financial aid: (414) 229-4541
Application deadline: 01/01
In-state tuition: full time: N/A; part
time: $10,239
Out-of-state tuition: full time: N/A
Room/board/expenses: $12,000
College-funded aid: Yes
International student aid: Yes
**Average student indebtedness at
graduation:** $15,315
Full-time enrollment: N/A
men: N/A; women: N/A;
minorities: N/A; international: N/A
Part-time enrollment: 572
men: 59%; women: 41%;
minorities: 8%; international: 5%
Average GMAT (part-time): 552
TOEFL requirement: Yes
Minimum TOEFL score: 550
Most popular departments: account-
ing, finance, general management,
marketing, tax

University of Wisconsin–Oshkosh[1]

800 Algoma Boulevard
Oshkosh, WI 54901
http://www.uwosh.edu/coba/
Public
Admissions: (800) 633-1430
E-mail: mba@uwosh.edu
Financial aid: (920) 424-3377
Tuition: N/A
Room/board/expenses: N/A
Enrollment: N/A

University of Wisconsin–Parkside

PO Box 2000
Kenosha, WI 53141-2000
http://www.uwp.edu/
departments/business
Public
Admissions: (262) 595-2046
E-mail: baldwin@uwp.edu
Financial aid: (262) 595-2574
Application deadline: 08/01
In-state tuition: full time:
$396/credit hour; part time:
$396/credit hour
Out-of-state tuition: full time:
$986/credit hour
Room/board/expenses: N/A
College-funded aid: No
International student aid: No

Full-time enrollment: 8
men: 63%; women: 38%;
minorities: 0%; international: 75%
Part-time enrollment: 69
men: 57%; women: 43%;
minorities: 16%; international: 0%
Acceptance rate (full-time): 100%
Average GMAT (part-time): 450
Average GPA (full-time): 3.15
TOEFL requirement: Yes
Minimum TOEFL score: 550

University of Wisconsin–River Falls
410 S. Third Street
River Falls, WI 54022-5001
http://www.uwrf.edu/cbe/masters
Private
Admissions: (715) 425-3335
E-mail: mmcbe@uwrf.edu
Financial aid: N/A
Application deadline: rolling
Tuition: full time: N/A; part time:
$445/credit hour

Room/board/expenses: N/A
College-funded aid: Yes
International student aid: Yes
Full-time enrollment: N/A
men: N/A; women: N/A;
minorities: N/A; international: N/A
Part-time enrollment: 79
men: 49%; women: 51%;
minorities: 1%; international: 5%
Average GMAT (part-time): 426
TOEFL requirement: Yes
Minimum TOEFL score: 550

University of Wisconsin–Whitewater
800 W. Main Street
Whitewater, WI 53190
http://www.uww.edu/
Public
Admissions: (262) 472-1945
E-mail: zahnd@uww.edu
Financial aid: (262) 472-1130
Application deadline: 07/15

In-state tuition: full time: $414/credit
hour; part time: $414/credit hour
Out-of-state tuition: full time:
$1,006/credit hour
Room/board/expenses: $8,600
College-funded aid: Yes
International student aid: Yes
Full-time enrollment: 53
men: 55%; women: 45%;
minorities: 25%; international: 58%
Part-time enrollment: 477
men: 53%; women: 47%;
minorities: 4%; international: 1%
Acceptance rate (full-time): 92%
Average GPA (full-time): 3.15
**Average age of entrants to full-time
program:** 24
**Average months of prior work
experience (full-time):** 27
TOEFL requirement: Yes
Minimum TOEFL score: 550
Most popular departments: finance,
general management, human resources management, marketing,
operations management

University of Wyoming[1]
PO Box 3275
Laramie, WY 82071-3275
http://business.uwyo.edu/
MBA_index.html
Public
Admissions: (307) 766-2449
E-mail: mba@uwyo.edu
Financial aid: (307) 766-3886
Tuition: N/A
Room/board/expenses: N/A
Enrollment: N/A

EDUCATION

The education school directory lists 278 schools nationwide that offer doctoral programs in education. Two hundred forty-five schools responded to the *U.S. News* survey, which was conducted in the fall of 2007 and early 2008. Their data, including information on entrance requirements, enrollment, the cost of attendance, fellowships and assistantships, and areas of student specialization, are reported below. Schools that did not respond to the survey have abbreviated entries.

TERMINOLOGY

1 A school whose name has been footnoted with the numeral 1 did not return the *U.S. News* statistical survey; limited data appear in its entry.

N/A. Not available from the school or not applicable.

Admissions. The office phone number.

E-mail. The electronic address of the admissions office. If, instead of an E-mail address, a website is listed, the website will automatically present an E-mail screen programmed to reach the admissions office.

Financial aid. The financial aid office phone number.

Application deadline. For fall 2009 enrollment. "Rolling" means there is no application deadline; the school acts on applications as they are received. "Varies" means deadlines vary according to department or whether applicants are U.S. citizens or foreign nationals.

Tuition. For the 2007–2008 academic year. Includes fees.

Credit hour. The cost per credit hour for the 2007–2008 academic year.

Room/board/expenses. For the 2007–2008 academic year.

Enrollment. Full and part time for fall 2007.

Minorities. For fall 2007, percentage of students who are Asian-American, African-American, Hispanic, or American Indian. (When the U.S. Department of Education calculates minority enrollment percentages, these are the demographic groupings it uses.)

Acceptance rate. Percentage of applicants who were accepted for fall 2007

master's and doctoral programs.

Entrance test required. "GRE" means that Graduate Record Examinations scores are required by some or all departments. "MAT" means that the Miller Analogies Test is required by some or all departments. "GRE or MAT" means that some or all departments require either the GRE or MAT.

Average GRE scores. Average verbal and quantitative scores for students who entered in fall 2007. Averages are based on the number of students who provided the school with scores. That number may be less than the total number of students entering in fall 2007. The GRE scores published in the ranking table refer to the scores of a school's entering doctoral students and may not be the same as the average GRE scores for the overall entering class printed in the directory.

Total research assistantships. For the 2007–2008 academic year.

Students reporting specialty. The percentage of graduate students, both full and part time, reporting a program specialization in fall 2007. If this figure is less than 50 percent, this entry and the specialties do not appear.

Student specialties. Proportion of students in the specialty-reporting population (not necessarily the entire student body) who are enrolled in a particular specialty. Numbers may not add up to 100 because of rounding or students enrolled in multiple specialties. The largest specialty areas in graduate education are listed.

ALABAMA

Alabama State University
915 S. Jackson Street
Montgomery, AL 36101
http://www.alasu.edu/Education/
Public
Admissions: (334) 229-4275
Financial aid: (334) 229-4324
Application deadline: rolling
In-state tuition: full time: $192/credit hour; part time: $192/credit hour
Out-of-state tuition: full time: $384/credit hour
Room/board/expenses: $6,330
Full-time enrollment: 230
doctoral students: 8%; master's students: 90%; education specialists: 2%; men: 30%; women: 70%; minorities: 93%; international: 0%
Part-time enrollment: 594
doctoral students: 7%; master's students: 76%; education specialists: 16%; men: 22%; women: 78%; minorities: 90%; international: 0%
Acceptance rate (master's): 87%
Acceptance rate (doctoral): 98%
Entrance test required: GRE or MAT
Avg. GRE (of all entering students with scores): quantitative: 423; verbal: 366
Students reporting specialty: 100%
Students specializing in: admin.: 23%; counseling: 6%; elementary: 13%; secondary: 22%; special: 10%; instructional media design: 5%; other: 22%

Auburn University– Main Campus
3084 Haley Center
Auburn , AL 36849-5218
http://www.auburn.edu/
Public
Admissions: (334) 844-4700
E-mail: gradadm@auburn.edu
Financial aid: (334) 844-4367
Application deadline: rolling
In-state tuition: full time: $5,754; part time: $217/credit hour
Out-of-state tuition: full time: $16,254
Room/board/expenses: $10,916
Full-time enrollment: 340
doctoral students: 29%; master's students: 70%; education specialists: 1%; men: 31%; women: 69%; minorities: 18%; international: 4%
Part-time enrollment: 415
doctoral students: 50%; master's students: 44%; education specialists: 6%; men: 34%; women: 66%; minorities: 24%; international: 2%
Acceptance rate (master's): 68%
Acceptance rate (doctoral): 30%
Entrance test required: GRE
Avg. GRE (of all entering students with scores): quantitative: 487; verbal: 428
Research assistantships: 29
Students reporting specialty: 100%
Students specializing in: admin.: 6%; counseling: 8%; educational psych: 8%; elementary: 14%; higher education admin.: 9%; secondary: 13%; special: 18%; technical (vocational): 12%; instructional media design: 2%; other: 9%

Auburn University– Montgomery
7051 Senators Drive
Montgomery, AL 36117
http://www.aum.edu
Public
Admissions: (334) 244-3615
E-mail: admitme@mail.aum.edu
Financial aid: (334) 244-3571
Application deadline: rolling
In-state tuition: full time: $4,770; part time: $189/credit hour
Out-of-state tuition: full time: $13,842
Room/board/expenses: $7,840
Full-time enrollment: N/A
doctoral students: N/A; master's students: N/A; education specialists: N/A; men: N/A; women: N/A; minorities: N/A; international: N/A
Part-time enrollment: N/A
doctoral students: N/A; master's students: N/A; education specialists: N/A; men: N/A; women: N/A; minorities: N/A; international: N/A
Acceptance rate (master's): N/A
Acceptance rate (doctoral): N/A
Entrance test required: GRE or MAT
Avg. GRE (of all entering students with scores): quantitative: N/A; verbal: N/A
Research assistantships: 0
Students reporting specialty: 100%
Students specializing in: admin.: 23%; counseling: 13%; elementary: 37%; secondary: 27%

Samford University (Beeson)
800 Lakeshore Drive
Birmingham, AL 35229
http://dlserver.samford.edu/
Private
Admissions: (205) 726-2019
E-mail: jmpersal@samford.edu
Financial aid: (205) 726-2905
Application deadline: rolling
Tuition: full time: $520/credit hour; part time: $520/credit hour
Room/board/expenses: $9,877
Full-time enrollment: 90
doctoral students: 89%; master's students: 11%; education specialists: 0%; men: 24%; women: 76%; minorities: 10%; international: N/A
Part-time enrollment: 79
doctoral students: 0%; master's students: 46%; education specialists: 54%; men: 19%; women: 81%; minorities: 16%; international: 1%
Acceptance rate (master's): 88%
Acceptance rate (doctoral): 78%
Entrance test required: GRE or MAT
Avg. GRE (of all entering students with scores): quantitative: 476; verbal: 483
Research assistantships: 1
Students reporting specialty: 100%
Students specializing in: admin.: 75%; elementary: 7%; other: 18%

University of Alabama
Box 870231
Tuscaloosa, AL 35487-0231
http://graduate.ua.edu
Public
Admissions: (205) 348-5921
E-mail: intergradapply@aalan.ua.edu
Financial aid: (205) 348-6756
Application deadline: N/A
In-state tuition: full time: $5,700; part time: N/A
Out-of-state tuition: full time: $16,518
Room/board/expenses: $11,095

Full-time enrollment: 324
doctoral students: 52%; master's students: 41%; education specialists: 8%; men: 31%; women: 69%; minorities: 22%; international: 3%
Part-time enrollment: 621
doctoral students: 49%; master's students: 34%; education specialists: 17%; men: 30%; women: 70%; minorities: 15%; international: 2%
Acceptance rate (master's): 72%
Acceptance rate (doctoral): 65%
Entrance test required: GRE or MAT
Avg. GRE (of all entering students with scores): quantitative: 508; verbal: 435
Research assistantships: 48
Students reporting specialty: 90%
Students specializing in: admin.: 29%; counseling: 5%; evaluation/research/statistics: 1%; educational psych: 4%; elementary: 13%; higher education admin.: 15%; secondary: 16%; special: 6%; other: 19%

University of Alabama–Birmingham

1530 Third Avenue S, EB 217
Birmingham, AL 35294-1250
http://www.uab.edu/graduate
Public
Admissions: (205) 934-8227
E-mail: gradschool@uab.edu
Financial aid: (205) 934-8223
Application deadline: rolling
In-state tuition: full time: $3,920; part time: $182/credit hour
Out-of-state tuition: full time: $8,834
Room/board/expenses: $11,324
Full-time enrollment: 244
doctoral students: 7%; master's students: 89%; education specialists: 4%; men: 18%; women: 82%; minorities: 26%; international: 3%
Part-time enrollment: 542
doctoral students: 17%; master's students: 74%; education specialists: 9%; men: 23%; women: 77%; minorities: 25%; international: 1%
Acceptance rate (master's): N/A
Acceptance rate (doctoral): N/A
Entrance test required: N/A
Avg. GRE (of all entering students with scores): quantitative: N/A; verbal: N/A
Students reporting specialty: 0%
Students specializing in: N/A

University of South Alabama

UCOM 3600
Mobile, AL 36688
http://www.southalabama.edu/
Public
Admissions: (251) 460-6141
E-mail: admiss@usouthal.edu
Financial aid: (251) 460-6231
Application deadline: 07/15
In-state tuition: full time: $176/credit hour; part time: $176/credit hour
Out-of-state tuition: full time: $352/credit hour
Room/board/expenses: N/A
Full-time enrollment: 387
doctoral students: 4%; master's students: 88%; education specialists: 8%; men: 16%; women: 84%; minorities: 31%; international: 4%
Part-time enrollment: 331
doctoral students: 15%; master's students: 69%; education specialists: 16%; men: 15%; women: 85%; minorities: 23%; international: 2%
Acceptance rate (master's): 46%
Acceptance rate (doctoral): 33%
Entrance test required: GRE or MAT
Avg. GRE (of all entering students with scores): quantitative: N/A; verbal: N/A
Students reporting specialty: 100%
Students specializing in: admin.: 4%; counseling: 15%; elementary: 16%; secondary: 9%; special: 18%; other: 38%

ARIZONA

Arizona State University

PO Box 870211
Tempe, AZ 85287-0211
http://www.asu.edu/graduate
Public
Admissions: (480) 965-6113
E-mail: asugrad@asu.edu
Financial aid: (480) 965-3521
Application deadline: rolling
In-state tuition: full time: $6,377; part time: $326/credit hour
Out-of-state tuition: full time: $18,070
Room/board/expenses: $15,660
Full-time enrollment: 625
doctoral students: 54%; master's students: 46%; education specialists: N/A; men: 25%; women: 75%; minorities: 20%; international: 11%
Part-time enrollment: 674
doctoral students: 35%; master's students: 65%; education specialists: N/A; men: 24%; women: 76%; minorities: 22%; international: 3%
Acceptance rate (master's): 62%
Acceptance rate (doctoral): 25%
Entrance test required: GRE or MAT
Avg. GRE (of all entering students with scores): quantitative: N/A; verbal: N/A
Research assistantships: 179
Students reporting specialty: 83%
Students specializing in: admin.: 21%; counseling: 13%; curriculum/instr.: 40%; evaluation/research/statistics: 4%; social/philosophical foundations: 1%; policy: 5%; educational tech.: 4%; educational psych: 5%; elementary: 10%; higher education admin.: 7%; secondary: 0%; special: 4%; instructional media design: 1%; other: 0%

Northern Arizona University

PO Box 5774
Flagstaff, AZ 86011-5774
http://coe.nau.edu/aboutCOE.php
Public
Admissions: (928) 523-6728
E-mail: Graduate.College@nau.edu
Financial aid: (928) 523-4951
Application deadline: rolling
In-state tuition: full time: $5,212; part time: $328/credit hour
Out-of-state tuition: full time: $14,894
Room/board/expenses: $13,757
Full-time enrollment: 959
doctoral students: 5%; master's students: 95%; education specialists: N/A; men: 20%; women: 80%; minorities: 31%; international: 1%
Part-time enrollment: 2,134
doctoral students: 6%; master's students: 94%; education specialists: N/A; men: 24%; women: 76%; minorities: 25%; international: 0%
Acceptance rate (master's): N/A
Acceptance rate (doctoral): N/A
Entrance test required: GRE or MAT
Avg. GRE (of all entering students with scores): quantitative: N/A; verbal: N/A
Research assistantships: 4
Students reporting specialty: 99%
Students specializing in: admin.: 19%; counseling: 14%; curriculum/instr.: 2%; educational tech.: 1%; educational psych: 1%; elementary: 23%; secondary: 7%; special: 6%; other: 27%

University of Arizona

Box 210069
1430 E. Second Street
Tucson, AZ 85721-0069
http://coe.arizona.edu/
Public
Admissions: (520) 626-8857
E-mail: tembry@grad.arizona.edu
Financial aid: (520) 621-5200
Application deadline: N/A
In-state tuition: full time: $5,868; part time: $365/credit hour
Out-of-state tuition: full time: $16,674
Room/board/expenses: $10,566
Full-time enrollment: 393
doctoral students: 34%; master's students: 61%; education specialists: 5%; men: 23%; women: 77%; minorities: 39%; international: 15%
Part-time enrollment: 343
doctoral students: 71%; master's students: 26%; education specialists: 4%; men: 32%; women: 68%; minorities: 28%; international: 7%
Acceptance rate (master's): 100%
Acceptance rate (doctoral): 55%
Entrance test required: GRE or MAT
Avg. GRE (of all entering students with scores): quantitative: 617; verbal: 484
Research assistantships: 34
Students reporting specialty: 100%
Students specializing in: admin.: 10%; counseling: 3%; curriculum/instr.: 21%; social/philosophical foundations: 19%; policy: 3%; educational psych: 5%; elementary: 4%; higher education admin.: 15%; junior high: 2%; secondary: 4%; special: 32%; instructional media design: 2%

ARKANSAS

University of Arkansas–Fayetteville

324 Graduate Education Building
Fayetteville, AR 72701
http://coehp.uark.edu
Public
Admissions: (479) 575-4401
E-mail: gradinfo@cavern.uark.edu
Financial aid: (479) 575-3806
Application deadline: 08/01
In-state tuition: full time: $281/credit hour; part time: $281/credit hour
Out-of-state tuition: full time: $664/credit hour
Room/board/expenses: $10,018
Full-time enrollment: 271
doctoral students: 23%; master's students: 76%; education specialists: 1%; men: 28%; women: 72%; minorities: 13%; international: 10%
Part-time enrollment: 404
doctoral students: 34%; master's students: 59%; education specialists: 7%; men: 29%; women: 71%; minorities: 22%; international: 0%
Acceptance rate (master's): N/A
Acceptance rate (doctoral): N/A
Entrance test required: GRE or MAT
Avg. GRE (of all entering students with scores): quantitative: N/A; verbal: N/A
Research assistantships: 33
Students reporting specialty: 100%
Students specializing in: admin.: 12%; counseling: 8%; curriculum/instr.: 9%; evaluation/research/statistics: 1%; elementary: 12%; higher education admin.: 12%; junior high: 1%; secondary: 9%; special: 7%; technical (vocational): 0%; instructional media design: 2%; other: 28%

University of Arkansas–Little Rock[1]

2801 S. University Avenue
Little Rock, AR 72204
http://www.ualr.edu/%7Egraddept/gsprodegs.html
Public
Admissions: (501) 569-3127
E-mail: gradinfo@ualr.edu
Financial aid: (501) 569-3450
Tuition: N/A
Room/board/expenses: N/A
Enrollment: N/A

University of Central Arkansas

201 Donaghey Avenue
Conway, AR 72035
http://www.uca.edu/index.php
Public
Admissions: (501) 450-5065
E-mail: bherring@uca.edu
Financial aid: (501) 450-3140
Application deadline: rolling
In-state tuition: full time: $201/credit hour; part time: $201/credit hour
Out-of-state tuition: full time: $402/credit hour
Room/board/expenses: $10,611
Full-time enrollment: N/A
doctoral students: N/A; master's students: N/A; education specialists: N/A; men: N/A; women: N/A; minorities: N/A; international: N/A
Part-time enrollment: N/A
doctoral students: N/A; master's students: N/A; education specialists: N/A; men: N/A; women: N/A; minorities: N/A; international: N/A
Acceptance rate (master's): N/A
Acceptance rate (doctoral): N/A
Entrance test required: GRE or MAT
Avg. GRE (of all entering students with scores): quantitative: N/A; verbal: N/A
Research assistantships: 22
Students reporting specialty: 100%
Students specializing in: admin.: 12%; counseling: 10%; curriculum/instr.: 18%; educational psych: 6%; elementary: 6%; special: 9%; instructional media design: 16%; other: 23%

CALIFORNIA

Alliant International University–San Diego

1 Beach Street
San Francisco, CA 94133-1221
http://www.alliant.edu/
Private
Admissions: (866) 825-5426
E-mail: admissions@alliant.edu
Financial aid: (858) 635-4559
Application deadline: rolling
Tuition: full time: $500/credit hour; part time: $500/credit hour
Room/board/expenses: $18,888
Full-time enrollment: 185
doctoral students: 29%; master's students: 71%; education specialists: N/A; men: 18%; women: 82%; minorities: 27%; international: 14%
Part-time enrollment: 349
doctoral students: 47%; master's students: 53%; education specialists: N/A; men: 28%; women: 72%; minorities: 31%; international: 6%
Acceptance rate (master's): 78%
Acceptance rate (doctoral): 71%
Entrance test required: N/A
Avg. GRE (of all entering students with scores): quantitative: N/A; verbal: N/A
Research assistantships: 7
Students reporting specialty: 100%
Students specializing in: admin.: 16%; educational psych: 9%; elementary: 1%; higher education admin.: 4%; other: 70%

California Polytechnic State University–San Luis Obispo

1 Grand Avenue
San Luis Obispo, CA 93407
http://www.calpoly.edu
Public
Admissions: (805) 756-2913
E-mail: admissions@calpoly.edu
Financial aid: (805) 756-2927
Application deadline: rolling
In-state tuition: full time: $4,605; part time: $4,605
Out-of-state tuition: full time: $226/credit hour
Room/board/expenses: $13,236
Full-time enrollment: 106
doctoral students: 29%; master's students: 71%; education specialists: N/A; men: 29%; women: 71%; minorities: 20%; international: 1%
Part-time enrollment: 25
doctoral students: 0%; master's students: 100%; education specialists: N/A; men: 20%; women: 80%; minorities: 20%; international: N/A
Acceptance rate (master's): 53%
Acceptance rate (doctoral): 100%
Entrance test required: GRE
Avg. GRE (of all entering students with scores): quantitative: N/A; verbal: N/A
Research assistantships: 0
Students reporting specialty: 38%
Students specializing in: N/A

California State University–Fullerton[1]

800 N. State College Boulevard
Fullerton, CA 92831-3599
http://hdcs.fullerton.edu/Education/
Public
Admissions: (714) 278-3352
E-mail: schofedgrad@fullerton.edu
Financial aid: (714) 278-3128
Tuition: N/A
Room/board/expenses: N/A
Enrollment: N/A

California State University–Long Beach

1250 Bellflower Boulevard
Long Beach, CA 90840
http://www.ced.csulb.edu
Public
Admissions: (562) 985-4547
E-mail: nmcgloth@csulb.edu
Financial aid: (562) 985-8403
Application deadline: rolling
In-state tuition: full time: $3,758; part time: $2,324
Out-of-state tuition: full time: $9,860
Room/board/expenses: N/A
Full-time enrollment: 231
doctoral students: 0%; master's students: 100%; education specialists: N/A; men: 23%; women: 77%; minorities: 64%; international: 4%
Part-time enrollment: 561
doctoral students: 5%; master's students: 95%; education specialists: N/A; men: 18%; women: 82%; minorities: 52%; international: 1%
Acceptance rate (master's): 49%
Acceptance rate (doctoral): 38%
Entrance test required: GRE
Avg. GRE (of all entering students with scores): quantitative: N/A; verbal: N/A
Research assistantships: 1
Students reporting specialty: 96%
Students specializing in: admin.: 8%; counseling: 16%; social/philosophical foundations: 6%; educational tech.: 4%; educational psych: 7%; elementary: 31%; higher education admin.: 2%; secondary: 7%; special: 5%; other: 13%

California State University–Los Angeles

5151 State University Drive
Los Angeles, CA 90032
http://www.calstatela.edu/academic/ccoe/
Public
Admissions: (323) 343-3940
Financial aid: (323) 343-3245
Application deadline: rolling
In-state tuition: full time: $4,536; part time: $3,102
Out-of-state tuition: full time: $9,960
Room/board/expenses: N/A
Full-time enrollment: 907
doctoral students: 0%; master's students: 98%; education specialists: 2%; men: 24%; women: 76%; minorities: 64%; international: 4%

Part-time enrollment: 593
doctoral students: 1%; master's students: 81%; education specialists: 18%; men: 28%; women: 72%; minorities: 62%; international: 4%
Acceptance rate (master's): 76%
Acceptance rate (doctoral): 100%
Entrance test required: GRE
Avg. GRE (of all entering students with scores): quantitative: N/A; verbal: N/A
Students reporting specialty: 100%
Students specializing in: admin.: 5%; counseling: 23%; curriculum/instr.: 18%; evaluation/research/statistics: 0%; educational psych: 1%; elementary: 8%; secondary: 13%; special: 17%; instructional media design: 1%; other: 12%

Chapman University
1 University Drive
Orange, CA 92866
http://www.chapman.edu/educ
Private
Admissions: (888) 282-7759
E-mail: admit@chapman.edu
Financial aid: (714) 997-6741
Application deadline: rolling
Tuition: full time: $520/credit hour; part time: $520/credit hour
Room/board/expenses: N/A
Full-time enrollment: 205
doctoral students: 4%; master's students: 73%; education specialists: 23%; men: 13%; women: 87%; minorities: 27%; international: 1%
Part-time enrollment: 180
doctoral students: 9%; master's students: 86%; education specialists: 5%; men: 22%; women: 78%; minorities: 32%; international: 1%
Acceptance rate (master's): 90%
Acceptance rate (doctoral): 58%
Entrance test required: GRE or MAT
Avg. GRE (of all entering students with scores): quantitative: 506; verbal: 494
Research assistantships: 1
Students reporting specialty: 100%
Students specializing in: admin.: 7%; counseling: 9%; curriculum/instr.: 9%; educational psych: 13%; elementary: 28%; secondary: 17%; special: 21%; other: 2%

Claremont Graduate University
150 E. 10th Street
Claremont, CA 91711
http://www.cgu.edu/pages/267.asp
Private
Admissions: (909) 621-8263
E-mail: admiss@cgu.edu
Financial aid: (909) 621-8337
Application deadline: rolling
Tuition: full time: $31,930; part time: $1,376/credit hour
Room/board/expenses: N/A
Full-time enrollment: 265
doctoral students: 85%; master's students: 12%; education specialists: 3%; men: 32%; women: 68%; minorities: 41%; international: 2%
Part-time enrollment: 181
doctoral students: 38%; master's students: 45%; education specialists: 17%; men: 33%; women: 67%; minorities: 38%; international: 1%
Acceptance rate (master's): 82%
Acceptance rate (doctoral): 80%
Entrance test required: GRE
Avg. GRE (of all entering students with scores): quantitative: 509; verbal: 488
Research assistantships: 4
Students reporting specialty: 59%
Students specializing in: admin.: 20%; curriculum/instr.: 3%; evaluation/research/statistics: 0%; policy: 2%; elementary: 10%; higher education admin.: 11%; secondary: 25%; special: 16%; other: 13%

Fielding Graduate University
2112 Santa Barbara Street
Santa Barbara, CA 93105
http://www.fielding.edu/schoolelc/index.htm
Private
Admissions: (800) 340-1099
E-mail: admission@fielding.edu
Financial aid: (805) 898-4008
Application deadline: 07/31
Tuition: full time: $17,640; part time: N/A
Room/board/expenses: $23,785
Full-time enrollment: 364
doctoral students: 80%; master's students: 20%; education specialists: N/A; men: 27%; women: 73%; minorities: 46%; international: N/A
Part-time enrollment: N/A
doctoral students: N/A; master's students: N/A; education specialists: N/A; men: N/A; women: N/A; minorities: N/A; international: N/A
Acceptance rate (master's): 93%
Acceptance rate (doctoral): 88%
Entrance test required: N/A
Avg. GRE (of all entering students with scores): quantitative: N/A; verbal: N/A
Research assistantships: 2
Students reporting specialty: 55%
Students specializing in: higher education admin.: 23%; instructional media design: 11%; other: 67%

Loyola Marymount University
1 LMU Drive
Los Angeles, CA 90045
http://www.lmu.edu
Private
Admissions: (310) 338-2721
E-mail: graduate@lmu.edu
Financial aid: (310) 338-2753
Application deadline: 06/15
Tuition: full time: $830/credit hour; part time: $830/credit hour
Room/board/expenses: $17,877
Full-time enrollment: 675
doctoral students: 2%; master's students: 98%; education specialists: N/A; men: 24%; women: 76%; minorities: 54%; international: 1%
Part-time enrollment: 286
doctoral students: 10%; master's students: 90%; education specialists: N/A; men: 29%; women: 71%; minorities: 46%; international: 3%
Acceptance rate (master's): 35%
Acceptance rate (doctoral): 75%
Entrance test required: GRE
Avg. GRE (of all entering students with scores): quantitative: 510; verbal: 462
Research assistantships: 16
Students reporting specialty: 100%
Students specializing in: admin.: 11%; counseling: 11%; policy: 4%; educational psych: 4%; elementary: 27%; secondary: 26%; special: 10%; other: 9%

Mills College
5000 MacArthur Boulevard
Oakland, CA 94613
http://www.mills.edu/
Private
Admissions: (510) 430-3309
E-mail: grad-studies@mills.edu
Financial aid: (510) 430-2000
Application deadline: 02/01
Tuition: full time: $25,710; part time: $5,702/credit hour
Room/board/expenses: $15,120
Full-time enrollment: 102
doctoral students: 19%; master's students: 81%; education specialists: N/A; men: 10%; women: 90%; minorities: 38%; international: 3%
Part-time enrollment: 62
doctoral students: 55%; master's students: 45%; education specialists: N/A; men: 13%; women: 87%; minorities: 50%; international: N/A
Acceptance rate (master's): 98%
Acceptance rate (doctoral): 91%
Entrance test required: N/A
Avg. GRE (of all entering students with scores): quantitative: N/A; verbal: N/A
Research assistantships: 22
Students reporting specialty: 73%
Students specializing in: admin.: 10%; elementary: 22%; higher education admin.: 47%; secondary: 16%; special: 5%

Pepperdine University
6100 Center Drive
Los Angeles, CA 90045-4301
http://gsep.pepperdine.edu/
Private
Admissions: (310) 568-5600
E-mail: gsep@pepperdine.edu
Financial aid: (310) 258-2848
Application deadline: rolling
Tuition: full time: $795/credit hour; part time: N/A
Room/board/expenses: $24,255
Full-time enrollment: 681
doctoral students: 67%; master's students: 33%; education specialists: N/A; men: 36%; women: 64%; minorities: 35%; international: 4%
Part-time enrollment: 21
doctoral students: 29%; master's students: 71%; education specialists: N/A; men: 38%; women: 62%; minorities: 29%; international: N/A
Acceptance rate (master's): 50%
Acceptance rate (doctoral): 89%
Entrance test required: GRE or MAT
Avg. GRE (of all entering students with scores): quantitative: 534; verbal: 440
Research assistantships: 39
Students reporting specialty: 55%
Students specializing in: admin.: 18%; educational tech.: 25%; elementary: 37%; junior high: 37%; secondary: 37%; other: 57%

San Diego State University
5500 Campanile Drive
San Diego, CA 92182
http://edweb.sdsu.edu/
Public
Admissions: (619) 594-4287
E-mail: scook@mail.sdsu.edu
Financial aid: (619) 594-6323
Application deadline: N/A
In-state tuition: full time: $4,070; part time: $2,636
Out-of-state tuition: full time: $14,240
Room/board/expenses: $15,566
Full-time enrollment: 330
doctoral students: 0%; master's students: 88%; education specialists: 12%; men: 26%; women: 74%; minorities: 59%; international: 10%
Part-time enrollment: 430
doctoral students: 17%; master's students: 82%; education specialists: 0%; men: 20%; women: 80%; minorities: 42%; international: 5%
Acceptance rate (master's): 62%
Acceptance rate (doctoral): 71%
Entrance test required: GRE
Avg. GRE (of all entering students with scores): quantitative: 477; verbal: 435
Research assistantships: 23
Students reporting specialty: 31%
Students specializing in: N/A

San Francisco State University
1600 Holloway Avenue
San Francisco, CA 94132
http://www.sfsu.edu/~gradstdy
Public
Admissions: (415) 338-2234
E-mail: gradstdy@sfsu.edu
Financial aid: (415) 338-7000
Application deadline: N/A
In-state tuition: full time: $1,893/credit hour; part time: $1,242/credit hour
Out-of-state tuition: full time: $2,232/credit hour
Room/board/expenses: $15,636
Full-time enrollment: N/A
doctoral students: N/A; master's students: N/A; education specialists: N/A; men: N/A; women: N/A; minorities: N/A; international: N/A
Part-time enrollment: N/A
doctoral students: N/A; master's students: N/A; education specialists: N/A; men: N/A; women: N/A; minorities: N/A; international: N/A
Acceptance rate (master's): 58%
Acceptance rate (doctoral): 32%
Entrance test required: GRE
Avg. GRE (of all entering students with scores): quantitative: 500; verbal: 520
Students reporting specialty: 0%
Students specializing in: N/A

Stanford University
485 Lasuen Mall
Stanford, CA 94305-3096
http://ed.stanford.edu
Private
Admissions: (650) 723-4794
E-mail: info@suse.stanford.edu
Financial aid: (650) 723-4794
Application deadline: 01/06
Tuition: full time: $35,049; part time: N/A
Room/board/expenses: $20,700
Full-time enrollment: 414
doctoral students: 47%; master's students: 53%; education specialists: N/A; men: 30%; women: 70%; minorities: 36%; international: 11%
Part-time enrollment: N/A
doctoral students: N/A; master's students: N/A; education specialists: N/A; men: N/A; women: N/A; minorities: N/A; international: N/A
Acceptance rate (master's): 49%
Acceptance rate (doctoral): 7%
Entrance test required: GRE
Avg. GRE (of all entering students with scores): quantitative: 677; verbal: 580
Research assistantships: 259
Students reporting specialty: 100%
Students specializing in: curriculum/instr.: 11%; social/philosophical foundations: 14%; policy: 14%; educational psych: 8%; elementary: 6%; secondary: 17%; instructional media design: 10%; other: 19%

University of California–Berkeley
1600 Tolman Hall
MC #1670
Berkeley, CA 94720-1670
http://gse.berkeley.edu
Public
Admissions: (510) 642-0841
E-mail: gse_info@berkeley.edu
Financial aid: (510) 643-1720
Application deadline: N/A
In-state tuition: full time: $9,578; part time: N/A
Out-of-state tuition: full time: $24,272
Room/board/expenses: $21,052
Full-time enrollment: 431
doctoral students: 62%; master's students: 38%; education specialists: N/A; men: 28%; women: 72%; minorities: 39%; international: 6%
Part-time enrollment: N/A
doctoral students: N/A; master's students: N/A; education specialists: N/A; men: N/A; women: N/A; minorities: N/A; international: N/A
Acceptance rate (master's): 42%
Acceptance rate (doctoral): 22%
Entrance test required: GRE
Avg. GRE (of all entering students with scores): quantitative: 628; verbal: 582
Research assistantships: 193
Students reporting specialty: 100%
Students specializing in: admin.: 16%; evaluation/research/statistics: 4%; social/philosophical foundations: 7%; policy: 6%; educational psych: 13%; elementary: 10%; secondary: 14%; special: 4%; other: 25%

University of California–Davis
2060 Academic Surge
1 Shields Avenue
Davis, CA 95616
http://education.ucdavis.edu
Public
Admissions: (530) 752-0757
E-mail: eduadvising@ucdavis.edu
Financial aid: (530) 752-2694
Application deadline: 12/15
In-state tuition: full time: $19,302; part time: $15,975
Out-of-state tuition: full time: $34,290
Room/board/expenses: $16,046
Full-time enrollment: 147
doctoral students: 93%; master's students: 7%; education specialists: N/A; men: 34%; women: 66%; minorities: 31%; international: 8%
Part-time enrollment: 116
doctoral students: 3%; master's students: 97%; education specialists: N/A; men: 21%; women: 79%; minorities: 28%; international: 4%
Acceptance rate (master's): 73%
Acceptance rate (doctoral): 51%
Entrance test required: GRE or MAT
Avg. GRE (of all entering students with scores): quantitative: 520; verbal: 542
Research assistantships: 79
Students reporting specialty: 0%
Students specializing in: N/A

University of California–Irvine
2001 Berkeley Place
Irvine, CA 92697-5500
http://www.gse.uci.edu/
Public
Admissions: (949) 824-7832
E-mail: scarolan@uci.edu
Financial aid: (949) 824-8262
Application deadline: rolling
In-state tuition: full time: $8,210; part time: $4,883
Out-of-state tuition: full time: $23,198
Room/board/expenses: $16,513
Full-time enrollment: 131
doctoral students: 46%; master's students: 54%; education specialists: N/A; men: 32%; women: 68%; minorities: 47%; international: 2%
Part-time enrollment: 25
doctoral students: 100%; master's students: 0%; education specialists: N/A; men: 28%; women: 72%; minorities: 36%; international: N/A
Acceptance rate (master's): 87%
Acceptance rate (doctoral): 27%
Entrance test required: GRE
Avg. GRE (of all entering students with scores): quantitative: 588; verbal: 480
Research assistantships: 3
Students reporting specialty: 100%
Students specializing in: admin.: 23%; other: 77%

University of California–Los Angeles
1009 Moore Hall
MB 951521
Los Angeles, CA 90095-1521
http://www.gseis.ucla.edu
Public
Admissions: (310) 825-8326
E-mail: info@gseis.ucla.edu
Financial aid: (310) 206-0400
Application deadline: 12/01
In-state tuition: full time: $8,967; part time: N/A
Out-of-state tuition: full time: $23,661
Room/board/expenses: $19,725
Full-time enrollment: 760
doctoral students: 42%; master's students: 58%; education specialists: N/A; men: 26%; women: 74%; minorities: 61%; international: 3%

Part-time enrollment: 97
doctoral students: 100%; master's students: 0%; education specialists: N/A; men: 41%; women: 59%; minorities: 37%; international: N/A
Acceptance rate (master's): 59%
Acceptance rate (doctoral): 36%
Entrance test required: GRE
Avg. GRE (of all entering students with scores): quantitative: 573; verbal: 533
Research assistantships: 153
Students reporting specialty: 100%
Students specializing in: admin.: 14%; counseling: 2%; curriculum/instr.: 6%; evaluation/research/statistics: 5%; social/philosophical foundations: 11%; policy: 10%; educational tech.: 0%; educational psych: 7%; elementary: 18%; higher education admin.: 10%; secondary: 22%; special: 1%; instructional media design: 1%

University of California–Riverside

1207 Sproul Hall
Riverside, CA 92521
http://www.education.ucr.edu
Public
Admissions: (951) 827-6362
E-mail: edgrad@ucr.edu
Financial aid: (951) 827-6362
Application deadline: N/A
In-state tuition: full time: $9,814; part time: N/A
Out-of-state tuition: full time: $24,802
Room/board/expenses: $16,900
Full-time enrollment: 199
doctoral students: 60%; master's students: 40%; education specialists: N/A; men: 24%; women: 76%; minorities: 31%; international: 3%
Part-time enrollment: 1
doctoral students: 0%; master's students: 100%; education specialists: N/A; men: N/A; women: 100%; minorities: N/A; international: N/A
Acceptance rate (master's): 59%
Acceptance rate (doctoral): 49%
Entrance test required: GRE
Avg. GRE (of all entering students with scores): quantitative: 596; verbal: 515
Research assistantships: 31
Students reporting specialty: 100%
Students specializing in: N/A

University of California–Santa Barbara (Gevirtz)

Phelps Hall 1190
Santa Barbara, CA 93106-9490
http://www.education.ucsb.edu
Public
Admissions: (805) 893-2137
E-mail: sao@education.ucsb.edu
Financial aid: (805) 893-2432
Application deadline: N/A
In-state tuition: full time: $10,108; part time: N/A
Out-of-state tuition: full time: $25,096
Room/board/expenses: $20,913
Full-time enrollment: 401
doctoral students: 62%; master's students: 35%; education specialists: 4%; men: 23%; women: 77%; minorities: 29%; international: 1%
Part-time enrollment: N/A
doctoral students: N/A; master's students: N/A; education specialists: N/A; men: N/A; women: N/A; minorities: N/A; international: N/A
Acceptance rate (master's): 82%
Acceptance rate (doctoral): 26%
Entrance test required: GRE or MAT
Avg. GRE (of all entering students with scores): quantitative: 592; verbal: 487
Research assistantships: 80
Students reporting specialty: 100%
Students specializing in: admin.: 8%; counseling: 11%; curriculum/instr.: 15%; evaluation/research/statistics: 1%; social/philosophical foundations: 10%; policy: 6%; elementary: 12%; secondary: 13%; special: 11%; other: 13%

University of California–Santa Cruz

1156 High Street
Santa Cruz, CA 95064
http://www.graddiv.ucsc.edu/
Public
Admissions: (831) 459-5905
E-mail: gradadm@ucsc.edu
Financial aid: (831) 459-2963
Application deadline: N/A
In-state tuition: full time: $10,731; part time: $10,731
Out-of-state tuition: full time: $25,425
Room/board/expenses: $19,125
Full-time enrollment: 124
doctoral students: 33%; master's students: 67%; education specialists: N/A; men: 23%; women: 77%; minorities: 27%; international: 1%
Part-time enrollment: 1
doctoral students: 100%; master's students: 0%; education specialists: N/A; men: N/A; women: 100%; minorities: N/A; international: N/A
Acceptance rate (master's): 68%
Acceptance rate (doctoral): 41%
Entrance test required: GRE
Avg. GRE (of all entering students with scores): quantitative: 624; verbal: 561
Research assistantships: 9
Students reporting specialty: 89%
Students specializing in: elementary: 43%; secondary: 32%; other: 25%

University of La Verne

1950 Third Street
La Verne, CA 91750
http://www.ulv.edu/education
Private
Admissions: (909) 593-3511
E-mail: gradadmt@ulv.edu
Financial aid: (909) 593-3511
Application deadline: rolling
Tuition: full time: $640/credit hour; part time: $640/credit hour
Room/board/expenses: N/A
Full-time enrollment: 495
doctoral students: 29%; master's students: 71%; education specialists: N/A; men: 20%; women: 80%; minorities: 43%; international: 0%
Part-time enrollment: 755
doctoral students: 18%; master's students: 82%; education specialists: N/A; men: 23%; women: 77%; minorities: 45%; international: 0%
Acceptance rate (master's): 57%
Acceptance rate (doctoral): 81%
Entrance test required: GRE or MAT
Avg. GRE (of all entering students with scores): quantitative: N/A; verbal: N/A
Students reporting specialty: 100%
Students specializing in: admin.: 28%; counseling: 36%; educational psych: 2%; other: 34%

University of San Diego

5998 Alcala Park
San Diego, CA 92110-2492
http://www.sandiego.edu/academics/soles/
Private
Admissions: (619) 260-4506
E-mail: grads@sandiego.edu
Financial aid: (619) 260-4514
Application deadline: N/A
Tuition: full time: $1,085/credit hour; part time: $1,085/credit hour
Room/board/expenses: $13,818
Full-time enrollment: 181
doctoral students: 2%; master's students: 98%; education specialists: N/A; men: 17%; women: 83%; minorities: 25%; international: 5%
Part-time enrollment: 310
doctoral students: 33%; master's students: 67%; education specialists: N/A; men: 25%; women: 75%; minorities: 25%; international: 1%
Acceptance rate (master's): 63%
Acceptance rate (doctoral): 65%
Entrance test required: GRE
Avg. GRE (of all entering students with scores): quantitative: 544; verbal: 454
Research assistantships: 9
Students reporting specialty: 98%
Students specializing in: admin.: 6%; counseling: 8%; curriculum/instr.: 15%; educational tech.: 2%; elementary: 6%; secondary: 3%; special: 10%; other: 55%

University of San Francisco

2130 Fulton Street
San Francisco, CA 94117-1080
http://www.usfca.edu
Private
Admissions: (415) 422-6563
E-mail: graduate@usfca.edu
Financial aid: (415) 422-6303
Application deadline: N/A
Tuition: full time: $890/credit hour; part time: $890/credit hour
Room/board/expenses: $16,720
Full-time enrollment: 586
doctoral students: 28%; master's students: 72%; education specialists: N/A; men: 22%; women: 78%; minorities: 31%; international: 8%
Part-time enrollment: 299
doctoral students: 37%; master's students: 63%; education specialists: N/A; men: 27%; women: 73%; minorities: 38%; international: 4%
Acceptance rate (master's): 66%
Acceptance rate (doctoral): 66%
Entrance test required: GRE or MAT
Avg. GRE (of all entering students with scores): quantitative: N/A; verbal: N/A
Research assistantships: 10
Students reporting specialty: 100%
Students specializing in: admin.: 4%; counseling: 4%; curriculum/instr.: 10%; educational psych: 28%; elementary: 9%; higher education admin.: 15%; secondary: 6%; special: 4%; instructional media design: 1%; other: 20%

University of Southern California (Rossier)

3470 Trousdale Parkway
Waite Phillips Hall
Los Angeles, CA 90089-0031
http://www.usc.edu/dept/education/
Private
Admissions: (213) 740-0224
E-mail: soeinfo@usc.edu
Financial aid: (213) 740-0224
Application deadline: N/A
Tuition: full time: $1,185/credit hour; part time: $1,185/credit hour
Room/board/expenses: $18,010
Full-time enrollment: 686
doctoral students: 47%; master's students: 53%; education specialists: N/A; men: 28%; women: 72%; minorities: 47%; international: 12%
Part-time enrollment: 383
doctoral students: 79%; master's students: 21%; education specialists: N/A; men: 34%; women: 66%; minorities: 56%; international: 4%
Acceptance rate (master's): 79%
Acceptance rate (doctoral): 51%
Entrance test required: GRE
Avg. GRE (of all entering students with scores): quantitative: 567; verbal: 488
Research assistantships: 22
Students reporting specialty: 96%
Students specializing in: admin.: 54%; counseling: 13%; curriculum/instr.: 0%; policy: 3%; educational tech.: 4%; educational psych: 0%; elementary: 4%; higher education admin.: 11%; secondary: 4%; other: 6%

University of the Pacific

3601 Pacific Avenue
Stockton, CA 95211
http://www.pacific.edu
Private
Admissions: (209) 946-2683
E-mail: gradschool@pacific.edu
Financial aid: (209) 946-2421
Application deadline: rolling
Tuition: full time: $890/credit hour; part time: $890/credit hour
Room/board/expenses: N/A
Full-time enrollment: 80
doctoral students: 13%; master's students: 78%; education specialists: 10%; men: 20%; women: 80%; minorities: 38%; international: 1%
Part-time enrollment: 112
doctoral students: 84%; master's students: 11%; education specialists: 5%; men: 34%; women: 66%; minorities: 31%; international: 2%
Acceptance rate (master's): 86%
Acceptance rate (doctoral): 65%
Entrance test required: GRE
Avg. GRE (of all entering students with scores): quantitative: 555; verbal: 437
Research assistantships: 13
Students reporting specialty: 100%
Students specializing in: admin.: 58%; curriculum/instr.: 20%; educational psych: 2%; elementary: 4%; special: 3%; other: 13%

COLORADO

Colorado State University

Room 111 Education Building
Fort Collins, CO 80523-2015
http://www.colostate.edu/
Public
Admissions: (970) 491-6909
E-mail: gschool@grad.colostate.edu
Financial aid: (970) 491-6321
Application deadline: rolling
In-state tuition: full time: $271/credit hour; part time: $271/credit hour
Out-of-state tuition: full time: $913/credit hour
Room/board/expenses: N/A
Full-time enrollment: 140
doctoral students: 27%; master's students: 73%; education specialists: N/A; men: 31%; women: 69%; minorities: N/A; international: N/A
Part-time enrollment: 406
doctoral students: 50%; master's students: 50%; education specialists: N/A; men: 39%; women: 61%; minorities: N/A; international: N/A
Acceptance rate (master's): 37%
Acceptance rate (doctoral): 63%
Entrance test required: N/A
Avg. GRE (of all entering students with scores): quantitative: N/A; verbal: N/A
Research assistantships: 6
Students reporting specialty: 47%
Students specializing in: N/A

University of Colorado–Boulder

Campus Box 249
Boulder, CO 80309-0249
http://www.colorado.edu/education
Public
Admissions: (303) 492-6555
E-mail: edadvise@colorado.edu
Financial aid: (303) 492-5091
Application deadline: 01/01
In-state tuition: full time: $8,256; part time: $1,172/credit hour
Out-of-state tuition: full time: $23,170
Room/board/expenses: $14,998
Full-time enrollment: 173
doctoral students: 37%; master's students: 63%; education specialists: N/A; men: 25%; women: 75%; minorities: 21%; international: 3%
Part-time enrollment: 166
doctoral students: 4%; master's students: 96%; education specialists: N/A; men: 15%; women: 85%; minorities: 12%; international: 1%
Acceptance rate (master's): 85%
Acceptance rate (doctoral): 29%
Entrance test required: GRE
Avg. GRE (of all entering students with scores): quantitative: 693; verbal: 609
Research assistantships: 114
Students reporting specialty: 89%
Students specializing in: curriculum/instr.: 43%; evaluation/research/statistics: 5%; social/philosophical foundations: 13%; policy: 9%; educational psych: 3%; secondary: 20%; special: 8%; other: 22%

University of Colorado–Denver

PO Box 173364
Campus Box 106
Denver, CO 80217-3364
http://www.cudenver.edu/sehd
Public
Admissions: (303) 556-2717
E-mail: education@cudenver.edu
Financial aid: (303) 556-2886
Application deadline: rolling
In-state tuition: full time: $6,729; part time: $340/credit hour
Out-of-state tuition: full time: $18,897
Room/board/expenses: $11,276
Full-time enrollment: 454
doctoral students: 3%; master's students: 78%; education specialists: 19%; men: 20%; women: 80%; minorities: 13%; international: 0%
Part-time enrollment: 911
doctoral students: 8%; master's students: 88%; education specialists: 4%; men: 17%; women: 83%; minorities: 12%; international: 1%
Acceptance rate (master's): 86%
Acceptance rate (doctoral): 71%
Entrance test required: GRE or MAT
Avg. GRE (of all entering students with scores): quantitative: 565; verbal: 493
Research assistantships: 6
Students reporting specialty: 92%
Students specializing in: N/A

University of Denver (Morgridge)

Graduate Office
A. Hyde Building
Denver, CO 80208
http://www.du.edu/education/
Private
Admissions: (303) 871-2509
E-mail: edinfo@du.edu
Financial aid: (303) 871-2337
Application deadline: N/A
Tuition: full time: $873/credit hour; part time: $873/credit hour
Room/board/expenses: $12,480
Full-time enrollment: 221
doctoral students: 24%; master's students: 63%; education specialists: 12%; men: 21%; women: 79%; minorities: 13%; international: 5%
Part-time enrollment: 323
doctoral students: 53%; master's students: 45%; education specialists: 2%; men: 23%; women: 77%; minorities: 16%; international: 1%
Acceptance rate (master's): 81%
Acceptance rate (doctoral): 56%
Entrance test required: GRE or MAT
Avg. GRE (of all entering students with scores): quantitative: 548; verbal: 487
Research assistantships: 1
Students reporting specialty: 100%
Students specializing in: admin.: 31%; counseling: 13%; curriculum/instr.: 19%; evaluation/research/statistics: 2%; educational psych: 8%; elementary: 6%; higher education admin.: 11%; junior high: 4%; secondary: 5%

MORE AT WWW.USNEWS.COM

University of Northern Colorado
McKee 125
Greeley, CO 80639
http://www.unco.edu/grad/general/home.htm
Public
Admissions: (970) 351-2831
E-mail: gradsch@unco.edu
Financial aid: (970) 351-2502
Application deadline: rolling
In-state tuition: full time: $4,705; part time: $222/credit hour
Out-of-state tuition: full time: $11,990
Room/board/expenses: $12,677
Full-time enrollment: 426
doctoral students: 27%; master's students: 67%; education specialists: 6%; men: 24%; women: 76%; minorities: 14%; international: 8%
Part-time enrollment: 509
doctoral students: 21%; master's students: 69%; education specialists: 10%; men: 21%; women: 79%; minorities: 7%; international: 2%
Acceptance rate (master's): 83%
Acceptance rate (doctoral): 72%
Entrance test required: GRE
Avg. GRE (of all entering students with scores): quantitative: 543; verbal: 467
Students reporting specialty: 96%
Students specializing in: admin.: 10%; counseling: 29%; evaluation/research/statistics: 4%; educational tech.: 4%; educational psych: 12%; elementary: 9%; higher education admin.: 2%; special: 27%; instructional media design: 2%; other: 4%

CONNECTICUT

Central Connecticut State University
1615 Stanley Street
New Britain, CT 06050
http://www.ccsu.edu/grad/
Public
Admissions: (860) 832-2350
E-mail: graduateadmissions@mail.ccsu.edu
Financial aid: (860) 832-2200
Application deadline: 07/01
In-state tuition: full time: $7,491; part time: $400/credit hour
Out-of-state tuition: full time: $14,936
Room/board/expenses: $10,900
Full-time enrollment: 97
doctoral students: 0%; master's students: 100%; education specialists: N/A; men: 24%; women: 76%; minorities: 12%; international: 5%
Part-time enrollment: 680
doctoral students: 8%; master's students: 92%; education specialists: N/A; men: 23%; women: 77%; minorities: 8%; international: 0%
Acceptance rate (master's): 61%
Acceptance rate (doctoral): 44%
Entrance test required: GRE
Avg. GRE (of all entering students with scores): quantitative: N/A; verbal: N/A
Students reporting specialty: 0%
Students specializing in: N/A

Southern Connecticut State University
501 Crescent Street
New Haven, CT 06515
http://www.southernct.edu/
Public
Admissions: (203) 392-5240
E-mail: GradInfo@southernCT.edu
Financial aid: (203) 392-5222
Application deadline: rolling
In-state tuition: full time: $7,370; part time: $428/credit hour
Out-of-state tuition: full time: $14,815
Room/board/expenses: $11,423
Full-time enrollment: 305
doctoral students: 0%; master's students: 92%; education specialists: 8%; men: 20%; women: 80%; minorities: 10%; international: 2%
Part-time enrollment: 902
doctoral students: 1%; master's students: 65%; education specialists: 34%; men: 23%; women: 77%; minorities: 8%; international: 0%
Acceptance rate (master's): 27%
Acceptance rate (doctoral): N/A
Entrance test required: GRE
Avg. GRE (of all entering students with scores): quantitative: N/A; verbal: N/A
Research assistantships: 11
Students reporting specialty: 100%
Students specializing in: admin.: 16%; counseling: 4%; evaluation/research/statistics: 2%; social/philosophical foundations: 1%; educational psych: 4%; elementary: 14%; secondary: 2%; special: 24%; other: 35%

University of Bridgeport
126 Park Avenue
Bridgeport, CT 06604
http://www.bridgeport.edu/
Private
Admissions: (203) 576-4552
E-mail: admit@bridgeport.edu
Financial aid: (203) 576-4568
Application deadline: rolling
Tuition: full time: $505/credit hour; part time: $505/credit hour
Room/board/expenses: $13,100
Full-time enrollment: 298
doctoral students: N/A; master's students: 98%; education specialists: 2%; men: 29%; women: 71%; minorities: 13%; international: 10%
Part-time enrollment: 458
doctoral students: 6%; master's students: 70%; education specialists: 24%; men: 26%; women: 74%; minorities: 20%; international: 2%
Acceptance rate (master's): 55%
Acceptance rate (doctoral): 30%
Entrance test required: MAT
Avg. GRE (of all entering students with scores): quantitative: N/A; verbal: N/A
Students reporting specialty: 98%
Students specializing in: admin.: 14%; counseling: 13%; curriculum/instr.: 18%; educational tech.: 2%; elementary: 35%; junior high: 3%; secondary: 16%

University of Connecticut (Neag)
249 Glenbrook Road
Storrs, CT 06269-2064
http://www.grad.uconn.edu
Public
Admissions: (860) 486-3617
E-mail: gradschool@uconn.edu
Financial aid: (860) 486-2819
Application deadline: 02/01
In-state tuition: full time: $10,052; part time: $469/credit hour
Out-of-state tuition: full time: $23,534
Room/board/expenses: $12,296
Full-time enrollment: 438
doctoral students: 24%; master's students: 76%; education specialists: N/A; men: 30%; women: 70%; minorities: 12%; international: 4%
Part-time enrollment: 219
doctoral students: 41%; master's students: 59%; education specialists: N/A; men: 31%; women: 69%; minorities: 13%; international: 2%
Acceptance rate (master's): 54%
Acceptance rate (doctoral): 23%
Entrance test required: GRE
Avg. GRE (of all entering students with scores): quantitative: 659; verbal: 584
Research assistantships: 140
Students reporting specialty: 94%
Students specializing in: admin.: 16%; counseling: 6%; curriculum/instr.: 3%; evaluation/research/statistics: 1%; social/philosophical foundations: 0%; educational tech.: 5%; educational psych: 13%; elementary: 6%; higher education admin.: 4%; secondary: 15%; special: 5%; other: 25%

University of Hartford
200 Bloomfield Avenue
Room 200
West Hartford, CT 06117
http://www.hartford.edu/enhp/
Private
Admissions: (860) 768-4371
E-mail: enhp@hartford.edu
Financial aid: (860) 768-4296
Application deadline: rolling
Tuition: full time: $365/credit hour; part time: $365/credit hour
Room/board/expenses: N/A
Full-time enrollment: 119
doctoral students: 42%; master's students: 37%; education specialists: 21%; men: 24%; women: 76%; minorities: 13%; international: 2%
Part-time enrollment: 165
doctoral students: 26%; master's students: 45%; education specialists: 29%; men: 19%; women: 81%; minorities: 10%; international: 1%
Acceptance rate (master's): 76%
Acceptance rate (doctoral): 66%
Entrance test required: GRE or MAT
Avg. GRE (of all entering students with scores): quantitative: N/A; verbal: N/A
Students reporting specialty: 91%
Students specializing in: admin.: 32%; counseling: 11%; educational tech.: 7%; educational psych: 12%; elementary: 28%; other: 10%

Western Connecticut State University
181 White Street
Danbury, CT 06810
http://www.wcsu.edu
Public
Admissions: (203) 837-9000
Financial aid: (203) 837-8528
Application deadline: 05/01
In-state tuition: full time: $8,682; part time: $363/credit hour
Out-of-state tuition: full time: $16,127
Room/board/expenses: $9,400
Full-time enrollment: 16
doctoral students: 0%; master's students: 100%; education specialists: N/A; men: 19%; women: 81%; minorities: 6%; international: N/A
Part-time enrollment: 285
doctoral students: 18%; master's students: 82%; education specialists: N/A; men: 25%; women: 75%; minorities: 4%; international: 0%
Acceptance rate (master's): 100%
Acceptance rate (doctoral): 100%
Entrance test required: GRE or MAT
Avg. GRE (of all entering students with scores): quantitative: N/A; verbal: N/A
Students reporting specialty: 78%
Students specializing in: admin.: 17%; counseling: 16%; curriculum/instr.: 21%; educational tech.: 9%; special: 11%; other: 27%

DELAWARE

University of Delaware
113 Willard Hall Education Building
Newark, DE 19716
http://www.udel.edu/gradoffice/applicants/degreesmajors.html
Public
Admissions: (302) 831-2129
E-mail: marym@udel.edu
Financial aid: (302) 831-2129
Application deadline: N/A
In-state tuition: full time: $7,994; part time: $408/credit hour
Out-of-state tuition: full time: $19,244
Room/board/expenses: $11,312
Full-time enrollment: 176
doctoral students: 47%; master's students: 49%; education specialists: 5%; men: 27%; women: 73%; minorities: 17%; international: 14%
Part-time enrollment: 407
doctoral students: 36%; master's students: 62%; education specialists: 2%; men: 30%; women: 70%; minorities: 12%; international: 2%
Acceptance rate (master's): 45%
Acceptance rate (doctoral): 33%
Entrance test required: GRE
Avg. GRE (of all entering students with scores): quantitative: 615; verbal: 523
Research assistantships: 29
Students reporting specialty: 95%
Students specializing in: admin.: 28%; counseling: 4%; curriculum/instr.: 6%; evaluation/research/statistics: 11%; educational tech.: 5%; special: 7%; other: 39%

Wilmington University
320 DuPont Highway
Wilmington, DE 19720
http://www.wilmu.edu
Private
Admissions: (302) 328-9407
E-mail: inquire@wilmcoll.edu
Financial aid: (302) 328-9437
Application deadline: rolling
Tuition: full time: $347/credit hour; part time: $347/credit hour
Room/board/expenses: $1,000
Full-time enrollment: 739
doctoral students: 23%; master's students: 77%; education specialists: N/A; men: 28%; women: 72%; minorities: N/A; international: N/A
Part-time enrollment: 1,493
doctoral students: 7%; master's students: 93%; education specialists: N/A; men: 26%; women: 74%; minorities: N/A; international: N/A
Acceptance rate (master's): 90%
Acceptance rate (doctoral): 24%
Entrance test required: N/A
Avg. GRE (of all entering students with scores): quantitative: N/A; verbal: N/A
Students reporting specialty: 0%
Students specializing in: N/A

DISTRICT OF COLUMBIA

American University
4400 Massachusetts Avenue NW
Washington, DC 20016-8030
http://www.american.edu/education
Private
Admissions: (202) 885-3621
E-mail: casgrad@american.edu
Financial aid: (202) 885-6100
Application deadline: 02/01
Tuition: full time: $20,378; part time: $13,712
Room/board/expenses: $18,260
Full-time enrollment: 44
doctoral students: N/A; master's students: 100%; education specialists: N/A; men: 20%; women: 80%; minorities: 16%; international: 7%
Part-time enrollment: 255
doctoral students: N/A; master's students: 100%; education specialists: N/A; men: 23%; women: 77%; minorities: 25%; international: 2%
Acceptance rate (master's): 84%
Acceptance rate (doctoral): N/A
Entrance test required: GRE
Avg. GRE (of all entering students with scores): quantitative: 589; verbal: 525
Students reporting specialty: 100%
Students specializing in: admin.: 5%; curriculum/instr.: 0%; elementary: 33%; secondary: 45%; special: 8%; other: 14%

Catholic University of America
Cardinal Station
Washington, DC 20064
http://admissions.cua.edu/graduate/
Private
Admissions: (800) 673-2772
E-mail: cua-admissions@cua.edu
Financial aid: (202) 319-5307
Application deadline: rolling
Tuition: full time: $28,840; part time: $1,045/credit hour
Room/board/expenses: $16,980
Full-time enrollment: 14
doctoral students: 43%; master's students: 57%; education specialists: N/A; men: 36%; women: 64%; minorities: 7%; international: 14%
Part-time enrollment: 77
doctoral students: 51%; master's students: 38%; education specialists: 12%; men: 29%; women: 71%; minorities: 25%; international: 4%
Acceptance rate (master's): 60%
Acceptance rate (doctoral): 43%
Entrance test required: GRE or MAT
Avg. GRE (of all entering students with scores): quantitative: N/A; verbal: N/A
Research assistantships: 2
Students reporting specialty: 80%
Students specializing in: admin.: 21%; counseling: 1%; curriculum/instr.: 1%; educational psych: 22%; secondary: 11%; special: 8%; other: 36%

Gallaudet University[1]
800 Florida Avenue NE
Washington, DC 20002-3695
http://gradschool.gallaudet.edu
Private
Admissions: (202) 651-5717
E-mail: graduate.school@gallaudet.edu
Financial aid: (202) 651-5290
Tuition: N/A
Room/board/expenses: N/A
Enrollment: N/A

George Washington University
2134 G Street NW
Washington, DC 20052
http://gsehd.gwu.edu
Private
Admissions: (202) 994-9283
E-mail: gsehdapp@gwu.edu
Financial aid: (202) 994-6822
Application deadline: rolling
Tuition: full time: $1,012/credit hour; part time: $1,012/credit hour
Room/board/expenses: $19,070
Full-time enrollment: 422
doctoral students: 24%; master's students: 73%; education specialists: 3%; men: 21%; women: 79%; minorities: 24%; international: 5%
Part-time enrollment: 1,243
doctoral students: 36%; master's students: 61%; education specialists: 4%; men: 31%; women: 69%; minorities: 29%; international: 3%
Acceptance rate (master's): 73%
Acceptance rate (doctoral): 51%
Entrance test required: GRE or MAT
Avg. GRE (of all entering students with scores): quantitative: 572; verbal: 516
Research assistantships: 20
Students reporting specialty: 89%
Students specializing in: admin.: 21%; counseling: 26%; curriculum/instr.: 3%; policy: 1%; educational tech.: 4%; elementary: 2%; higher education admin.: 10%; secondary: 7%; special: 18%; other: 8%

Howard University
2441 Fourth Street NW
Washington, DC 20059
http://www.howard.edu/schooleducation
Private
Admissions: (202) 806-7340

E-mail: hugsadmission@howard.edu
Financial aid: (202) 806-2820
Application deadline: rolling
Tuition: full time: $16,980; part time: $899/credit hour
Room/board/expenses: $9,425
Full-time enrollment: 103
doctoral students: 51%; master's students: 49%; education specialists: N/A; men: 28%; women: 72%; minorities: 95%; international: 4%
Part-time enrollment: 78
doctoral students: 50%; master's students: 50%; education specialists: N/A; men: 27%; women: 73%; minorities: 96%; international: 1%
Acceptance rate (master's): 71%
Acceptance rate (doctoral): 41%
Entrance test required: GRE
Avg. GRE (of all entering students with scores): quantitative: 449; verbal: 390
Research assistantships: 14
Students reporting specialty: 100%
Students specializing in: admin.: 29%; counseling: 41%; educational psych: 9%; elementary: 9%; secondary: 7%; special: 2%; other: 3%

FLORIDA

Barry University (Dominican)[1]
11300 N.E. Second Avenue
Miami Shores, FL 33161-6695
http://www.barry.edu/ed/
Private
Admissions: (305) 899-3100
E-mail: admissions@mail.barry.edu
Financial aid: (305) 899-3673
Tuition: N/A
Room/board/expenses: N/A
Enrollment: N/A

Florida A&M University
Gore Education Center
Tallahassee, FL 32307
http://www.famu.edu/education/
Public
Admissions: (850) 599-3315
E-mail: adm@famu.edu
Financial aid: (850) 599-3730
Application deadline: 04/01
In-state tuition: full time: $214/credit hour; part time: $214/credit hour
Out-of-state tuition: full time: $835/credit hour
Room/board/expenses: $11,400
Full-time enrollment: 83
doctoral students: 17%; master's students: 61%; education specialists: 22%; men: 29%; women: 71%; minorities: 94%; international: 6%
Part-time enrollment: 85
doctoral students: 28%; master's students: 71%; education specialists: 1%; men: 26%; women: 74%; minorities: 91%; international: N/A
Acceptance rate (master's): 65%
Acceptance rate (doctoral): 35%
Entrance test required: GRE
Avg. GRE (of all entering students with scores): quantitative: N/A; verbal: 733
Students reporting specialty: 100%
Students specializing in: admin.: 48%; counseling: 19%; elementary: 4%; secondary: 6%; technical (vocational): 2%; other: 21%

Florida Atlantic University
777 Glades Road
PO Box 3091
Boca Raton, FL 33431-0991
http://www.coe.fau.edu/menu.htm
Public
Admissions: (561) 297-3624
E-mail: gradadm@fau.edu
Financial aid: (561) 297-3131
Application deadline: 07/01
In-state tuition: full time: $256/credit hour; part time: $256/credit hour
Out-of-state tuition: full time: $915/credit hour
Room/board/expenses: $13,085
Full-time enrollment: 316
doctoral students: 15%; master's students: 80%; education specialists: 5%; men: 19%; women: 81%; minorities: 29%; international: 3%
Part-time enrollment: 571
doctoral students: 27%; master's students: 67%; education specialists: 6%; men: 20%; women: 80%; minorities: 27%; international: 1%
Acceptance rate (master's): 56%
Acceptance rate (doctoral): 63%
Entrance test required: GRE
Avg. GRE (of all entering students with scores): quantitative: 513; verbal: 443
Research assistantships: 36
Students reporting specialty: 90%
Students specializing in: admin.: 31%; counseling: 18%; curriculum/instr.: 17%; evaluation/research/statistics: 0%; social/philosophical foundations: 1%; educational tech.: 2%; educational psych: 2%; elementary: 7%; higher education admin.: 7%; secondary: 2%; special: 6%; other: 8%

Florida Institute of Technology–Melbourne
150 W. University Boulevard
Melbourne, FL 32901
http://www.fit.edu
Private
Admissions: (321) 674-7578
E-mail: grad-admissions@fit.edu
Financial aid: (321) 674-8070
Application deadline: rolling
Tuition: full time: $945/credit hour; part time: $945/credit hour
Room/board/expenses: $11,470
Full-time enrollment: 17
doctoral students: 53%; master's students: 47%; education specialists: N/A; men: 35%; women: 65%; minorities: N/A; international: 29%
Part-time enrollment: 22
doctoral students: 68%; master's students: 32%; education specialists: N/A; men: 59%; women: 41%; minorities: 5%; international: 18%
Acceptance rate (master's): 38%
Acceptance rate (doctoral): 67%
Entrance test required: GRE
Avg. GRE (of all entering students with scores): quantitative: N/A; verbal: N/A
Research assistantships: 3
Students reporting specialty: 100%
Students specializing in: secondary: 5%; other: 95%

Florida International University
11200 S.W. Eighth Street
Miami, FL 33199
http://education.fiu.edu
Public
Admissions: (305) 348-7442
E-mail: gradadm@fiu.edu
Financial aid: (305) 348-7272
Application deadline: rolling
In-state tuition: full time: $273/credit hour; part time: $273/credit hour
Out-of-state tuition: full time: $777/credit hour
Room/board/expenses: $16,450
Full-time enrollment: 216
doctoral students: 16%; master's students: 83%; education specialists: 1%; men: 19%; women: 81%; minorities: 69%; international: 9%
Part-time enrollment: 627
doctoral students: 25%; master's students: 70%; education specialists: 5%; men: 22%; women: 78%; minorities: 72%; international: 0%
Acceptance rate (master's): 60%
Acceptance rate (doctoral): 11%
Entrance test required: GRE
Avg. GRE (of all entering students with scores): quantitative: N/A; verbal: N/A
Research assistantships: 27
Students reporting specialty: 100%
Students specializing in: admin.: 12%; counseling: 14%; curriculum/instr.: 15%; elementary: 5%; higher education admin.: 17%; special: 8%; technical (vocational): 26%; other: 3%

Florida State University
236 Stone Building
Tallahassee, FL 32306-4450
http://www.coe.fsu.edu
Public
Admissions: (850) 644-3760
E-mail: admissions@admin.fsu.edu
Financial aid: (850) 644-0539
Application deadline: N/A
In-state tuition: full time: $210/credit hour; part time: $210/credit hour
Out-of-state tuition: full time: $841/credit hour
Room/board/expenses: $12,938
Full-time enrollment: 629
doctoral students: 39%; master's students: 55%; education specialists: 6%; men: 37%; women: 63%; minorities: 21%; international: 18%
Part-time enrollment: 620
doctoral students: 29%; master's students: 67%; education specialists: 3%; men: 27%; women: 73%; minorities: 20%; international: 5%
Acceptance rate (master's): 54%
Acceptance rate (doctoral): 44%
Entrance test required: GRE
Avg. GRE (of all entering students with scores): quantitative: 566; verbal: 461
Research assistantships: 274
Students reporting specialty: 69%
Students specializing in: admin.: 11%; counseling: 14%; evaluation/research/statistics: 4%; social/philosophical foundations: 5%; policy: 11%; educational psych: 8%; elementary: 6%; higher education admin.: 11%; special: 15%; instructional media design: 15%

Lynn University[1]
3601 North Military Trail
Boca Raton, FL 33431
http://www.lynn.edu
Private
Admissions: (561) 237-7900
E-mail: admission@lynn.edu
Financial aid: (561) 237-7816
Tuition: N/A
Room/board/expenses: N/A
Enrollment: N/A

Nova Southeastern University (Fischler)
3301 College Avenue
Fort Lauderdale, FL 33314
http://www.schoolofed.nova.edu
Private
Admissions: (954) 262-8500
Financial aid: (954) 262-3380
Application deadline: rolling
Tuition: full time: $470/credit hour; part time: $470/credit hour
Room/board/expenses: $12,520
Full-time enrollment: 4,150
doctoral students: 62%; master's students: 27%; education specialists: 11%; men: 22%; women: 78%; minorities: 56%; international: 2%
Part-time enrollment: 5,610
doctoral students: 26%; master's students: 59%; education specialists: 15%; men: 17%; women: 83%; minorities: 50%; international: 3%
Acceptance rate (master's): 59%
Acceptance rate (doctoral): 59%
Entrance test required: GRE or MAT
Avg. GRE (of all entering students with scores): quantitative: N/A; verbal: N/A
Research assistantships: 2
Students reporting specialty: 55%
Students specializing in: admin.: 60%; counseling: 3%; curriculum/instr.: 3%; elementary: 11%; higher education admin.: 3%; special: 15%; technical (vocational): 4%; instructional media design: 1%

University of Central Florida
4000 Central Florida Boulevard
Orlando, FL 32816-1250
http://www.graduate.ucf.edu
Public
Admissions: (407) 823-2781
E-mail: graduate@mail.ucf.edu
Financial aid: (407) 823-2827
Application deadline: 07/15
In-state tuition: full time: $270/credit hour; part time: $270/credit hour
Out-of-state tuition: full time: $997/credit hour
Room/board/expenses: $13,498
Full-time enrollment: 524
doctoral students: 35%; master's students: 56%; education specialists: 9%; men: 23%; women: 77%; minorities: 19%; international: 5%
Part-time enrollment: 773
doctoral students: 19%; master's students: 78%; education specialists: 3%; men: 20%; women: 80%; minorities: 17%; international: 1%
Acceptance rate (master's): 65%
Acceptance rate (doctoral): 54%
Entrance test required: GRE
Avg. GRE (of all entering students with scores): quantitative: 546; verbal: 473
Research assistantships: 91
Students reporting specialty: 96%
Students specializing in: admin.: 16%; counseling: 9%; curriculum/instr.: 2%; educational tech.: 4%; educational psych: 3%; elementary: 6%; junior high: 1%; secondary: 5%; special: 11%; technical (vocational): 1%; instructional media design: 2%; other: 40%

University of Florida
140 Norman Hall
PO Box 117040
Gainesville, FL 32611-7040
http://www.coe.ufl.edu
Public
Admissions: (352) 392-0726
E-mail: tla@coe.ufl.edu
Financial aid: (352) 392-0726
Application deadline: 06/01
In-state tuition: full time: $299/credit hour; part time: $299/credit hour
Out-of-state tuition: full time: $942/credit hour
Room/board/expenses: $11,980
Full-time enrollment: 654
doctoral students: 31%; master's students: 57%; education specialists: 12%; men: 19%; women: 81%; minorities: 20%; international: 8%
Part-time enrollment: 458
doctoral students: 52%; master's students: 33%; education specialists: 16%; men: 26%; women: 74%; minorities: 22%; international: 1%
Acceptance rate (master's): 70%
Acceptance rate (doctoral): 64%
Entrance test required: GRE
Avg. GRE (of all entering students with scores): quantitative: 592; verbal: 506
Research assistantships: 44
Students reporting specialty: 93%
Students specializing in: admin.: 11%; counseling: 7%; curriculum/instr.: 21%; evaluation/research/statistics: 1%; social/philosophical foundations: 0%; educational psych: 2%; elementary: 14%; higher education admin.: 7%; secondary: 7%; special: 12%; other: 16%

University of Miami
PO Box 248065
Coral Gables, FL 33124
http://www.education.miami.edu
Private
Admissions: (305) 284-5990
E-mail: soe@miami.edu
Financial aid: (305) 284-5212
Application deadline: rolling
Tuition: full time: $24,768; part time: $1,350/credit hour
Room/board/expenses: $15,700
Full-time enrollment: 169
doctoral students: 53%; master's students: 47%; education specialists: 0%; men: 27%; women: 73%; minorities: 29%; international: 12%
Part-time enrollment: 132
doctoral students: 3%; master's students: 92%; education specialists: 5%; men: 18%; women: 82%; minorities: 48%; international: 2%
Acceptance rate (master's): 41%
Acceptance rate (doctoral): 21%
Entrance test required: GRE
Avg. GRE (of all entering students with scores): quantitative: 608; verbal: 518
Research assistantships: 20
Students reporting specialty: 77%
Students specializing in: counseling: 34%; evaluation/research/statistics: 3%; elementary: 7%; higher education admin.: 9%; special: 10%; other: 51%

University of North Florida
1 UNF Drive
Jacksonville, FL 32224-2676
http://www.unf.edu/graduatestudies
Public
Admissions: (904) 620-1360
E-mail: graduatestudies@unf.edu
Financial aid: (904) 620-5555
Application deadline: N/A
In-state tuition: full time: $266/credit hour; part time: $266/credit hour
Out-of-state tuition: full time: $858/credit hour
Room/board/expenses: $12,000
Full-time enrollment: 117
doctoral students: 5%; master's students: 95%; education specialists: N/A; men: 12%; women: 88%; minorities: 17%; international: 6%
Part-time enrollment: 331
doctoral students: 29%; master's students: 71%; education specialists: N/A; men: 19%; women: 81%; minorities: 23%; international: 1%
Acceptance rate (master's): 54%
Acceptance rate (doctoral): 56%
Entrance test required: GRE
Avg. GRE (of all entering students with scores): quantitative: 473; verbal: 436
Research assistantships: 7
Students reporting specialty: 100%
Students specializing in: admin.: 48%; counseling: 21%; elementary: 12%; secondary: 9%; special: 10%

University of South Florida
4202 E. Fowler Avenue
EDU 162
Tampa, FL 33620
http://www.grad.usf.edu
Public
Admissions: (813) 974-8800
E-mail: admissions@grad.usf.edu
Financial aid: (813) 974-4700
Application deadline: rolling
In-state tuition: full time: $252/credit hour; part time: $252/credit hour
Out-of-state tuition: full time: $897/credit hour
Room/board/expenses: $14,020
Full-time enrollment: 698
doctoral students: 27%; master's students: 71%; education specialists: 2%; men: 22%; women: 78%; minorities: 27%; international: 5%

MORE AT WWW.USNEWS.COM

Part-time enrollment: 1,332
doctoral students: 23%; master's students: 75%; education specialists: 2%; men: 23%; women: 77%; minorities: 23%; international: 2%
Acceptance rate (master's): 81%
Acceptance rate (doctoral): 60%
Entrance test required: GRE
Avg. GRE (of all entering students with scores): quantitative: 531; verbal: 475
Research assistantships: 60
Students reporting specialty: 100%
Students specializing in: N/A

University of West Florida
11000 University Parkway
Pensacola, FL 32514-5750
http://uwf.edu
Public
Admissions: (850) 474-2230
E-mail: admissions@uwf.edu
Financial aid: (850) 474-2400
Application deadline: 06/01
In-state tuition: full time: $252/credit hour; part time: $252/credit hour
Out-of-state tuition: full time: $912/credit hour
Room/board/expenses: $10,450
Full-time enrollment: 131
doctoral students: 15%; master's students: 78%; education specialists: 8%; men: 26%; women: 74%; minorities: 21%; international: 2%
Part-time enrollment: 502
doctoral students: 36%; master's students: 54%; education specialists: 10%; men: 26%; women: 74%; minorities: 23%; international: 0%
Acceptance rate (master's): 71%
Acceptance rate (doctoral): 63%
Entrance test required: GRE
Avg. GRE (of all entering students with scores): quantitative: N/A; verbal: N/A
Research assistantships: 8
Students reporting specialty: 100%
Students specializing in: admin.: 15%; counseling: 5%; curriculum/instr.: 60%; special: 8%; instructional media design: 6%; other: 6%

GEORGIA

Clark Atlanta University
223 James P. Brawley Drive, SW
Atlanta, GA 30314
http://www.cau.edu/
Private
Admissions: (404) 880-6605
Financial aid: (404) 880-8992
Application deadline: rolling
Tuition: full time: $648/credit hour; part time: $648/credit hour
Room/board/expenses: $9,228
Full-time enrollment: 155
doctoral students: 48%; master's students: 50%; education specialists: 1%; men: 12%; women: 88%; minorities: 100%; international: N/A
Part-time enrollment: 41
doctoral students: 24%; master's students: 76%; education specialists: 0%; men: 15%; women: 85%; minorities: 100%; international: N/A
Acceptance rate (master's): 78%
Acceptance rate (doctoral): 75%
Entrance test required: GRE
Avg. GRE (of all entering students with scores): quantitative: N/A; verbal: N/A
Research assistantships: 0
Students reporting specialty: 80%
Students specializing in: admin.: 63%; counseling: 28%; elementary: 6%; secondary: 3%

Emory University[1]
North Decatur Building
Suite 240
Atlanta, GA 30322
http://www.emory.edu/EDUCATION/
Private
Admissions: (404) 727-6468
E-mail: gavant@emory.edu
Financial aid: (404) 727-6039
Tuition: N/A
Room/board/expenses: N/A
Enrollment: N/A

Georgia State University
PO Box 3980
Atlanta, GA 30302-3980
http://education.gsu.edu/coe/
Public
Admissions: (404) 413-8000
E-mail: educadmissions@gsu.edu
Financial aid: (404) 413-2400
Application deadline: N/A
In-state tuition: full time: $6,286; part time: $221/credit hour
Out-of-state tuition: full time: $22,170
Room/board/expenses: $11,562
Full-time enrollment: 877
doctoral students: 23%; master's students: 73%; education specialists: 4%; men: 20%; women: 80%; minorities: 28%; international: 4%
Part-time enrollment: 742
doctoral students: 35%; master's students: 59%; education specialists: 6%; men: 21%; women: 79%; minorities: 28%; international: 2%
Acceptance rate (master's): 67%
Acceptance rate (doctoral): 40%
Entrance test required: GRE or MAT
Avg. GRE (of all entering students with scores): quantitative: 542; verbal: 479
Research assistantships: 313
Students reporting specialty: 88%
Students specializing in: admin.: 13%; counseling: 7%; evaluation/research/statistics: 2%; social/philosophical foundations: 2%; policy: 4%; educational psych: 6%; elementary: 8%; higher education admin.: 1%; junior high: 4%; secondary: 20%; special: 9%; technical (vocational): 2%; instructional media design: 9%; other: 13%

University of Georgia
G-3 Aderhold Hall
Athens, GA 30602-7101
http://www.gradsch.uga.edu
Public
Admissions: (706) 542-1739
E-mail: gradadm@uga.edu
Financial aid: (706) 542-6147
Application deadline: 07/01
In-state tuition: full time: $6,170; part time: $211/credit hour
Out-of-state tuition: full time: $21,424
Room/board/expenses: $10,292
Full-time enrollment: 865
doctoral students: 44%; master's students: 55%; education specialists: 0%; men: 30%; women: 70%; minorities: 19%; international: 15%
Part-time enrollment: 1,149
doctoral students: 38%; master's students: 46%; education specialists: 16%; men: 30%; women: 70%; minorities: 15%; international: 2%
Acceptance rate (master's): 47%
Acceptance rate (doctoral): 34%
Entrance test required: GRE or MAT
Avg. GRE (of all entering students with scores): quantitative: 559; verbal: 496
Research assistantships: 167
Students reporting specialty: 96%
Students specializing in: admin.: 10%; counseling: 11%; evaluation/research/statistics: 1%; social/philosophical foundations: 1%; policy: 0%; educational tech.: 4%; educational psych: 4%; elementary: 7%; higher education admin.: 2%; junior high: 2%; secondary: 24%; special: 12%; technical (vocational): 8%; instructional media design: 2%; other: 13%

University of West Georgia
1601 Maple Street
Carrollton, GA 30118
http://coe.westga.edu
Public
Admissions: (678) 839-6419
E-mail: cthill@westga.edu
Financial aid: (678) 839-6421
Application deadline: rolling
In-state tuition: full time: $3,408; part time: $136/credit hour
Out-of-state tuition: full time: $10,734
Room/board/expenses: $6,776
Full-time enrollment: 228
doctoral students: 0%; master's students: 83%; education specialists: 17%; men: 17%; women: 83%; minorities: 26%; international: 1%
Part-time enrollment: 758
doctoral students: 9%; master's students: 61%; education specialists: 29%; men: 18%; women: 82%; minorities: 25%; international: N/A
Acceptance rate (master's): N/A
Acceptance rate (doctoral): N/A
Entrance test required: GRE
Avg. GRE (of all entering students with scores): quantitative: N/A; verbal: N/A
Students reporting specialty: 100%
Students specializing in: admin.: 7%; counseling: 9%; elementary: 8%; junior high: 3%; secondary: 2%; special: 8%; instructional media design: 12%; other: 50%

HAWAII

University of Hawaii–Manoa
1776 University Avenue
Everly Hall 128
Honolulu, HI 96822
http://www.hawaii.edu/graduatestudies/fields/html/fields.htm
Public
Admissions: (808) 956-8544
E-mail: admissions@grad.hawaii.edu
Financial aid: (808) 956-3993
Application deadline: 03/01
In-state tuition: full time: $7,134; part time: $286/credit hour
Out-of-state tuition: full time: $16,590
Room/board/expenses: $10,207
Full-time enrollment: 329
doctoral students: 18%; master's students: 82%; education specialists: N/A; men: 27%; women: 73%; minorities: 56%; international: 17%
Part-time enrollment: 607
doctoral students: 20%; master's students: 80%; education specialists: N/A; men: 26%; women: 74%; minorities: 66%; international: 2%
Acceptance rate (master's): 72%
Acceptance rate (doctoral): 36%
Entrance test required: GRE
Avg. GRE (of all entering students with scores): quantitative: 562; verbal: 541
Research assistantships: 38
Students reporting specialty: 95%
Students specializing in: admin.: 16%; counseling: 3%; curriculum/instr.: 27%; social/philosophical foundations: 9%; policy: 1%; educational tech.: 4%; educational psych: 4%; elementary: 2%; higher education admin.: 3%; junior high: 3%; secondary: 6%; special: 8%; other: 14%

IDAHO

Boise State University[1]
1910 University Drive
Boise, ID 83725-1700
http://www.boisestate.edu/gradcoll/3admis.html
Public
Admissions: (208) 426-1337
E-mail: gradcoll@boisestate.edu
Financial aid: (208) 426-1664
Tuition: N/A
Room/board/expenses: N/A
Enrollment: N/A

Idaho State University
921 S. Eighth Avenue
Pocatello, ID 83209-8059
http://www.isu.edu/departments/graduate
Public
Admissions: (208) 282-2150
E-mail: graddean@isu.edu
Financial aid: (208) 282-2756
Application deadline: 07/01
In-state tuition: full time: $5,160; part time: $259/credit hour
Out-of-state tuition: full time: $13,844
Room/board/expenses: $12,144
Full-time enrollment: 68
doctoral students: 16%; master's students: 66%; education specialists: 18%; men: 44%; women: 56%; minorities: 9%; international: 13%
Part-time enrollment: 354
doctoral students: 23%; master's students: 65%; education specialists: 12%; men: 41%; women: 59%; minorities: 5%; international: 3%
Acceptance rate (master's): 100%
Acceptance rate (doctoral): 100%
Entrance test required: GRE or MAT
Avg. GRE (of all entering students with scores): quantitative: 490; verbal: 459
Research assistantships: 1
Students reporting specialty: 0%
Students specializing in: N/A

University of Idaho
PO Box 443080
Moscow, ID 83844-3080
http://coe.ed.uidaho.edu/
Public
Admissions: (208) 885-4001
E-mail: gadms@uidaho.edu
Financial aid: (208) 885-6312
Application deadline: N/A
In-state tuition: full time: $4,950; part time: $4,950
Out-of-state tuition: full time: $15,030
Room/board/expenses: $13,582
Full-time enrollment: 134
doctoral students: 17%; master's students: 71%; education specialists: 12%; men: 38%; women: 62%; minorities: 10%; international: 7%
Part-time enrollment: 501
doctoral students: 35%; master's students: 52%; education specialists: 13%; men: 39%; women: 61%; minorities: 4%; international: 4%
Acceptance rate (master's): 61%
Acceptance rate (doctoral): 28%
Entrance test required: GRE
Avg. GRE (of all entering students with scores): quantitative: 539; verbal: 523
Research assistantships: 1
Students reporting specialty: 98%
Students specializing in: admin.: 26%; counseling: 9%; curriculum/instr.: 10%; educational tech.: 1%; elementary: 1%; special: 3%; technical (vocational): 5%; other: 51%

ILLINOIS

Aurora University[1]
347 S. Gladstone Avenue
Aurora, IL 60506-4892
http://www.aurora.edu
Private
Admissions: (630) 844-5533
E-mail: admission@aurora.edu
Financial aid: (630) 844-5448
Tuition: N/A
Room/board/expenses: N/A
Enrollment: N/A

Concordia University
7400 Augusta Street
River Forest, IL 60305-1499
http://www.cuchicago.edu/academics/college_of_education/index.asp
Private
Admissions: (708) 209-4093
E-mail: grad.admission@cuchicago.edu
Financial aid: (708) 209-3347
Application deadline: 08/15
Tuition: full time: $416/credit hour; part time: $416/credit hour
Room/board/expenses: $8,692
Full-time enrollment: 358
doctoral students: 0%; master's students: 100%; education specialists: N/A; men: 27%; women: 73%; minorities: 23%; international: 1%
Part-time enrollment: 2,373
doctoral students: 1%; master's students: 99%; education specialists: N/A; men: 18%; women: 82%; minorities: 23%; international: N/A
Acceptance rate (master's): 58%
Acceptance rate (doctoral): 30%
Entrance test required: GRE or MAT
Avg. GRE (of all entering students with scores): quantitative: N/A; verbal: N/A
Students reporting specialty: 88%
Students specializing in: admin.: 33%; counseling: 8%; curriculum/instr.: 36%; elementary: 4%; secondary: 1%; other: 18%

DePaul University
1 E. Jackson Boulevard
Chicago, IL 60604-2287
http://education.depaul.edu
Private
Admissions: (773) 325-4405
E-mail: edgradadmissions@depaul.edu
Financial aid: N/A
Application deadline: rolling
Tuition: full time: $478/credit hour; part time: $478/credit hour
Room/board/expenses: N/A
Full-time enrollment: 866
doctoral students: 3%; master's students: 97%; education specialists: N/A; men: 19%; women: 81%; minorities: 16%; international: 2%
Part-time enrollment: 462
doctoral students: 10%; master's students: 90%; education specialists: N/A; men: 26%; women: 74%; minorities: 25%; international: 1%
Acceptance rate (master's): 78%
Acceptance rate (doctoral): 38%
Entrance test required: N/A
Avg. GRE (of all entering students with scores): quantitative: N/A; verbal: N/A
Research assistantships: 9
Students reporting specialty: 100%
Students specializing in: admin.: 10%; counseling: 14%; curriculum/instr.: 5%; social/philosophical foundations: 2%; elementary: 26%; secondary: 25%; special: 10%; other: 9%

Illinois State University
Campus Box 5300
Normal, IL 61790-5300
http://www.ilstu.edu
Public
Admissions: (309) 438-2181
E-mail: gradinfo@ilstu.edu

Financial aid: (309) 438-2231
Application deadline: rolling
In-state tuition: full time: $6,344; part time: $194/credit hour
Out-of-state tuition: full time: $11,384
Room/board/expenses: $10,809
Full-time enrollment: 205
doctoral students: 29%; master's students: 71%; education specialists: N/A; men: 20%; women: 80%; minorities: 11%; international: 6%
Part-time enrollment: 593
doctoral students: 39%; master's students: 61%; education specialists: N/A; men: 26%; women: 74%; minorities: 9%; international: 1%
Acceptance rate (master's): 50%
Acceptance rate (doctoral): 67%
Entrance test required: GRE
Avg. GRE (of all entering students with scores): quantitative: 554; verbal: 455
Research assistantships: 35
Students reporting specialty: 100%
Students specializing in: admin.: 28%; counseling: 3%; curriculum/instr.: 12%; special: 18%; instructional media design: 0%; other: 38%

Loyola University Chicago

820 N. Michigan Avenue
Chicago, IL 60611
http://www.luc.edu/education/
Private
Admissions: (312) 915-6880
E-mail: schleduc@luc.edu
Financial aid: (773) 508-3155
Application deadline: N/A
Tuition: full time: $710/credit hour; part time: $710/credit hour
Room/board/expenses: N/A
Full-time enrollment: 287
doctoral students: 22%; master's students: 64%; education specialists: 14%; men: 24%; women: 76%; minorities: 20%; international: 11%
Part-time enrollment: 558
doctoral students: 50%; master's students: 50%; education specialists: 0%; men: 29%; women: 71%; minorities: 27%; international: N/A
Acceptance rate (master's): 72%
Acceptance rate (doctoral): 28%
Entrance test required: GRE or MAT
Avg. GRE (of all entering students with scores): quantitative: N/A; verbal: N/A
Research assistantships: 31
Students reporting specialty: 97%
Students specializing in: admin.: 20%; counseling: 14%; curriculum/instr.: 16%; evaluation/research/statistics: 2%; social/philosophical foundations: 10%; educational tech.: 1%; educational psych: 5%; elementary: 5%; higher education admin.: 14%; secondary: 6%; special: 3%; other: 7%

National-Louis University

122 S. Michigan Avenue
Chicago, IL 60603
http://www.nl.edu/academics/nce/index.cfm
Private
Admissions: (888) 658-8632
E-mail: nluinfo@nl.edu
Financial aid: (888) 658-8632
Application deadline: rolling
Tuition: full time: $588/credit hour; part time: $588/credit hour
Room/board/expenses: N/A
Full-time enrollment: 921
doctoral students: 2%; master's students: 95%; education specialists: 3%; men: 26%; women: 74%; minorities: 14%; international: N/A
Part-time enrollment: 2,547
doctoral students: 8%; master's students: 82%; education specialists: 11%; men: 24%; women: 76%; minorities: 21%; international: N/A
Acceptance rate (master's): N/A
Acceptance rate (doctoral): N/A
Entrance test required: GRE or MAT
Avg. GRE (of all entering students with scores): quantitative: 498; verbal: 462
Students reporting specialty: 98%
Students specializing in: admin.: 16%; curriculum/instr.: 8%; educational tech.: 2%; educational psych: 3%; elementary: 22%; junior high: 0%; secondary: 16%; special: 6%; other: 27%

Northern Illinois University

321 Graham Hall
DeKalb, IL 60115
http://www.niu.edu
Public
Admissions: (815) 753-8301
E-mail: gradsch@niu.edu
Financial aid: (815) 753-1300
Application deadline: rolling
In-state tuition: full time: $5,280; part time: $227/credit hour
Out-of-state tuition: full time: $10,560
Room/board/expenses: $9,687
Full-time enrollment: 291
doctoral students: 24%; master's students: 76%; education specialists: 0%; men: 39%; women: 61%; minorities: 22%; international: 10%
Part-time enrollment: 1,552
doctoral students: 28%; master's students: 66%; education specialists: 5%; men: 29%; women: 71%; minorities: 19%; international: 0%
Acceptance rate (master's): 61%
Acceptance rate (doctoral): 45%
Entrance test required: GRE or MAT
Avg. GRE (of all entering students with scores): quantitative: N/A; verbal: N/A
Research assistantships: 31
Students reporting specialty: 82%
Students specializing in: admin.: 46%; counseling: 10%; curriculum/instr.: 14%; evaluation/research/statistics: 1%; social/philosophical foundations: 1%; educational psych: 2%; elementary: 5%; special: 10%; instructional media design: 10%; other: 3%

Northwestern University

2120 Campus Drive
Evanston, IL 60208
http://www.sesp.northwestern.edu
Private
Admissions: (847) 491-3783
E-mail: sesp@northwestern.edu
Financial aid: (847) 491-3783
Application deadline: rolling
Tuition: full time: $35,304; part time: $3,896/credit hour
Room/board/expenses: N/A
Full-time enrollment: 154
doctoral students: 45%; master's students: 55%; education specialists: N/A; men: 23%; women: 77%; minorities: 20%; international: 8%
Part-time enrollment: 117
doctoral students: 1%; master's students: 99%; education specialists: N/A; men: 50%; women: 50%; minorities: 18%; international: 2%
Acceptance rate (master's): 66%
Acceptance rate (doctoral): 12%
Entrance test required: GRE
Avg. GRE (of all entering students with scores): quantitative: 661; verbal: 616
Research assistantships: 19
Students reporting specialty: 38%
Students specializing in: N/A

Roosevelt University

430 S. Michigan Avenue
Chicago, IL 60605
http://www.roosevelt.edu
Private
Admissions: (877) 277-5978
E-mail: applyRU@roosevelt.edu
Financial aid: (866) 421-0935
Application deadline: rolling
Tuition: full time: $16,980; part time: $600/credit hour
Room/board/expenses: N/A
Full-time enrollment: 271
doctoral students: 22%; master's students: 78%; education specialists: N/A; men: 19%; women: 81%; minorities: 36%; international: N/A
Part-time enrollment: 466
doctoral students: 2%; master's students: 98%; education specialists: N/A; men: 21%; women: 79%; minorities: 28%; international: 0%
Acceptance rate (master's): 58%
Acceptance rate (doctoral): 75%
Entrance test required: GRE or MAT
Avg. GRE (of all entering students with scores): quantitative: N/A; verbal: N/A
Research assistantships: 13
Students reporting specialty: 100%
Students specializing in: admin.: 20%; counseling: 9%; elementary: 25%; secondary: 16%; special: 9%; other: 21%

Southern Illinois University–Carbondale

Wham Building 115
Carbondale, IL 62901-4624
http://web.coehs.siu.edu/Public/
Public
Admissions: (618) 536-7791
E-mail: gradschl@siu.edu
Financial aid: (618) 453-4334
Application deadline: rolling
In-state tuition: full time: $275/credit hour; part time: $275/credit hour
Out-of-state tuition: full time: $688/credit hour
Room/board/expenses: $12,135
Full-time enrollment: 449
doctoral students: 17%; master's students: 83%; education specialists: N/A; men: 28%; women: 72%; minorities: 15%; international: 11%
Part-time enrollment: 840
doctoral students: 27%; master's students: 73%; education specialists: N/A; men: 33%; women: 67%; minorities: 25%; international: 5%
Acceptance rate (master's): 68%
Acceptance rate (doctoral): 65%
Entrance test required: GRE or MAT
Avg. GRE (of all entering students with scores): quantitative: N/A; verbal: N/A
Research assistantships: 155
Students reporting specialty: 73%
Students specializing in: admin.: 3%; curriculum/instr.: 21%; educational psych: 13%; higher education admin.: 3%; secondary: 6%; special: 4%; technical (vocational): 2%; other: 47%

University of Illinois–Chicago

1040 W. Harrison Street
Chicago, IL 60607-7133
http://www.education.uic.edu
Public
Admissions: (312) 996-4532
E-mail: jeisen@uic.edu
Financial aid: (312) 996-3126
Application deadline: 01/01
In-state tuition: full time: $10,912; part time: $8,316
Out-of-state tuition: full time: $22,910
Room/board/expenses: $12,000
Full-time enrollment: 148
doctoral students: 41%; master's students: 59%; education specialists: N/A; men: 28%; women: 72%; minorities: 36%; international: 7%
Part-time enrollment: 487
doctoral students: 38%; master's students: 62%; education specialists: N/A; men: 20%; women: 80%; minorities: 32%; international: 3%
Acceptance rate (master's): 78%
Acceptance rate (doctoral): 49%
Entrance test required: GRE
Avg. GRE (of all entering students with scores): quantitative: 533; verbal: 488
Research assistantships: 285
Students reporting specialty: 100%
Students specializing in: admin.: 9%; curriculum/instr.: 12%; social/philosophical foundations: 3%; educational psych: 9%; elementary: 12%; higher education admin.: 0%; secondary: 7%; special: 19%; other: 28%

University of Illinois–Urbana-Champaign

1310 S. Sixth Street
Champaign, IL 61820
http://www.ed.uiuc.edu/saao
Public
Admissions: (217) 333-2267
E-mail: saao@ed.uiuc.edu
Financial aid: (217) 333-2267
Application deadline: N/A
In-state tuition: full time: $11,330; part time: $8,540
Out-of-state tuition: full time: $24,170
Room/board/expenses: $15,402
Full-time enrollment: 443
doctoral students: 73%; master's students: 27%; education specialists: N/A; men: 31%; women: 69%; minorities: 36%; international: 25%
Part-time enrollment: 659
doctoral students: 36%; master's students: 64%; education specialists: N/A; men: 28%; women: 72%; minorities: 21%; international: 5%
Acceptance rate (master's): 72%
Acceptance rate (doctoral): 44%
Entrance test required: GRE
Avg. GRE (of all entering students with scores): quantitative: N/A; verbal: N/A
Research assistantships: 224
Students reporting specialty: 95%
Students specializing in: admin.: 14%; counseling: 4%; curriculum/instr.: 19%; evaluation/research/statistics: 3%; social/philosophical foundations: 15%; policy: 15%; educational tech.: 5%; educational psych: 13%; elementary: 9%; higher education admin.: 8%; junior high: 16%; secondary: 10%; special: 8%; technical (vocational): 0%; other: 22%

INDIANA

Ball State University

Muncie, IN 47306
http://www.bsu.edu/gradschool/
Public
Admissions: (765) 285-1297
E-mail: pwhitena@bsu.edu
Financial aid: (765) 295-5600
Application deadline: rolling
In-state tuition: full time: $8,736; part time: $6,132
Out-of-state tuition: full time: $19,804
Room/board/expenses: $11,740
Full-time enrollment: 281
doctoral students: 21%; master's students: 76%; education specialists: 3%; men: 33%; women: 67%; minorities: N/A; international: N/A
Part-time enrollment: 1,077
doctoral students: 14%; master's students: 83%; education specialists: 3%; men: 35%; women: 65%; minorities: N/A; international: N/A
Acceptance rate (master's): 59%
Acceptance rate (doctoral): 25%
Entrance test required: GRE
Avg. GRE (of all entering students with scores): quantitative: 574; verbal: 483
Research assistantships: 18
Students reporting specialty: N/A
Students specializing in: N/A

Indiana State University

Terre Haute, IN 47809
http://www.indstate.edu/academic/grad.htm#Education
Public
Admissions: (800) 444-4723
E-mail: grdstudy@isugw.indstate.edu
Financial aid: (800) 841-4744
Application deadline: rolling
In-state tuition: full time: $294/credit hour; part time: $294/credit hour
Out-of-state tuition: full time: $584/credit hour
Room/board/expenses: $6,756
Full-time enrollment: 218
doctoral students: 51%; master's students: 40%; education specialists: 9%; men: 37%; women: 63%; minorities: 17%; international: 16%
Part-time enrollment: 394
doctoral students: 29%; master's students: 59%; education specialists: 12%; men: 30%; women: 70%; minorities: 12%; international: 2%
Acceptance rate (master's): N/A
Acceptance rate (doctoral): N/A
Entrance test required: GRE or MAT
Avg. GRE (of all entering students with scores): quantitative: 511; verbal: 441
Research assistantships: 10
Students reporting specialty: 99%
Students specializing in: admin.: 28%; counseling: 22%; curriculum/instr.: 12%; elementary: 3%; special: 3%; instructional media design: 9%; other: 23%

Indiana University–Bloomington

201 N. Rose Avenue
Bloomington, IN 47405-1006
http://education.indiana.edu/
Public
Admissions: (812) 856-8504
E-mail: educate@indiana.edu
Financial aid: (812) 855-3278
Application deadline: rolling
In-state tuition: full time: $269/credit hour; part time: $269/credit hour
Out-of-state tuition: full time: $784/credit hour
Room/board/expenses: $19,400
Full-time enrollment: 867
doctoral students: 56%; master's students: 40%; education specialists: 3%; men: 34%; women: 66%; minorities: 13%; international: 25%
Part-time enrollment: 268
doctoral students: 55%; master's students: 40%; education specialists: 6%; men: 32%; women: 68%; minorities: 13%; international: 16%
Acceptance rate (master's): 58%
Acceptance rate (doctoral): 41%
Entrance test required: GRE
Avg. GRE (of all entering students with scores): quantitative: 608; verbal: 515
Research assistantships: 87
Students reporting specialty: 97%
Students specializing in: admin.: 8%; counseling: 19%; curriculum/instr.: 31%; evaluation/research/statistics: 2%; social/philosophical foundations: 5%; educational psych: 8%; elementary: 5%; higher education admin.: 7%; secondary: 3%; special: 3%; instructional media design: 11%; other: 0%

Purdue University–West Lafayette

100 N. University Street
West Lafayette, IN 47907-2098
http://www.education.purdue.edu/
Public
Admissions: (765) 494-2345
E-mail: education-gradoffice@purdue.edu
Financial aid: (765) 494-5050
Application deadline: rolling

In-state tuition: full time: $7,416; part time: $266/credit hour
Out-of-state tuition: full time: $22,224
Room/board/expenses: $10,550
Full-time enrollment: 136
doctoral students: 76%; master's students: 24%; education specialists: 0%; men: 26%; women: 74%; minorities: 15%; international: 33%
Part-time enrollment: 216
doctoral students: 74%; master's students: 25%; education specialists: 1%; men: 40%; women: 60%; minorities: 12%; international: 11%
Acceptance rate (master's): 58%
Acceptance rate (doctoral): 68%
Entrance test required: GRE
Avg. GRE (of all entering students with scores): quantitative: 627; verbal: 480
Research assistantships: 51
Students reporting specialty: 91%
Students specializing in: admin.: 17%; counseling: 15%; curriculum/instr.: 30%; social/philosophical foundations: 1%; educational tech.: 9%; educational psych: 13%; elementary: 1%; higher education admin.: 3%; special: 7%; technical (vocational): 3%

IOWA

Drake University
3206 University Avenue
Des Moines, IA 50311-4505
http://www.educ.drake.edu
Private
Admissions: (515) 271-3871
E-mail: gradadmission@drake.edu
Financial aid: (515) 271-2905
Application deadline: rolling
Tuition: full time: $23,692; part time: $450/credit hour
Room/board/expenses: $10,920
Full-time enrollment: 96
doctoral students: 1%; master's students: 97%; education specialists: 2%; men: 31%; women: 69%; minorities: 9%; international: 5%
Part-time enrollment: 502
doctoral students: 4%; master's students: 84%; education specialists: 12%; men: 28%; women: 72%; minorities: 7%; international: 0%
Acceptance rate (master's): 95%
Acceptance rate (doctoral): N/A
Entrance test required: GRE or MAT
Avg. GRE (of all entering students with scores): quantitative: N/A; verbal: N/A
Research assistantships: 7
Students reporting specialty: 0%
Students specializing in: N/A

Iowa State University
E262 Lagomarcino Hall
Ames, IA 50011
http://www.grad-college.iastate.edu/
Public
Admissions: (515) 294-5836
E-mail: admissions@iastate.edu
Financial aid: (515) 294-2223
Application deadline: rolling
In-state tuition: full time: $7,215; part time: $347/credit hour
Out-of-state tuition: full time: $17,875
Room/board/expenses: $14,010
Full-time enrollment: 198
doctoral students: 44%; master's students: 56%; education specialists: N/A; men: 37%; women: 63%; minorities: 22%; international: 19%
Part-time enrollment: 284
doctoral students: 43%; master's students: 57%; education specialists: N/A; men: 35%; women: 65%; minorities: 7%; international: 1%
Acceptance rate (master's): 88%
Acceptance rate (doctoral): 84%
Entrance test required: GRE
Avg. GRE (of all entering students with scores): quantitative: 475; verbal: 432
Research assistantships: 43
Students reporting specialty: 74%
Students specializing in: admin.: 18%; curriculum/instr.: 10%; social/philosophical foundations: 1%; educational psych: 1%; higher education admin.: 49%; junior high: 5%; secondary: 5%; special: 6%; instructional media design: 15%; other: 3%

University of Iowa
Lindquist Center
Iowa City, IA 52242
http://www.education.uiowa.edu
Public
Admissions: (319) 335-5359
E-mail: coe-tess@uiowa.edu
Financial aid: (319) 335-1450
Application deadline: rolling
In-state tuition: full time: $7,296; part time: $349/credit hour
Out-of-state tuition: full time: $19,282
Room/board/expenses: $14,350
Full-time enrollment: 547
doctoral students: 56%; master's students: 44%; education specialists: 0%; men: 32%; women: 68%; minorities: 12%; international: 17%
Part-time enrollment: 212
doctoral students: 64%; master's students: 33%; education specialists: 3%; men: 30%; women: 70%; minorities: 12%; international: 10%
Acceptance rate (master's): 65%
Acceptance rate (doctoral): 50%
Entrance test required: GRE
Avg. GRE (of all entering students with scores): quantitative: 618; verbal: 502
Research assistantships: 155
Students reporting specialty: 100%
Students specializing in: admin.: 8%; counseling: 12%; curriculum/instr.: 1%; evaluation/research/statistics: 8%; social/philosophical foundations: 6%; educational psych: 4%; elementary: 6%; higher education admin.: 8%; secondary: 21%; special: 7%; instructional media design: 0%; other: 20%

University of Northern Iowa
205 Schindler Center
Cedar Falls, IA 50614-0610
http://www.uni.edu/coe
Public
Admissions: (319) 273-2623
E-mail: admissions@uni.edu
Financial aid: (800) 772-2736
Application deadline: N/A
In-state tuition: full time: $7,084; part time: $813/credit hour
Out-of-state tuition: full time: $15,392
Room/board/expenses: $11,263
Full-time enrollment: 192
doctoral students: 7%; master's students: 89%; education specialists: 4%; men: 34%; women: 66%; minorities: 9%; international: 11%
Part-time enrollment: 452
doctoral students: 18%; master's students: 80%; education specialists: 2%; men: 30%; women: 70%; minorities: 4%; international: 2%
Acceptance rate (master's): 74%
Acceptance rate (doctoral): 65%
Entrance test required: GRE
Avg. GRE (of all entering students with scores): quantitative: 565; verbal: 462
Research assistantships: 0
Students reporting specialty: 60%
Students specializing in: admin.: 43%; counseling: 13%; curriculum/instr.: 8%; social/philosophical foundations: 10%; educational psych: 2%; elementary: 4%; junior high: 1%; special: 13%; instructional media design: 6%

KANSAS

Kansas State University
18 Bluemont Hall
Manhattan, KS 66506
http://www.ksu.edu/
Public
Admissions: (785) 532-5595
E-mail: coegrads@ksu.edu
Financial aid: (785) 532-6420
Application deadline: rolling
In-state tuition: full time: $255/credit hour; part time: $255/credit hour
Out-of-state tuition: full time: $586/credit hour
Room/board/expenses: $10,784
Full-time enrollment: 21
doctoral students: 52%; master's students: 48%; education specialists: N/A; men: 33%; women: 67%; minorities: N/A; international: 100%
Part-time enrollment: 988
doctoral students: 32%; master's students: 68%; education specialists: N/A; men: 36%; women: 64%; minorities: 16%; international: N/A
Acceptance rate (master's): 69%
Acceptance rate (doctoral): 35%
Entrance test required: GRE or MAT
Avg. GRE (of all entering students with scores): quantitative: 426; verbal: 430
Research assistantships: 12
Students reporting specialty: 0%
Students specializing in: N/A

University of Kansas
217 Joseph R. Pearson Hall
Lawrence, KS 66045
http://www.soe.ku.edu
Public
Admissions: (785) 864-4510
E-mail: jlicht@ku.edu
Financial aid: (785) 864-4700
Application deadline: N/A
In-state tuition: full time: $241/credit hour; part time: $241/credit hour
Out-of-state tuition: full time: $575/credit hour
Room/board/expenses: N/A
Full-time enrollment: 544
doctoral students: 30%; master's students: 67%; education specialists: 3%; men: 0%; women: 3%; minorities: 0%; international: 0%
Part-time enrollment: 666
doctoral students: 43%; master's students: 57%; education specialists: N/A; men: N/A; women: N/A; minorities: N/A; international: N/A
Acceptance rate (master's): 89%
Acceptance rate (doctoral): 66%
Entrance test required: GRE or MAT
Avg. GRE (of all entering students with scores): quantitative: 590; verbal: 470
Research assistantships: 57
Students reporting specialty: 100%
Students specializing in: admin.: 1%; counseling: 10%; curriculum/instr.: 40%; evaluation/research/statistics: 1%; social/philosophical foundations: 1%; policy: 13%; educational psych: 0%; higher education admin.: 5%; special: 20%; other: 8%

Wichita State University[1]
1845 N. Fairmount
Wichita, KS 67260-0131
http://www.wichita.edu/my/visitors/
Public
Admissions: N/A
Financial aid: N/A
Tuition: N/A
Room/board/expenses: N/A
Enrollment: N/A

KENTUCKY

Spalding University
851 S. Fourth Street
Louisville, KY 40203
http://www.spalding.edu/admissions
Private
Admissions: (502) 585-7111
E-mail: admissions@spalding.edu
Financial aid: (502) 585-9911
Application deadline: rolling
Tuition: full time: $595/credit hour; part time: N/A
Room/board/expenses: $7,140
Full-time enrollment: 103
doctoral students: 28%; master's students: 72%; education specialists: N/A; men: 42%; women: 58%; minorities: 27%; international: N/A
Part-time enrollment: 147
doctoral students: 49%; master's students: 51%; education specialists: N/A; men: 31%; women: 69%; minorities: 43%; international: 2%
Acceptance rate (master's): N/A
Acceptance rate (doctoral): N/A
Entrance test required: GRE or MAT
Avg. GRE (of all entering students with scores): quantitative: N/A; verbal: N/A
Students reporting specialty: 100%
Students specializing in: admin.: 44%; curriculum/instr.: 6%; elementary: 6%; junior high: 5%; secondary: 12%; special: 26%; other: 1%

University of Kentucky
103 Dickey Hall
Lexington, KY 40506-0033
http://www.gradschool.uky.edu/
Public
Admissions: (859) 257-4905
E-mail: Brian.Jackson@uky.edu
Financial aid: (859) 257-3172
Application deadline: rolling
In-state tuition: full time: $7,719; part time: $401/credit hour
Out-of-state tuition: full time: $16,187
Room/board/expenses: $10,350
Full-time enrollment: 479
doctoral students: 39%; master's students: 56%; education specialists: 5%; men: 29%; women: 71%; minorities: 17%; international: 3%
Part-time enrollment: 266
doctoral students: 44%; master's students: 51%; education specialists: 5%; men: 32%; women: 68%; minorities: 11%; international: N/A
Acceptance rate (master's): 41%
Acceptance rate (doctoral): 30%
Entrance test required: GRE
Avg. GRE (of all entering students with scores): quantitative: 520; verbal: 444
Research assistantships: 55
Students reporting specialty: 100%
Students specializing in: admin.: 16%; counseling: 9%; curriculum/instr.: 3%; evaluation/research/statistics: 10%; social/philosophical foundations: 0%; educational psych: 9%; elementary: 2%; higher education admin.: 2%; junior high: 0%; secondary: 7%; special: 8%; other: 32%

University of Louisville
Cardinal Boulevard and First Street
Louisville, KY 40292
http://www.louisville.edu/edu/
Public
Admissions: (502) 852-3101
E-mail: gradadm@louisville.edu
Financial aid: (502) 852-5511
Application deadline: rolling
In-state tuition: full time: $7,528; part time: $419/credit hour
Out-of-state tuition: full time: $18,090
Room/board/expenses: $12,812
Full-time enrollment: 490
doctoral students: 21%; master's students: 79%; education specialists: 0%; men: 31%; women: 69%; minorities: 14%; international: 6%
Part-time enrollment: 775
doctoral students: 21%; master's students: 78%; education specialists: 1%; men: 29%; women: 71%; minorities: 10%; international: 1%
Acceptance rate (master's): 66%
Acceptance rate (doctoral): 37%
Entrance test required: GRE
Avg. GRE (of all entering students with scores): quantitative: 515; verbal: 451
Research assistantships: 29
Students reporting specialty: 100%
Students specializing in: admin.: 12%; counseling: 19%; curriculum/instr.: 5%; elementary: 8%; higher education admin.: 5%; junior high: 5%; secondary: 11%; special: 15%; other: 20%

Western Kentucky University
1906 College Heights Boulevard
Bowling Green, KY 42101
http://edtech.wku.edu/
Public
Admissions: (270) 745-2446
E-mail: graduate.studies@wku.edu
Financial aid: (270) 745-2755
Application deadline: 06/15
In-state tuition: full time: $7,014; part time: $351/credit hour
Out-of-state tuition: full time: $7,678
Room/board/expenses: $7,531
Full-time enrollment: 86
doctoral students: 2%; master's students: 76%; education specialists: 22%; men: 21%; women: 79%; minorities: 10%; international: 1%
Part-time enrollment: 497
doctoral students: 7%; master's students: 90%; education specialists: 4%; men: 29%; women: 71%; minorities: 6%; international: 1%
Acceptance rate (master's): 83%
Acceptance rate (doctoral): N/A
Entrance test required: GRE
Avg. GRE (of all entering students with scores): quantitative: 509; verbal: 438
Research assistantships: 30
Students reporting specialty: 100%
Students specializing in: admin.: 24%; counseling: 8%; elementary: 15%; junior high: 3%; secondary: 8%; special: 19%; instructional media design: 0%; other: 23%

LOUISIANA

Grambling State University
GSU Box 4305
Grambling, LA 71245
http://www.gram.edu/
Public
Admissions: (318) 274-2457
E-mail: gsugrad@gram.edu
Financial aid: (318) 274-6190
Application deadline: 07/01
In-state tuition: full time: $3,457; part time: $3,573
Out-of-state tuition: full time: $7,471
Room/board/expenses: $9,576
Full-time enrollment: 36
doctoral students: 28%; master's students: 72%; education specialists: N/A; men: 31%; women: 69%; minorities: 86%; international: 8%
Part-time enrollment: 83
doctoral students: 70%; master's students: 30%; education specialists: N/A; men: 29%; women: 71%; minorities: 73%; international: 2%
Acceptance rate (master's): N/A
Acceptance rate (doctoral): N/A
Entrance test required: GRE or MAT
Avg. GRE (of all entering students with scores): quantitative: N/A; verbal: N/A
Research assistantships: 40
Students reporting specialty: 100%

Students specializing in: admin.: 10%; curriculum/instr.: 3%; other: 87%

Louisiana State University–Baton Rouge

221 Peabody Hall
Baton Rouge, LA 70803
http://www.lsu.edu/coe
Public
Admissions: (225) 578-1641
E-mail: graddeanoffice@lsu.edu
Financial aid: (225) 578-3103
Application deadline: 05/15
In-state tuition: full time: $4,432; part time: $2,765
Out-of-state tuition: full time: $12,732
Room/board/expenses: $11,020
Full-time enrollment: 236
doctoral students: 43%; master's students: 56%; education specialists: 2%; men: 25%; women: 75%; minorities: 15%; international: 9%
Part-time enrollment: 245
doctoral students: 38%; master's students: 53%; education specialists: 9%; men: 20%; women: 80%; minorities: 17%; international: 2%
Acceptance rate (master's): 71%
Acceptance rate (doctoral): 50%
Entrance test required: GRE
Avg. GRE (of all entering students with scores): quantitative: 537; verbal: 455
Research assistantships: 29
Students reporting specialty: 95%
Students specializing in: admin.: 5%; counseling: 4%; curriculum/instr.: 11%; evaluation/research/statistics: 14%; educational tech.: 5%; educational psych: 2%; elementary: 4%; higher education admin.: 8%; secondary: 2%; special: 3%; other: 41%

Louisiana Tech University

PO Box 3163
Ruston, LA 71272-0001
http://www.latech.edu/tech/education/
Public
Admissions: (318) 257-2924
E-mail: gschool@latech.edu
Financial aid: (318) 257-2641
Application deadline: 08/01
In-state tuition: full time: $5,172; part time: $4,270
Out-of-state tuition: full time: $8,752
Room/board/expenses: $10,868
Full-time enrollment: 221
doctoral students: 9%; master's students: 91%; education specialists: N/A; men: 27%; women: 73%; minorities: 26%; international: 0%
Part-time enrollment: 177
doctoral students: 16%; master's students: 84%; education specialists: N/A; men: 22%; women: 78%; minorities: 22%; international: N/A
Acceptance rate (master's): N/A
Acceptance rate (doctoral): 45%
Entrance test required: GRE
Avg. GRE (of all entering students with scores): quantitative: 453; verbal: 405
Research assistantships: 3
Students reporting specialty: 100%
Students specializing in: admin.: 3%; counseling: 10%; curriculum/instr.: 7%; educational psych: 0%; elementary: 1%; junior high: 1%; secondary: 3%; special: 1%; other: 75%

University of Louisiana–Monroe

Strauss Hall
Monroe, LA 71209-0001
http://www.ulm.edu
Public
Admissions: (318) 342-5252
E-mail: admissions@ulm.edu
Financial aid: (318) 342-5320
Application deadline: N/A
In-state tuition: full time: $3,859; part time: $289/credit hour
Out-of-state tuition: full time: $9,817
Room/board/expenses: $6,220
Full-time enrollment: 143
doctoral students: 17%; master's students: 82%; education specialists: 1%; men: 27%; women: 73%; minorities: 30%; international: 2%
Part-time enrollment: 233
doctoral students: 18%; master's students: 78%; education specialists: 4%; men: 21%; women: 79%; minorities: 33%; international: 1%
Acceptance rate (master's): N/A
Acceptance rate (doctoral): 80%
Entrance test required: GRE
Avg. GRE (of all entering students with scores): quantitative: 492; verbal: 428
Research assistantships: 30
Students reporting specialty: 55%
Students specializing in: admin.: 4%; counseling: 23%; curriculum/instr.: 8%; educational psych: 5%; elementary: 20%; secondary: 11%; special: 14%; other: 33%

University of New Orleans

2000 Lakeshore Drive
New Orleans, LA 70148
http://www.uno.edu
Public
Admissions: (504) 280-6595
E-mail: admissions@uno.edu
Financial aid: (504) 280-6603
Application deadline: rolling
In-state tuition: full time: N/A; part time: N/A
Out-of-state tuition: full time: N/A
Room/board/expenses: N/A
Full-time enrollment: 135
doctoral students: 40%; master's students: 60%; education specialists: N/A; men: 21%; women: 79%; minorities: 51%; international: 3%
Part-time enrollment: 326
doctoral students: 41%; master's students: 59%; education specialists: N/A; men: 21%; women: 79%; minorities: 53%; international: 1%
Acceptance rate (master's): N/A
Acceptance rate (doctoral): N/A
Entrance test required: GRE
Avg. GRE (of all entering students with scores): quantitative: N/A; verbal: N/A
Research assistantships: 8
Students reporting specialty: 98%
Students specializing in: admin.: 18%; counseling: 10%; curriculum/instr.: 13%; evaluation/research/statistics: 0%; higher education admin.: 3%; special: 6%; other: 51%

MAINE

University of Maine–Orono

Shibles Hall
Orono, ME 04469-5766
http://www.umaine.edu/about/academicprograms/edudevelop.htm
Public
Admissions: (207) 581-3219
E-mail: graduate@maine.edu
Financial aid: (207) 581-1324
Application deadline: rolling
In-state tuition: full time: $325/credit hour; part time: $325/credit hour
Out-of-state tuition: full time: $936/credit hour
Room/board/expenses: $11,530
Full-time enrollment: 229
doctoral students: 12%; master's students: 83%; education specialists: 4%; men: 22%; women: 78%; minorities: 5%; international: 4%
Part-time enrollment: 393
doctoral students: 11%; master's students: 75%; education specialists: 15%; men: 26%; women: 74%; minorities: 1%; international: 0%
Acceptance rate (master's): 70%
Acceptance rate (doctoral): 40%
Entrance test required: GRE or MAT
Avg. GRE (of all entering students with scores): quantitative: 537; verbal: 487
Research assistantships: 4
Students reporting specialty: 100%
Students specializing in: admin.: 28%; counseling: 17%; curriculum/instr.: 2%; elementary: 2%; higher education admin.: 8%; secondary: 4%; special: 10%; instructional media design: 3%; other: 45%

MARYLAND

Johns Hopkins University

6740 Alexander Bell Drive
Suite 110
Columbia, MD 21046-2100
http://education.jhu.edu/admission/
Private
Admissions: (410) 516-9796
E-mail: onestop.admissions@jhu.edu
Financial aid: (410) 516-9806
Application deadline: rolling
Tuition: full time: N/A; part time: $428/credit hour
Room/board/expenses: N/A
Full-time enrollment: N/A
doctoral students: N/A; master's students: N/A; education specialists: N/A; men: N/A; women: N/A; minorities: N/A; international: N/A
Part-time enrollment: 1,641
doctoral students: 2%; master's students: 98%; education specialists: N/A; men: 22%; women: 78%; minorities: 21%; international: 4%
Acceptance rate (master's): 96%
Acceptance rate (doctoral): 43%
Entrance test required: GRE
Avg. GRE (of all entering students with scores): quantitative: N/A; verbal: N/A
Students reporting specialty: 96%
Students specializing in: admin.: 17%; counseling: 10%; curriculum/instr.: 8%; elementary: 10%; secondary: 16%; special: 16%; other: 24%

Morgan State University

1700 E. Cold Spring Lane
Baltimore, MD 21251
http://www.morgan.edu/academics/Grad-Studies/default.asp
Public
Admissions: (443) 885-3185
E-mail: pshicks@moac.morgan.edu
Financial aid: (443) 885-3185
Application deadline: rolling
In-state tuition: full time: $283/credit hour; part time: $283/credit hour
Out-of-state tuition: full time: $502/credit hour
Room/board/expenses: $16,730
Full-time enrollment: 54
doctoral students: 93%; master's students: 7%; education specialists: N/A; men: 39%; women: 61%; minorities: 89%; international: 6%
Part-time enrollment: 109
doctoral students: 94%; master's students: 6%; education specialists: N/A; men: 32%; women: 68%; minorities: 88%; international: 1%
Acceptance rate (master's): N/A
Acceptance rate (doctoral): N/A
Entrance test required: GRE or MAT
Avg. GRE (of all entering students with scores): quantitative: N/A; verbal: N/A
Research assistantships: 4
Students reporting specialty: 100%
Students specializing in: admin.: 34%; higher education admin.: 37%; secondary: 2%; other: 27%

Towson University

8000 York Road
Towson, MD 21252
http://www.grad.towson.edu
Public
Admissions: (410) 704-2501
E-mail: grads@towson.edu
Financial aid: (410) 704-4236
Application deadline: rolling
In-state tuition: full time: $286/credit hour; part time: $286/credit hour
Out-of-state tuition: full time: $600/credit hour
Room/board/expenses: $12,337
Full-time enrollment: 317
doctoral students: 13%; master's students: 84%; education specialists: 3%; men: 15%; women: 85%; minorities: 15%; international: N/A
Part-time enrollment: 1,214
doctoral students: 2%; master's students: 92%; education specialists: 6%; men: 14%; women: 86%; minorities: 13%; international: 3%
Acceptance rate (master's): 81%
Acceptance rate (doctoral): 62%
Entrance test required: GRE
Avg. GRE (of all entering students with scores): quantitative: N/A; verbal: N/A
Research assistantships: 6
Students reporting specialty: 97%
Students specializing in: admin.: 10%; educational tech.: 2%; educational psych: 3%; elementary: 4%; secondary: 4%; special: 5%; instructional media design: 13%; other: 60%

University of Maryland–College Park

3119 Benjamin Building
College Park, MD 20742-1121
http://www.education.umd.edu
Public
Admissions: (301) 405-2358
E-mail: kangel@umd.edu
Financial aid: (301) 314-9000
Application deadline: 12/01
In-state tuition: full time: $427/credit hour; part time: $427/credit hour
Out-of-state tuition: full time: $921/credit hour
Room/board/expenses: $12,903
Full-time enrollment: 744
doctoral students: 66%; master's students: 34%; education specialists: 0%; men: 24%; women: 76%; minorities: 25%; international: 15%
Part-time enrollment: 451
doctoral students: 33%; master's students: 66%; education specialists: 1%; men: 22%; women: 78%; minorities: 28%; international: 2%
Acceptance rate (master's): 49%
Acceptance rate (doctoral): 33%
Entrance test required: GRE or MAT
Avg. GRE (of all entering students with scores): quantitative: 610; verbal: 522
Research assistantships: 89
Students reporting specialty: 100%
Students specializing in: admin.: 7%; counseling: 14%; evaluation/research/statistics: 4%; social/philosophical foundations: 4%; policy: 9%; educational psych: 8%; elementary: 5%; higher education admin.: 5%; secondary: 34%; special: 11%

University of Maryland–Eastern Shore

1 Backbone Road
Princess Anne, MD 21853
http://www.umes.edu/deps/arts_n_professions/index.html
Public
Admissions: (410) 651-6507
E-mail: cdignasias@umes.edu
Financial aid: (410) 651-6174
Application deadline: rolling
In-state tuition: full time: $6,068; part time: $225/credit hour
Out-of-state tuition: full time: $12,635
Room/board/expenses: $1,700
Full-time enrollment: 27
doctoral students: 0%; master's students: 100%; education specialists: N/A; men: 33%; women: 67%; minorities: 56%; international: 7%
Part-time enrollment: 80
doctoral students: 28%; master's students: 73%; education specialists: N/A; men: 21%; women: 79%; minorities: 44%; international: 1%
Acceptance rate (master's): 56%
Acceptance rate (doctoral): N/A
Entrance test required: N/A
Avg. GRE (of all entering students with scores): quantitative: N/A; verbal: N/A
Students reporting specialty: 100%
Students specializing in: admin.: 21%; counseling: 35%; secondary: 18%; special: 11%; technical (vocational): 16%

MASSACHUSETTS

American International College

1000 State Street
Springfield, MA 01109
http://www.aic.edu/pages/399.html
Private
Admissions: (413) 205-3535
E-mail: ellen.noonan@aic.edu
Financial aid: (413) 205-3270
Application deadline: rolling
Tuition: full time: $615/credit hour; part time: $615/credit hour
Room/board/expenses: $10,542
Full-time enrollment: 37
doctoral students: 41%; master's students: 59%; education specialists: N/A; men: 24%; women: 76%; minorities: 3%; international: 3%
Part-time enrollment: 453
doctoral students: 4%; master's students: 96%; education specialists: N/A; men: 12%; women: 88%; minorities: 10%; international: N/A
Acceptance rate (master's): 96%
Acceptance rate (doctoral): 60%
Entrance test required: GRE
Avg. GRE (of all entering students with scores): quantitative: N/A; verbal: N/A
Research assistantships: 0
Students reporting specialty: 0%
Students specializing in: N/A

Boston College (Lynch)

Campion Hall
Chestnut Hill, MA 02467-3813
http://www.bc.edu/education
Private
Admissions: (617) 552-4214
E-mail: grad.ed.info@bc.edu
Financial aid: (617) 552-3300
Application deadline: N/A
Tuition: full time: $970/credit hour; part time: $970/credit hour
Room/board/expenses: $20,111
Full-time enrollment: 673
doctoral students: 35%; master's students: 63%; education specialists: 2%; men: 24%; women: 76%; minorities: 16%; international: 11%
Part-time enrollment: 185
doctoral students: 15%; master's students: 79%; education specialists: 5%; men: 28%; women: 72%; minorities: 11%; international: 1%
Acceptance rate (master's): 78%
Acceptance rate (doctoral): 12%
Entrance test required: GRE or MAT
Avg. GRE (of all entering students with scores): quantitative: 589; verbal: 519
Research assistantships: 355
Students reporting specialty: 100%
Students specializing in: admin.: 10%; counseling: 24%; curriculum/instr.: 17%; evaluation/research/statistics: 5%; educational psych: 4%; elementary: 7%; higher education admin.: 12%; secondary: 11%; special: 7%; other: 4%

Boston University
2 Sherborn Street
Boston, MA 02215
http://www.bu.edu/education/
Private
Admissions: (617) 353-4237
E-mail: sedgrad@bu.edu
Financial aid: (617) 353-4238
Application deadline: rolling
Tuition: full time: $35,300; part time: $546/credit hour
Room/board/expenses: $16,387
Full-time enrollment: 265
doctoral students: 25%; master's students: 75%; education specialists: 0%; men: 22%; women: 78%; minorities: 12%; international: 27%
Part-time enrollment: 285
doctoral students: 35%; master's students: 61%; education specialists: 4%; men: 31%; women: 69%; minorities: 12%; international: 2%
Acceptance rate (master's): 70%
Acceptance rate (doctoral): 50%
Entrance test required: GRE or MAT
Avg. GRE (of all entering students with scores): quantitative: 585; verbal: 520
Research assistantships: 11
Students reporting specialty: 85%
Students specializing in: admin.: 7%; counseling: 12%; curriculum/instr.: 11%; policy: 6%; elementary: 2%; higher education admin.: 6%; special: 9%; instructional media design: 3%; other: 45%

Harvard University
Appian Way
Cambridge, MA 02138
http://www.gse.harvard.edu
Private
Admissions: (617) 495-3414
E-mail: gseadmissions@harvard.edu
Financial aid: (617) 495-3416
Application deadline: 12/15
Tuition: full time: $34,484; part time: $18,636
Room/board/expenses: $20,644
Full-time enrollment: 808
doctoral students: 36%; master's students: 64%; education specialists: N/A; men: 26%; women: 74%; minorities: 25%; international: 13%
Part-time enrollment: 100
doctoral students: 29%; master's students: 71%; education specialists: N/A; men: 24%; women: 76%; minorities: 24%; international: 3%
Acceptance rate (master's): 61%
Acceptance rate (doctoral): 12%
Entrance test required: GRE
Avg. GRE (of all entering students with scores): quantitative: 646; verbal: 591
Research assistantships: 44
Students reporting specialty: 96%
Students specializing in: admin.: 23%; counseling: 8%; curriculum/instr.: 10%; evaluation/research/statistics: 2%; policy: 21%; educational tech.: 4%; educational psych: 23%; higher education admin.: 7%; secondary: 5%; other: 13%

Lesley University
29 Everett Street
Cambridge, MA 02138-2790
http://www.lesley.edu/soe.html
Private
Admissions: (617) 349-8544
E-mail: learn@lesley.edu
Financial aid: (800) 999-1959
Application deadline: rolling
Tuition: full time: $735/credit hour; part time: $735/credit hour
Room/board/expenses: N/A
Full-time enrollment: 454
doctoral students: 0%; master's students: 95%; education specialists: 5%; men: 11%; women: 89%; minorities: 7%; international: 2%
Part-time enrollment: 3,422
doctoral students: 2%; master's students: 94%; education specialists: 4%; men: 13%; women: 87%; minorities: 10%; international: 0%
Acceptance rate (master's): 68%
Acceptance rate (doctoral): 56%
Entrance test required: GRE or MAT
Avg. GRE (of all entering students with scores): quantitative: N/A; verbal: N/A
Students reporting specialty: 78%
Students specializing in: counseling: 1%; curriculum/instr.: 15%; educational tech.: 22%; elementary: 10%; junior high: 1%; special: 7%; other: 44%

Tufts University[1]
Paige Hall
12 Upper Campus Road
Medford, MA 02155
http://ase.tufts.edu/GradStudy/programs.htm
Private
Admissions: (617) 627-3395
Financial aid: (617) 627-2000
Tuition: N/A
Room/board/expenses: N/A
Enrollment: N/A

University of Massachusetts–Amherst
Furcolo Hall
813 N. Pleasant Street
Amherst, MA 01003-9308
http://www.umass.edu/education
Public
Admissions: (413) 545-0721
E-mail: gradadm@resgs.umass.edu
Financial aid: (413) 577-0555
Application deadline: 01/15
In-state tuition: full time: $10,096; part time: $110/credit hour
Out-of-state tuition: full time: $17,393
Room/board/expenses: $11,000
Full-time enrollment: 420
doctoral students: 35%; master's students: 65%; education specialists: N/A; men: 30%; women: 70%; minorities: 15%; international: 15%
Part-time enrollment: 416
doctoral students: 53%; master's students: 47%; education specialists: N/A; men: 30%; women: 70%; minorities: 17%; international: 9%
Acceptance rate (master's): 72%
Acceptance rate (doctoral): 48%
Entrance test required: GRE
Avg. GRE (of all entering students with scores): quantitative: 591; verbal: 512
Research assistantships: 90
Students reporting specialty: 98%
Students specializing in: admin.: 10%; counseling: 3%; curriculum/instr.: 23%; evaluation/research/statistics: 2%; social/philosophical foundations: 7%; policy: 28%; educational tech.: 2%; educational psych: 4%; elementary: 10%; higher education admin.: 11%; secondary: 14%; special: 1%; other: 5%

University of Massachusetts–Lowell
510 O'Leary Library
61 Wilder Street
Lowell, MA 01854
http://gse.uml.edu
Public
Admissions: (978) 934-4601
E-mail: donald_pierson@uml.edu
Financial aid: (978) 934-4220
Application deadline: rolling
In-state tuition: full time: $91/credit hour; part time: $91/credit hour
Out-of-state tuition: full time: $357/credit hour
Room/board/expenses: N/A
Full-time enrollment: 128
doctoral students: 5%; master's students: 95%; education specialists: N/A; men: 34%; women: 66%; minorities: 5%; international: 4%
Part-time enrollment: 259
doctoral students: 52%; master's students: 48%; education specialists: N/A; men: 25%; women: 75%; minorities: 7%; international: N/A
Acceptance rate (master's): 80%
Acceptance rate (doctoral): 60%
Entrance test required: GRE
Avg. GRE (of all entering students with scores): quantitative: 555; verbal: 525
Research assistantships: 2
Students reporting specialty: 88%
Students specializing in: admin.: 16%; curriculum/instr.: 7%; policy: 22%; elementary: 9%; secondary: 27%; other: 19%

MICHIGAN

Andrews University
Berrien Springs, MI 49104-0100
http://www.andrews.edu/
Private
Admissions: (800) 253-2874
E-mail: enroll@andrews.edu
Financial aid: (269) 471-3334
Application deadline: rolling
Tuition: full time: $849/credit hour; part time: $849/credit hour
Room/board/expenses: $8,510
Full-time enrollment: 140
doctoral students: 61%; master's students: 26%; education specialists: 13%; men: 37%; women: 63%; minorities: 25%; international: 22%
Part-time enrollment: 136
doctoral students: 76%; master's students: 21%; education specialists: 4%; men: 47%; women: 53%; minorities: 24%; international: 13%
Acceptance rate (master's): 44%
Acceptance rate (doctoral): 63%
Entrance test required: GRE
Avg. GRE (of all entering students with scores): quantitative: 450; verbal: 441
Research assistantships: 10
Students reporting specialty: 0%
Students specializing in: N/A

Eastern Michigan University[1]
310 Porter Building
Ypsilanti, MI 48197
http://www.gradord.emich.edu
Public
Admissions: (734) 487-3400
E-mail: graduate.admissions@emich.edu
Financial aid: (734) 487-0455
Tuition: N/A
Room/board/expenses: N/A
Enrollment: N/A

Michigan State University
501 Erickson Hall
East Lansing, MI 48824-1034
http://www.educ.msu.edu
Public
Admissions: (517) 355-8332
E-mail: admis@msu.edu
Financial aid: (517) 353-5940
Application deadline: N/A
In-state tuition: full time: $412/credit hour; part time: $412/credit hour
Out-of-state tuition: full time: $833/credit hour
Room/board/expenses: $13,554
Full-time enrollment: 906
doctoral students: 55%; master's students: 42%; education specialists: 3%; men: 32%; women: 68%; minorities: 15%; international: 16%
Part-time enrollment: 198
doctoral students: 21%; master's students: 71%; education specialists: 9%; men: 29%; women: 71%; minorities: 11%; international: 2%
Acceptance rate (master's): 62%
Acceptance rate (doctoral): 47%
Entrance test required: GRE
Avg. GRE (of all entering students with scores): quantitative: 600; verbal: 524
Research assistantships: 244
Students reporting specialty: 63%
Students specializing in: admin.: 10%; counseling: 11%; curriculum/instr.: 26%; evaluation/research/statistics: 3%; social/philosophical foundations: 2%; policy: 2%; educational tech.: 2%; educational psych: 4%; elementary: 5%; higher education admin.: 15%; secondary: 3%; special: 7%; other: 9%

Oakland University
415 Pawley Hall
Rochester, MI 48309-4494
http://www.oakland.edu/grad
Public
Admissions: (248) 370-3167
E-mail: gradmail@oakland.edu
Financial aid: (248) 370-2550
Application deadline: rolling
In-state tuition: full time: $11,340; part time: $473/credit hour
Out-of-state tuition: full time: $19,548
Room/board/expenses: $9,382
Full-time enrollment: 570
doctoral students: 6%; master's students: 94%; education specialists: 0%; men: 14%; women: 86%; minorities: 12%; international: 2%
Part-time enrollment: 1,321
doctoral students: 9%; master's students: 80%; education specialists: 11%; men: 16%; women: 84%; minorities: 9%; international: 0%
Acceptance rate (master's): 89%
Acceptance rate (doctoral): 56%
Entrance test required: GRE or MAT
Avg. GRE (of all entering students with scores): quantitative: N/A; verbal: N/A
Students reporting specialty: 100%
Students specializing in: admin.: 14%; counseling: 22%; curriculum/instr.: 6%; elementary: 5%; higher education admin.: 0%; secondary: 4%; special: 14%; other: 35%

University of Michigan–Ann Arbor
610 E. University Street
Ann Arbor, MI 48109-1259
http://www.soe.umich.edu/
Public
Admissions: (734) 764-7563
E-mail: ed.grad.admit@umich.edu
Financial aid: (734) 764-7563
Application deadline: N/A
In-state tuition: full time: $16,582; part time: $843/credit hour
Out-of-state tuition: full time: $32,824
Room/board/expenses: $15,980
Full-time enrollment: 456
doctoral students: 61%; master's students: 39%; education specialists: N/A; men: 29%; women: 71%; minorities: 24%; international: 11%
Part-time enrollment: 44
doctoral students: 25%; master's students: 75%; education specialists: N/A; men: 34%; women: 66%; minorities: 9%; international: 7%
Acceptance rate (master's): 65%
Acceptance rate (doctoral): 20%
Entrance test required: GRE
Avg. GRE (of all entering students with scores): quantitative: 635; verbal: 547
Research assistantships: 205
Students reporting specialty: 94%
Students specializing in: admin.: 4%; curriculum/instr.: 27%; evaluation/research/statistics: 3%; social/philosophical foundations: 6%; educational tech.: 3%; educational psych: 5%; elementary: 11%; higher education admin.: 27%; secondary: 13%; special: 1%; other: 5%

Wayne State University
Detroit, MI 48202-3489
http://www.coe.wayne.edu/
Public
Admissions: (313) 577-1605
Financial aid: (313) 577-3378
Application deadline: 07/01
In-state tuition: full time: $403/credit hour; part time: $403/credit hour
Out-of-state tuition: full time: $890/credit hour
Room/board/expenses: $11,457
Full-time enrollment: 692
doctoral students: 15%; master's students: 75%; education specialists: 10%; men: 27%; women: 73%; minorities: 35%; international: 7%
Part-time enrollment: 1,733
doctoral students: 10%; master's students: 75%; education specialists: 14%; men: 26%; women: 74%; minorities: 40%; international: 2%
Acceptance rate (master's): 64%
Acceptance rate (doctoral): 10%
Entrance test required: GRE or MAT
Avg. GRE (of all entering students with scores): quantitative: 461; verbal: 432
Research assistantships: 10
Students reporting specialty: 93%
Students specializing in: admin.: 13%; counseling: 1%; curriculum/instr.: 5%; evaluation/research/statistics: 1%; social/philosophical foundations: 0%; educational psych: 3%; elementary: 12%; secondary: 14%; special: 2%; technical (vocational): 1%; instructional media design: 9%; other: 40%

Western Michigan University
1903 W. Michigan Avenue
Kalamazoo, MI 49008-5229
http://www.wmich.edu/coe
Public
Admissions: (269) 387-2000
E-mail: ask-wmu@wmich.edu
Financial aid: (269) 387-6000
Application deadline: 12/03
In-state tuition: full time: $345/credit hour; part time: $345/credit hour
Out-of-state tuition: full time: $730/credit hour
Room/board/expenses: $11,807
Full-time enrollment: 714
doctoral students: 17%; master's students: 83%; education specialists: 0%; men: 29%; women: 71%; minorities: 16%; international: 6%
Part-time enrollment: 947
doctoral students: 21%; master's students: 78%; education specialists: 1%; men: 30%; women: 70%; minorities: 15%; international: 1%
Acceptance rate (master's): 74%
Acceptance rate (doctoral): 20%
Entrance test required: GRE
Avg. GRE (of all entering students with scores): quantitative: 518; verbal: 453
Research assistantships: 13
Students reporting specialty: 100%
Students specializing in: admin.: 20%; counseling: 21%; evaluation/research/statistics: 3%; social/philosophical foundations: 1%; elementary: 2%; higher education admin.: 3%; junior high: 1%; special: 7%; instructional media design: 5%; other: 38%

MINNESOTA

Bethel University
3900 Bethel Drive
St. Paul, MN 55112-6999
http://gs.bethel.edu
Private
Admissions: (651) 635-8000
E-mail: gs@bethel.edu
Financial aid: (651) 638-6241
Application deadline: rolling
Tuition: full time: $415/credit hour; part time: $415/credit hour
Room/board/expenses: N/A
Full-time enrollment: 161
doctoral students: 34%; master's students: 66%; education specialists: N/A; men: 37%; women: 63%; minorities: 5%; international: N/A

Part-time enrollment: 56
doctoral students: 20%; master's students: 80%; education specialists: N/A; men: 39%; women: 61%; minorities: 11%; international: N/A
Acceptance rate (master's): 94%
Acceptance rate (doctoral): 69%
Entrance test required: GRE or MAT
Avg. GRE (of all entering students with scores): quantitative: N/A; verbal: N/A
Students reporting specialty: 100%
Students specializing in: admin.: 35%; special: 38%; other: 27%

Hamline University
1536 Hewitt Avenue
St. Paul, MN 55104-1284
http://www.hamline.edu
Private
Admissions: (651) 523-2900
E-mail: gradprog@hamline.edu
Financial aid: (651) 523-3000
Application deadline: rolling
Tuition: full time: $396/credit hour; part time: $396/credit hour
Room/board/expenses: $8,060
Full-time enrollment: 33
doctoral students: 9%; master's students: 91%; education specialists: N/A; men: 18%; women: 82%; minorities: 6%; international: 9%
Part-time enrollment: 465
doctoral students: 15%; master's students: 85%; education specialists: N/A; men: 22%; women: 78%; minorities: 7%; international: 2%
Acceptance rate (master's): 86%
Acceptance rate (doctoral): 80%
Entrance test required: N/A
Avg. GRE (of all entering students with scores): quantitative: N/A; verbal: N/A
Research assistantships: 0
Students reporting specialty: 100%
Students specializing in: admin.: 5%; elementary: 6%; secondary: 12%; other: 76%

University of Minnesota–Twin Cities
104 Burton Hall
178 Pillsbury Drive SE
Minneapolis, MN 55455
http://education.umn.edu/
Public
Admissions: (612) 625-6501
E-mail: spsinfo@umn.edu
Financial aid: (612) 624-1111
Application deadline: 12/17
In-state tuition: full time: $11,484; part time: $812/credit hour
Out-of-state tuition: full time: $18,582
Room/board/expenses: $12,134
Full-time enrollment: 1,231
doctoral students: 49%; master's students: 50%; education specialists: 1%; men: 28%; women: 72%; minorities: 12%; international: 13%
Part-time enrollment: 860
doctoral students: 57%; master's students: 42%; education specialists: 1%; men: 28%; women: 72%; minorities: 13%; international: 8%
Acceptance rate (master's): 59%
Acceptance rate (doctoral): 47%
Entrance test required: GRE
Avg. GRE (of all entering students with scores): quantitative: 610; verbal: 518
Research assistantships: 330
Students reporting specialty: 99%
Students specializing in: admin.: 7%; counseling: 4%; curriculum/instr.: 7%; evaluation/research/statistics: 1%; social/philosophical foundations: 4%; educational tech.: 1%; educational psych: 4%; elementary: 6%; higher education admin.: 4%; secondary: 15%; special: 6%; instructional media design: 0%; other: 41%

University of St. Thomas
1000 LaSalle Avenue
Minneapolis, MN 55403
http://www.stthomas.edu/education
Private
Admissions: (651) 962-4550
E-mail: education@stthomas.edu
Financial aid: (651) 962-6550
Application deadline: 06/01
Tuition: full time: $573/credit hour; part time: $573/credit hour
Room/board/expenses: $900
Full-time enrollment: 610
doctoral students: 6%; master's students: 84%; education specialists: 10%; men: 30%; women: 70%; minorities: 12%; international: 2%
Part-time enrollment: 584
doctoral students: 24%; master's students: 67%; education specialists: 9%; men: 30%; women: 70%; minorities: 11%; international: 1%
Acceptance rate (master's): 96%
Acceptance rate (doctoral): 90%
Entrance test required: GRE or MAT
Avg. GRE (of all entering students with scores): quantitative: N/A; verbal: N/A
Research assistantships: 29
Students reporting specialty: 98%
Students specializing in: admin.: 14%; curriculum/instr.: 11%; evaluation/research/statistics: 9%; policy: 2%; educational tech.: 2%; elementary: 14%; higher education admin.: 3%; junior high: 1%; secondary: 14%; special: 29%

MISSISSIPPI

Delta State University
1003 W. Sunflower Road
Cleveland, MS 38733
http://www.deltastate.edu/pages/251.asp
Public
Admissions: (662) 846-4875
E-mail: grad-info@deltastate.edu
Financial aid: (662) 846-4670
Application deadline: N/A
In-state tuition: full time: $4,248; part time: $236/credit hour
Out-of-state tuition: full time: $10,258
Room/board/expenses: $6,360
Full-time enrollment: 104
doctoral students: 5%; master's students: 91%; education specialists: 4%; men: 32%; women: 68%; minorities: 59%; international: N/A
Part-time enrollment: 286
doctoral students: 13%; master's students: 71%; education specialists: 16%; men: 10%; women: 90%; minorities: 73%; international: N/A
Acceptance rate (master's): N/A
Acceptance rate (doctoral): N/A
Entrance test required: GRE
Avg. GRE (of all entering students with scores): quantitative: N/A; verbal: N/A
Students reporting specialty: 100%
Students specializing in: admin.: 14%; counseling: 26%; elementary: 15%; secondary: 5%; special: 19%; other: 22%

Mississippi State University
PO Box 9710
Mississippi State, MS 39762
http://www.educ.msstate.edu/
Public
Admissions: (662) 325-2224
E-mail: admit@admissions.msstate.edu
Financial aid: (662) 325-2450
Application deadline: N/A
In-state tuition: full time: $4,929; part time: $274/credit hour
Out-of-state tuition: full time: $11,420
Room/board/expenses: $4,164
Full-time enrollment: 337
doctoral students: 27%; master's students: 64%; education specialists: 9%; men: 31%; women: 69%; minorities: 34%; international: 4%
Part-time enrollment: 614
doctoral students: 54%; master's students: 36%; education specialists: 11%; men: 25%; women: 75%; minorities: 42%; international: N/A
Acceptance rate (master's): 51%
Acceptance rate (doctoral): 33%
Entrance test required: GRE
Avg. GRE (of all entering students with scores): quantitative: 451; verbal: 375
Research assistantships: 13
Students reporting specialty: 100%
Students specializing in: admin.: 26%; counseling: 19%; curriculum/instr.: 2%; educational psych: 4%; elementary: 5%; secondary: 8%; special: 1%; technical (vocational): 2%; other: 32%

University of Mississippi
222 Guyton Hall
University, MS 38677
http://www.olemiss.edu/depts/educ_school2/
Public
Admissions: (662) 915-7226
E-mail: admissions@olemiss.edu
Financial aid: (662) 915-5788
Application deadline: 04/01
In-state tuition: full time: $4,932; part time: $274/credit hour
Out-of-state tuition: full time: $11,440
Room/board/expenses: $3,550
Full-time enrollment: 158
doctoral students: 27%; master's students: 69%; education specialists: 4%; men: 22%; women: 78%; minorities: 39%; international: 9%
Part-time enrollment: 401
doctoral students: 23%; master's students: 69%; education specialists: 9%; men: 25%; women: 75%; minorities: 33%; international: 1%
Acceptance rate (master's): 41%
Acceptance rate (doctoral): 25%
Entrance test required: GRE
Avg. GRE (of all entering students with scores): quantitative: 538; verbal: 440
Research assistantships: 9
Students reporting specialty: 100%
Students specializing in: admin.: 20%; counseling: 17%; curriculum/instr.: 57%; higher education admin.: 6%

University of Southern Mississippi
118 College Drive
Box 5023
Hattiesburg, MS 39406
http://www.usm.edu
Public
Admissions: (601) 266-4369
Financial aid: (601) 266-4774
Application deadline: rolling
In-state tuition: full time: $5,174; part time: $205/credit hour
Out-of-state tuition: full time: $11,952
Room/board/expenses: $9,114
Full-time enrollment: 276
doctoral students: 29%; master's students: 63%; education specialists: 8%; men: 21%; women: 79%; minorities: 26%; international: 6%
Part-time enrollment: 574
doctoral students: 35%; master's students: 53%; education specialists: 12%; men: 21%; women: 79%; minorities: 23%; international: 1%
Acceptance rate (master's): 41%
Acceptance rate (doctoral): 30%
Entrance test required: GRE or MAT
Avg. GRE (of all entering students with scores): quantitative: 481; verbal: 450
Research assistantships: 71
Students reporting specialty: 99%
Students specializing in: admin.: 8%; counseling: 8%; curriculum/instr.: 3%; educational tech.: 1%; higher education admin.: 4%; secondary: 1%; special: 5%; instructional media design: 1%; other: 70%

MISSOURI

St. Louis University
3750 Lindell Boulevard
St. Louis, MO 63108-3412
http://www.slu.edu/colleges/cops/es/grad.html
Private
Admissions: (314) 977-2240
E-mail: grequest@slu.edu
Financial aid: (314) 977-2350
Application deadline: rolling
Tuition: full time: $845/credit hour; part time: $845/credit hour
Room/board/expenses: $12,553
Full-time enrollment: 181
doctoral students: 60%; master's students: 40%; education specialists: 0%; men: 29%; women: 71%; minorities: 13%; international: 3%
Part-time enrollment: 275
doctoral students: 81%; master's students: 17%; education specialists: 2%; men: 50%; women: 50%; minorities: 15%; international: N/A
Acceptance rate (master's): 63%
Acceptance rate (doctoral): 68%
Entrance test required: GRE or MAT
Avg. GRE (of all entering students with scores): quantitative: N/A; verbal: N/A
Research assistantships: 13
Students reporting specialty: 64%
Students specializing in: admin.: 111%; counseling: 17%

University of Central Missouri
Lovinger 2190
Warrensburg, MO 64093
http://www.ucmo.edu/graduate
Public
Admissions: (660) 543-4621
E-mail: Gradinfo@ucmo.edu
Financial aid: (660) 543-4040
Application deadline: rolling
In-state tuition: full time: $236/credit hour; part time: $236/credit hour
Out-of-state tuition: full time: $471/credit hour
Room/board/expenses: $6,646
Full-time enrollment: 112
doctoral students: N/A; master's students: 93%; education specialists: 7%; men: 31%; women: 69%; minorities: 12%; international: 2%
Part-time enrollment: 843
doctoral students: 1%; master's students: 84%; education specialists: 16%; men: 25%; women: 75%; minorities: 5%; international: 0%
Acceptance rate (master's): N/A
Acceptance rate (doctoral): N/A
Entrance test required: GRE
Avg. GRE (of all entering students with scores): quantitative: N/A; verbal: N/A
Students reporting specialty: 99%
Students specializing in: admin.: 20%; counseling: 2%; elementary: 2%; higher education admin.: 4%; secondary: 2%; special: 4%; instructional media design: 3%; other: 64%

University of Missouri–Columbia
118 Hill Hall
Columbia, MO 65211
http://www.coe.missouri.edu
Public
Admissions: (573) 882-2961
E-mail: lewistj@missouri.edu
Financial aid: (573) 882-7506
Application deadline: rolling
In-state tuition: full time: $287/credit hour; part time: $287/credit hour
Out-of-state tuition: full time: $741/credit hour
Room/board/expenses: $14,461
Full-time enrollment: 696
doctoral students: 21%; master's students: 77%; education specialists: 2%; men: 23%; women: 77%; minorities: 10%; international: 8%
Part-time enrollment: 1,358
doctoral students: 34%; master's students: 59%; education specialists: 6%; men: 27%; women: 73%; minorities: 6%; international: 4%
Acceptance rate (master's): 74%
Acceptance rate (doctoral): 44%
Entrance test required: GRE
Avg. GRE (of all entering students with scores): quantitative: 539; verbal: 475
Research assistantships: 138
Students reporting specialty: 0%
Students specializing in: N/A

University of Missouri–Kansas City
5100 Rockhill Road
Kansas City, MO 64110-2499
http://www.umkc.edu/
Public
Admissions: (816) 235-1111
E-mail: admit@umkc.edu
Financial aid: (816) 235-1154
Application deadline: rolling
In-state tuition: full time: $287/credit hour; part time: $287/credit hour
Out-of-state tuition: full time: $741/credit hour
Room/board/expenses: $15,684
Full-time enrollment: 208
doctoral students: 9%; master's students: 83%; education specialists: 8%; men: 23%; women: 77%; minorities: 27%; international: 4%
Part-time enrollment: 443
doctoral students: 7%; master's students: 75%; education specialists: 18%; men: 29%; women: 71%; minorities: 22%; international: 1%
Acceptance rate (master's): 72%
Acceptance rate (doctoral): 8%
Entrance test required: GRE
Avg. GRE (of all entering students with scores): quantitative: 539; verbal: 463
Research assistantships: 15
Students reporting specialty: 100%
Students specializing in: admin.: 16%; counseling: 14%; curriculum/instr.: 19%; special: 6%; other: 46%

University of Missouri–St. Louis
1 University Boulevard
St. Louis, MO 63121
http://coe.umsl.edu
Public
Admissions: (314) 516-5483
E-mail: gradadm@umsl.edu
Financial aid: (314) 516-5508
Application deadline: rolling
In-state tuition: full time: $287/credit hour; part time: $287/credit hour
Out-of-state tuition: full time: $741/credit hour
Room/board/expenses: $15,335
Full-time enrollment: 212
doctoral students: 16%; master's students: 74%; education specialists: 10%; men: 22%; women: 78%; minorities: 20%; international: 5%
Part-time enrollment: 805
doctoral students: 25%; master's students: 71%; education specialists: 5%; men: 26%; women: 74%; minorities: 26%; international: 1%
Acceptance rate (master's): 78%
Acceptance rate (doctoral): 40%
Entrance test required: GRE
Avg. GRE (of all entering students with scores): quantitative: 543; verbal: 454
Research assistantships: 35
Students reporting specialty: 100%
Students specializing in: admin.: 12%; counseling: 21%; curriculum/

instr.: 6%; policy: 5%; educational psych: 4%; elementary: 9%; higher education admin.: 7%; junior high: 1%; secondary: 17%; special: 5%; other: 12%

Washington University in St. Louis

1 Brookings Drive
Box 1183
St. Louis, MO 63130-4899
http://www.artsci.wustl.edu/~educ/
Private
Admissions: (314) 935-6791
E-mail: nkolk@artsci.wustl.edu
Financial aid: (314) 935-5900
Application deadline: 01/01
Tuition: full time: $35,179; part time: $1,438/credit hour
Room/board/expenses: N/A
Full-time enrollment: 13
doctoral students: 46%; master's students: 54%; education specialists: N/A; men: 38%; women: 62%; minorities: 15%; international: 8%
Part-time enrollment: 7
doctoral students: 0%; master's students: 100%; education specialists: N/A; men: N/A; women: 100%; minorities: 29%; international: N/A
Acceptance rate (master's): 74%
Acceptance rate (doctoral): 33%
Entrance test required: GRE or MAT
Avg. GRE (of all entering students with scores): quantitative: 674; verbal: 601
Research assistantships: 2
Students reporting specialty: 100%
Students specializing in: elementary: 32%; secondary: 32%; other: 36%

MONTANA

Montana State University[1]

215 Reid Hall
Bozeman, MT 59717
http://www.montana.edu/wwweduc/
Public
Admissions: (406) 994-4145
E-mail: gradstudy@montana.edu
Financial aid: (406) 994-2845
Tuition: N/A
Room/board/expenses: N/A
Enrollment: N/A

University of Montana

Education Building
Room 109
Missoula, MT 59812
http://www.soe.umt.edu
Public
Admissions: (406) 243-2572
E-mail: gradschl@mso.umt.edu
Financial aid: (406) 243-5373
Application deadline: rolling
In-state tuition: full time: $5,827; part time: N/A
Out-of-state tuition: full time: $17,225
Room/board/expenses: $10,750
Full-time enrollment: 96
doctoral students: 15%; master's students: 85%; education specialists: 0%; men: 28%; women: 72%; minorities: 15%; international: 3%
Part-time enrollment: 188
doctoral students: 40%; master's students: 56%; education specialists: 3%; men: 37%; women: 63%; minorities: 10%; international: 1%
Acceptance rate (master's): 81%
Acceptance rate (doctoral): 71%
Entrance test required: GRE or MAT
Avg. GRE (of all entering students with scores): quantitative: 535; verbal: 489
Research assistantships: 0
Students reporting specialty: 87%
Students specializing in: admin.: 38%; counseling: 18%; curriculum/instr.: 44%

NEBRASKA

University of Nebraska–Lincoln

233 Mabel Lee Hall
Lincoln, NE 68588-0234
http://cehs.unl.edu
Public
Admissions: (402) 472-2878
E-mail: graduate@unl.edu
Financial aid: (402) 472-2030
Application deadline: rolling
In-state tuition: full time: $224/credit hour; part time: $224/credit hour
Out-of-state tuition: full time: $604/credit hour
Room/board/expenses: $7,553
Full-time enrollment: 271
doctoral students: 39%; master's students: 60%; education specialists: 1%; men: 21%; women: 79%; minorities: 14%; international: 10%
Part-time enrollment: 519
doctoral students: 58%; master's students: 39%; education specialists: 2%; men: 32%; women: 68%; minorities: 8%; international: 4%
Acceptance rate (master's): 83%
Acceptance rate (doctoral): 63%
Entrance test required: GRE
Avg. GRE (of all entering students with scores): quantitative: 542; verbal: 484
Research assistantships: 114
Students reporting specialty: 98%
Students specializing in: admin.: 12%; counseling: 8%; curriculum/instr.: 24%; evaluation/research/statistics: 2%; policy: 1%; educational tech.: 2%; educational psych: 8%; elementary: 1%; higher education admin.: 16%; junior high: 1%; secondary: 4%; special: 19%; instructional media design: 3%

University of Nebraska–Omaha

6001 Dodge Street
Omaha, NE 68182
http://www.unomaha.edu
Public
Admissions: (402) 554-2341
E-mail: graduate@unomaha.edu
Financial aid: (402) 554-3408
Application deadline: rolling
In-state tuition: full time: $193/credit hour; part time: $193/credit hour
Out-of-state tuition: full time: $507/credit hour
Room/board/expenses: $10,800
Full-time enrollment: 86
doctoral students: 1%; master's students: 99%; education specialists: 0%; men: 17%; women: 83%; minorities: 6%; international: 2%
Part-time enrollment: 614
doctoral students: 7%; master's students: 92%; education specialists: 1%; men: 20%; women: 80%; minorities: 8%; international: N/A
Acceptance rate (master's): 95%
Acceptance rate (doctoral): 83%
Entrance test required: GRE or MAT
Avg. GRE (of all entering students with scores): quantitative: 509; verbal: 426
Research assistantships: 9
Students reporting specialty: 100%
Students specializing in: admin.: 23%; counseling: 22%; educational psych: 3%; elementary: 17%; secondary: 15%; special: 8%; other: 12%

NEVADA

University of Nevada–Las Vegas

4505 Maryland Parkway
Box 453001
Las Vegas, NV 89154-3001
http://www.unlv.edu/colleges/graduate
Public
Admissions: (702) 895-3320
E-mail: gradcollege@ccmail.nevada.edu
Financial aid: (702) 895-3424
Application deadline: 06/15
In-state tuition: full time: $3,646; part time: $176/credit hour
Out-of-state tuition: full time: $14,457
Room/board/expenses: $12,738
Full-time enrollment: 440
doctoral students: 10%; master's students: 84%; education specialists: 6%; men: 25%; women: 75%; minorities: 27%; international: 2%
Part-time enrollment: 1,000
doctoral students: 23%; master's students: 75%; education specialists: 3%; men: 31%; women: 69%; minorities: 19%; international: 2%
Acceptance rate (master's): 74%
Acceptance rate (doctoral): 46%
Entrance test required: GRE
Avg. GRE (of all entering students with scores): quantitative: N/A; verbal: N/A
Research assistantships: 91
Students reporting specialty: 100%
Students specializing in: admin.: 22%; counseling: 3%; curriculum/instr.: 43%; evaluation/research/statistics: 9%; special: 20%; other: 3%

University of Nevada–Reno

MS278
Reno, NV 89557-0278
http://www.unr.edu/grad
Public
Admissions: (775) 784-6869
E-mail: gradadmissions@unr.edu
Financial aid: (775) 784-4666
Application deadline: rolling
In-state tuition: full time: $176/credit hour; part time: $176/credit hour
Out-of-state tuition: full time: $190/credit hour
Room/board/expenses: N/A
Full-time enrollment: 228
doctoral students: 36%; master's students: 63%; education specialists: 1%; men: 27%; women: 73%; minorities: 9%; international: 6%
Part-time enrollment: 194
doctoral students: 25%; master's students: 70%; education specialists: 5%; men: 21%; women: 79%; minorities: 13%; international: 4%
Acceptance rate (master's): 63%
Acceptance rate (doctoral): 50%
Entrance test required: GRE
Avg. GRE (of all entering students with scores): quantitative: N/A; verbal: N/A
Students reporting specialty: 0%
Students specializing in: N/A

NEW HAMPSHIRE

University of New Hampshire

Morrill Hall
Durham, NH 03824-3595
http://www.unh.edu/education/
Public
Admissions: (603) 862-2381
Financial aid: (603) 862-3600
Application deadline: N/A
In-state tuition: full time: $10,516; part time: $506/credit hour
Out-of-state tuition: full time: $23,476
Room/board/expenses: $12,700
Full-time enrollment: 201
doctoral students: 20%; master's students: 79%; education specialists: 1%; men: 21%; women: 79%; minorities: 2%; international: 1%
Part-time enrollment: 304
doctoral students: 6%; master's students: 83%; education specialists: 11%; men: 28%; women: 72%; minorities: 2%; international: 1%
Acceptance rate (master's): 79%
Acceptance rate (doctoral): 52%
Entrance test required: GRE
Avg. GRE (of all entering students with scores): quantitative: 536; verbal: 483
Research assistantships: 3
Students reporting specialty: 100%
Students specializing in: N/A

NEW JERSEY

Montclair State University

1 Normal Avenue
Upper Montclair, NJ 07043
http://cehs.montclair.edu/
Public
Admissions: (973) 655-5147
E-mail: Graduate.School@montclair.edu
Financial aid: (973) 655-4461
Application deadline: rolling
In-state tuition: full time: $477/credit hour; part time: $477/credit hour
Out-of-state tuition: full time: $737/credit hour
Room/board/expenses: $13,601
Full-time enrollment: 294
doctoral students: 2%; master's students: 98%; education specialists: N/A; men: 22%; women: 78%; minorities: 16%; international: 3%
Part-time enrollment: 965
doctoral students: 1%; master's students: 99%; education specialists: N/A; men: 22%; women: 78%; minorities: 17%; international: 1%
Acceptance rate (master's): 64%
Acceptance rate (doctoral): 40%
Entrance test required: GRE or MAT
Avg. GRE (of all entering students with scores): quantitative: 523; verbal: 434
Students reporting specialty: 100%
Students specializing in: admin.: 17%; counseling: 25%; special: 5%; technical (vocational): 8%; instructional media design: 0%; other: 45%

Rowan University

201 Mullica Hill Road
Glassboro, NJ 08028
http://www.rowan.edu/
Public
Admissions: (856) 256-4050
E-mail: gradoffice@rowan.edu
Financial aid: (856) 256-4250
Application deadline: 02/15
In-state tuition: full time: $12,682; part time: $590/credit hour
Out-of-state tuition: full time: $12,682
Room/board/expenses: $11,142
Full-time enrollment: 128
doctoral students: 14%; master's students: 69%; education specialists: 17%; men: 22%; women: 78%; minorities: 20%; international: N/A
Part-time enrollment: 399
doctoral students: 22%; master's students: 70%; education specialists: 8%; men: 20%; women: 80%; minorities: 16%; international: N/A
Acceptance rate (master's): 85%
Acceptance rate (doctoral): 84%
Entrance test required: GRE or MAT
Avg. GRE (of all entering students with scores): quantitative: N/A; verbal: N/A
Research assistantships: 16
Students reporting specialty: 100%
Students specializing in: admin.: 30%; counseling: 10%; curriculum/instr.: 3%; educational tech.: 0%; educational psych: 13%; elementary: 5%; higher education admin.: 5%; junior high: 3%; secondary: 0%; special: 15%; other: 15%

Rutgers, the State University of New Jersey–New Brunswick

10 Seminary Place
New Brunswick, NJ 08901-1183
http://www.gse.rutgers.edu
Public
Admissions: (732) 932-7711
E-mail: gradadm@rci.rutgers.edu
Financial aid: (732) 932-7057
Application deadline: 02/01
In-state tuition: full time: $13,561; part time: $516/credit hour
Out-of-state tuition: full time: $19,587
Room/board/expenses: $13,620
Full-time enrollment: 320
doctoral students: 15%; master's students: 85%; education specialists: N/A; men: 23%; women: 77%; minorities: 16%; international: 8%
Part-time enrollment: 460
doctoral students: 44%; master's students: 56%; education specialists: N/A; men: 28%; women: 72%; minorities: 13%; international: 2%
Acceptance rate (master's): 65%
Acceptance rate (doctoral): 28%
Entrance test required: GRE
Avg. GRE (of all entering students with scores): quantitative: 575; verbal: 479
Research assistantships: 6
Students reporting specialty: 100%
Students specializing in: admin.: 22%; counseling: 6%; curriculum/instr.: 0%; evaluation/research/statistics: 2%; social/philosophical foundations: 5%; policy: 1%; educational psych: 5%; elementary: 9%; secondary: 24%; special: 15%; other: 11%

Seton Hall University[1]

400 S. Orange Avenue
South Orange, NJ 07079
http://education.shu.edu
Private
Admissions: (973) 761-9668
E-mail: educate@shu.edu
Financial aid: (973) 761-9332
Tuition: N/A
Room/board/expenses: N/A
Enrollment: N/A

NEW MEXICO

New Mexico State University

Las Cruces, NM 88003-8001
http://education.nmsu.edu
Public
Admissions: (505) 646-2736
E-mail: gradinfo@nmsu.edu
Financial aid: (505) 646-4105
Application deadline: N/A
In-state tuition: full time: $5,609; part time: $189/credit hour
Out-of-state tuition: full time: $15,239
Room/board/expenses: $10,262
Full-time enrollment: 282
doctoral students: 25%; master's students: 69%; education specialists: 6%; men: 25%; women: 75%; minorities: 39%; international: 13%
Part-time enrollment: 607
doctoral students: 27%; master's students: 68%; education specialists: 5%; men: 25%; women: 75%; minorities: 45%; international: 2%
Acceptance rate (master's): 42%
Acceptance rate (doctoral): 46%
Entrance test required: GRE or MAT
Avg. GRE (of all entering students with scores): quantitative: N/A; verbal: N/A
Research assistantships: 19
Students reporting specialty: 100%
Students specializing in: admin.: 15%; counseling: 7%; curriculum/instr.: 71%; other: 7%

University of New Mexico
MSC05 3040
College of Education
Albuquerque, NM 87131-0001
http://www.unm.edu
Public
Admissions: (505) 277-8392
E-mail: apply@unm.edu
Financial aid: (505) 277-3012
Application deadline: 06/15
In-state tuition: full time: $4,061; part time: $169/credit hour
Out-of-state tuition: full time: $14,399
Room/board/expenses: $12,196
Full-time enrollment: 335
doctoral students: 28%; master's students: 72%; education specialists: 0%; men: 33%; women: 67%; minorities: 37%; international: 6%
Part-time enrollment: 802
doctoral students: 25%; master's students: 72%; education specialists: 3%; men: 26%; women: 74%; minorities: 36%; international: 4%
Acceptance rate (master's): 56%
Acceptance rate (doctoral): 43%
Entrance test required: GRE or MAT
Avg. GRE (of all entering students with scores): quantitative: 483; verbal: 505
Research assistantships: 11
Students reporting specialty: 100%
Students specializing in: admin.: 8%; counseling: 7%; curriculum /instr.: 2%; social/philosophical foundations: 16%; educational psych: 3%; elementary: 14%; secondary: 10%; special: 15%; technical (vocational): 8%; other: 20%

NEW YORK

Binghamton University[1]
School of Education
Binghamton, NY 13902-6000
http://soe.binghamton.edu
Public
Admissions: (607) 777-2151
E-mail: gradad@binghamton.edu
Financial aid: (607) 777-2428
Tuition: N/A
Room/board/expenses: N/A
Enrollment: N/A

Cornell University
Kennedy Hall
Ithaca, NY 14853
http://www.education.cornell.edu
Private
Admissions: (607) 255-4278
E-mail: rh22@cornell.edu
Financial aid: (607) 255-0441
Application deadline: 01/15
Tuition: full time: $20,868; part time: N/A
Room/board/expenses: $21,035
Full-time enrollment: 59
doctoral students: 51%; master's students: 49%; education specialists: N/A; men: 29%; women: 71%; minorities: 17%; international: 7%
Part-time enrollment: 12
doctoral students: 58%; master's students: 42%; education specialists: N/A; men: 25%; women: 75%; minorities: N/A; international: N/A
Acceptance rate (master's): 61%
Acceptance rate (doctoral): 38%
Entrance test required: GRE
Avg. GRE (of all entering students with scores): quantitative: 610; verbal: 538
Research assistantships: 8
Students reporting specialty: 94%
Students specializing in: curriculum/instr.: 21%; social/philosophical foundations: 1%; policy: 10%; educational psych: 6%; higher education admin.: 4%; secondary: 37%; other: 22%

CUNY–Graduate Center
365 Fifth Avenue
New York, NY 10016
http://www.gc.cuny.edu
Public
Admissions: (212) 817-7470
E-mail: admissions@gc.cuny.edu
Financial aid: (212) 817-7460
Application deadline: 01/15
In-state tuition: full time: $6,003; part time: $325/credit hour
Out-of-state tuition: full time: $560/credit hour
Room/board/expenses: $12,916
Full-time enrollment: 122
doctoral students: 100%; master's students: N/A; education specialists: N/A; men: 20%; women: 80%; minorities: 8%; international: 7%
Part-time enrollment: 12
doctoral students: 100%; master's students: N/A; education specialists: N/A; men: 17%; women: 83%; minorities: 8%; international: 8%
Acceptance rate (master's): N/A
Acceptance rate (doctoral): 37%
Entrance test required: GRE
Avg. GRE (of all entering students with scores): quantitative: 635; verbal: 564
Research assistantships: 1
Students reporting specialty: 100%
Students specializing in: educational psych: 100%

D'Youville College
1 D'Youville Square
320 Porter Avenue
Buffalo, NY 14201-1084
http://www.dyc.edu/academics/education/index.asp
Private
Admissions: (716) 829-7676
E-mail: graduateadmissions@dyc.edu
Financial aid: (716) 829-7500
Application deadline: rolling
Tuition: full time: $635/credit hour; part time: $635/credit hour
Room/board/expenses: $11,550
Full-time enrollment: 230
doctoral students: 0%; master's students: 100%; education specialists: N/A; men: 23%; women: 77%; minorities: 22%; international: 73%
Part-time enrollment: 215
doctoral students: 16%; master's students: 84%; education specialists: N/A; men: 30%; women: 70%; minorities: 27%; international: 45%
Acceptance rate (master's): 53%
Acceptance rate (doctoral): 58%
Entrance test required: N/A
Avg. GRE (of all entering students with scores): quantitative: N/A; verbal: N/A
Research assistantships: 0
Students reporting specialty: 100%
Students specializing in: admin.: 4%; elementary: 49%; secondary: 37%; special: 10%; other: 0%

Fordham University
113 W. 60th Street
New York, NY 10023
http://www.fordham.edu/gse
Private
Admissions: (212) 636-6400
E-mail: gse_admiss@fordham.edu
Financial aid: (212) 636-6400
Application deadline: rolling
Tuition: full time: $875/credit hour; part time: $875/credit hour
Room/board/expenses: $21,100
Full-time enrollment: 168
doctoral students: 26%; master's students: 48%; education specialists: 26%; men: 9%; women: 91%; minorities: 20%; international: 7%
Part-time enrollment: 1,114
doctoral students: 30%; master's students: 66%; education specialists: 4%; men: 21%; women: 79%; minorities: 27%; international: N/A
Acceptance rate (master's): 81%
Acceptance rate (doctoral): 41%
Entrance test required: GRE or MAT
Avg. GRE (of all entering students with scores): quantitative: N/A; verbal: N/A
Research assistantships: 90
Students reporting specialty: 100%
Students specializing in: admin.: 18%; counseling: 27%; curriculum/instr.: 5%; educational psych: 4%; elementary: 16%; junior high: 0%; secondary: 12%; special: 5%; other: 13%

Hofstra University
Hagedorn Hall
Hempstead, NY 11549
http://www.hofstra.edu/graduate
Private
Admissions: (800) 463-7872
E-mail: gradstudent@hofstra.edu
Financial aid: (516) 463-6680
Application deadline: rolling
Tuition: full time: $790/credit hour; part time: $790/credit hour
Room/board/expenses: $14,040
Full-time enrollment: 730
doctoral students: 1%; master's students: 99%; education specialists: N/A; men: 24%; women: 76%; minorities: 15%; international: 3%
Part-time enrollment: 783
doctoral students: 11%; master's students: 89%; education specialists: N/A; men: 22%; women: 78%; minorities: 16%; international: 1%
Acceptance rate (master's): 84%
Acceptance rate (doctoral): 64%
Entrance test required: GRE or MAT
Avg. GRE (of all entering students with scores): quantitative: N/A; verbal: N/A
Research assistantships: 45
Students reporting specialty: 100%
Students specializing in: admin.: 6%; counseling: 4%; social/philosophical foundations: 1%; elementary: 9%; junior high: 0%; secondary: 1%; special: 14%; other: 65%

New York University (Steinhardt)
82 Washington Square E
Fourth Floor
New York, NY 10003
http://www.steinhardt.nyu.edu/
Private
Admissions: (212) 998-5030
E-mail: steinhardt.gradadmission@nyu.edu
Financial aid: (212) 998-4444
Application deadline: rolling
Tuition: full time: $28,291; part time: $1,097/credit hour
Room/board/expenses: $23,928
Full-time enrollment: 2,076
doctoral students: 14%; master's students: 86%; education specialists: N/A; men: 20%; women: 80%; minorities: 22%; international: 23%
Part-time enrollment: 1,446
doctoral students: 20%; master's students: 80%; education specialists: N/A; men: 22%; women: 78%; minorities: 24%; international: 13%
Acceptance rate (master's): 58%
Acceptance rate (doctoral): 16%
Entrance test required: GRE
Avg. GRE (of all entering students with scores): quantitative: 610; verbal: 538
Research assistantships: 37
Students reporting specialty: 98%
Students specializing in: admin.: 2%; counseling: 6%; curriculum/instr.: 10%; social/philosophical foundations: 1%; educational tech.: 2%; educational psych: 4%; elementary: 3%; higher education admin.: 3%; secondary: 9%; special: 3%; other: 58%

St. John's University
8000 Utopia Parkway
Queens, NY 11439
http://www.stjohns.edu
Private
Admissions: (718) 990-2304
E-mail: ronaynek@stjohns.edu
Financial aid: (718) 990-2000
Application deadline: rolling
Tuition: full time: $19,980; part time: $820/credit hour
Room/board/expenses: $3,700
Full-time enrollment: 124
doctoral students: 5%; master's students: 94%; education specialists: 2%; men: 17%; women: 83%; minorities: 24%; international: 8%
Part-time enrollment: 1,268
doctoral students: 14%; master's students: 83%; education specialists: 3%; men: 24%; women: 76%; minorities: 26%; international: 2%
Acceptance rate (master's): 82%
Acceptance rate (doctoral): 53%
Entrance test required: GRE
Avg. GRE (of all entering students with scores): quantitative: N/A; verbal: N/A
Students reporting specialty: 100%
Students specializing in: admin.: 26%; counseling: 9%; curriculum/instr.: 6%; elementary: 11%; secondary: 10%; special: 7%; other: 31%

SUNY–Albany
1400 Washington Avenue
ED 212
Albany, NY 12222
http://www.albany.edu/education
Public
Admissions: (518) 442-3980
E-mail: graduate@uamail.albany.edu
Financial aid: (518) 442-5757
Application deadline: rolling
In-state tuition: full time: $7,988; part time: $288/credit hour
Out-of-state tuition: full time: $12,008
Room/board/expenses: $11,738
Full-time enrollment: 438
doctoral students: 24%; master's students: 68%; education specialists: 9%; men: 24%; women: 76%; minorities: 9%; international: 12%
Part-time enrollment: 644
doctoral students: 34%; master's students: 61%; education specialists: 5%; men: 23%; women: 77%; minorities: 7%; international: 3%
Acceptance rate (master's): 64%
Acceptance rate (doctoral): 30%
Entrance test required: GRE
Avg. GRE (of all entering students with scores): quantitative: 591; verbal: 496
Research assistantships: 123
Students reporting specialty: 100%
Students specializing in: admin.: 7%; counseling: 13%; curriculum/instr.: 17%; evaluation/research/statistics: 0%; policy: 2%; educational psych: 5%; elementary: 1%; higher education admin.: 5%; secondary: 14%; special: 8%; other: 27%

Syracuse University
230 Huntington Hall
Syracuse, NY 13244-2340
http://soe.syr.edu
Private
Admissions: (315) 443-2505
E-mail: gradrcrt@gwmail.syr.edu
Financial aid: (315) 443-1513
Application deadline: rolling
Tuition: full time: $1,012/credit hour; part time: $1,012/credit hour
Room/board/expenses: $16,174
Full-time enrollment: 355
doctoral students: 31%; master's students: 69%; education specialists: N/A; men: 29%; women: 71%; minorities: 9%; international: 13%
Part-time enrollment: 325
doctoral students: 41%; master's students: 59%; education specialists: N/A; men: 29%; women: 71%; minorities: 12%; international: 6%
Acceptance rate (master's): 77%
Acceptance rate (doctoral): 44%
Entrance test required: GRE
Avg. GRE (of all entering students with scores): quantitative: 586; verbal: 495
Research assistantships: 9
Students reporting specialty: 94%
Students specializing in: admin.: 10%; counseling: 7%; curriculum/instr.: 6%; social/philosophical foundations: 14%; elementary: 6%; higher education admin.: 10%; secondary: 23%; special: 12%; instructional media design: 12%; other: 7%

Teachers College, Columbia University
525 W. 120th Street
New York, NY 10027
http://www.tc.columbia.edu/
Private
Admissions: (212) 678-3710
E-mail: tcinfo@tc.columbia.edu
Financial aid: (212) 678-3714
Application deadline: rolling
Tuition: full time: $1,030/credit hour; part time: $1,030/credit hour
Room/board/expenses: $21,785
Full-time enrollment: 1,573
doctoral students: 27%; master's students: 73%; education specialists: N/A; men: 23%; women: 77%; minorities: 29%; international: 14%
Part-time enrollment: 3,147
doctoral students: 39%; master's students: 61%; education specialists: N/A; men: 24%; women: 76%; minorities: 28%; international: 11%
Acceptance rate (master's): 59%
Acceptance rate (doctoral): 23%
Entrance test required: GRE
Avg. GRE (of all entering students with scores): quantitative: 632; verbal: 540
Research assistantships: 100
Students reporting specialty: 95%
Students specializing in: admin.: 6%; counseling: 14%; curriculum/instr.: 10%; evaluation/research/statistics: 1%; social/philosophical foundations: 11%; policy: 1%; educational tech.: 2%; educational psych: 7%; elementary: 11%; higher education admin.: 5%; secondary: 16%; special: 5%; instructional media design: 2%; other: 10%

University at Buffalo–SUNY
367 Baldy Hall
Buffalo, NY 14260-1000
http://www.gse.buffalo.edu
Public
Admissions: (716) 645-2110
E-mail: gseinfo@buffalo.edu
Financial aid: (716) 645-2450
Application deadline: rolling
In-state tuition: full time: $8,289; part time: $288/credit hour
Out-of-state tuition: full time: $12,309
Room/board/expenses: $14,890
Full-time enrollment: 542
doctoral students: 24%; master's students: 76%; education specialists: N/A; men: 23%; women: 77%; minorities: 13%; international: 13%
Part-time enrollment: 538
doctoral students: 42%; master's students: 58%; education specialists: N/A; men: 29%; women: 71%; minorities: 10%; international: 10%
Acceptance rate (master's): 67%
Acceptance rate (doctoral): 40%
Entrance test required: GRE or MAT
Avg. GRE (of all entering students with scores): quantitative: 576; verbal: 486
Research assistantships: 104
Students reporting specialty: 100%
Students specializing in: admin.: 8%; counseling: 18%; curriculum/instr.: 18%; social/philosophical foundations: 5%; educational tech.: 0%; educational psych: 2%; elementary: 15%; higher education admin.: 8%; secondary: 25%; special: 1%; other: 0%

University of Rochester (Warner)[1]

2-147 Dewey Hall
Rochester, NY 14627
http://www.rochester.edu/warner/
Private
Admissions: (716) 275-3950
E-mail: tmug@dbl.cc.rochester.edu
Financial aid: (716) 275-3226
Tuition: N/A
Room/board/expenses: N/A
Enrollment: N/A

Yeshiva University (Azrieli)[1]

245 Lexington Avenue
New York, NY 10016
http://www.yu.edu/azrieli/
Private
Admissions: (212) 340-7705
Financial aid: (212) 960-5269
Tuition: N/A
Room/board/expenses: N/A
Enrollment: N/A

NORTH CAROLINA

Appalachian State University (Reich)[1]

Edwin Duncan Hall
Boone, NC 28608-2068
http://www.graduate.appstate.edu
Public
Admissions: (828) 262-2130
E-mail: hirsthp@appstate.edu
Financial aid: (828) 262-2190
Tuition: N/A
Room/board/expenses: N/A
Enrollment: N/A

East Carolina University

E. Fifth Street
Greenville, NC 27858
http://www.ecu.edu/gradschool/
Public
Admissions: N/A
Financial aid: N/A
Application deadline: 06/01
In-state tuition: full time: $4,699; part time: $182/credit hour
Out-of-state tuition: full time: $15,015
Room/board/expenses: $10,950
Full-time enrollment: 383
doctoral students: 9%; master's students: 90%; education specialists: 1%; men: 14%; women: 86%; minorities: 1%; international: 0%
Part-time enrollment: 1,315
doctoral students: 5%; master's students: 92%; education specialists: 2%; men: 18%; women: 82%; minorities: 1%; international: N/A
Acceptance rate (master's): N/A
Acceptance rate (doctoral): N/A
Entrance test required: GRE or MAT
Avg. GRE (of all entering students with scores): quantitative: N/A; verbal: N/A
Research assistantships: 36
Students reporting specialty: 62%
Students specializing in: admin.: 33%; counseling: 6%; educational tech.: 4%; elementary: 6%; junior high: 1%; special: 5%; technical (vocational): 2%; instructional media design: 9%; other: 33%

Gardner-Webb University

110 S. Main Street
Boiling Springs, NC 28017
http://www.gardner-webb.edu
Private
Admissions: (800) 492-4723
E-mail: gradschool@gardner-webb.edu
Financial aid: (704) 406-3271
Application deadline: rolling
Tuition: full time: $275/credit hour; part time: $275/credit hour
Room/board/expenses: $4,000
Full-time enrollment: N/A
doctoral students: N/A; master's students: N/A; education specialists: N/A; men: N/A; women: N/A; minorities: N/A; international: N/A
Part-time enrollment: 449
doctoral students: 14%; master's students: 86%; education specialists: N/A; men: 29%; women: 71%; minorities: 32%; international: 0%
Acceptance rate (master's): 70%
Acceptance rate (doctoral): 38%
Entrance test required: GRE or MAT
Avg. GRE (of all entering students with scores): quantitative: N/A; verbal: N/A
Students reporting specialty: 100%
Students specializing in: admin.: 82%; counseling: 10%; curriculum/instr.: 4%; elementary: 10%; junior high: 3%

North Carolina State University–Raleigh

Campus Box 7801
Raleigh, NC 27695-7801
http://ced.ncsu.edu/
Public
Admissions: (919) 515-2872
E-mail: graduate_admissions@ncsu.edu
Financial aid: (919) 515-3325
Application deadline: N/A
In-state tuition: full time: $5,636; part time: $3,502
Out-of-state tuition: full time: $17,684
Room/board/expenses: $15,694
Full-time enrollment: 327
doctoral students: 36%; master's students: 64%; education specialists: N/A; men: 26%; women: 74%; minorities: 26%; international: 4%
Part-time enrollment: 651
doctoral students: 43%; master's students: 57%; education specialists: N/A; men: 28%; women: 72%; minorities: 26%; international: 1%
Acceptance rate (master's): 53%
Acceptance rate (doctoral): 39%
Entrance test required: GRE or MAT
Avg. GRE (of all entering students with scores): quantitative: 559; verbal: 486
Research assistantships: 41
Students reporting specialty: 83%
Students specializing in: admin.: 42%; counseling: 10%; curriculum/instr.: 10%; evaluation/research/statistics: 3%; policy: 3%; educational tech.: 3%; elementary: 1%; higher education admin.: 9%; junior high: 1%; secondary: 3%; special: 4%; instructional media design: 1%; other: 12%

University of North Carolina–Chapel Hill

CB#3500
101 Peabody Hall
Chapel Hill, NC 27599-3500
http://soe.unc.edu
Public
Admissions: (919) 966-7000
E-mail: ed@unc.edu
Financial aid: (919) 966-1346
Application deadline: rolling
In-state tuition: full time: $6,236; part time: $5,083
Out-of-state tuition: full time: $20,234
Room/board/expenses: $17,300
Full-time enrollment: 357
doctoral students: 49%; master's students: 51%; education specialists: N/A; men: 26%; women: 74%; minorities: 26%; international: 4%
Part-time enrollment: 176
doctoral students: 24%; master's students: 76%; education specialists: N/A; men: 21%; women: 79%; minorities: 26%; international: 1%
Acceptance rate (master's): 52%
Acceptance rate (doctoral): 30%
Entrance test required: GRE or MAT
Avg. GRE (of all entering students with scores): quantitative: N/A; verbal: N/A
Research assistantships: 43
Students reporting specialty: 100%
Students specializing in: admin.: 22%; counseling: 3%; curriculum/instr.: 4%; evaluation/research/statistics: 5%; social/philosophical foundations: 11%; educational psych: 8%; junior high: 5%; secondary: 12%; special: 1%; other: 30%

University of North Carolina–Charlotte

9201 University City Boulevard
Charlotte, NC 28223
http://education.uncc.edu/coe/
Public
Admissions: (704) 687-3366
E-mail: gradadm@email.uncc.edu
Financial aid: (704) 687-2461
Application deadline: rolling
In-state tuition: full time: $4,547; part time: $357/credit hour
Out-of-state tuition: full time: $14,754
Room/board/expenses: $8,734
Full-time enrollment: 204
doctoral students: 22%; master's students: 78%; education specialists: N/A; men: 20%; women: 80%; minorities: 18%; international: 2%
Part-time enrollment: 743
doctoral students: 18%; master's students: 82%; education specialists: N/A; men: 16%; women: 84%; minorities: 19%; international: 1%
Acceptance rate (master's): 76%
Acceptance rate (doctoral): 62%
Entrance test required: GRE or MAT
Avg. GRE (of all entering students with scores): quantitative: 543; verbal: 466
Research assistantships: 12
Students reporting specialty: 18%
Students specializing in: N/A

University of North Carolina–Greensboro

329 Curry Building
Greensboro, NC 27402
http://www.uncg.edu/grs
Public
Admissions: (336) 334-5596
E-mail: inquiries@uncg.edu
Financial aid: (336) 334-5702
Application deadline: rolling
In-state tuition: full time: $4,075; part time: $2,654
Out-of-state tuition: full time: $15,125
Room/board/expenses: $11,032
Full-time enrollment: 285
doctoral students: 27%; master's students: 68%; education specialists: 5%; men: 22%; women: 78%; minorities: 18%; international: 5%
Part-time enrollment: 678
doctoral students: 26%; master's students: 67%; education specialists: 6%; men: 17%; women: 83%; minorities: 18%; international: 1%
Acceptance rate (master's): 58%
Acceptance rate (doctoral): 53%
Entrance test required: GRE
Avg. GRE (of all entering students with scores): quantitative: 514; verbal: 486
Research assistantships: 30
Students reporting specialty: 100%
Students specializing in: admin.: 13%; counseling: 12%; curriculum/instr.: 12%; evaluation/research/statistics: 3%; elementary: 4%; higher education admin.: 5%; junior high: 6%; special: 5%; instructional media design: 0%; other: 39%

Western Carolina University

Killian Building
Room 222
Cullowhee, NC 28723
http://www.wcu.edu/
Public
Admissions: (828) 227-7398
E-mail: gradsch@email.wcu.edu
Financial aid: (828) 227-7290
Application deadline: rolling
In-state tuition: full time: $6,258; part time: $361/credit hour
Out-of-state tuition: full time: $15,843
Room/board/expenses: $9,336
Full-time enrollment: 192
doctoral students: 2%; master's students: 98%; education specialists: 0%; men: 22%; women: 78%; minorities: 10%; international: 2%
Part-time enrollment: 486
doctoral students: 15%; master's students: 83%; education specialists: 2%; men: 25%; women: 75%; minorities: 20%; international: 1%
Acceptance rate (master's): 73%
Acceptance rate (doctoral): 73%
Entrance test required: GRE
Avg. GRE (of all entering students with scores): quantitative: 509; verbal: 465
Research assistantships: 91
Students reporting specialty: 100%
Students specializing in: admin.: 34%; counseling: 4%; elementary: 5%; junior high: 3%; special: 12%; other: 43%

NORTH DAKOTA

North Dakota State University

PO Box 5057
Fargo, ND 58105-5057
http://www.ndsu.edu/gradschool/
Public
Admissions: (702) 231-7033
E-mail: ndsu.grad.school@ndsu.nodak.edu
Financial aid: (701) 231-7533
Application deadline: rolling
In-state tuition: full time: $5,975; part time: $209/credit hour
Out-of-state tuition: full time: $14,346
Room/board/expenses: $10,055
Full-time enrollment: 19
doctoral students: 16%; master's students: 84%; education specialists: N/A; men: 11%; women: 89%; minorities: 5%; international: 26%
Part-time enrollment: 220
doctoral students: 40%; master's students: 56%; education specialists: 4%; men: 40%; women: 60%; minorities: 4%; international: 2%
Acceptance rate (master's): 76%
Acceptance rate (doctoral): 63%
Entrance test required: GRE or MAT
Avg. GRE (of all entering students with scores): quantitative: N/A; verbal: N/A
Research assistantships: 6
Students reporting specialty: 100%
Students specializing in: admin.: 32%; counseling: 12%; curriculum/instr.: 24%; evaluation/research/statistics: 13%; higher education admin.: 3%; secondary: 4%; other: 13%

University of North Dakota

Box 7189
Grand Forks, ND 58202-7189
http://www.und.edu/dept/ehd/
Public
Admissions: (701) 777-2945
E-mail: gradschool@und.edu
Financial aid: (701) 777-3121
Application deadline: rolling
In-state tuition: full time: $225/credit hour; part time: $225/credit hour
Out-of-state tuition: full time: $601/credit hour
Room/board/expenses: $13,600
Full-time enrollment: 138
doctoral students: 22%; master's students: 75%; education specialists: 3%; men: 22%; women: 78%; minorities: 36%; international: 12%
Part-time enrollment: 419
doctoral students: 38%; master's students: 59%; education specialists: 2%; men: 26%; women: 74%; minorities: 7%; international: 0%
Acceptance rate (master's): 43%
Acceptance rate (doctoral): 24%
Entrance test required: N/A
Avg. GRE (of all entering students with scores): quantitative: 536; verbal: 485
Research assistantships: 36
Students reporting specialty: 0%
Students specializing in: N/A

OHIO

Ashland University (Schar)

401 College Avenue
Ashland, OH 44805
http://www.ashland.edu
Private
Admissions: (419) 289-5386
E-mail: fslater@ashland.edu
Financial aid: (419) 289-5002
Application deadline: rolling
Tuition: full time: $419/credit hour; part time: $419/credit hour
Room/board/expenses: $11,810
Full-time enrollment: 466
doctoral students: 4%; master's students: 96%; education specialists: N/A; men: 25%; women: 75%; minorities: 7%; international: 2%
Part-time enrollment: 919
doctoral students: 4%; master's students: 96%; education specialists: N/A; men: 26%; women: 74%; minorities: 6%; international: 0%
Acceptance rate (master's): 99%
Acceptance rate (doctoral): 100%
Entrance test required: GRE or MAT
Avg. GRE (of all entering students with scores): quantitative: N/A; verbal: N/A
Research assistantships: 0
Students reporting specialty: 59%
Students specializing in: admin.: 34%; curriculum/instr.: 45%; educational tech.: 2%; junior high: 0%; special: 17%; other: 3%

Bowling Green State University[1]

444 Education Building
Bowling Green, OH 43403
http://www.bgsu.edu/colleges/edhd/
Public
Admissions: (419) 372-2791
E-mail: prospct@bgnet.bgsu.edu
Financial aid: (419) 372-2651
Tuition: N/A
Room/board/expenses: N/A
Enrollment: N/A

Cleveland State University[1]

2121 Euclid Avenue
RT 1416
Cleveland, OH 44115
http://www.csuohio.edu/coehs/
Public
Admissions: (216) 687-5599
E-mail: graduate.admissions@csuohio.edu
Financial aid: (216) 687-3764
Tuition: N/A
Room/board/expenses: N/A
Enrollment: N/A

Kent State University

PO Box 5190
Kent, OH 44242-0001
http://www.ehhs.kent.edu
Public
Admissions: (330) 672-2576
E-mail: ogs@kent.edu

Financial aid: (330) 672-2972
Application deadline: rolling
In-state tuition: full time: $8,430; part time: $384/credit hour
Out-of-state tuition: full time: $15,862
Room/board/expenses: $10,040
Full-time enrollment: 801
doctoral students: 36%; master's students: 60%; education specialists: 4%; men: 22%; women: 78%; minorities: 9%; international: 6%
Part-time enrollment: 806
doctoral students: 12%; master's students: 86%; education specialists: 2%; men: 19%; women: 81%; minorities: 7%; international: 6%
Acceptance rate (master's): N/A
Acceptance rate (doctoral): N/A
Entrance test required: GRE
Avg. GRE (of all entering students with scores): quantitative: 509; verbal: 464
Research assistantships: 125
Students reporting specialty: 100%
Students specializing in: admin.: 10%; counseling: 9%; curriculum/instr.: 9%; evaluation/research/statistics: 2%; educational psych: 1%; higher education admin.: 6%; secondary: 1%; special: 7%; instructional media design: 2%; other: 58%

Miami University–Oxford
207 McGuffey Hall
Oxford, OH 45056
http://www.muohio.edu/graduateschool/
Public
Admissions: (513) 529-3734
E-mail: gradschool@muohio.edu
Financial aid: (513) 529-8734
Application deadline: N/A
In-state tuition: full time: $11,267; part time: $469/credit hour
Out-of-state tuition: full time: $24,127
Room/board/expenses: $11,440
Full-time enrollment: 167
doctoral students: 15%; master's students: 69%; education specialists: 16%; men: 34%; women: 66%; minorities: 23%; international: 7%
Part-time enrollment: 165
doctoral students: 22%; master's students: 78%; education specialists: 0%; men: 30%; women: 70%; minorities: 22%; international: N/A
Acceptance rate (master's): 75%
Acceptance rate (doctoral): 32%
Entrance test required: GRE or MAT
Avg. GRE (of all entering students with scores): quantitative: 568; verbal: 526
Research assistantships: 50
Students reporting specialty: 97%
Students specializing in: admin.: 19%; counseling: 17%; curriculum/instr.: 7%; educational tech.: 0%; educational psych: 7%; elementary: 4%; higher education admin.: 11%; secondary: 15%; special: 0%; other: 20%

Ohio State University
1945 N. High Street
Columbus, OH 43210-1172
http://www.coe.ohio-state.edu
Public
Admissions: (614) 292-9444
E-mail: domestic.grad@osu.edu
Financial aid: (614) 292-0300
Application deadline: N/A
In-state tuition: full time: $9,972; part time: $414/credit hour
Out-of-state tuition: full time: $24,126
Room/board/expenses: $12,108
Full-time enrollment: 546
doctoral students: 52%; master's students: 48%; education specialists: N/A; men: 26%; women: 74%; minorities: 16%; international: 27%
Part-time enrollment: 480
doctoral students: 39%; master's students: 61%; education specialists: N/A; men: 28%; women: 73%; minorities: 14%; international: 8%
Acceptance rate (master's): 57%
Acceptance rate (doctoral): 43%
Entrance test required: GRE
Avg. GRE (of all entering students with scores): quantitative: 607; verbal: 508
Research assistantships: 82
Students reporting specialty: 66%
Students specializing in: admin.: 7%; counseling: 8%; curriculum/instr.: 1%; evaluation/research/statistics: 3%; social/philosophical foundations: 2%; policy: 1%; educational tech.: 13%; elementary: 8%; higher education admin.: 9%; junior high: 8%; secondary: 27%; special: 6%; technical (vocational): 4%; instructional media design: 2%

Ohio University
133 McCracken Hall
Athens, OH 45701-2979
http://www.coe.ohiou.edu
Public
Admissions: (740) 593-2800
E-mail: graduate@ohio.edu
Financial aid: (740) 593-4141
Application deadline: 01/15
In-state tuition: full time: $9,378; part time: $387/credit hour
Out-of-state tuition: full time: $17,370
Room/board/expenses: $11,550
Full-time enrollment: 440
doctoral students: 25%; master's students: 75%; education specialists: N/A; men: 33%; women: 68%; minorities: 12%; international: 11%
Part-time enrollment: 242
doctoral students: 40%; master's students: 60%; education specialists: N/A; men: 40%; women: 60%; minorities: 10%; international: 20%
Acceptance rate (master's): 76%
Acceptance rate (doctoral): 67%
Entrance test required: GRE or MAT
Avg. GRE (of all entering students with scores): quantitative: 527; verbal: 471
Research assistantships: 33
Students reporting specialty: 86%
Students specializing in: admin.: 13%; counseling: 13%; curriculum/instr.: 3%; evaluation/research/statistics: 1%; educational tech.: 14%; elementary: 0%; higher education admin.: 12%; junior high: 4%; secondary: 5%; special: 7%; other: 28%

University of Akron
302 Buchtel Common
Akron, OH 44325-4201
http://www.uakron.edu/gradsch
Public
Admissions: (330) 972-7663
E-mail: gradschool@uakron.edu
Financial aid: (330) 972-7032
Application deadline: rolling
In-state tuition: full time: $342/credit hour; part time: $342/credit hour
Out-of-state tuition: full time: $588/credit hour
Room/board/expenses: $12,785
Full-time enrollment: 347
doctoral students: 13%; master's students: 87%; education specialists: N/A; men: 28%; women: 72%; minorities: 14%; international: 6%
Part-time enrollment: 724
doctoral students: 17%; master's students: 83%; education specialists: N/A; men: 26%; women: 74%; minorities: 11%; international: 1%
Acceptance rate (master's): 77%
Acceptance rate (doctoral): 41%
Entrance test required: GRE or MAT
Avg. GRE (of all entering students with scores): quantitative: 457; verbal: 416
Research assistantships: 65
Students reporting specialty: 83%
Students specializing in: admin.: 16%; counseling: 8%; social/philosophical foundations: 7%; elementary: 4%; higher education admin.: 5%; secondary: 10%; special: 12%; technical (vocational): 2%; other: 37%

University of Cincinnati
PO Box 210002
Cincinnati, OH 45221-0002
http://www.cech.uc.edu
Public
Admissions: (513) 556-3857
E-mail: donald.wagner@uc.edu
Financial aid: (513) 556-2327
Application deadline: rolling
In-state tuition: full time: $13,614; part time: $404/credit hour
Out-of-state tuition: full time: $23,448
Room/board/expenses: $16,748
Full-time enrollment: 456
doctoral students: 40%; master's students: 53%; education specialists: 7%; men: 30%; women: 70%; minorities: 17%; international: 1%
Part-time enrollment: 249
doctoral students: 41%; master's students: 55%; education specialists: 4%; men: 25%; women: 75%; minorities: 20%; international: N/A
Acceptance rate (master's): 47%
Acceptance rate (doctoral): 36%
Entrance test required: GRE
Avg. GRE (of all entering students with scores): quantitative: 572; verbal: 500
Research assistantships: 73
Students reporting specialty: 100%
Students specializing in: admin.: 4%; counseling: 10%; curriculum/instr.: 7%; social/philosophical foundations: 16%; educational psych: 7%; elementary: 0%; junior high: 8%; secondary: 8%; special: 7%; other: 32%

University of Dayton
300 College Park
Dayton, OH 45469-0510
http://soeap.udayton.edu/
Private
Admissions: (937) 229-4411
E-mail: gradadmission@udayton.edu
Financial aid: (937) 229-4311
Application deadline: rolling
Tuition: full time: $435/credit hour; part time: $435/credit hour
Room/board/expenses: N/A
Full-time enrollment: 140
doctoral students: 80%; master's students: 20%; education specialists: 0%; men: 31%; women: 69%; minorities: 4%; international: 6%
Part-time enrollment: 1,149
doctoral students: 0%; master's students: 98%; education specialists: 2%; men: 22%; women: 78%; minorities: 9%; international: 1%
Acceptance rate (master's): N/A
Acceptance rate (doctoral): N/A
Entrance test required: GRE or MAT
Avg. GRE (of all entering students with scores): quantitative: N/A; verbal: N/A
Research assistantships: 11
Students reporting specialty: 78%
Students specializing in: admin.: 34%; counseling: 42%; curriculum/instr.: 1%; educational tech.: 1%; educational psych: 4%; elementary: 4%; higher education admin.: 1%; junior high: 3%; secondary: 4%; special: 4%; other: 1%

University of Toledo
2801 W. Bancroft Street
Toledo, OH 43606
http://gradschool.utoledo.edu
Public
Admissions: (419) 530-4723
E-mail: grdsch@utnet.utoledo.edu
Financial aid: (419) 530-5812
Application deadline: rolling
In-state tuition: full time: $9,828; part time: $409/credit hour
Out-of-state tuition: full time: $18,639
Room/board/expenses: $6,170
Full-time enrollment: 252
doctoral students: 25%; master's students: 68%; education specialists: 7%; men: 28%; women: 72%; minorities: 18%; international: 4%
Part-time enrollment: 543
doctoral students: 34%; master's students: 60%; education specialists: 6%; men: 28%; women: 72%; minorities: 16%; international: 1%
Acceptance rate (master's): 59%
Acceptance rate (doctoral): 81%
Entrance test required: GRE
Avg. GRE (of all entering students with scores): quantitative: 505; verbal: 437
Research assistantships: 63
Students reporting specialty: 98%
Students specializing in: admin.: 23%; curriculum/instr.: 14%; evaluation/research/statistics: 0%; social/philosophical foundations: 3%; educational psych: 0%; elementary: 2%; higher education admin.: 6%; junior high: 2%; secondary: 5%; special: 16%; instructional media design: 2%; other: 29%

Youngstown State University[1]
1 University Plaza
Youngstown, OH 44555
http://www.coe.ysu.edu/
Public
Admissions: (330) 742-3091
E-mail: graduateschool@cc.ysu.edu
Financial aid: (330) 941-3505
Tuition: N/A
Room/board/expenses: N/A
Enrollment: N/A

OKLAHOMA

Oklahoma State University
325 Willard Hall
Stillwater, OK 74078-4033
http://www.okstate.edu/education/
Public
Admissions: (405) 744-6368
E-mail: grad-i@okstate.edu
Financial aid: (405) 744-6604
Application deadline: rolling
In-state tuition: full time: $148/credit hour; part time: $148/credit hour
Out-of-state tuition: full time: $555/credit hour
Room/board/expenses: $8,843
Full-time enrollment: 194
doctoral students: 53%; master's students: 44%; education specialists: 3%; men: 29%; women: 71%; minorities: 19%; international: 3%
Part-time enrollment: 614
doctoral students: 54%; master's students: 43%; education specialists: 2%; men: 31%; women: 69%; minorities: 19%; international: 0%
Acceptance rate (master's): 56%
Acceptance rate (doctoral): 56%
Entrance test required: GRE or MAT
Avg. GRE (of all entering students with scores): quantitative: 533; verbal: 482
Research assistantships: 28
Students reporting specialty: 94%
Students specializing in: admin.: 2%; counseling: 21%; curriculum/instr.: 11%; evaluation/research/statistics: 4%; social/philosophical foundations: 4%; educational tech.: 0%; educational psych: 30%; elementary: 4%; higher education admin.: 8%; secondary: 4%; special: 2%; technical (vocational): 10%

Oral Roberts University
7777 S. Lewis Avenue
Tulsa, OK 74171
http://www.oru.edu/
Private
Admissions: (918) 495-6553
E-mail: gradedu@oru.edu
Financial aid: (918) 495-6602
Application deadline: rolling
Tuition: full time: $460/credit hour; part time: $460/credit hour
Room/board/expenses: $4,536
Full-time enrollment: 187
doctoral students: 76%; master's students: 24%; education specialists: N/A; men: 35%; women: 65%; minorities: 42%; international: 16%
Part-time enrollment: 186
doctoral students: 38%; master's students: 62%; education specialists: N/A; men: 31%; women: 69%; minorities: 34%; international: 10%
Acceptance rate (master's): 100%
Acceptance rate (doctoral): 90%
Entrance test required: GRE or MAT
Avg. GRE (of all entering students with scores): quantitative: N/A; verbal: N/A
Students reporting specialty: 0%
Students specializing in: N/A

University of Oklahoma
820 Van Vleet Oval No. 100
Norman, OK 73019-2041
http://www.ou.edu/education
Public
Admissions: (405) 325-2252
E-mail: admission@ou.edu
Financial aid: (405) 325-4521
Application deadline: rolling
In-state tuition: full time: $5,376; part time: $144/credit hour
Out-of-state tuition: full time: $14,357
Room/board/expenses: $14,747
Full-time enrollment: 460
doctoral students: 42%; master's students: 58%; education specialists: N/A; men: 29%; women: 71%; minorities: 25%; international: 5%
Part-time enrollment: 229
doctoral students: 63%; master's students: 37%; education specialists: N/A; men: 29%; women: 71%; minorities: 20%; international: 5%
Acceptance rate (master's): 16%
Acceptance rate (doctoral): 6%
Entrance test required: GRE or MAT
Avg. GRE (of all entering students with scores): quantitative: 533; verbal: 476
Research assistantships: 89
Students reporting specialty: 95%
Students specializing in: admin.: 22%; counseling: 12%; curriculum/instr.: 24%; evaluation/research/statistics: 8%; social/philosophical foundations: 5%; higher education admin.: 23%; special: 7%

OREGON

Lewis and Clark College
0615 S.W. Palatine Hill Road
Portland, OR 97219-7899
http://education.lclark.edu/
Private
Admissions: (503) 768-6200
E-mail: gseadmit@lclark.edu
Financial aid: (503) 768-7090
Application deadline: rolling
Tuition: full time: $645/credit hour; part time: $645/credit hour
Room/board/expenses: $4,953
Full-time enrollment: 204
doctoral students: 2%; master's students: 85%; education specialists: 13%; men: 25%; women: 75%; minorities: 9%; international: N/A
Part-time enrollment: 122
doctoral students: 30%; master's students: 58%; education specialists: 11%; men: 20%; women: 80%; minorities: 14%; international: 1%
Acceptance rate (master's): 93%
Acceptance rate (doctoral): 71%
Entrance test required: GRE
Avg. GRE (of all entering students with scores): quantitative: 510; verbal: 506
Research assistantships: 1
Students reporting specialty: 100%
Students specializing in: admin.: 32%; counseling: 19%; elementary: 12%; secondary: 13%; special: 5%; other: 20%

Oregon State University
Education Hall
Corvallis, OR 97331-3502
http://oregonstate.edu/education/
Public
Admissions: (541) 737-4411
E-mail: osuadmit@oregonstate.edu
Financial aid: (541) 737-2241
Application deadline: rolling
In-state tuition: full time: $10,573; part time: $338/credit hour
Out-of-state tuition: full time: $16,243
Room/board/expenses: $11,454
Full-time enrollment: 260
doctoral students: 8%; master's students: 92%; education specialists: N/A; men: 20%; women: 80%; minorities: 25%; international: N/A
Part-time enrollment: 226
doctoral students: 41%; master's students: 59%; education specialists: N/A; men: 28%; women: 72%; minorities: 22%; international: N/A
Acceptance rate (master's): N/A
Acceptance rate (doctoral): N/A
Entrance test required: N/A
Avg. GRE (of all entering students with scores): quantitative: N/A; verbal: N/A
Research assistantships: 2
Students reporting specialty: 100%
Students specializing in: counseling: 45%; elementary: 15%; higher education admin.: 15%; other: 26%

Portland State University
PO Box 751
Portland, OR 97207-0751
http://www.ed.pdx.edu/admissions.shtml
Public
Admissions: (503) 725-3511
E-mail: adm@pdx.edu
Financial aid: (503) 725-3461
Application deadline: rolling
In-state tuition: full time: $8,432; part time: $173/credit hour
Out-of-state tuition: full time: $12,563
Room/board/expenses: $13,155
Full-time enrollment: 418
doctoral students: 7%; master's students: 93%; education specialists: N/A; men: 26%; women: 74%; minorities: 15%; international: 4%
Part-time enrollment: 648
doctoral students: 9%; master's students: 91%; education specialists: N/A; men: 24%; women: 76%; minorities: 13%; international: 1%
Acceptance rate (master's): 92%
Acceptance rate (doctoral): 59%
Entrance test required: GRE or MAT
Avg. GRE (of all entering students with scores): quantitative: 551; verbal: 530
Research assistantships: 5
Students reporting specialty: 100%
Students specializing in: admin.: 5%; counseling: 10%; curriculum/instr.: 18%; policy: 23%; elementary: 11%; higher education admin.: 2%; secondary: 13%; special: 15%; instructional media design: 3%; other: 1%

University of Oregon
1215 University of Oregon
Eugene, OR 97403-1215
http://education.uoregon.edu/path.htm?setpath=19
Public
Admissions: (541) 346-3201
E-mail: uoadmit@oregon.uoregon.edu
Financial aid: (541) 346-3221
Application deadline: N/A
In-state tuition: full time: $11,577; part time: $372/credit hour
Out-of-state tuition: full time: $16,341
Room/board/expenses: $11,394
Full-time enrollment: 431
doctoral students: 30%; master's students: 70%; education specialists: N/A; men: 26%; women: 74%; minorities: 18%; international: 5%
Part-time enrollment: 145
doctoral students: 37%; master's students: 63%; education specialists: N/A; men: 43%; women: 57%; minorities: 40%; international: 11%
Acceptance rate (master's): 56%
Acceptance rate (doctoral): 16%
Entrance test required: GRE or MAT
Avg. GRE (of all entering students with scores): quantitative: 567; verbal: 483
Students reporting specialty: 100%
Students specializing in: admin.: 34%; policy: 14%; elementary: 8%; junior high: 14%; special: 13%; other: 20%

PENNSYLVANIA

Arcadia University
450 S. Easton Road
Glenside, PA 19038-3295
http://www.arcadia.edu/
Private
Admissions: (877) 272-2342
E-mail: admiss@arcadia.edu
Financial aid: (215) 572-2980
Application deadline: rolling
Tuition: full time: $610/credit hour; part time: $610/credit hour
Room/board/expenses: N/A
Full-time enrollment: 121
doctoral students: N/A; master's students: 52%; education specialists: 48%; men: 23%; women: 77%; minorities: 8%; international: N/A
Part-time enrollment: 514
doctoral students: 6%; master's students: 53%; education specialists: 41%; men: 24%; women: 76%; minorities: 15%; international: N/A
Acceptance rate (master's): 96%
Acceptance rate (doctoral): 50%
Entrance test required: GRE or MAT
Avg. GRE (of all entering students with scores): quantitative: N/A; verbal: N/A
Research assistantships: 0
Students reporting specialty: 99%
Students specializing in: admin.: 22%; counseling: 6%; educational tech.: 1%; elementary: 17%; secondary: 13%; special: 31%; other: 46%

Drexel University
3141 Chestnut Street
Philadelphia, PA 19104
http://www.drexel.edu/academics/soe
Private
Admissions: (215) 895-2400
E-mail: admissions@drexel.edu
Financial aid: (215) 895-1627
Application deadline: rolling
Tuition: full time: $835/credit hour; part time: $835/credit hour
Room/board/expenses: N/A
Full-time enrollment: 61
doctoral students: 20%; master's students: 79%; education specialists: 2%; men: 26%; women: 74%; minorities: 16%; international: 2%
Part-time enrollment: 465
doctoral students: 2%; master's students: 90%; education specialists: 7%; men: 25%; women: 75%; minorities: 19%; international: 1%
Acceptance rate (master's): 89%
Acceptance rate (doctoral): 7%
Entrance test required: GRE
Avg. GRE (of all entering students with scores): quantitative: N/A; verbal: N/A
Research assistantships: 3
Students reporting specialty: 98%
Students specializing in: admin.: 14%; counseling: 2%; curriculum/instr.: 5%; evaluation/research/statistics: 5%; social/philosophical foundations: 0%; policy: 4%; educational tech.: 2%; elementary: 32%; higher education admin.: 16%; secondary: 16%; instructional media design: 7%; other: 11%

Duquesne University
600 Forbes Avenue
Pittsburgh, PA 15282
http://www.education.duq.edu/index.html
Private
Admissions: (412) 396-6091
E-mail: black@duq.edu
Financial aid: (412) 396-6607
Application deadline: rolling
Tuition: full time: $774/credit hour; part time: $774/credit hour
Room/board/expenses: $10,546
Full-time enrollment: 483
doctoral students: 32%; master's students: 54%; education specialists: 14%; men: 31%; women: 69%; minorities: 10%; international: 1%
Part-time enrollment: 375
doctoral students: 21%; master's students: 57%; education specialists: 22%; men: 31%; women: 69%; minorities: 6%; international: N/A
Acceptance rate (master's): 84%
Acceptance rate (doctoral): 20%
Entrance test required: GRE or MAT
Avg. GRE (of all entering students with scores): quantitative: 560; verbal: 530
Research assistantships: 0
Students reporting specialty: 91%
Students specializing in: admin.: 7%; counseling: 13%; curriculum/instr.: 0%; evaluation/research/statistics: 0%; educational tech.: 9%; educational psych: 9%; elementary: 7%; higher education admin.: 9%; secondary: 14%; special: 3%; other: 29%

East Stroudsburg University of Pennsylvania
200 Prospect Street
East Stroudsburg, PA 18301-2999
http://www.esu.edu
Public
Admissions: (570) 422-3536
E-mail: grad@po-box.esu.edu
Financial aid: N/A
Application deadline: 07/31
In-state tuition: full time: $7,655; part time: $345/credit hour
Out-of-state tuition: full time: $11,385
Room/board/expenses: N/A
Full-time enrollment: 112
doctoral students: N/A; master's students: 97%; education specialists: 3%; men: 38%; women: 62%; minorities: 10%; international: N/A
Part-time enrollment: 422
doctoral students: N/A; master's students: 89%; education specialists: 11%; men: 16%; women: 84%; minorities: 6%; international: 0%
Acceptance rate (master's): N/A
Acceptance rate (doctoral): N/A
Entrance test required: GRE
Avg. GRE (of all entering students with scores): quantitative: N/A; verbal: N/A
Students reporting specialty: 100%
Students specializing in: admin.: 8%; elementary: 13%; secondary: 23%; special: 16%; instructional media design: 3%; other: 37%

Indiana University of Pennsylvania
104 Stouffer Hall
Indiana, PA 15705-1083
http://www.iup.edu/graduate
Public
Admissions: (724) 357-2222
E-mail: graduate-admissions@iup.edu
Financial aid: (724) 357-2218
Application deadline: rolling
In-state tuition: full time: $7,544; part time: $345/credit hour
Out-of-state tuition: full time: $11,274
Room/board/expenses: $9,369
Full-time enrollment: 251
doctoral students: 5%; master's students: 90%; education specialists: 5%; men: 22%; women: 78%; minorities: 7%; international: 5%
Part-time enrollment: 537
doctoral students: 32%; master's students: 60%; education specialists: 8%; men: 29%; women: 71%; minorities: 6%; international: 0%
Acceptance rate (master's): 44%
Acceptance rate (doctoral): 51%
Entrance test required: GRE or MAT
Avg. GRE (of all entering students with scores): quantitative: 542; verbal: 449
Research assistantships: 64
Students reporting specialty: 100%
Students specializing in: admin.: 12%; counseling: 20%; educational psych: 3%; elementary: 13%; special: 5%; other: 46%

Lehigh University
111 Research Drive
Bethlehem, PA 18015
http://www.lehigh.edu/collegeofeducation
Private
Admissions: (610) 758-3231
E-mail: ineduc@lehigh.edu
Financial aid: (610) 758-3181
Application deadline: rolling
Tuition: full time: $510/credit hour; part time: $510/credit hour
Room/board/expenses: $16,600
Full-time enrollment: 173
doctoral students: 35%; master's students: 55%; education specialists: 9%; men: 20%; women: 80%; minorities: 13%; international: 11%
Part-time enrollment: 388
doctoral students: 23%; master's students: 77%; education specialists: 0%; men: 34%; women: 66%; minorities: 7%; international: 8%
Acceptance rate (master's): N/A
Acceptance rate (doctoral): 14%
Entrance test required: GRE or MAT
Avg. GRE (of all entering students with scores): quantitative: 610; verbal: 525
Research assistantships: 51
Students reporting specialty: 96%
Students specializing in: admin.: 34%; counseling: 16%; curriculum/instr.: 0%; educational tech.: 4%; educational psych: 8%; elementary: 3%; secondary: 7%; special: 13%; instructional media design: 2%; other: 12%

Pennsylvania State University–Harrisburg
777 W. Harrisburg Pike
Middletown, PA 17057
http://www.hbg.psu.edu/bsed/
Public
Admissions: (717) 948-6250
E-mail: hbgadmit@psu.edu
Financial aid: (717) 948-6307
Application deadline: rolling
In-state tuition: full time: $581/credit hour; part time: $581/credit hour
Out-of-state tuition: full time: $822/credit hour
Room/board/expenses: $2,750
Full-time enrollment: 21
doctoral students: 14%; master's students: 86%; education specialists: N/A; men: 33%; women: 67%; minorities: 14%; international: 10%
Part-time enrollment: 752
doctoral students: 8%; master's students: 92%; education specialists: N/A; men: 19%; women: 81%; minorities: 4%; international: 0%
Acceptance rate (master's): 91%
Acceptance rate (doctoral): 53%
Entrance test required: GRE or MAT
Avg. GRE (of all entering students with scores): quantitative: N/A; verbal: N/A
Research assistantships: 6
Students reporting specialty: 0%
Students specializing in: N/A

Pennsylvania State University–University Park
274 Chambers Building
University Park, PA 16802-3206
http://www.ed.psu.edu
Public
Admissions: (814) 865-1795
E-mail: gadm@psu.edu
Financial aid: (814) 863-1489
Application deadline: rolling
In-state tuition: full time: $14,508; part time: $581/credit hour
Out-of-state tuition: full time: $25,710
Room/board/expenses: $11,800
Full-time enrollment: 517
doctoral students: 68%; master's students: 32%; education specialists: N/A; men: 34%; women: 66%; minorities: 13%; international: 25%
Part-time enrollment: 515
doctoral students: 48%; master's students: 52%; education specialists: N/A; men: 35%; women: 65%; minorities: 9%; international: 2%
Acceptance rate (master's): 44%
Acceptance rate (doctoral): 28%
Entrance test required: GRE or MAT
Avg. GRE (of all entering students with scores): quantitative: 580; verbal: 509
Research assistantships: 124
Students reporting specialty: 91%
Students specializing in: admin.: 7%; counseling: 13%; curriculum/instr.: 24%; evaluation/research/statistics: 2%; social/philosophical foundations: 2%; policy: 4%; educational tech.: 1%; educational psych: 6%; elementary: 8%; higher education admin.: 6%; junior high: 1%; secondary: 7%; special: 5%; technical (vocational): 8%; instructional media design: 10%; other: 21%

Robert Morris University
6001 University Boulevard
Moon Township, PA 15108-1189
http://www.rmu.edu
Private
Admissions: (412) 397-5200
E-mail: admissions@rmu.edu
Financial aid: (412) 262-8212
Application deadline: rolling
Tuition: full time: $595/credit hour; part time: $595/credit hour
Room/board/expenses: $12,720
Full-time enrollment: N/A
doctoral students: N/A; master's students: N/A; education specialists: N/A; men: N/A; women: N/A; minorities: N/A; international: N/A
Part-time enrollment: 291
doctoral students: 13%; master's students: 87%; education specialists: N/A; men: 36%; women: 64%; minorities: 7%; international: 0%
Acceptance rate (master's): 98%
Acceptance rate (doctoral): 46%
Entrance test required: N/A
Avg. GRE (of all entering students with scores): quantitative: N/A; verbal: N/A
Research assistantships: 0
Students reporting specialty: 100%
Students specializing in: curriculum/instr.: 62%; elementary: 1%; secondary: 37%

St. Joseph's University[1]
5600 City Avenue
Philadelphia, PA 19131
http://www.sju.edu
Private
Admissions: (610) 660-1101
E-mail: graduate@sju.edu
Financial aid: (610) 660-1555
Tuition: N/A
Room/board/expenses: N/A
Enrollment: N/A

Temple University
OSS RA238
Philadelphia, PA 19122
http://www.temple.edu/
Public
Admissions: (215) 204-8011
E-mail:
educate@blue.vm.temple.edu
Financial aid: (215) 204-1492
Application deadline: rolling
In-state tuition: full time: $541/credit hour; part time: $541/credit hour
Out-of-state tuition: full time: $790/credit hour
Room/board/expenses: $15,912
Full-time enrollment: 158
doctoral students: 33%; master's students: 67%; education specialists: 0%; men: 28%; women: 72%; minorities: 26%; international: 4%
Part-time enrollment: 514
doctoral students: 40%; master's students: 60%; education specialists: 0%; men: 32%; women: 68%; minorities: 17%; international: 2%
Acceptance rate (master's): 48%
Acceptance rate (doctoral): 36%
Entrance test required: GRE or MAT
Avg. GRE (of all entering students with scores): quantitative: 583; verbal: 519
Research assistantships: 21
Students reporting specialty: 69%
Students specializing in: admin.: 30%; educational psych: 11%; elementary: 14%; technical (vocational): 0%; other: 45%

University of Pennsylvania
3700 Walnut Street
Philadelphia, PA 19104-6216
http://www.gse.upenn.edu
Private
Admissions: (215) 898-6455
E-mail: admissions@gse.upenn.edu
Financial aid: (215) 898-6455
Application deadline: 02/15
Tuition: full time: $35,640; part time: $6,268
Room/board/expenses: $20,750
Full-time enrollment: 414
doctoral students: 21%; master's students: 79%; education specialists: N/A; men: 23%; women: 77%; minorities: 17%; international: 29%
Part-time enrollment: 506
doctoral students: 41%; master's students: 59%; education specialists: N/A; men: 25%; women: 75%; minorities: 13%; international: 7%
Acceptance rate (master's): 76%
Acceptance rate (doctoral): 22%
Entrance test required: GRE
Avg. GRE (of all entering students with scores): quantitative: 626; verbal: 538
Research assistantships: 80
Students reporting specialty: 100%
Students specializing in: admin.: 5%; counseling: 10%; curriculum/instr.: 34%; evaluation/research/statistics: 2%; social/philosophical foundations: 3%; policy: 3%; educational tech.: 0%; educational psych: 3%; elementary: 8%; higher education admin.: 10%; secondary: 23%

University of Pittsburgh
5601 Wesley W. Posvar Hall
Pittsburgh, PA 15260
http://www.education.pitt.edu
Public
Admissions: (412) 648-2230
E-mail: soeinfo@pitt.edu
Financial aid: (412) 648-2230
Application deadline: rolling
In-state tuition: full time: $15,530; part time: $604/credit hour
Out-of-state tuition: full time: $27,570
Room/board/expenses: $15,190
Full-time enrollment: 416
doctoral students: 31%; master's students: 69%; education specialists: N/A; men: 26%; women: 74%; minorities: 9%; international: 17%
Part-time enrollment: 473
doctoral students: 38%; master's students: 62%; education specialists: N/A; men: 26%; women: 74%; minorities: 10%; international: 1%
Acceptance rate (master's): 89%
Acceptance rate (doctoral): 71%
Entrance test required: GRE
Avg. GRE (of all entering students with scores): quantitative: 556; verbal: 488
Research assistantships: 40
Students reporting specialty: 100%
Students specializing in: admin.: 15%; curriculum/instr.: 3%; evaluation/research/statistics: 3%; social/philosophical foundations: 5%; policy: 0%; educational psych: 8%; elementary: 9%; higher education admin.: 7%; secondary: 18%; special: 14%; instructional media design: 0%; other: 22%

Widener University
1 University Place
Chester, PA 19013-5792
http://www.widener.edu
Private
Admissions: (610) 499-4251
E-mail: j.j.edgette@widener.edu
Financial aid: (610) 499-4174
Application deadline: rolling
Tuition: full time: $570/credit hour; part time: $570/credit hour
Room/board/expenses: N/A
Full-time enrollment: 123
doctoral students: 73%; master's students: 27%; education specialists: N/A; men: 33%; women: 67%; minorities: 9%; international: N/A
Part-time enrollment: 369
doctoral students: 70%; master's students: 30%; education specialists: N/A; men: 30%; women: 70%; minorities: 11%; international: N/A
Acceptance rate (master's): 58%
Acceptance rate (doctoral): 82%
Entrance test required: GRE or MAT
Avg. GRE (of all entering students with scores): quantitative: N/A; verbal: 552
Students reporting specialty: 68%
Students specializing in: admin.: 26%; counseling: 4%; curriculum/instr.: 10%; educational psych: 1%; elementary: 4%; higher education admin.: 18%; special: 3%; other: 34%

RHODE ISLAND

University of Rhode Island/ Rhode Island College (Feinstein)
600 Mount Pleasant Avenue
Providence, RI 02908
http://www.ric.edu/fsehd
Public
Admissions: (401) 456-8896
E-mail: mdarcy@ric.edu
Financial aid: (401) 456-8033
Application deadline: 04/01
In-state tuition: full time: $260/credit hour; part time: $260/credit hour
Out-of-state tuition: full time: $546/credit hour
Room/board/expenses: $9,000
Full-time enrollment: N/A
doctoral students: N/A; master's students: N/A; education specialists: N/A; men: N/A; women: N/A; minorities: N/A; international: N/A
Part-time enrollment: N/A
doctoral students: N/A; master's students: N/A; education specialists: N/A; men: N/A; women: N/A; minorities: N/A; international: N/A
Acceptance rate (master's): N/A
Acceptance rate (doctoral): N/A
Entrance test required: GRE or MAT
Avg. GRE (of all entering students with scores): quantitative: N/A; verbal: N/A
Students reporting specialty: 100%
Students specializing in: admin.: 2%; counseling: 2%; educational psych: 10%; elementary: 10%; secondary: 5%; special: 12%; technical (vocational): 0%; other: 58%

SOUTH CAROLINA

Clemson University (Moore)
102 Tillman Hall
Clemson, SC 29634-0702
http://www.grad.clemson.edu
Public
Admissions: (864) 656-3195
E-mail: grdapp@clemson.edu
Financial aid: (864) 656-2280
Application deadline: rolling
In-state tuition: full time: $7,282; part time: $440/credit hour
Out-of-state tuition: full time: $14,570
Room/board/expenses: $11,294
Full-time enrollment: 218
doctoral students: 21%; master's students: 79%; education specialists: 0%; men: 32%; women: 68%; minorities: 15%; international: 3%
Part-time enrollment: 365
doctoral students: 25%; master's students: 71%; education specialists: 4%; men: 34%; women: 66%; minorities: 14%; international: 1%
Acceptance rate (master's): 72%
Acceptance rate (doctoral): 55%
Entrance test required: GRE
Avg. GRE (of all entering students with scores): quantitative: 534; verbal: 438
Research assistantships: 35
Students reporting specialty: 100%
Students specializing in: admin.: 32%; counseling: 28%; curriculum/instr.: 6%; elementary: 1%; junior high: 10%; secondary: 2%; special: 5%; other: 17%

South Carolina State University
PO Box 7298
300 College Street, NE
Orangeburg, SC 29117
http://www.scsu.edu/Academics/Colleges/index.cfm?ID=1
Public
Admissions: (803) 536-7186
E-mail: admissions@scsu.edu
Financial aid: (803) 536-7067
Application deadline: 07/31
In-state tuition: full time: $7,538; part time: $407/credit hour
Out-of-state tuition: full time: $14,582
Room/board/expenses: $3,500
Full-time enrollment: 143
doctoral students: 10%; master's students: 71%; education specialists: 18%; men: 13%; women: 87%; minorities: 92%; international: N/A
Part-time enrollment: 251
doctoral students: 35%; master's students: 22%; education specialists: 43%; men: 27%; women: 73%; minorities: 83%; international: N/A
Acceptance rate (master's): 64%
Acceptance rate (doctoral): 64%
Entrance test required: GRE or MAT
Avg. GRE (of all entering students with scores): quantitative: N/A; verbal: N/A
Research assistantships: 10
Students reporting specialty: 100%
Students specializing in: admin.: 60%; counseling: 22%; elementary: 7%; secondary: 5%; special: 0%; other: 6%

University of South Carolina–Columbia
Wardlaw Building
Columbia, SC 29208
http://www.ed.sc.edu
Public
Admissions: (803) 777-4243
E-mail: gradapp@sc.edu
Financial aid: (803) 777-8134
Application deadline: 07/01
In-state tuition: full time: $9,088; part time: $440/credit hour
Out-of-state tuition: full time: $19,380
Room/board/expenses: $14,305
Full-time enrollment: 453
doctoral students: 17%; master's students: 71%; education specialists: 12%; men: 24%; women: 76%; minorities: 14%; international: 2%
Part-time enrollment: 647
doctoral students: 35%; master's students: 40%; education specialists: 24%; men: 23%; women: 77%; minorities: 22%; international: 1%
Acceptance rate (master's): 58%
Acceptance rate (doctoral): 40%
Entrance test required: GRE or MAT
Avg. GRE (of all entering students with scores): quantitative: 537; verbal: 463
Research assistantships: 38
Students reporting specialty: 98%
Students specializing in: admin.: 27%; counseling: 9%; curriculum/instr.: 4%; evaluation/research/statistics: 0%; social/philosophical foundations: 1%; educational tech.: 1%; educational psych: 3%; elementary: 4%; higher education admin.: 3%; secondary: 4%; special: 5%; other: 39%

SOUTH DAKOTA

University of South Dakota
414 E. Clark Street
Vermillion, SD 57069
http://www.usd.edu
Public
Admissions: (605) 677-6287
E-mail: gradsch@usd.edu
Financial aid: (605) 677-5446
Application deadline: rolling
In-state tuition: full time: $125/credit hour; part time: $125/credit hour
Out-of-state tuition: full time: $369/credit hour
Room/board/expenses: $8,161
Full-time enrollment: 169
doctoral students: 31%; master's students: 54%; education specialists: 15%; men: 31%; women: 69%; minorities: 9%; international: 5%
Part-time enrollment: 293
doctoral students: 46%; master's students: 42%; education specialists: 12%; men: 30%; women: 70%; minorities: 5%; international: 1%
Acceptance rate (master's): 88%
Acceptance rate (doctoral): 89%
Entrance test required: GRE or MAT
Avg. GRE (of all entering students with scores): quantitative: 519; verbal: 441
Research assistantships: 15
Students reporting specialty: 98%
Students specializing in: admin.: 20%; counseling: 8%; curriculum/instr.: 12%; educational tech.: 0%; educational psych: 1%; elementary: 5%; higher education admin.: 26%; secondary: 1%; special: 6%; instructional media design: 4%; other: 16%

TENNESSEE

East Tennessee State University (Clemmer)
PO Box 70720
Johnson City, TN 37614-0720
http://www.etsu.edu/coe/
Public
Admissions: (423) 439-4221
E-mail: gradsch@etsu.edu
Financial aid: (423) 439-4300
Application deadline: rolling
In-state tuition: full time: $6,275; part time: $288/credit hour
Out-of-state tuition: full time: $16,551
Room/board/expenses: $12,022
Full-time enrollment: 337
doctoral students: 5%; master's students: 94%; education specialists: 1%; men: 31%; women: 69%; minorities: 6%; international: 4%
Part-time enrollment: 388
doctoral students: 42%; master's students: 52%; education specialists: 6%; men: 22%; women: 78%; minorities: 6%; international: 0%
Acceptance rate (master's): 63%
Acceptance rate (doctoral): 43%
Entrance test required: GRE
Avg. GRE (of all entering students with scores): quantitative: 502; verbal: 422
Students reporting specialty: 100%
Students specializing in: admin.: 30%; counseling: 10%; elementary: 16%; secondary: 12%; special: 5%; instructional media design: 7%; other: 20%

Tennessee State University
3500 John A. Merritt Boulevard
Nashville, TN 37209-1561
http://www.tnstate.edu
Public
Admissions: (615) 963-5901
E-mail: gradschool@tnstate.edu
Financial aid: (615) 963-5701
Application deadline: rolling
In-state tuition: full time: $7,010; part time: $490/credit hour
Out-of-state tuition: full time: $17,286
Room/board/expenses: $13,752
Full-time enrollment: 272
doctoral students: 19%; master's students: 75%; education specialists: 5%; men: 24%; women: 76%; minorities: 63%; international: 1%
Part-time enrollment: 615
doctoral students: 33%; master's students: 57%; education specialists: 9%; men: 26%; women: 74%; minorities: 60%; international: 0%
Acceptance rate (master's): 63%
Acceptance rate (doctoral): 37%
Entrance test required: GRE or MAT
Avg. GRE (of all entering students with scores): quantitative: N/A; verbal: 469
Research assistantships: 11
Students reporting specialty: 100%
Students specializing in: admin.: 34%; counseling: 4%; curriculum/instr.: 29%; educational psych: 19%; elementary: 6%; special: 5%; other: 3%

Tennessee Technological University
Box 5036
Cookeville, TN 38505-0001
http://www.tntech.edu/
Public
Admissions: (931) 372-3233
E-mail: gradstudies@tntech.edu
Financial aid: (931) 372-3073
Application deadline: 08/01
In-state tuition: full time: $9,450; part time: $347/credit hour
Out-of-state tuition: full time: $24,864
Room/board/expenses: $12,200
Full-time enrollment: 416
doctoral students: 3%; master's students: 61%; education specialists: 36%; men: 26%; women: 74%; minorities: 8%; international: 1%
Part-time enrollment: 555
doctoral students: 4%; master's students: 68%; education specialists: 28%; men: 25%; women: 75%; minorities: 5%; international: 0%
Acceptance rate (master's): 93%
Acceptance rate (doctoral): 39%
Entrance test required: GRE or MAT
Avg. GRE (of all entering students with scores): quantitative: N/A; verbal: N/A
Research assistantships: 14
Students reporting specialty: 56%

Students specializing in: admin.: 59%; counseling: 5%; curriculum/instr.: 17%; evaluation/research/statistics: 4%; educational psych: 4%; elementary: 2%; secondary: 4%; special: 4%; other: 2%

Trevecca Nazarene University[1]
333 Murfreesboro Road
Nashville, TN 37210
http://www.trevecca.edu
Private
Admissions: (800) 284-1594
E-mail: admissions_ged.@trevecca.edu
Financial aid: (615) 248-1242
Tuition: N/A
Room/board/expenses: N/A
Enrollment: N/A

Union University
1050 Union University Drive
Jackson, TN 38305
http://www.uu.edu/
Private
Admissions: (731) 661-5374
E-mail: hfowler@uu.edu
Financial aid: (731) 661-5015
Application deadline: rolling
Tuition: full time: $330/credit hour; part time: $330/credit hour
Room/board/expenses: N/A
Full-time enrollment: 260
doctoral students: 27%; master's students: 44%; education specialists: 28%; men: 20%; women: 80%; minorities: N/A; international: N/A
Part-time enrollment: 162
doctoral students: 0%; master's students: 100%; education specialists: 0%; men: 33%; women: 67%; minorities: N/A; international: N/A
Acceptance rate (master's): N/A
Acceptance rate (doctoral): N/A
Entrance test required: GRE or MAT
Avg. GRE (of all entering students with scores): quantitative: N/A; verbal: N/A
Research assistantships: 0
Students reporting specialty: 89%
Students specializing in: admin.: 23%; curriculum/instr.: 6%; higher education admin.: 5%; other: 66%

University of Memphis[1]
215 Ball Hall
Memphis, TN 38152-6015
http://coe.memphis.edu/
Public
Admissions: (901) 678-2911
E-mail: gradsch@memphis.edu
Financial aid: (901) 678-4825
Tuition: N/A
Room/board/expenses: N/A
Enrollment: N/A

University of Tennessee–Knoxville
335 Claxton Complex
Knoxville, TN 37996-3400
http://cehhs.utk.edu
Public
Admissions: (865) 974-3251
E-mail: nfox@utk.edu
Financial aid: (865) 974-3131
Application deadline: rolling
In-state tuition: full time: $10,081; part time: $329/credit hour
Out-of-state tuition: full time: $29,661
Room/board/expenses: $13,844
Full-time enrollment: 393
doctoral students: 38%; master's students: 60%; education specialists: 2%; men: 23%; women: 77%; minorities: 11%; international: 5%
Part-time enrollment: 242
doctoral students: 51%; master's students: 38%; education specialists: 11%; men: 38%; women: 62%; minorities: 6%; international: 4%
Acceptance rate (master's): 86%
Acceptance rate (doctoral): 56%
Entrance test required: GRE
Avg. GRE (of all entering students with scores): quantitative: 629; verbal: 503
Research assistantships: 14
Students reporting specialty: 100%
Students specializing in: admin.: 2%; counseling: 17%; educational psych: 5%; higher education admin.: 1%; instructional media design: 6%; other: 69%

Vanderbilt University (Peabody)
PO Box 327
Nashville, TN 37203-9418
http://peabody.vanderbilt.edu
Private
Admissions: (615) 322-8410
E-mail: peabody.admissions@vanderbilt.edu
Financial aid: (615) 322-8400
Application deadline: 12/31
Tuition: full time: $1,434/credit hour; part time: $1,434/credit hour
Room/board/expenses: $17,499
Full-time enrollment: 544
doctoral students: 44%; master's students: 56%; education specialists: N/A; men: 24%; women: 76%; minorities: 12%; international: 8%
Part-time enrollment: 144
doctoral students: 49%; master's students: 51%; education specialists: N/A; men: 37%; women: 63%; minorities: 17%; international: N/A
Acceptance rate (master's): 64%
Acceptance rate (doctoral): 9%
Entrance test required: GRE or MAT
Avg. GRE (of all entering students with scores): quantitative: 639; verbal: 549
Research assistantships: 190
Students reporting specialty: 100%
Students specializing in: admin.: 6%; counseling: 6%; curriculum/instr.: 4%; evaluation/research/statistics: 18%; policy: 12%; elementary: 5%; higher education admin.: 13%; secondary: 6%; special: 19%; other: 11%

TEXAS

Baylor University
1 Bear Place
#97304
Waco, TX 76798-7304
http://www.baylor.edu/SOE/
Private
Admissions: (254) 710-3584
E-mail: graduate_school@baylor.edu
Financial aid: (254) 710-2611
Application deadline: 02/15
Tuition: full time: $925/credit hour; part time: $925/credit hour
Room/board/expenses: $7,913
Full-time enrollment: 161
doctoral students: 40%; master's students: 50%; education specialists: 10%; men: 32%; women: 68%; minorities: 26%; international: 7%
Part-time enrollment: 55
doctoral students: 16%; master's students: 84%; education specialists: 0%; men: 49%; women: 51%; minorities: 9%; international: N/A
Acceptance rate (master's): 59%
Acceptance rate (doctoral): 54%
Entrance test required: GRE or MAT
Avg. GRE (of all entering students with scores): quantitative: 592; verbal: 477
Research assistantships: 75
Students reporting specialty: 100%
Students specializing in: admin.: 23%; curriculum/instr.: 19%; educational psych: 19%; other: 38%

Lamar University
PO Box 10034
Lamar University Station
Beaumont, TX 77710
http://dept.lamar.edu/education/
Public
Admissions: (409) 880-8356
E-mail: gradmissions@hal.lamar.edu
Financial aid: (409) 880-8450
Application deadline: rolling
In-state tuition: full time: $3,664; part time: $1,854
Out-of-state tuition: full time: $10,336
Room/board/expenses: $7,900
Full-time enrollment: 85
doctoral students: 40%; master's students: 60%; education specialists: N/A; men: 33%; women: 67%; minorities: 25%; international: 4%
Part-time enrollment: 507
doctoral students: 5%; master's students: 95%; education specialists: N/A; men: 21%; women: 79%; minorities: 27%; international: 0%
Acceptance rate (master's): N/A
Acceptance rate (doctoral): N/A
Entrance test required: GRE
Avg. GRE (of all entering students with scores): quantitative: 490; verbal: 438
Students reporting specialty: 6%
Students specializing in: N/A

Our Lady of the Lake University
411 S.W. 24th Street
San Antonio, TX 78207
http://www.ollusa.edu
Private
Admissions: (210) 431-3961
E-mail: gradadm@lake.ollusa.edu
Financial aid: (210) 431-3960
Application deadline: rolling
Tuition: full time: $11,932; part time: $628/credit hour
Room/board/expenses: $8,994
Full-time enrollment: 58
doctoral students: N/A; master's students: 100%; education specialists: N/A; men: 3%; women: 97%; minorities: 48%; international: N/A
Part-time enrollment: 218
doctoral students: N/A; master's students: 100%; education specialists: N/A; men: 19%; women: 81%; minorities: 44%; international: 0%
Acceptance rate (master's): 78%
Acceptance rate (doctoral): N/A
Entrance test required: GRE or MAT
Avg. GRE (of all entering students with scores): quantitative: N/A; verbal: N/A
Research assistantships: 0
Students reporting specialty: 100%
Students specializing in: admin.: 8%; counseling: 9%; curriculum/instr.: 45%; junior high: 5%; secondary: 4%; special: 24%; other: 10%

Sam Houston State University
PO Box 2119
Huntsville, TX 77341
http://www.shsu.edu/~grs_www
Public
Admissions: (936) 294-1971
E-mail: mmuehsam@shsu.edu
Financial aid: (936) 294-1724
Application deadline: N/A
In-state tuition: full time: $6,018; part time: $3,367
Out-of-state tuition: full time: $13,246
Room/board/expenses: $10,432
Full-time enrollment: 126
doctoral students: 19%; master's students: 79%; education specialists: 2%; men: 21%; women: 79%; minorities: 37%; international: 3%
Part-time enrollment: 975
doctoral students: 12%; master's students: 87%; education specialists: 1%; men: 19%; women: 81%; minorities: 27%; international: 1%
Acceptance rate (master's): N/A
Acceptance rate (doctoral): N/A
Entrance test required: GRE or MAT
Avg. GRE (of all entering students with scores): quantitative: N/A; verbal: N/A
Students reporting specialty: 0%
Students specializing in: N/A

Stephen F. Austin State University
PO Box 13024
SFA Station
Nacogdoches, TX 75962
http://www.sfasu.edu/graduate
Public
Admissions: (936) 468-2807
E-mail: gschool@sfasu.edu
Financial aid: (936) 468-2403
Application deadline: rolling
In-state tuition: full time: $177/credit hour; part time: $177/credit hour
Out-of-state tuition: full time: $455/credit hour
Room/board/expenses: $10,788
Full-time enrollment: 160
doctoral students: 16%; master's students: 84%; education specialists: N/A; men: 25%; women: 75%; minorities: 21%; international: 3%
Part-time enrollment: 384
doctoral students: 5%; master's students: 95%; education specialists: N/A; men: 28%; women: 72%; minorities: 16%; international: N/A
Acceptance rate (master's): 80%
Acceptance rate (doctoral): 50%
Entrance test required: GRE
Avg. GRE (of all entering students with scores): quantitative: 507; verbal: 441
Research assistantships: 3
Students reporting specialty: 76%
Students specializing in: admin.: 41%; elementary: 24%; secondary: 16%; special: 13%; other: 6%

Tarleton State University
Box T-0350
Stephenville, TX 76402
http://www.tarleton.edu/~graduate
Public
Admissions: (254) 968-9104
E-mail: ljones@tarleton.edu
Financial aid: (254) 968-9070
Application deadline: rolling
In-state tuition: full time: $130/credit hour; part time: $130/credit hour
Out-of-state tuition: full time: $398/credit hour
Room/board/expenses: $3,731
Full-time enrollment: 180
doctoral students: 21%; master's students: 79%; education specialists: N/A; men: 28%; women: 72%; minorities: 18%; international: N/A
Part-time enrollment: 823
doctoral students: 4%; master's students: 96%; education specialists: N/A; men: 23%; women: 77%; minorities: 25%; international: 1%
Acceptance rate (master's): 91%
Acceptance rate (doctoral): 54%
Entrance test required: GRE
Avg. GRE (of all entering students with scores): quantitative: 468; verbal: 435
Students reporting specialty: 80%
Students specializing in: admin.: 54%; counseling: 16%; curriculum/instr.: 27%; educational psych: 4%

Texas A&M University–College Station
4222 TAMUS
College Station, TX 77843-4222
http://www.cehd.tamu.edu/
Public
Admissions: (979) 845-1071
E-mail: admissions@tamu.edu
Financial aid: (979) 845-3236
Application deadline: rolling
In-state tuition: full time: $206/credit hour; part time: $206/credit hour
Out-of-state tuition: full time: $484/credit hour
Room/board/expenses: $12,657
Full-time enrollment: 536
doctoral students: 49%; master's students: 51%; education specialists: N/A; men: 35%; women: 65%; minorities: 22%; international: 23%
Part-time enrollment: 695
doctoral students: 60%; master's students: 40%; education specialists: N/A; men: 26%; women: 74%; minorities: 31%; international: 2%
Acceptance rate (master's): 76%
Acceptance rate (doctoral): 62%
Entrance test required: GRE
Avg. GRE (of all entering students with scores): quantitative: 530; verbal: 475
Research assistantships: 123
Students reporting specialty: 100%
Students specializing in: admin.: 22%; curriculum/instr.: 31%; educational psych: 15%; instructional media design: 2%; other: 30%

Texas A&M University–Commerce
PO Box 3011
Commerce, TX 75429-3011
http://www.tamu-commerce.edu
Public
Admissions: (903) 886-5167
E-mail: graduate_school@tamu-commerce.edu
Financial aid: (903) 886-5096
Application deadline: rolling
In-state tuition: full time: $4,300; part time: N/A
Out-of-state tuition: full time: N/A
Room/board/expenses: N/A
Full-time enrollment: 188
doctoral students: 19%; master's students: 81%; education specialists: N/A; men: 12%; women: 88%; minorities: 10%; international: 2%
Part-time enrollment: 575
doctoral students: 52%; master's students: 48%; education specialists: N/A; men: 30%; women: 70%; minorities: 27%; international: 1%
Acceptance rate (master's): N/A
Acceptance rate (doctoral): N/A
Entrance test required: GRE
Avg. GRE (of all entering students with scores): quantitative: N/A; verbal: N/A
Students reporting specialty: 0%
Students specializing in: N/A

Texas A&M University–Corpus Christi[1]
6300 Ocean Drive
Corpus Christi, TX 78412
http://www.tamucc.edu/~gradweb
Public
Admissions: (361) 825-2177
E-mail: Harvey.Knull@mail.tamucc.edu
Financial aid: (361) 825-2332
Tuition: N/A
Room/board/expenses: N/A
Enrollment: N/A

Texas A&M University–Kingsville[1]
700 University Boulevard
Kingsville, TX 78363
http://www.tamuk.edu
Public
Admissions: (361) 593-2811
Financial aid: (361) 593-3911
Tuition: N/A
Room/board/expenses: N/A
Enrollment: N/A

Texas Christian University
3000 Bellaire Drive North
Fort Worth, TX 76129
http://www.sofe.tcu.edu
Private
Admissions: (817) 257-7661

E-mail: ed_grad@TCU.edu
Financial aid: (817) 257-7872
Application deadline: 07/16
Tuition: full time: $865/credit hour; part time: $865/credit hour
Room/board/expenses: $12,260
Full-time enrollment: 89
doctoral students: 9%; master's students: 91%; education specialists: N/A; men: 13%; women: 87%; minorities: 17%; international: 3%
Part-time enrollment: 100
doctoral students: 14%; master's students: 86%; education specialists: N/A; men: 18%; women: 82%; minorities: 29%; international: 2%
Acceptance rate (master's): 88%
Acceptance rate (doctoral): 42%
Entrance test required: GRE
Avg. GRE (of all entering students with scores): quantitative: 570; verbal: 540
Students reporting specialty: 100%
Students specializing in: admin.: 37%; counseling: 22%; social/philosophical foundations: 6%; elementary: 10%; junior high: 5%; secondary: 5%; special: 12%; other: 4%

Texas Southern University[1]

3100 Cleburne Street
Houston, TX 77004
http://www.tsu.edu/
Public
Admissions: (713) 313-7435
E-mail: admissions@tsu.edu
Financial aid: (713) 313-7530
Tuition: N/A
Room/board/expenses: N/A
Enrollment: N/A

Texas State University–San Marcos

601 University Drive
San Marcos, TX 78666
http://www.txstate.edu
Public
Admissions: (512) 245-2581
E-mail: gradcollege@txstate.edu
Financial aid: (512) 245-2315
Application deadline: rolling
In-state tuition: full time: $5,006; part time: $210/credit hour
Out-of-state tuition: full time: $10,010
Room/board/expenses: $11,022
Full-time enrollment: 393
doctoral students: 6%; master's students: 94%; education specialists: N/A; men: 24%; women: 76%; minorities: 25%; international: 3%
Part-time enrollment: 787
doctoral students: 10%; master's students: 90%; education specialists: N/A; men: 22%; women: 78%; minorities: 26%; international: 1%
Acceptance rate (master's): 89%
Acceptance rate (doctoral): 41%
Entrance test required: GRE
Avg. GRE (of all entering students with scores): quantitative: 504; verbal: 457
Research assistantships: 38
Students reporting specialty: 100%
Students specializing in: admin.: 24%; counseling: 7%; curriculum/instr.: 2%; elementary: 21%; secondary: 7%; special: 5%; instructional media design: 3%; other: 31%

Texas Tech University

Box 41071
Lubbock, TX 79409-1071
http://www.educ.ttu.edu/
Public
Admissions: (806) 742-1998
E-mail: gradschool@ttu.edu
Financial aid: (806) 742-3681
Application deadline: rolling
In-state tuition: full time: $194/credit hour; part time: $194/credit hour
Out-of-state tuition: full time: $472/credit hour
Room/board/expenses: $11,381
Full-time enrollment: 190
doctoral students: 43%; master's students: 57%; education specialists: N/A; men: 29%; women: 71%; minorities: 21%; international: 14%
Part-time enrollment: 437
doctoral students: 45%; master's students: 55%; education specialists: N/A; men: 26%; women: 74%; minorities: 16%; international: 1%
Acceptance rate (master's): 58%
Acceptance rate (doctoral): 53%
Entrance test required: GRE
Avg. GRE (of all entering students with scores): quantitative: 518; verbal: 467
Research assistantships: 42
Students reporting specialty: 71%
Students specializing in: admin.: 15%; counseling: 12%; curriculum/instr.: 14%; evaluation/research/statistics: 14%; educational psych: 6%; elementary: 5%; secondary: 2%; special: 17%; instructional media design: 11%; other: 4%

Texas Woman's University

PO Box 425769
Denton, TX 76204-5769
http://www.twu.edu/admissions/
Public
Admissions: (940) 898-3188
E-mail: admissions@twu.edu
Financial aid: (940) 898-3050
Application deadline: rolling
In-state tuition: full time: $5,832; part time: $183/credit hour
Out-of-state tuition: full time: $9,792
Room/board/expenses: $9,434
Full-time enrollment: 211
doctoral students: 8%; master's students: 92%; education specialists: N/A; men: 18%; women: 82%; minorities: 31%; international: 7%
Part-time enrollment: 696
doctoral students: 7%; master's students: 93%; education specialists: N/A; men: 9%; women: 91%; minorities: 31%; international: 1%
Acceptance rate (master's): 87%
Acceptance rate (doctoral): 56%
Entrance test required: GRE
Avg. GRE (of all entering students with scores): quantitative: 463; verbal: 430
Research assistantships: 1
Students reporting specialty: 26%
Students specializing in: N/A

University of Houston–Main Campus

4800 Calhoun Road
Farish Hall
Houston, TX 77204-5023
http://www.coe.uh.edu/
Public
Admissions: (713) 743-1010
E-mail: admissions@uh.edu
Financial aid: (713) 743-9090
Application deadline: rolling
In-state tuition: full time: $262/credit hour; part time: $262/credit hour
Out-of-state tuition: full time: $541/credit hour
Room/board/expenses: $10,745
Full-time enrollment: 292
doctoral students: 41%; master's students: 59%; education specialists: N/A; men: 22%; women: 78%; minorities: 32%; international: 7%
Part-time enrollment: 648
doctoral students: 37%; master's students: 63%; education specialists: N/A; men: 24%; women: 76%; minorities: 32%; international: 1%
Acceptance rate (master's): 52%
Acceptance rate (doctoral): 78%
Entrance test required: GRE or MAT
Avg. GRE (of all entering students with scores): quantitative: 588; verbal: 493
Research assistantships: 0
Students reporting specialty: 77%
Students specializing in: admin.: 17%; curriculum/instr.: 42%; educational tech.: 2%; educational psych: 6%; elementary: 2%; higher education admin.: 3%; secondary: 1%; special: 2%; other: 26%

University of North Texas

PO Box 311337
Denton, TX 76203-1337
http://www.unt.edu
Public
Admissions: (940) 565-2383
E-mail: gradsch@unt.edu
Financial aid: (940) 565-2302
Application deadline: N/A
In-state tuition: full time: $195/credit hour; part time: $195/credit hour
Out-of-state tuition: full time: $473/credit hour
Room/board/expenses: $10,790
Full-time enrollment: 327
doctoral students: 35%; master's students: 65%; education specialists: N/A; men: 25%; women: 75%; minorities: 23%; international: 14%
Part-time enrollment: 1,253
doctoral students: 28%; master's students: 72%; education specialists: N/A; men: 26%; women: 74%; minorities: 29%; international: 3%
Acceptance rate (master's): 41%
Acceptance rate (doctoral): 26%
Entrance test required: GRE
Avg. GRE (of all entering students with scores): quantitative: 465; verbal: 432
Students reporting specialty: 100%
Students specializing in: admin.: 27%; counseling: 20%; curriculum/instr.: 10%; evaluation/research/statistics: 1%; educational psych: 2%; higher education admin.: 8%; secondary: 4%; special: 8%; instructional media design: 3%; other: 18%

University of Texas–Austin

1 University Station, D5000
Sanchez Building Room 210
Austin, TX 78712
http://www.utexas.edu/student/admissions
Public
Admissions: (512) 475-7398
E-mail: adgrd@utxdp.dp.utexas.edu
Financial aid: (512) 475-6282
Application deadline: rolling
In-state tuition: full time: $6,007; part time: $5,555
Out-of-state tuition: full time: $12,803
Room/board/expenses: $12,846
Full-time enrollment: 772
doctoral students: 67%; master's students: 33%; education specialists: N/A; men: 30%; women: 70%; minorities: 25%; international: 21%
Part-time enrollment: 505
doctoral students: 64%; master's students: 36%; education specialists: N/A; men: 31%; women: 69%; minorities: 26%; international: 7%
Acceptance rate (master's): 50%
Acceptance rate (doctoral): 41%
Entrance test required: GRE
Avg. GRE (of all entering students with scores): quantitative: 591; verbal: 496
Research assistantships: 160
Students reporting specialty: 96%
Students specializing in: admin.: 6%; counseling: 2%; curriculum/instr.: 30%; evaluation/research/statistics: 2%; policy: 4%; educational tech.: 4%; educational psych: 17%; higher education admin.: 11%; special: 11%; other: 14%

University of Texas–El Paso

500 W. University Avenue
El Paso, TX 79968
http://teach.education.utep.edu/
Public
Admissions: (915) 747-5572
E-mail: gradschool@utep.edu
Financial aid: (915) 747-5204
Application deadline: N/A
In-state tuition: full time: N/A; part time: N/A
Out-of-state tuition: full time: N/A
Room/board/expenses: N/A
Full-time enrollment: 55
doctoral students: 20%; master's students: 80%; education specialists: N/A; men: 33%; women: 67%; minorities: 111%; international: 20%
Part-time enrollment: 511
doctoral students: 10%; master's students: 90%; education specialists: N/A; men: 23%; women: 77%; minorities: 143%; international: 4%
Acceptance rate (master's): 80%
Acceptance rate (doctoral): 59%
Entrance test required: GRE
Avg. GRE (of all entering students with scores): quantitative: 424; verbal: 398
Students reporting specialty: 100%
Students specializing in: admin.: 18%; counseling: 13%; curriculum/instr.: 30%; elementary: 0%; secondary: 0%; special: 5%; other: 33%

University of Texas–Pan American

1201 W. University Drive
Edinburg, TX 78541-2999
http://www.utpa.edu/colleges/coe/
Public
Admissions: (956) 381-3661
E-mail: admissions@utpa.edu
Financial aid: (956) 381-2501
Application deadline: rolling
In-state tuition: full time: $4,365; part time: $159/credit hour
Out-of-state tuition: full time: $9,369
Room/board/expenses: $9,866
Full-time enrollment: 128
doctoral students: 9%; master's students: 91%; education specialists: N/A; men: 25%; women: 75%; minorities: 86%; international: 2%
Part-time enrollment: 769
doctoral students: 6%; master's students: 94%; education specialists: N/A; men: 25%; women: 75%; minorities: 87%; international: 2%
Acceptance rate (master's): 92%
Acceptance rate (doctoral): 49%
Entrance test required: N/A
Avg. GRE (of all entering students with scores): quantitative: 337; verbal: 348
Research assistantships: 7
Students reporting specialty: 100%
Students specializing in: admin.: 33%; counseling: 29%; elementary: 2%; secondary: 2%; special: 6%; other: 28%

University of Texas–San Antonio

1 UTSA Circle
San Antonio, TX 78249-0617
http://www.utsa.edu/graduate
Public
Admissions: (210) 458-4330
E-mail: graduatestudies@utsa.edu
Financial aid: (210) 458-4154
Application deadline: 07/01
In-state tuition: full time: $201/credit hour; part time: $201/credit hour
Out-of-state tuition: full time: $757/credit hour
Room/board/expenses: $12,080
Full-time enrollment: 252
doctoral students: 18%; master's students: 82%; education specialists: N/A; men: 21%; women: 79%; minorities: 50%; international: 8%
Part-time enrollment: 1,002
doctoral students: 7%; master's students: 93%; education specialists: N/A; men: 21%; women: 79%; minorities: 59%; international: 0%
Acceptance rate (master's): 90%
Acceptance rate (doctoral): 54%
Entrance test required: GRE
Avg. GRE (of all entering students with scores): quantitative: 491; verbal: 447
Research assistantships: 14
Students reporting specialty: 98%
Students specializing in: admin.: 24%; counseling: 31%; curriculum/instr.: 10%; elementary: 3%; higher education admin.: 5%; special: 3%; other: 25%

University of the Incarnate Word[1]

4301 Broadway
San Antonio, TX 78209
http://www.uiw.edu
Private
Admissions: (210) 829-6005
E-mail: admis@universe.uiwtx.edu
Financial aid: (210) 829-6008
Tuition: N/A
Room/board/expenses: N/A
Enrollment: N/A

UTAH

Brigham Young University–Provo (McKay)

301 MCKB
Provo, UT 84602
http://www.byu.edu/gradstudies
Private
Admissions: (801) 422-4091
E-mail: admissions@byu.edu
Financial aid: (801) 422-4104
Application deadline: N/A
Tuition: full time: $7,872; part time: $270/credit hour
Room/board/expenses: $17,580
Full-time enrollment: 212
doctoral students: 29%; master's students: 54%; education specialists: 17%; men: 33%; women: 67%; minorities: 10%; international: 5%
Part-time enrollment: 132
doctoral students: 46%; master's students: 54%; education specialists: 0%; men: 41%; women: 59%; minorities: 4%; international: 6%
Acceptance rate (master's): 59%
Acceptance rate (doctoral): 38%
Entrance test required: GRE or MAT
Avg. GRE (of all entering students with scores): quantitative: 588; verbal: 529
Research assistantships: 57
Students reporting specialty: 62%
Students specializing in: admin.: 16%; evaluation/research/statistics: 6%; policy: 1%; educational tech.: 10%; special: 6%; instructional media design: 12%; other: 49%

University of Utah

1705 Campus Center Drive
Room 225
Salt Lake City, UT 84112-9251
http://www.sa.utah.edu/admiss/index.htm
Public
Admissions: (801) 581-7281
E-mail: uadmiss@sa.utah.edu
Financial aid: (801) 581-6211
Application deadline: N/A
In-state tuition: full time: $4,773; part time: $456/credit hour
Out-of-state tuition: full time: $13,500
Room/board/expenses: $10,716
Full-time enrollment: 237
doctoral students: 30%; master's students: 70%; education specialists: N/A; men: 26%; women: 74%; minorities: 18%; international: 6%
Part-time enrollment: 357
doctoral students: 38%; master's students: 62%; education specialists: N/A; men: 29%; women: 71%; minorities: 12%; international: 2%
Acceptance rate (master's): 65%
Acceptance rate (doctoral): 30%
Entrance test required: GRE

Avg. GRE (of all entering students with scores): quantitative: 532; verbal: 492
Research assistantships: 28
Students reporting specialty: 100%
Students specializing in: admin.: 11%; counseling: 17%; curriculum/instr.: 17%; evaluation/research/statistics: 3%; social/philosophical foundations: 12%; educational psych: 36%; elementary: 2%; higher education admin.: 9%; secondary: 3%; special: 11%; instructional media design: 5%; other: 14%

Utah State University

2800 Old Main Hill
Logan, UT 84322-2800
http://www.usu.edu/gradsch
Public
Admissions: (435) 797-1189
E-mail: gradsch@cc.usu.edu
Financial aid: (435) 797-0173
Application deadline: rolling
In-state tuition: full time: $4,557; part time: $4,263
Out-of-state tuition: full time: $14,487
Room/board/expenses: $9,090
Full-time enrollment: 306
doctoral students: 35%; master's students: 64%; education specialists: 1%; men: 40%; women: 60%; minorities: 5%; international: 6%
Part-time enrollment: 640
doctoral students: 25%; master's students: 75%; education specialists: 0%; men: 34%; women: 66%; minorities: 3%; international: 4%
Acceptance rate (master's): 62%
Acceptance rate (doctoral): 40%
Entrance test required: GRE or MAT
Avg. GRE (of all entering students with scores): quantitative: 559; verbal: 514
Research assistantships: 51
Students reporting specialty: 65%
Students specializing in: admin.: 5%; counseling: 17%; curriculum/instr.: 14%; evaluation/research/statistics: 0%; elementary: 17%; junior high: 0%; secondary: 6%; special: 20%; instructional media design: 21%

VERMONT

University of Vermont[1]

309 Waterman Building
Burlington, VT 05405-0160
http://www.uvm.edu/~gradcoll
Public
Admissions: (802) 656-2699
E-mail: graduate.admissions@uvm.edu
Financial aid: (802) 656-3156
Tuition: N/A
Room/board/expenses: N/A
Enrollment: N/A

VIRGINIA

College of William and Mary

PO Box 8795
Williamsburg, VA 23187-8795
http://www.education.wm.edu/
Public
Admissions: (757) 221-2317
E-mail: GradEd@wm.edu
Financial aid: (757) 221-2317
Application deadline: 01/15
In-state tuition: full time: $11,312; part time: $275/credit hour
Out-of-state tuition: full time: $24,526
Room/board/expenses: $14,134
Full-time enrollment: 183
doctoral students: 25%; master's students: 68%; education specialists: 7%; men: 21%; women: 79%; minorities: 11%; international: 2%
Part-time enrollment: 204
doctoral students: 56%; master's students: 37%; education specialists: 7%; men: 26%; women: 74%; minorities: 20%; international: 0%
Acceptance rate (master's): 58%
Acceptance rate (doctoral): 59%
Entrance test required: GRE or MAT
Avg. GRE (of all entering students with scores): quantitative: 606; verbal: 546
Students reporting specialty: 100%
Students specializing in: admin.: 52%; counseling: 19%; curriculum/instr.: 19%; other: 10%

George Mason University

4400 University Drive
MSN 2F1
Fairfax, VA 22030-4444
http://gse.gmu.edu
Public
Admissions: (703) 993-2010
E-mail: gseadmit@gmu.edu
Financial aid: (703) 993-2353
Application deadline: N/A
In-state tuition: full time: $512/credit hour; part time: $512/credit hour
Out-of-state tuition: full time: $920/credit hour
Room/board/expenses: $19,700
Full-time enrollment: 288
doctoral students: 14%; master's students: 86%; education specialists: N/A; men: 14%; women: 86%; minorities: 12%; international: 10%
Part-time enrollment: 2,222
doctoral students: 7%; master's students: 93%; education specialists: N/A; men: 21%; women: 79%; minorities: 14%; international: 2%
Acceptance rate (master's): 67%
Acceptance rate (doctoral): 50%
Entrance test required: GRE
Avg. GRE (of all entering students with scores): quantitative: 581; verbal: 538
Research assistantships: 104
Students reporting specialty: 96%
Students specializing in: admin.: 12%; counseling: 6%; curriculum/instr.: 42%; special: 20%; other: 20%

Liberty University

1971 University Boulevard
Lynchburg, VA 24502
http://www.liberty.edu/academics/graduate
Private
Admissions: (800) 424-9596
E-mail: gradadmissions@liberty.edu
Financial aid: (434) 582-2270
Application deadline: rolling
Tuition: full time: $395/credit hour; part time: $395/credit hour
Room/board/expenses: $7,025
Full-time enrollment: 346
doctoral students: 39%; master's students: 53%; education specialists: 8%; men: 64%; women: 36%; minorities: 18%; international: 1%
Part-time enrollment: 785
doctoral students: 16%; master's students: 64%; education specialists: 20%; men: 69%; women: 31%; minorities: 18%; international: 2%
Acceptance rate (master's): 99%
Acceptance rate (doctoral): 88%
Entrance test required: GRE
Avg. GRE (of all entering students with scores): quantitative: N/A; verbal: N/A
Research assistantships: 1
Students reporting specialty: 98%
Students specializing in: admin.: 52%; counseling: 9%; curriculum/instr.: 11%; elementary: 10%; secondary: 8%; special: 7%; other: 3%

Old Dominion University (Darden)

Hampton Boulevard
Norfolk, VA 23529
http://education.odu.edu
Public
Admissions: (757) 683-3685
E-mail: admit@odu.edu
Financial aid: (757) 683-3683
Application deadline: 06/01
In-state tuition: full time: $211/credit hour; part time: $211/credit hour
Out-of-state tuition: full time: $304/credit hour
Room/board/expenses: $10,975
Full-time enrollment: 435
doctoral students: 2%; master's students: 97%; education specialists: 1%; men: 20%; women: 80%; minorities: 15%; international: 1%
Part-time enrollment: 937
doctoral students: 8%; master's students: 85%; education specialists: 7%; men: 23%; women: 77%; minorities: 20%; international: 1%
Acceptance rate (master's): 63%
Acceptance rate (doctoral): 57%
Entrance test required: GRE or MAT
Avg. GRE (of all entering students with scores): quantitative: 540; verbal: 470
Research assistantships: 58
Students reporting specialty: 60%
Students specializing in: admin.: 16%; counseling: 8%; elementary: 23%; secondary: 17%; special: 10%; other: 27%

Regent University

1000 Regent University Drive
Virginia Beach, VA 23464
http://www.regent.edu/acad/schedu
Private
Admissions: (800) 373-5504
E-mail: admissions@regent.edu
Financial aid: (757) 226-4140
Application deadline: rolling
Tuition: full time: $560/credit hour; part time: $560/credit hour
Room/board/expenses: N/A
Full-time enrollment: 189
doctoral students: 2%; master's students: 92%; education specialists: 7%; men: 17%; women: 83%; minorities: 52%; international: 3%
Part-time enrollment: 347
doctoral students: 44%; master's students: 52%; education specialists: 4%; men: 25%; women: 75%; minorities: 35%; international: 2%
Acceptance rate (master's): 65%
Acceptance rate (doctoral): 11%
Entrance test required: GRE
Avg. GRE (of all entering students with scores): quantitative: 473; verbal: 440
Students reporting specialty: 100%
Students specializing in: admin.: 14%; educational psych: 3%; higher education admin.: 3%; special: 11%; other: 70%

Shenandoah University

1460 University Drive
Winchester, VA 22601
http://www.su.edu
Private
Admissions: (540) 665-4581
E-mail: admit@su.edu
Financial aid: (540) 665-4538
Application deadline: rolling
Tuition: full time: $11,320; part time: $640/credit hour
Room/board/expenses: $12,090
Full-time enrollment: 13
doctoral students: 8%; master's students: 92%; education specialists: N/A; men: 31%; women: 69%; minorities: 8%; international: 31%
Part-time enrollment: 316
doctoral students: 28%; master's students: 72%; education specialists: N/A; men: 36%; women: 64%; minorities: 3%; international: 5%
Acceptance rate (master's): 87%
Acceptance rate (doctoral): 100%
Entrance test required: N/A
Avg. GRE (of all entering students with scores): quantitative: N/A; verbal: N/A
Research assistantships: 0
Students reporting specialty: 90%
Students specializing in: admin.: 15%; secondary: 0%; other: 85%

University of Virginia (Curry)

405 Emmet Street S
Charlottesville, VA 22903-2495
http://curry.edschool.virginia.edu/
Public
Admissions: (434) 924-3334
E-mail: curry@virginia.edu
Financial aid: (434) 982-6000
Application deadline: rolling
In-state tuition: full time: $11,250; part time: $5,904
Out-of-state tuition: full time: $21,015
Room/board/expenses: $18,584
Full-time enrollment: 662
doctoral students: 45%; master's students: 55%; education specialists: 0%; men: 24%; women: 76%; minorities: 10%; international: 5%
Part-time enrollment: 172
doctoral students: 71%; master's students: 28%; education specialists: 1%; men: 42%; women: 58%; minorities: 4%; international: N/A
Acceptance rate (master's): 62%
Acceptance rate (doctoral): 55%
Entrance test required: GRE
Avg. GRE (of all entering students with scores): quantitative: 592; verbal: 528
Research assistantships: 57
Students reporting specialty: 100%
Students specializing in: admin.: 8%; counseling: 7%; curriculum/instr.: 11%; evaluation/research/statistics: 2%; social/philosophical foundations: 7%; policy: 1%; educational psych: 5%; elementary: 9%; higher education admin.: 6%; secondary: 12%; special: 7%; instructional media design: 4%; other: 20%

Virginia Commonwealth University

1015 W. Main Street
PO Box 842020
Richmond, VA 23284-2020
http://www.soe.vcu.edu
Public
Admissions: (804) 828-3382
E-mail: htclark@vcu.edu
Financial aid: (804) 828-6181
Application deadline: N/A
In-state tuition: full time: $8,904; part time: $401/credit hour
Out-of-state tuition: full time: $17,584
Room/board/expenses: $11,575
Full-time enrollment: 279
doctoral students: 11%; master's students: 89%; education specialists: N/A; men: 26%; women: 74%; minorities: 18%; international: 6%
Part-time enrollment: 601
doctoral students: 22%; master's students: 78%; education specialists: N/A; men: 24%; women: 76%; minorities: 18%; international: 4%
Acceptance rate (master's): 75%
Acceptance rate (doctoral): 48%
Entrance test required: GRE or MAT
Avg. GRE (of all entering students with scores): quantitative: 508; verbal: 446
Research assistantships: 28
Students reporting specialty: 95%
Students specializing in: admin.: 25%; counseling: 6%; curriculum/instr.: 2%; evaluation/research/statistics: 0%; elementary: 5%; junior high: 0%; secondary: 4%; special: 5%; instructional media design: 1%; other: 52%

Virginia State University[1]

1 Hayden Street
Petersburg, VA 23806
http://www.vsu.edu/
Public
Admissions: (804) 524-5901
E-mail: admiss@vsu.edu
Financial aid: (804) 524-5990
Tuition: N/A
Room/board/expenses: N/A
Enrollment: N/A

Virginia Tech

226 War Memorial Hall (0313)
Blacksburg, VA 24061-0313
http://www.grads.vt.edu/
Public
Admissions: (540) 231-8636
E-mail: gradappl@vt.edu
Financial aid: (540) 231-4558
Application deadline: rolling
In-state tuition: full time: $8,986; part time: $409/credit hour
Out-of-state tuition: full time: $15,181
Room/board/expenses: $6,332
Full-time enrollment: 445
doctoral students: 45%; master's students: 55%; education specialists: 0%; men: 33%; women: 67%; minorities: 22%; international: 9%
Part-time enrollment: 685
doctoral students: 35%; master's students: 59%; education specialists: 7%; men: 30%; women: 70%; minorities: 19%; international: 1%
Acceptance rate (master's): 69%
Acceptance rate (doctoral): 51%
Entrance test required: N/A
Avg. GRE (of all entering students with scores): quantitative: N/A; verbal: N/A
Research assistantships: 20
Students reporting specialty: 100%
Students specializing in: admin.: 27%; counseling: 9%; curriculum/instr.: 43%; evaluation/research/statistics: 2%; other: 19%

WASHINGTON

Gonzaga University[1]

502 E. Boone Avenue
Spokane, WA 99258-0025
http://www.gonzaga.edu/Academics/Graduate/default.htm
Private
Admissions: (509) 323-6572
E-mail: soriet@soe.gonzaga.edu
Financial aid: (509) 323-6582
Tuition: N/A
Room/board/expenses: N/A
Enrollment: N/A

Seattle Pacific University

3307 Third Avenue W
Seattle, WA 98119-1997
http://www.spu.edu
Private
Admissions: (206) 378-5478
E-mail: hiemstra@spu.edu
Financial aid: (206) 281-2061
Application deadline: rolling
Tuition: full time: $440/credit hour; part time: $440/credit hour
Room/board/expenses: $10,638
Full-time enrollment: 59
doctoral students: 8%; master's students: 92%; education specialists: N/A; men: 41%; women: 59%; minorities: 7%; international: N/A
Part-time enrollment: 270
doctoral students: 18%; master's students: 82%; education specialists: N/A; men: 29%; women: 71%; minorities: 10%; international: 1%
Acceptance rate (master's): 84%
Acceptance rate (doctoral): 88%
Entrance test required: GRE or MAT
Avg. GRE (of all entering students with scores): quantitative: 596; verbal: 489
Research assistantships: 0
Students reporting specialty: 82%

Students specializing in: admin.: 45%; counseling: 10%; secondary: 42%; other: 3%

University of Washington
PO Box 353600
206 Miller
Seattle, WA 98195-3600
http://depts.washington.edu/coe
Public
Admissions: (206) 543-7834
E-mail: edinfo@u.washington.edu
Financial aid: (206) 543-7834
Application deadline: N/A
In-state tuition: full time: $10,460; part time: $472/credit hour
Out-of-state tuition: full time: $22,507
Room/board/expenses: $16,626
Full-time enrollment: 487
doctoral students: 35%; master's students: 65%; education specialists: N/A; men: 28%; women: 72%; minorities: 20%; international: 6%
Part-time enrollment: 319
doctoral students: 57%; master's students: 43%; education specialists: N/A; men: 33%; women: 67%; minorities: 22%; international: 3%
Acceptance rate (master's): 54%
Acceptance rate (doctoral): 32%
Entrance test required: GRE
Avg. GRE (of all entering students with scores): quantitative: 565; verbal: 525
Research assistantships: 70
Students reporting specialty: 98%
Students specializing in: admin.: 9%; curriculum/instr.: 16%; evaluation/research/statistics: 1%; social/philosophical foundations: 1%; policy: 8%; educational tech.: 2%; educational psych: 10%; elementary: 4%; higher education admin.: 3%; secondary: 10%; special: 11%; other: 26%

Washington State University
PO Box 642114
Pullman, WA 99164-2114
http://education.wsu.edu
Public
Admissions: (509) 335-7718
E-mail: gradsch@wsu.edu
Financial aid: (509) 335-9711
Application deadline: 01/10
In-state tuition: full time: $8,076; part time: $378/credit hour
Out-of-state tuition: full time: $18,924
Room/board/expenses: $13,532
Full-time enrollment: 236
doctoral students: 41%; master's students: 59%; education specialists: N/A; men: 31%; women: 69%; minorities: 16%; international: 7%

Part-time enrollment: 360
doctoral students: 26%; master's students: 74%; education specialists: N/A; men: 29%; women: 71%; minorities: 6%; international: 2%
Acceptance rate (master's): 79%
Acceptance rate (doctoral): 49%
Entrance test required: GRE or MAT
Avg. GRE (of all entering students with scores): quantitative: 480; verbal: 523
Research assistantships: 11
Students reporting specialty: 83%
Students specializing in: admin.: 22%; counseling: 14%; curriculum/instr.: 3%; evaluation/research/statistics: 2%; educational psych: 1%; elementary: 10%; higher education admin.: 9%; secondary: 9%; special: 4%; other: 26%

Marshall University
1 John Marshall Drive
Huntington, WV 25755
http://www.marshall.edu/gsepd
Public
Admissions: (800) 642-9842
E-mail: services@marshall.edu
Financial aid: (304) 696-3162
Application deadline: rolling
In-state tuition: full time: $4,606; part time: $240/credit hour
Out-of-state tuition: full time: $12,548
Room/board/expenses: $9,600
Full-time enrollment: 582
doctoral students: 3%; master's students: 92%; education specialists: 5%; men: 31%; women: 69%; minorities: 14%; international: 9%
Part-time enrollment: 1,200
doctoral students: 88%; master's students: 88%; education specialists: 3%; men: 22%; women: 78%; minorities: 2%; international: 0%
Acceptance rate (master's): 97%
Acceptance rate (doctoral): 97%
Entrance test required: GRE or MAT
Avg. GRE (of all entering students with scores): quantitative: 465; verbal: 416
Students reporting specialty: 55%
Students specializing in: admin.: 12%; counseling: 22%; elementary: 13%; higher education admin.: 5%; secondary: 10%; special: 37%

West Virginia University
802 Allen Hall
PO Box 6122
Morgantown, WV 26506-6122
http://www.wvu.edu
Public
Admissions: (304) 293-2124
Financial aid: (304) 293-5242
Application deadline: rolling

In-state tuition: full time: $5,196; part time: $292/credit hour
Out-of-state tuition: full time: $15,064
Room/board/expenses: $12,490
Full-time enrollment: 677
doctoral students: 20%; master's students: 80%; education specialists: N/A; men: 23%; women: 77%; minorities: 7%; international: 7%
Part-time enrollment: 677
doctoral students: 30%; master's students: 70%; education specialists: N/A; men: 20%; women: 80%; minorities: 7%; international: 1%
Acceptance rate (master's): N/A
Acceptance rate (doctoral): N/A
Entrance test required: GRE or MAT
Avg. GRE (of all entering students with scores): quantitative: 533; verbal: 486
Research assistantships: 33
Students reporting specialty: 74%
Students specializing in: admin.: 20%; counseling: 7%; curriculum/instr.: 7%; educational tech.: 3%; educational psych: 3%; elementary: 17%; secondary: 15%; special: 22%; other: 21%

Cardinal Stritch University[1]
6801 N. Yates Road
Milwaukee, WI 53217
http://www.stritch.edu/
Private
Admissions: N/A
Financial aid: N/A
Tuition: N/A
Room/board/expenses: N/A
Enrollment: N/A

Edgewood College[1]
1000 Edgewood College Drive
Madison, WI 53711
http://www.edgewood.edu
Private
Admissions: (608) 663-2294
E-mail: admissions@edgewood.edu
Financial aid: (608) 663-2206
Tuition: N/A
Room/board/expenses: N/A
Enrollment: N/A

Marquette University
Schroeder Complex
Box 1881
Milwaukee, WI 53201
http://www.grad.marquette.edu
Private
Admissions: (414) 288-7137
E-mail: mugs@marquette.edu
Financial aid: (414) 288-5325
Application deadline: rolling
Tuition: full time: $595/credit hour; part time: $595/credit hour

Room/board/expenses: $14,210
Full-time enrollment: 101
doctoral students: 21%; master's students: 78%; education specialists: 1%; men: 18%; women: 82%; minorities: 11%; international: 4%
Part-time enrollment: 143
doctoral students: 41%; master's students: 52%; education specialists: 7%; men: 26%; women: 74%; minorities: 7%; international: N/A
Acceptance rate (master's): N/A
Acceptance rate (doctoral): 16%
Entrance test required: GRE
Avg. GRE (of all entering students with scores): quantitative: 558; verbal: 490
Research assistantships: 38
Students reporting specialty: 100%
Students specializing in: admin.: 18%; counseling: 50%; curriculum/instr.: 13%; social/philosophical foundations: 2%; policy: 16%; educational admin.: 10%; higher education admin.: 1%; junior high: 10%; secondary: 11%

University of Wisconsin–Madison
123 Education Building
Madison, WI 53706-1398
http://www.education.wisc.edu
Public
Admissions: (608) 262-2433
E-mail: gradadmiss@bascom.wisc.edu
Financial aid: (608) 262-2087
Application deadline: rolling
In-state tuition: full time: $9,642; part time: $604/credit hour
Out-of-state tuition: full time: $24,912
Room/board/expenses: $10,500
Full-time enrollment: 728
doctoral students: 60%; master's students: 40%; education specialists: N/A; men: 33%; women: 67%; minorities: 16%; international: 16%
Part-time enrollment: 440
doctoral students: 42%; master's students: 58%; education specialists: N/A; men: 34%; women: 66%; minorities: 11%; international: 6%
Acceptance rate (master's): 40%
Acceptance rate (doctoral): 43%
Entrance test required: GRE
Avg. GRE (of all entering students with scores): quantitative: 605; verbal: 523
Research assistantships: 23
Students reporting specialty: 100%
Students specializing in: admin.: 26%; counseling: 8%; curriculum/instr.: 26%; policy: 6%; educational psych: 10%; special: 4%; other: 20%

University of Wisconsin–Milwaukee
PO Box 413
Milwaukee, WI 53201
http://www.graduateschool.uwm.edu
Public
Admissions: (414) 229-6569
E-mail: gradschool@uwm.edu
Financial aid: (414) 229-5840
Application deadline: rolling
In-state tuition: full time: $10,020; part time: $779/credit hour
Out-of-state tuition: full time: $24,384
Room/board/expenses: $10,250
Full-time enrollment: 211
doctoral students: 28%; master's students: 70%; education specialists: 2%; men: 20%; women: 80%; minorities: 22%; international: 7%
Part-time enrollment: 449
doctoral students: 26%; master's students: 73%; education specialists: 1%; men: 19%; women: 81%; minorities: 22%; international: 3%
Acceptance rate (master's): 49%
Acceptance rate (doctoral): 42%
Entrance test required: GRE
Avg. GRE (of all entering students with scores): quantitative: 545; verbal: 448
Students reporting specialty: 99%
Students specializing in: admin.: 29%; counseling: 13%; curriculum/instr.: 17%; evaluation/research/statistics: 2%; social/philosophical foundations: 5%; educational tech.: 1%; educational psych: 19%; higher education admin.: 1%; special: 12%; other: 1%

University of Wyoming[1]
Department 3374
1000 E. University Avenue
Laramie, WY 82071
http://uwadmnweb.uwyo.edu/uwgrad/
Public
Admissions: (307) 766-2287
E-mail: uwgrad@uwyo.edu
Financial aid: (307) 766-2118
Tuition: N/A
Room/board/expenses: N/A
Enrollment: N/A

ENGINEERING

The engineering school directory lists the 198 schools in the country that offer doctoral programs. One hundred ninety-three schools responded to the *U.S. News* survey, which was conducted in the fall of 2007 and early 2008. Information about entrance requirements, enrollment, the cost of attendance, assistantships and fellowships, and student areas of specialization is reported in the following pages. Institutions that did not respond to the survey have abbreviated entries.

TERMINOLOGY

1 A school whose name is footnoted with the numeral 1 did not return the *U.S. News* statistical survey; limited data appear in its entry.

N/A. Not available from the school or not applicable.

Admissions. The admissions office phone number.

E-mail. The electronic address of the admissions office. If, instead of an E-mail address, a website is listed, the website will automatically present an E-mail screen programmed to reach the admissions office.

Financial aid. The financial aid office phone number.

Application deadline. For fall 2009 enrollment. "Rolling" means there is no application deadline; the school acts on applications as they are received. "Varies" means deadlines vary according to department or whether applicants are U.S. citizens or foreign nationals.

Tuition. For the 2007–2008 academic year. Includes fees.

Credit hour. The cost per credit hour for the 2007–2008 academic year.

Room/board/expenses. For the 2007–2008 academic year.

Enrollment. Full and part time for fall 2007. The total is the combination of master's and doctoral students, if the school offers both degrees. Where available, the breakdown for men, women, minorities, and international students is provided. Percentages for men and women may not add to 100 because of rounding.

Minorities. For the fall of 2007, the percentage of students who are Asian-American, African-American, Hispanic, or American Indian. (When the U.S. Department of Education calculates minority enrollment percentages, these are the demographic groupings it uses.)

Acceptance rate. Percentage of applicants who were accepted for fall 2007 including both master's and doctoral degree programs.

GRE requirement. A "yes" means Graduate Record Examinations scores are required by some or all departments.

Average GRE scores. Combined for both master's and doctoral degree students who entered in fall 2007.

TOEFL requirement. A "yes" means that students from non-English-speaking countries must submit scores for the Test of English as a Foreign Language.

Minimum TOEFL score. The score listed is the minimum acceptable score for the paper TOEFL. (The computer-administered TOEFL is graded on a different scale.)

Total fellowships, teaching assistantships, and research assistantships. The number of student appointments for the 2007–2008 academic year. Students may hold multiple appointments and would therefore be counted more than once.

Student specialties. Proportion of master's and doctoral students, both full and part time, in the specialty-reporting population (not necessarily the entire student body) who are enrolled in a particular specialty in fall 2007. Specialty fields listed in engineering are aerospace/aeronautical/astronautical, agriculture, architectural engineering, bioengineering/biomedical, chemical, civil, computer engineering, computer science, electrical/electronic/communications, engineering management, engineering science and physics, environmental/environmental health, industrial/manufacturing, materials, mechanical, mining, nuclear, petroleum, and other. Numbers may not add to 100 because of rounding or students enrolled in multiple specialties.

ALABAMA

Auburn University (Ginn)
108 Ramsay Hall
Auburn University, AL 36849
http://www.grad.auburn.edu
Public
Admissions: (334) 844-4700
E-mail: gradadm@auburn.edu
Financial aid: (334) 844-4367
Application deadline: rolling
In-state tuition: full time: $5,754;
part time: $217/credit hour
Out-of-state tuition: full time:
$16,254
Room/board/expenses: $10,916
Full-time enrollment: 377
men: 74%; women: 26%;
minorities: 10%; international: 62%
Part-time enrollment: 317
men: 76%; women: 24%;
minorities: 11%; international: 35%
Acceptance rate: 47%
GRE requirement: Yes
Avg. GRE: quantitative: 707
TOEFL requirement: Yes
Minimum TOEFL score: 550
Fellowships: 503
Teaching assistantships: 156
Research assistantships: 363
Students specializing in: aerospace: 6%; chemical: 11%; civil: 11%; computer: 19%; electrical: 17%; industrial: 14%; materials: 8%; mechanical: 11%; other: 3%

Tuskegee University
202 Engineering Building
Tuskegee, AL 36088-1920
http://tuskegee.edu
Private
Admissions: (334) 727-8500
E-mail: adm@tuskegee.edu
Financial aid: (334) 727-8206
Application deadline: rolling
Tuition: full time: $14,120;
part time: $810/credit hour
Room/board/expenses: $11,494
Full-time enrollment: 49
men: 69%; women: 31%;
minorities: 90%; international:
55%
Part-time enrollment: 7
men: 86%; women: 14%;
minorities: 71%; international: 57%
Acceptance rate: 63%
GRE requirement: Yes
Avg. GRE: quantitative: N/A
TOEFL requirement: Yes
Minimum TOEFL score: 500
Fellowships: 10
Teaching assistantships: 13
Research assistantships: 19
Students specializing in: electrical: 38%; materials: 18%; mechanical: 45%

University of Alabama
Box 870200
Tuscaloosa, AL 35487-0200
http://www.coeweb.eng.ua.edu/
Public
Admissions: (205) 348-5921
E-mail:
intergradapply@aalan.ua.edu
Financial aid: (205) 348-2976
Application deadline: 07/01
In-state tuition: full time: $5,700;
part time: N/A
Out-of-state tuition: full time:
$16,518
Room/board/expenses: $11,095
Full-time enrollment: 199
men: 80%; women: 20%;
minorities: 12%; international: 58%

Part-time enrollment: 60
men: 73%; women: 27%;
minorities: 10%; international: 32%
Acceptance rate: 35%
GRE requirement: Yes
Avg. GRE: quantitative: 730
TOEFL requirement: Yes
Minimum TOEFL score: 550
Fellowships: 0
Teaching assistantships: 60
Research assistantships: 89
Students specializing in: aerospace: 14%; chemical: 8%; civil: 16%; computer science: 16%; electrical: 13%; industrial: 2%; materials: 11%; mechanical: 19%; other: 1%

University of Alabama–Birmingham
1530 Third Avenue S, HOEN 100
Birmingham, AL 35294-4440
http://www.eng.uab.edu
Public
Admissions: (205) 934-8232
E-mail: gradschool@uab.edu
Financial aid: (205) 934-8132
Application deadline: 08/15
In-state tuition: full time:
$198/credit hour; part time:
$198/credit hour
Out-of-state tuition: full time:
$471/credit hour
Room/board/expenses: $12,155
Full-time enrollment: 129
men: 76%; women: 24%;
minorities: 8%; international: 70%
Part-time enrollment: 100
men: 83%; women: 17%;
minorities: 18%; international: 24%
Acceptance rate: 34%
GRE requirement: Yes
Avg. GRE: quantitative: 705
TOEFL requirement: Yes
Minimum TOEFL score: 550
Fellowships: 26
Teaching assistantships: 5
Research assistantships: 69
Students specializing in: biomedical: 12%; civil: 19%; computer: 7%; electrical: 31%; environmental: 7%; materials: 14%; mechanical: 11%

University of Alabama–Huntsville
301 Sparkman Drive EB 102
Huntsville, AL 35899
http://www.uah.edu
Public
Admissions: (256) 824-6199
E-mail: biggsk@uah.edu
Financial aid: (256) 824-6241
Application deadline: 06/18
In-state tuition: full time: $6,548;
part time: $3,720
Out-of-state tuition: full time:
$13,466
Room/board/expenses: $8,961
Full-time enrollment: 255
men: 73%; women: 27%;
minorities: 9%; international: 61%
Part-time enrollment: 454
men: 81%; women: 19%;
minorities: 11%; international: 5%
Acceptance rate: 53%
GRE requirement: Yes
Avg. GRE: quantitative: 675
TOEFL requirement: Yes
Minimum TOEFL score: 500
Fellowships: 0
Teaching assistantships: 88
Research assistantships: 49
Students specializing in: aerospace: 9%; chemical: 2%; civil: 3%; computer: 5%; computer

science: 21%; electrical: 23%; management: 13%; industrial: 25%; mechanical: 10%; other: 3%

ALASKA

University of Alaska–Fairbanks
PO Box 755960
Fairbanks, AK 99775-5960
http://www.uaf.edu/cem
Public
Admissions: (800) 478-1823
E-mail: admissions@uaf.edu
Financial aid: (888) 474-7256
Application deadline: 06/01
In-state tuition: full time: $5,896; part time: N/A
Out-of-state tuition: full time: $11,278
Room/board/expenses: $9,380
Full-time enrollment: 80
men: 73%; women: 28%; minorities: 4%; international: 69%
Part-time enrollment: 38
men: 74%; women: 26%; minorities: 8%; international: 29%
Acceptance rate: 37%
GRE requirement: Yes
Avg. GRE: quantitative: 698
TOEFL requirement: Yes
Minimum TOEFL score: 550
Fellowships: 3
Teaching assistantships: 26
Research assistantships: 44
Students specializing in: civil: 31%; computer science: 5%; electrical: 20%; management: 7%; mining: 13%; petroleum: 21%; other: 4%

ARIZONA

Arizona State University (Fulton)
Box 879309
Tempe, AZ 85287-9309
http://www.fulton.asu.edu/fulton/
Public
Admissions: (480) 965-6113
E-mail: grad-q@asu.edu
Financial aid: (480) 965-3355
Application deadline: rolling
In-state tuition: full time: $7,178; part time: $426/credit hour
Out-of-state tuition: full time: $18,870
Room/board/expenses: $11,530
Full-time enrollment: 1,393
men: 77%; women: 23%; minorities: 5%; international: 76%
Part-time enrollment: 626
men: 83%; women: 17%; minorities: 15%; international: 27%
Acceptance rate: 51%
GRE requirement: Yes
Avg. GRE: quantitative: 763
TOEFL requirement: Yes
Minimum TOEFL score: 550
Teaching assistantships: 177
Research assistantships: 465
Students specializing in: aerospace: 2%; biomedical: 5%; chemical: 2%; civil: 3%; computer science: 20%; electrical: 39%; environmental: 3%; industrial: 9%; materials: 6%; mechanical: 5%; other: 7%

University of Arizona
Civil Engineering Building
Room 100
Tucson, AZ 85721-0072
http://grad.arizona.edu
Public
Admissions: (520) 621-3471
E-mail: gradadmission@grad.arizona.edu
Financial aid: (520) 621-1858
Application deadline: rolling
In-state tuition: full time: $6,002; part time: $365/credit hour
Out-of-state tuition: full time: $16,808
Room/board/expenses: $12,096
Full-time enrollment: 961
men: 76%; women: 24%; minorities: 11%; international: 49%

Part-time enrollment: N/A
men: N/A; women: N/A; minorities: N/A; international: N/A
Acceptance rate: 33%
GRE requirement: Yes
Avg. GRE: quantitative: 719
TOEFL requirement: Yes
Minimum TOEFL score: 550
Fellowships: 31
Teaching assistantships: 117
Research assistantships: 296
Students specializing in: aerospace: 3%; agriculture: 3%; biomedical: 2%; chemical: 3%; civil: 5%; computer: 19%; computer science: 8%; electrical: 19%; environmental: 3%; industrial: 1%; materials: 4%; mechanical: 7%; mining: 4%; nuclear: 0%; other: 37%

ARKANSAS

University of Arkansas–Fayetteville
Bell Engineering Center
Room 4183
Fayetteville, AR 72701
http://www.engr.uark.edu
Public
Admissions: (479) 575-4401
E-mail: gradinfo@cavern.uark.edu
Financial aid: (479) 575-3806
Application deadline: 07/24
In-state tuition: full time: $281/credit hour; part time: $281/credit hour
Out-of-state tuition: full time: $664/credit hour
Room/board/expenses: $9,731
Full-time enrollment: 419
men: 73%; women: 27%; minorities: 13%; international: 40%
Part-time enrollment: 333
men: 72%; women: 28%; minorities: 21%; international: 15%
Acceptance rate: 37%
GRE requirement: Yes
Avg. GRE: quantitative: 687
TOEFL requirement: Yes
Minimum TOEFL score: 550
Fellowships: 32
Teaching assistantships: 32
Research assistantships: 142
Students specializing in: biomedical: 5%; chemical: 3%; civil: 6%; computer: 3%; computer science: 5%; electrical: 13%; environmental: 1%; industrial: 60%; mechanical: 7%

CALIFORNIA

California Institute of Technology
1200 E. California Boulevard
Pasadena, CA 91125-4400
http://www.gradoffice.caltech.edu
Private
Admissions: (626) 395-6346
E-mail: gradofc@its.caltech.edu
Financial aid: (626) 395-3712
Application deadline: 01/01
Tuition: full time: $31,020; part time: N/A
Room/board/expenses: $21,326
Full-time enrollment: 536
men: 77%; women: 23%; minorities: 15%; international: 43%
Part-time enrollment: N/A
men: N/A; women: N/A; minorities: N/A; international: N/A
Acceptance rate: 13%
GRE requirement: Yes
Avg. GRE: quantitative: 800
TOEFL requirement: Yes
Minimum TOEFL score: 600
Fellowships: 184
Teaching assistantships: 215
Research assistantships: 613
Students specializing in: aerospace: 7%; biomedical: 8%; chemical: 11%; civil: 2%; computer science: 5%; electrical: 18%; environmental: 5%; materials: 9%; mechanical: 10%; other: 25%

California State University–Long Beach
1250 Bellflower Boulevard
Long Beach, CA 90840-8306
http://www.csulb.edu/colleges/coe/
Public
Admissions: N/A
Financial aid: N/A
Application deadline: 10/01
In-state tuition: full time: $3,400; part time: $2,100
Out-of-state tuition: full time: $11,000
Room/board/expenses: $7,550
Full-time enrollment: 655
men: 80%; women: 20%; minorities: 49%; international: 34%
Part-time enrollment: N/A
men: N/A; women: N/A; minorities: N/A; international: N/A
Acceptance rate: 33%
GRE requirement: Yes
Avg. GRE: quantitative: 702
TOEFL requirement: Yes
Minimum TOEFL score: 550
Fellowships: 7
Teaching assistantships: 15
Research assistantships: 15
Students specializing in: chemical: 0%; civil: 12%; computer science: 25%; electrical: 36%; mechanical: 27%

Naval Postgraduate School[1]
1 University Circle
Monterey, CA 93943-5001
http://www.nps.navy.mil/inps/GSEAS.htm
Public
Admissions: (831) 656-3093
E-mail: grad-ed@nps.navy.mil
Financial aid: N/A
Tuition: N/A
Room/board/expenses: N/A
Enrollment: N/A

San Diego State University
5500 Campanile Drive
San Diego, CA 92182
http://engineering.sdsu.edu
Public
Admissions: (619) 594-6061
Financial aid: (619) 594-6323
Application deadline: N/A
In-state tuition: full time: $3,428; part time: $2,264
Out-of-state tuition: full time: $339/credit hour
Room/board/expenses: $13,768
Full-time enrollment: 171
men: 70%; women: 30%; minorities: 6%; international: 76%
Part-time enrollment: 234
men: 78%; women: 22%; minorities: 24%; international: 45%
Acceptance rate: 54%
GRE requirement: Yes
Avg. GRE: quantitative: 698
TOEFL requirement: Yes
Minimum TOEFL score: 550
Students specializing in: aerospace: 4%; civil: 10%; electrical: 62%; science and physics: 2%; environmental: 5%; industrial: 4%; mechanical: 14%

Santa Clara University
500 El Camino Real
Santa Clara, CA 95053-0583
http://www.scu.edu/engineering/graduate
Private
Admissions: (408) 554-4313
E-mail: gradengineer@scu.edu
Financial aid: (408) 554-4505
Application deadline: 08/14
Tuition: full time: $669/credit hour; part time: $669/credit hour
Room/board/expenses: $12,290
Full-time enrollment: 126
men: 76%; women: 24%; minorities: 38%; international: 41%

Part-time enrollment: 364
men: 78%; women: 22%; minorities: 38%; international: 19%
Acceptance rate: 58%
GRE requirement: Yes
Avg. GRE: quantitative: 710
TOEFL requirement: Yes
Minimum TOEFL score: 550
Fellowships: 3
Teaching assistantships: 16
Research assistantships: 19
Students specializing in: civil: 0%; computer: 23%; electrical: 27%; management: 34%; mechanical: 14%; other: 1%

Stanford University
Terman Engineering Center
Room 214
Stanford, CA 94305-4027
http://soe.stanford.edu/
Private
Admissions: (650) 723-4291
E-mail: gradadmissions@stanford.edu
Financial aid: (650) 723-3058
Application deadline: N/A
Tuition: full time: $37,199; part time: N/A
Room/board/expenses: $20,905
Full-time enrollment: 2,920
men: 77%; women: 23%; minorities: 16%; international: 50%
Part-time enrollment: 309
men: 83%; women: 17%; minorities: 28%; international: 23%
Acceptance rate: 28%
GRE requirement: Yes
Avg. GRE: quantitative: 780
TOEFL requirement: Yes
Minimum TOEFL score: 575
Fellowships: 736
Teaching assistantships: 373
Research assistantships: 976
Students specializing in: aerospace: 7%; biomedical: 2%; chemical: 3%; civil: 8%; computer science: 12%; electrical: 30%; management: 12%; materials: 4%; mechanical: 16%; petroleum: 2%; other: 4%

University of California–Berkeley
320 McLaughlin Hall # 1700
Berkeley, CA 94720-1700
http://www.grad.berkeley.edu/
Public
Admissions: (510) 642-7405
E-mail: gradadm@berkeley.edu
Financial aid: (510) 642-0485
Application deadline: N/A
In-state tuition: full time: $9,578; part time: N/A
Out-of-state tuition: full time: $24,576
Room/board/expenses: $18,482
Full-time enrollment: 1,720
men: 74%; women: 26%; minorities: 23%; international: 33%
Part-time enrollment: 60
men: 63%; women: 37%; minorities: 23%; international: 28%
Acceptance rate: 20%
GRE requirement: Yes
Avg. GRE: quantitative: 772
TOEFL requirement: Yes
Minimum TOEFL score: 570
Fellowships: 520
Teaching assistantships: 305
Research assistantships: 860
Students specializing in: biomedical: 9%; chemical: 6%; civil: 22%; computer: 12%; electrical: 17%; industrial: 4%; materials: 5%; mechanical: 19%; nuclear: 3%; other: 2%

University of California–Davis
1050 Kemper Hall
1 Shields Avenue
Davis, CA 95616-5294
http://engineering.ucdavis.edu
Public
Admissions: (530) 752-0655
Financial aid: (530) 752-0592
Application deadline: N/A

In-state tuition: full time: $9,651; part time: $6,324
Out-of-state tuition: full time: $24,639
Room/board/expenses: $16,046
Full-time enrollment: 1,068
men: 74%; women: 26%; minorities: 18%; international: 38%
Part-time enrollment: 56
men: 84%; women: 16%; minorities: 23%; international: 7%
Acceptance rate: 36%
GRE requirement: Yes
Avg. GRE: quantitative: 749
TOEFL requirement: Yes
Minimum TOEFL score: 550
Fellowships: 193
Teaching assistantships: 162
Research assistantships: 542
Students specializing in: aerospace: 13%; agriculture: 4%; biomedical: 10%; chemical: 5%; civil: 20%; computer: 17%; computer science: 18%; electrical: 17%; science and physics: 4%; environmental: 20%; materials: 4%; mechanical: 13%; other: 4%

University of California–Irvine (Samueli)
305 REC
Irvine, CA 92697-2700
http://www.eng.uci.edu
Public
Admissions: (949) 824-4334
E-mail: soegradinfo@soemail.eng.uci.edu
Financial aid: (949) 824-4889
Application deadline: 01/15
In-state tuition: full time: $10,716; part time: $7,389
Out-of-state tuition: full time: $25,704
Room/board/expenses: $16,513
Full-time enrollment: 893
men: 77%; women: 23%; minorities: 2%; international: 57%
Part-time enrollment: 91
men: 73%; women: 27%; minorities: 4%; international: 15%
Acceptance rate: 26%
GRE requirement: Yes
Avg. GRE: quantitative: 758
TOEFL requirement: Yes
Minimum TOEFL score: 550
Fellowships: 771
Teaching assistantships: 351
Research assistantships: 876
Students specializing in: aerospace: 3%; biomedical: 10%; chemical: 4%; civil: 7%; computer: 13%; computer science: 25%; electrical: 18%; environmental: 1%; materials: 7%; mechanical: 8%; other: 3%

University of California–Los Angeles (Samueli)
6426 Boelter Hall, Box 951601
Los Angeles, CA 90095-1601
http://www.engineer.ucla.edu
Public
Admissions: (310) 825-2514
E-mail: gradadm@ea.ucla.edu
Financial aid: (310) 206-0400
Application deadline: 12/15
In-state tuition: full time: $8,967; part time: N/A
Out-of-state tuition: full time: $23,955
Room/board/expenses: $19,725
Full-time enrollment: 1,388
men: 81%; women: 19%; minorities: 33%; international: 36%
Part-time enrollment: N/A
men: N/A; women: N/A; minorities: N/A; international: N/A
Acceptance rate: 36%
GRE requirement: Yes
Avg. GRE: quantitative: 768
TOEFL requirement: Yes
Minimum TOEFL score: 560
Fellowships: 567
Teaching assistantships: 540
Research assistantships: 1,910

Students specializing in: aerospace: 4%; biomedical: 8%; chemical: 5%; civil: 8%; computer science: 26%; electrical: 25%; materials: 6%; mechanical: 17%

University of California–Riverside (Bourns)
Riverside, CA 92521-0208
http://www.graddiv.ucr.edu
Public
Admissions: (951) 827-3313
E-mail: grdadmis@pop.ucr.edu
Financial aid: (951) 827-4302
Application deadline: 01/09
In-state tuition: full time: $19,628; part time: $16,301
Out-of-state tuition: full time: $34,617
Room/board/expenses: $16,550
Full-time enrollment: 325
men: 72%; women: 28%;
minorities: 12%; international: 60%
Part-time enrollment: 42
men: 79%; women: 21%;
minorities: 17%; international: 14%
Acceptance rate: 33%
GRE requirement: Yes
Avg. GRE: quantitative: 755
TOEFL requirement: Yes
Minimum TOEFL score: 550
Fellowships: 96
Teaching assistantships: 132
Research assistantships: 160
Students specializing in: biomedical: 3%; chemical: 19%; computer science: 35%; electrical: 28%; mechanical: 16%

University of California–San Diego (Jacobs)
9500 Gilman Drive
La Jolla, CA 92093-0403
http://www.jacobsschool.ucsd.edu
Public
Admissions: (858) 534-3555
E-mail: gradadmissions@ucsd.edu
Financial aid: (858) 534-4480
Application deadline: N/A
In-state tuition: full time: $9,429; part time: $9,429
Out-of-state tuition: full time: $24,123
Room/board/expenses: $15,659
Full-time enrollment: 1,213
men: 79%; women: 21%;
minorities: 23%; international: 36%
Part-time enrollment: N/A
men: N/A; women: N/A;
minorities: N/A; international: N/A
Acceptance rate: 25%
GRE requirement: Yes
Avg. GRE: quantitative: 765
TOEFL requirement: Yes
Minimum TOEFL score: 550
Fellowships: 230
Teaching assistantships: 280
Research assistantships: 610
Students specializing in: aerospace: 2%; biomedical: 16%; chemical: 1%; civil: 8%; computer: 3%; computer science: 20%; electrical: 29%; science and physics: 5%; materials: 5%; mechanical: 11%

University of California–San Francisco
1700 Fourth Street
San Francisco, CA 94158-2330
http://www.grad.berkeley.edu
Public
Admissions: (510) 642-7405
E-mail: gradadm@berkeley.edu
Financial aid: (415) 476-4181
Application deadline: 12/10
In-state tuition: full time: $9,822; part time: N/A
Out-of-state tuition: full time: $24,810
Room/board/expenses: N/A

Full-time enrollment: 171
men: 60%; women: 40%;
minorities: 47%; international: 10%
Part-time enrollment: N/A
men: N/A; women: N/A;
minorities: N/A; international: N/A
Acceptance rate: 15%
GRE requirement: Yes
Avg. GRE: quantitative: 774
TOEFL requirement: Yes
Minimum TOEFL score: 570
Fellowships: 21
Research assistantships: 38
Students specializing in: N/A

University of California–Santa Barbara
College of Engineering
Santa Barbara, CA 93106-5130
http://www.engineering.ucsb.edu
Public
Admissions: (805) 893-2277
E-mail: admissions@graddiv.ucsb.edu
Financial aid: (805) 893-2277
Application deadline: 12/15
In-state tuition: full time: $8,069; part time: N/A
Out-of-state tuition: full time: $23,057
Room/board/expenses: $11,532
Full-time enrollment: 724
men: 78%; women: 22%;
minorities: 10%; international: 48%
Part-time enrollment: N/A
men: N/A; women: N/A;
minorities: N/A; international: N/A
Acceptance rate: 28%
GRE requirement: Yes
Avg. GRE: quantitative: 773
TOEFL requirement: Yes
Minimum TOEFL score: 600
Fellowships: 121
Teaching assistantships: 114
Research assistantships: 350
Students specializing in: chemical: 11%; computer science: 19%; electrical: 44%; materials: 15%; mechanical: 11%

University of California–Santa Cruz (Baskin)
1156 High Street
Santa Cruz, CA 95064
http://www.soe.ucsc.edu/advising/graduate
Public
Admissions: (831) 459-4975
E-mail: soegradadm@soe.ucsc.edu
Financial aid: (831) 459-2963
Application deadline: 01/01
In-state tuition: full time: $10,728; part time: $10,728
Out-of-state tuition: full time: $25,422
Room/board/expenses: $17,424
Full-time enrollment: 246
men: 72%; women: 28%;
minorities: 21%; international: 39%
Part-time enrollment: 66
men: 83%; women: 17%;
minorities: 29%; international: 24%
Acceptance rate: 39%
GRE requirement: Yes
Avg. GRE: quantitative: 750
TOEFL requirement: Yes
Minimum TOEFL score: 570
Fellowships: 110
Teaching assistantships: 138
Research assistantships: 305
Students specializing in: biomedical: 13%; computer: 22%; computer science: 32%; electrical: 26%; other: 6%

University of Southern California (Viterbi)
University Park, Olin Hall 200
Los Angeles, CA 90089-1450
http://viterbi.usc.edu
Private
Admissions: (213) 740-4530

E-mail: viterbi.gradadmission@usc.edu
Financial aid: (213) 740-6241
Application deadline: rolling
Tuition: full time $24,355; part time: $1,263/credit hour
Room/board/expenses: $16,700
Full-time enrollment: 2,307
men: 80%; women: 20%;
minorities: 9%; international: 78%
Part-time enrollment: 1,638
men: 79%; women: 21%;
minorities: 31%; international: 29%
Acceptance rate: 47%
GRE requirement: Yes
Avg. GRE: quantitative: 753
TOEFL requirement: No
Minimum TOEFL score: N/A
Fellowships: 186
Teaching assistantships: 490
Research assistantships: 942
Students specializing in: aerospace: 5%; biomedical: 5%; chemical: 3%; civil: 5%; computer: 3%; computer science: 26%; electrical: 31%; management: 3%; environmental: 1%; industrial: 8%; materials: 2%; mechanical: 6%; petroleum: 1%

Colorado School of Mines
1500 Illinois Street
Golden, CO 80401-1887
http://www.mines.edu/admiss/grad/
Public
Admissions: (303) 273-3348
E-mail: grad-school@mines.edu
Financial aid: (303) 273-3207
Application deadline: 07/01
In-state tuition: full time: $10,250; part time: $498/credit hour
Out-of-state tuition: full time: $23,030
Room/board/expenses: $20,886
Full-time enrollment: 543
men: 76%; women: 24%;
minorities: 9%; international: 27%
Part-time enrollment: 303
men: 68%; women: 32%;
minorities: 8%; international: 16%
Acceptance rate: 70%
GRE requirement: Yes
Avg. GRE: quantitative: 717
TOEFL requirement: Yes
Minimum TOEFL score: 550
Fellowships: 52
Teaching assistantships: 178
Research assistantships: 277
Students specializing in: chemical: 5%; computer: 7%; environmental: 10%; materials: 12%; mining: 4%; nuclear: 0%; petroleum: 9%; other: 54%

Colorado State University
202 Engineering Building
Fort Collins, CO 80523-1301
http://www.engr.colostate.edu
Public
Admissions: (970) 491-6220
E-mail: tjs@engr.colostate.edu
Financial aid: (970) 491-6220
Application deadline: 02/01
In-state tuition: full time: $6,466; part time: $272/credit hour
Out-of-state tuition: full time: $18,004
Room/board/expenses: $11,752
Full-time enrollment: 359
men: 76%; women: 24%;
minorities: 12%; international: 29%
Part-time enrollment: 179
men: 78%; women: 22%;
minorities: 15%; international: 36%
Acceptance rate: 34%
GRE requirement: Yes
Avg. GRE: quantitative: 730
TOEFL requirement: Yes
Minimum TOEFL score: 550
Fellowships: 28
Teaching assistantships: 61
Research assistantships: 206

Students specializing in: biomedical: 1%; chemical: 4%; civil: 35%; electrical: 20%; mechanical: 22%; other: 17%

University of Colorado–Boulder
422 UCB
Boulder, CO 80309-0422
http://www.colorado.edu/engineering
Public
Admissions: (303) 492-5071
Financial aid: (303) 492-5091
Application deadline: 02/01
In-state tuition: full time: $10,279; part time: $7,321
Out-of-state tuition: full time: $24,979
Room/board/expenses: $17,908
Full-time enrollment: 1,167
men: 77%; women: 23%;
minorities: 10%; international: 33%
Part-time enrollment: 131
men: 81%; women: 19%;
minorities: 15%; international: 9%
Acceptance rate: 58%
GRE requirement: Yes
Avg. GRE: quantitative: 757
TOEFL requirement: Yes
Minimum TOEFL score: 600
Fellowships: 71
Teaching assistantships: 88
Research assistantships: 289
Students specializing in: aerospace: 11%; chemical: 8%; civil: 15%; computer science: 17%; electrical: 21%; management: 9%; mechanical: 8%; other: 12%

University of Colorado–Colorado Springs
1420 Austin Bluffs Parkway
Colorado Springs, CO 80918
http://www.uccs.edu
Public
Admissions: (719) 262-3383
E-mail: admrec@uccs.edu
Financial aid: (719) 262-3460
Application deadline: rolling
In-state tuition: full time: $4,570; part time: N/A
Out-of-state tuition: full time: $9,994
Room/board/expenses: $12,080
Full-time enrollment: 82
men: 77%; women: 23%;
minorities: 21%; international: 12%
Part-time enrollment: 103
men: 85%; women: 15%;
minorities: 9%; international: 3%
Acceptance rate: 86%
GRE requirement: Yes
Avg. GRE: quantitative: N/A
TOEFL requirement: Yes
Minimum TOEFL score: 550
Fellowships: 2
Teaching assistantships: 3
Research assistantships: 6
Students specializing in: computer: 25%; electrical: 23%; management: 25%; mechanical: 10%; other: 17%

University of Colorado–Denver
PO Box 173364, Campus Box 104
Denver, CO 80217-3364
http://www.cudenver.edu/
Public
Admissions: (303) 556-2704
E-mail: admissions@cudenver.edu
Financial aid: (303) 556-2886
Application deadline: rolling
In-state tuition: full time: $9,344; part time: $410/credit hour
Out-of-state tuition: full time: $19,170
Room/board/expenses: $14,270
Full-time enrollment: 48
men: 75%; women: 25%;
minorities: 13%; international: 50%
Part-time enrollment: 251
men: 74%; women: 26%;
minorities: 17%; international: 28%

Acceptance rate: 77%
GRE requirement: Yes
Avg. GRE: quantitative: N/A
TOEFL requirement: Yes
Minimum TOEFL score: 500
Fellowships: 0
Teaching assistantships: 2
Research assistantships: 15
Students specializing in: civil: 28%; computer science: 30%; electrical: 21%; mechanical: 21%

University of Denver
2390 York Street
Denver, CO 80208
http://www.du.edu/secs/
Private
Admissions: (303) 871-2831
E-mail: grad-info@du.edu
Financial aid: (303) 871-4020
Application deadline: rolling
Tuition: full time: $873/credit hour; part time: $873/credit hour
Room/board/expenses: $14,700
Full-time enrollment: 112
men: 80%; women: 20%;
minorities: 4%; international: 34%
Part-time enrollment: 61
men: 74%; women: 26%;
minorities: 23%; international: 13%
Acceptance rate: 56%
GRE requirement: Yes
Avg. GRE: quantitative: 740
TOEFL requirement: Yes
Minimum TOEFL score: 550
Fellowships: 0
Teaching assistantships: 20
Research assistantships: 17
Students specializing in: biomedical: 3%; computer: 6%; computer science: 25%; electrical: 9%; materials: 2%; mechanical: 12%; other: 46%

University of Bridgeport
221 University Avenue
Bridgeport, CT 06604
http://www.bridgeport.edu/sed
Private
Admissions: (203) 576-4552
E-mail: admit@bridgeport.edu
Financial aid: (203) 576-4568
Application deadline: 08/01
Tuition: full time: $575/credit hour; part time: $575/credit hour
Room/board/expenses: $13,100
Full-time enrollment: 936
men: 84%; women: 16%;
minorities: 1%; international: 99%
Part-time enrollment: 249
men: 82%; women: 18%;
minorities: 3%; international: 96%
Acceptance rate: 66%
GRE requirement: No
Avg. GRE: quantitative: N/A
TOEFL requirement: Yes
Minimum TOEFL score: 550
Teaching assistantships: 33
Research assistantships: 18
Students specializing in: computer: 2%; computer science: 25%; electrical: 38%; management: 16%; mechanical: 19%

University of Connecticut
261 Glenbrook Road, Unit 2237
Storrs, CT 06269-2237
http://www.uconn.edu
Public
Admissions: (860) 486-0974
E-mail: gradschool@uconn.edu
Financial aid: (860) 486-2819
Application deadline: 02/01
In-state tuition: full time: $10,052; part time: $469/credit hour
Out-of-state tuition: full time: $23,534
Room/board/expenses: $14,060
Full-time enrollment: 361
men: 74%; women: 26%;
minorities: 6%; international: 67%

Part-time enrollment: 153
men: 82%; women: 18%;
minorities: 16%; international: 13%
Acceptance rate: 30%
GRE requirement: Yes
Avg. GRE: quantitative: 750
TOEFL requirement: Yes
Minimum TOEFL score: 550
Fellowships: 19
Teaching assistantships: 51
Research assistantships: 234
Students specializing in: biomedical: 10%; chemical: 7%; civil: 8%; computer science: 18%; electrical: 21%; environmental: 5%; materials: 6%; mechanical: 15%; other: 11%

Yale University
226 Dunham Lab
10 Hillhouse Avenue
New Haven, CT 06520
http://www.eng.yale.edu
Private
Admissions: (203) 432-2771
E-mail: graduate.admissions@yale.edu
Financial aid: (203) 432-2739
Application deadline: 01/02
Tuition: full time: $30,500; part time: $3,813/credit hour
Room/board/expenses: $23,019
Full-time enrollment: 168
men: 64%; women: 36%;
minorities: 8%; international: 50%
Part-time enrollment: 4
men: 100%; women: 0%;
minorities: 0%; international: 50%
Acceptance rate: 15%
GRE requirement: Yes
Avg. GRE: quantitative: 772
TOEFL requirement: Yes
Minimum TOEFL score: 590
Fellowships: 58
Teaching assistantships: 100
Research assistantships: 103
Students specializing in: biomedical: 27%; chemical: 10%; electrical: 26%; environmental: 10%; mechanical: 16%; other: 10%

DELAWARE

University of Delaware
102 DuPont Hall
Newark, DE 19716-3101
http://www.engr.udel.edu
Public
Admissions: (302) 831-2129
Financial aid: (302) 831-8761
Application deadline: rolling
In-state tuition: full time: $7,994; part time: $408/credit hour
Out-of-state tuition: full time: $19,244
Room/board/expenses: $11,500
Full-time enrollment: 575
men: 74%; women: 26%;
minorities: 5%; international: 56%
Part-time enrollment: 54
men: 80%; women: 20%;
minorities: 2%; international: 11%
Acceptance rate: 27%
GRE requirement: Yes
Avg. GRE: quantitative: 748
TOEFL requirement: Yes
Minimum TOEFL score: 550
Fellowships: 23
Teaching assistantships: 54
Research assistantships: 385
Students specializing in: chemical: 18%; civil: 14%; computer science: 17%; electrical: 22%; materials: 12%; mechanical: 17%

DISTRICT OF COLUMBIA

Catholic University of America
620 Michigan Avenue NE
Washington, DC 20064
http://admissions.cua.edu/graduate/
Private
Admissions: (800) 673-2772
E-mail: cua-admissions@cua.edu
Financial aid: (202) 319-5307
Application deadline: rolling
Tuition: full time: $29,050; part time: $1,045/credit hour
Room/board/expenses: $18,180
Full-time enrollment: 48
men: 77%; women: 23%;
minorities: 15%; international: 48%
Part-time enrollment: 83
men: 82%; women: 18%;
minorities: 24%; international: 14%
Acceptance rate: 62%
GRE requirement: No
Avg. GRE: quantitative: 713
TOEFL requirement: Yes
Minimum TOEFL score: 550
Teaching assistantships: 7
Research assistantships: 14
Students specializing in: biomedical: 17%; civil: 18%; electrical: 38%; management: 15%; mechanical: 11%

George Washington University
725 23rd Street NW, Tompkins Hall
Washington, DC 20052
http://www.seas.gwu.edu/
Private
Admissions: (202) 994-8675
E-mail: engineering@gwu.edu
Financial aid: (202) 994-6822
Application deadline: 01/15
Tuition: full time: $1,012/credit hour; part time: $1,012/credit hour
Room/board/expenses: $19,070
Full-time enrollment: 347
men: 70%; women: 30%;
minorities: 16%; international: 57%
Part-time enrollment: 898
men: 75%; women: 25%;
minorities: 20%; international: 15%
Acceptance rate: 71%
GRE requirement: Yes
Avg. GRE: quantitative: 710
TOEFL requirement: Yes
Minimum TOEFL score: 550
Fellowships: 68
Teaching assistantships: 99
Research assistantships: 26
Students specializing in: civil: 5%; computer science: 22%; electrical: 17%; management: 51%; mechanical: 6%

Howard University
2366 Sixth Street NW, Suite 100
Washington, DC 20059
http://www.gs.howard.edu
Private
Admissions: (202) 806-7469
E-mail: hugsadmissions@howard.edu
Financial aid: (202) 806-2820
Application deadline: 02/01
Tuition: full time: $16,980; part time: $899/credit hour
Room/board/expenses: $15,683
Full-time enrollment: 51
men: 69%; women: 31%;
minorities: 49%; international: 51%
Part-time enrollment: 20
men: 75%; women: 25%;
minorities: 55%; international: 45%
Acceptance rate: 38%
GRE requirement: Yes
Avg. GRE: quantitative: 611
TOEFL requirement: Yes
Minimum TOEFL score: 550
Fellowships: 3
Teaching assistantships: 13
Research assistantships: 48
Students specializing in: chemical: 13%; civil: 14%; computer science: 30%; electrical: 28%; mechanical: 15%

FLORIDA

Florida Atlantic University
777 Glades Road
Boca Raton, FL 33431-0991
http://www.eng.fau.edu
Public
Admissions: (561) 297-3642
E-mail: gradadm@fau.edu
Financial aid: (561) 297-3530
Application deadline: 07/01
In-state tuition: full time: $256/credit hour; part time: $256/credit hour
Out-of-state tuition: full time: $915/credit hour
Room/board/expenses: $10,864
Full-time enrollment: 128
men: 78%; women: 22%;
minorities: 18%; international: 54%
Part-time enrollment: 131
men: 73%; women: 27%;
minorities: 36%; international: 24%
Acceptance rate: 50%
GRE requirement: Yes
Avg. GRE: quantitative: 694
TOEFL requirement: Yes
Minimum TOEFL score: 550
Fellowships: 0
Teaching assistantships: 21
Research assistantships: 61
Students specializing in: biomedical: 1%; civil: 9%; computer: 17%; computer science: 34%; electrical: 17%; mechanical: 8%; other: 14%

Florida Institute of Technology
150 W. University Boulevard
Melbourne, FL 32901-6975
http://coe.fit.edu
Private
Admissions: (800) 944-4348
E-mail: grad_admissions@fit.edu
Financial aid: (321) 674-8070
Application deadline: rolling
Tuition: full time: $945/credit hour; part time: $945/credit hour
Room/board/expenses: $11,470
Full-time enrollment: 234
men: 81%; women: 19%;
minorities: 7%; international: 54%
Part-time enrollment: 362
men: 79%; women: 21%;
minorities: 12%; international: 12%
Acceptance rate: 54%
GRE requirement: Yes
Avg. GRE: quantitative: 659
TOEFL requirement: Yes
Minimum TOEFL score: 550
Fellowships: 8
Teaching assistantships: 47
Research assistantships: 33
Students specializing in: aerospace: 5%; chemical: 3%; civil: 3%; computer: 5%; computer science: 17%; electrical: 15%; management: 12%; environmental: 2%; mechanical: 5%; other: 33%

Florida International University
10555 W. Flagler Street
Miami, FL 33174
http://www.eng.fiu.edu/
Public
Admissions: (305) 348-2363
E-mail: brownc@servms.fiu.edu
Financial aid: (305) 348-7272
Application deadline: 06/01
In-state tuition: full time: $7,006; part time: $273/credit hour
Out-of-state tuition: full time: $19,103
Room/board/expenses: $17,162
Full-time enrollment: 492
men: 75%; women: 25%;
minorities: 16%; international: 77%
Part-time enrollment: 356
men: 75%; women: 25%;
minorities: 60%; international: 22%
Acceptance rate: 57%
GRE requirement: Yes
Avg. GRE: quantitative: 702
TOEFL requirement: Yes
Minimum TOEFL score: 550
Fellowships: 6
Teaching assistantships: 118
Research assistantships: 133
Students specializing in: biomedical: 9%; civil: 16%; computer: 2%; computer science: 19%; electrical: 25%; management: 9%; environmental: 4%; industrial: 4%; materials: 2%; mechanical: 9%; other: 2%

Florida State University/Florida A&M University
2525 Pottsdamer Street
Tallahassee, FL 32310
http://www.eng.fsu.edu
Public
Admissions: (850) 644-3420
E-mail: gradadms@admin.fsu.edu
Financial aid: (850) 410-6423
Application deadline: 07/01
In-state tuition: full time: $250/credit hour; part time: $250/credit hour
Out-of-state tuition: full time: $880/credit hour
Room/board/expenses: $13,600
Full-time enrollment: 284
men: 79%; women: 21%;
minorities: 23%; international: 44%
Part-time enrollment: N/A
men: N/A; women: N/A;
minorities: N/A; international: N/A
Acceptance rate: 65%
GRE requirement: Yes
Avg. GRE: quantitative: 746
TOEFL requirement: Yes
Minimum TOEFL score: 550
Fellowships: 14
Teaching assistantships: 66
Research assistantships: 102
Students specializing in: biomedical: 3%; chemical: 5%; civil: 17%; electrical: 28%; industrial: 21%; mechanical: 26%

University of Central Florida
4000 Central Florida Boulevard
Orlando, FL 32816-2993
http://www.cecs.ucf.edu/graduate
Public
Admissions: (407) 823-2455
E-mail: gradengr@mail.ucf.edu
Financial aid: (407) 823-2827
Application deadline: 07/15
In-state tuition: full time: $270/credit hour; part time: $270/credit hour
Out-of-state tuition: full time: $997/credit hour
Room/board/expenses: $13,498
Full-time enrollment: 688
men: 79%; women: 21%;
minorities: 12%; international: 57%
Part-time enrollment: 289
men: 79%; women: 21%;
minorities: 27%; international: 0%
Acceptance rate: 50%
GRE requirement: Yes
Avg. GRE: quantitative: 711
TOEFL requirement: Yes
Minimum TOEFL score: 560
Fellowships: 63
Teaching assistantships: 113
Research assistantships: 601
Students specializing in: aerospace: 2%; civil: 10%; computer: 12%; computer science: 18%; electrical: 20%; environmental: 4%; industrial: 19%; materials: 7%; mechanical: 9%

University of Florida
300 Weil Hall
Gainesville, FL 32611-6550
http://www.eng.ufl.edu
Public
Admissions: (352) 392-0946
E-mail: admissions@eng.ufl.edu
Financial aid: (352) 392-0946
Application deadline: 06/01
In-state tuition: full time: $7,478; part time: $312/credit hour
Out-of-state tuition: full time: $22,603
Room/board/expenses: $13,010
Full-time enrollment: 2,474
men: 79%; women: 21%;
minorities: 11%; international: 56%
Part-time enrollment: N/A
men: N/A; women: N/A;
minorities: N/A; international: N/A
Acceptance rate: 40%
GRE requirement: Yes
Avg. GRE: quantitative: 758
TOEFL requirement: Yes
Minimum TOEFL score: 550
Fellowships: 396
Teaching assistantships: 197
Research assistantships: 1,028
Students specializing in: aerospace: 3%; agriculture: 2%; biomedical: 3%; chemical: 4%; civil: 10%; computer: 18%; computer science: 1%; electrical: 19%; management: 3%; environmental: 5%; industrial: 7%; materials: 11%; mechanical: 10%; nuclear: 3%

University of Miami
1251 Memorial Drive
Coral Gables, FL 33146
http://www.miami.edu/engineering
Private
Admissions: (305) 284-2942
E-mail: gradadm.eng@miami.edu
Financial aid: (305) 284-5212
Application deadline: 12/01
Tuition: full time: $1,350/credit hour; part time: $1,350/credit hour
Room/board/expenses: $25,898
Full-time enrollment: 214
men: 72%; women: 28%;
minorities: 21%; international: 52%
Part-time enrollment: 28
men: 71%; women: 29%;
minorities: 43%; international: 7%
Acceptance rate: 58%
GRE requirement: Yes
Avg. GRE: quantitative: 726
TOEFL requirement: Yes
Minimum TOEFL score: 550
Fellowships: 7
Teaching assistantships: 49
Research assistantships: 59
Students specializing in: biomedical: 22%; civil: 7%; computer science: 4%; electrical: 21%; industrial: 30%; mechanical: 15%; other: 1%

University of South Florida
4202 E. Fowler Avenue, ENB118
Tampa, FL 33620
http://admissions.grad.usf.edu/
Public
Admissions: (813) 974-8800
E-mail: admissions@grad.usf.edu
Financial aid: (813) 974-4700
Application deadline: 03/15
In-state tuition: full time: $6,124; part time: $267/credit hour
Out-of-state tuition: full time: $21,604
Room/board/expenses: $14,020
Full-time enrollment: 448
men: 69%; women: 31%;
minorities: 18%; international: 55%
Part-time enrollment: 322
men: 79%; women: 21%;
minorities: 26%; international: 25%
Acceptance rate: 68%
GRE requirement: Yes
Avg. GRE: quantitative: 705
TOEFL requirement: Yes
Minimum TOEFL score: 550
Fellowships: 71
Teaching assistantships: 192
Research assistantships: 337
Students specializing in: biomedical: 7%; chemical: 6%; civil: 18%; computer: 10%; computer science: 13%; electrical: 29%; management: 11%; science and physics: 2%; environmental: 2%; industrial: 6%; mechanical: 8%

GEORGIA

Georgia Institute of Technology
225 North Avenue
Atlanta, GA 30332-0360
http://www.grad.gatech.edu
Public
Admissions: (404) 894-3090
E-mail: gradstudies@gatech.edu
Financial aid: (404) 894-4160
Application deadline: rolling
In-state tuition: full time: $6,444; part time: $221/credit hour

Out-of-state tuition: full time: $23,334
Room/board/expenses: $9,794
Full-time enrollment: 3,407
men: 80%; women: 20%; minorities: 11%; international: 57%
Part-time enrollment: 896
men: 82%; women: 18%; minorities: 17%; international: 25%
Acceptance rate: 37%
GRE requirement: Yes
Avg. GRE: quantitative: 767
TOEFL requirement: Yes
Minimum TOEFL score: 550
Fellowships: 478
Teaching assistantships: 314
Research assistantships: 1,853
Students specializing in: aerospace: 11%; biomedical: 4%; chemical: 4%; civil: 5%; computer science: 17%; electrical: 26%; science and physics: 0%; environmental: 2%; industrial: 11%; materials: 3%; mechanical: 16%; nuclear: 1%; other: 1%

University of Georgia
Driftmier Engineering Center
Athens, GA 30602
http://www.engr.uga.edu
Public
Admissions: (706) 542-1739
E-mail: gradadm@uga.edu
Financial aid: (706) 542-6147
Application deadline: 01/30
In-state tuition: full time: $211/credit hour; part time: $211/credit hour
Out-of-state tuition: full time: $846/credit hour
Room/board/expenses: $10,432
Full-time enrollment: 40
men: 73%; women: 28%; minorities: 15%; international: 73%
Part-time enrollment: 8
men: 88%; women: 13%; minorities: 0%; international: 13%
Acceptance rate: 61%
GRE requirement: Yes
Avg. GRE: quantitative: 698
TOEFL requirement: Yes
Minimum TOEFL score: 550
Fellowships: 0
Teaching assistantships: 0
Research assistantships: 37
Students specializing in: N/A

HAWAII

University of Hawaii–Manoa
2540 Dole Street, Holmes Hall 240
Honolulu, HI 96822
http://www.eng.hawaii.edu/
Public
Admissions: (808) 956-8544
E-mail: admissions@hawaii.edu
Financial aid: (808) 956-5047
Application deadline: 05/11
In-state tuition: full time: $7,200; part time: $421/credit hour
Out-of-state tuition: full time: $16,868
Room/board/expenses: $15,619
Full-time enrollment: 72
men: 71%; women: 29%; minorities: 39%; international: 49%
Part-time enrollment: 103
men: 70%; women: 30%; minorities: 25%; international: 44%
Acceptance rate: 60%
GRE requirement: Yes
Avg. GRE: quantitative: 729
TOEFL requirement: Yes
Minimum TOEFL score: 500
Fellowships: 2
Teaching assistantships: 19
Research assistantships: 69
Students specializing in: civil: 35%; electrical: 41%; mechanical: 24%

IDAHO

Idaho State University
921 S. Eighth Street, MS 8060
Pocatello, ID 83209-8060
http://www.isu.edu/engineer/
Public
Admissions: (208) 282-2150
E-mail: graddean@isu.edu
Financial aid: (208) 282-2756
Application deadline: 12/30
In-state tuition: full time: $6,206; part time: $259/credit hour
Out-of-state tuition: full time: $14,890
Room/board/expenses: $8,600
Full-time enrollment: 33
men: 73%; women: 27%; minorities: 0%; international: 52%
Part-time enrollment: 54
men: 83%; women: 17%; minorities: 0%; international: 30%
Acceptance rate: 94%
GRE requirement: Yes
Avg. GRE: quantitative: N/A
TOEFL requirement: Yes
Minimum TOEFL score: 550
Fellowships: 5
Teaching assistantships: 5
Research assistantships: 6
Students specializing in: civil: 7%; science and physics: 34%; environmental: 16%; mechanical: 5%; nuclear: 20%; other: 18%

University of Idaho
PO Box 441011
Moscow, ID 83844-1011
http://www.engr.uidaho.edu/
Public
Admissions: (208) 885-4001
E-mail: gadms@uidaho.edu
Financial aid: (208) 885-6312
Application deadline: 02/01
In-state tuition: full time: $4,950; part time: $239/credit hour
Out-of-state tuition: full time: $15,030
Room/board/expenses: $13,582
Full-time enrollment: 121
men: N/A; women: N/A; minorities: N/A; international: N/A
Part-time enrollment: 229
men: N/A; women: N/A; minorities: N/A; international: N/A
Acceptance rate: 43%
GRE requirement: Yes
Avg. GRE: quantitative: 732
TOEFL requirement: Yes
Minimum TOEFL score: 550
Students specializing in: agriculture: 3%; chemical: 3%; civil: 19%; computer: 1%; computer science: 10%; electrical: 32%; management: 5%; environmental: 3%; materials: 5%; mechanical: 13%; nuclear: 4%; other: 3%

ILLINOIS

Illinois Institute of Technology (Armour)
10 W. 32nd Street
Engineering 1, Room 220
Chicago, IL 60616
http://www.iit.edu/%7Earmour/
Private
Admissions: (312) 567-3020
E-mail: gradstu@iit.edu
Financial aid: (312) 567-7219
Application deadline: rolling
Tuition: full time: $778/credit hour; part time: $778/credit hour
Room/board/expenses: $13,480
Full-time enrollment: 1,033
men: 78%; women: 22%; minorities: 2%; international: 92%
Part-time enrollment: 556
men: 83%; women: 17%; minorities: 14%; international: 49%
Acceptance rate: 51%
GRE requirement: Yes
Avg. GRE: quantitative: 744
TOEFL requirement: Yes
Minimum TOEFL score: 550
Fellowships: 8
Teaching assistantships: 119

Research assistantships: 206
Students specializing in: architectural: 1%; biomedical: 3%; chemical: 9%; civil: 8%; computer: 9%; computer science: 28%; electrical: 27%; environmental: 3%; industrial: 1%; materials: 2%; mechanical: 10%

Northwestern University (McCormick)
2145 Sheridan Road
Evanston, IL 60208
http://www.northwestern.edu
Private
Admissions: (847) 491-8532
E-mail: gradapp@northwestern.edu
Financial aid: (847) 491-7266
Application deadline: 12/31
Tuition: full time: $35,244; part time: $11,868
Room/board/expenses: $21,941
Full-time enrollment: 920
men: 73%; women: 27%; minorities: 18%; international: 45%
Part-time enrollment: 335
men: 76%; women: 24%; minorities: 24%; international: 9%
Acceptance rate: 28%
GRE requirement: Yes
Avg. GRE: quantitative: 779
TOEFL requirement: Yes
Minimum TOEFL score: 600
Fellowships: 149
Teaching assistantships: 119
Research assistantships: 294
Students specializing in: biomedical: 16%; chemical: 11%; civil: 8%; electrical: 25%; industrial: 6%; materials: 19%; mechanical: 10%; other: 5%

Southern Illinois University–Carbondale
Carbondale, IL 62901-6603
http://www.siu.edu/gradschl/
Public
Admissions: (618) 536-7791
E-mail: gradsch@siu.edu
Financial aid: (618) 453-4334
Application deadline: rolling
In-state tuition: full time: $275/credit hour; part time: $275/credit hour
Out-of-state tuition: full time: $688/credit hour
Room/board/expenses: $12,135
Full-time enrollment: 310
men: 80%; women: 20%; minorities: 2%; international: 90%
Part-time enrollment: 144
men: 77%; women: 23%; minorities: 7%; international: 69%
Acceptance rate: 59%
GRE requirement: Yes
Avg. GRE: quantitative: 700
TOEFL requirement: Yes
Minimum TOEFL score: 550
Fellowships: 16
Teaching assistantships: 218
Research assistantships: 88
Students specializing in: civil: 5%; computer: 7%; computer science: 14%; electrical: 66%; science and physics: 6%; mechanical: 7%; mining: 1%

University of Illinois–Chicago
851 S. Morgan Street
Chicago, IL 60607-7043
http://www.uic.edu/
Public
Admissions: (312) 996-5133
E-mail: uicgrad@uic.edu
Financial aid: (312) 996-5563
Application deadline: N/A
In-state tuition: full time: $12,812; part time: $9,582
Out-of-state tuition: full time: $24,810
Room/board/expenses: $14,702

Full-time enrollment: 635
men: 72%; women: 28%; minorities: 9%; international: 74%
Part-time enrollment: 293
men: 80%; women: 20%; minorities: 19%; international: 45%
Acceptance rate: 34%
GRE requirement: Yes
Avg. GRE: quantitative: 741
TOEFL requirement: Yes
Minimum TOEFL score: 600
Fellowships: 19
Teaching assistantships: 125
Research assistantships: 244
Students specializing in: biomedical: 18%; chemical: 5%; civil: 10%; computer science: 28%; electrical: 21%; mechanical: 13%; other: 5%

University of Illinois–Urbana-Champaign
1308 W. Green
Urbana, IL 61801
http://www.engr.uiuc.edu
Public
Admissions: (217) 333-0035
Financial aid: (217) 333-0100
Application deadline: rolling
In-state tuition: full time: $14,760; part time: $11,093
Out-of-state tuition: full time: $27,600
Room/board/expenses: $14,922
Full-time enrollment: 2,386
men: 82%; women: 18%; minorities: 18%; international: 47%
Part-time enrollment: 93
men: 83%; women: 17%; minorities: 11%; international: 39%
Acceptance rate: 19%
GRE requirement: Yes
Avg. GRE: quantitative: 774
TOEFL requirement: Yes
Minimum TOEFL score: 550
Fellowships: 240
Teaching assistantships: 551
Research assistantships: 1,419
Students specializing in: aerospace: 3%; agriculture: 2%; biomedical: 1%; chemical: 4%; civil: 12%; computer: 21%; computer science: 18%; electrical: 21%; science and physics: 14%; environmental: 3%; industrial: 1%; materials: 6%; mechanical: 10%; nuclear: 3%; other: 2%

INDIANA

Indiana University–Purdue University–Indianapolis
799 W. Michigan Street, ET 219
Indianapolis, IN 46202-5160
http://engr.iupui.edu
Public
Admissions: (317) 278-4961
E-mail: et_grad@iupui.edu
Financial aid: N/A
Application deadline: 05/01
In-state tuition: full time: $287/credit hour; part time: $287/credit hour
Out-of-state tuition: full time: $820/credit hour
Room/board/expenses: $2,255
Full-time enrollment: 103
men: 84%; women: 16%; minorities: 9%; international: 66%
Part-time enrollment: 60
men: 83%; women: 17%; minorities: 27%; international: 5%
Acceptance rate: 89%
GRE requirement: Yes
Avg. GRE: quantitative: N/A
TOEFL requirement: Yes
Minimum TOEFL score: 550
Fellowships: 3
Teaching assistantships: 6
Research assistantships: 25
Students specializing in: biomedical: 18%; computer: 15%; electrical: 36%; science and physics: 2%; mechanical: 42%; other: 9%

Purdue University–West Lafayette
701 W. Stadium Avenue
Suite 2000 ARMS
West Lafayette, IN 47907-2045
http://engineering.purdue.edu
Public
Admissions: (765) 494-5340
E-mail: graduate@ecn.purdue.edu
Financial aid: (765) 494-5340
Application deadline: 01/01
In-state tuition: full time: $8,044; part time: $266/credit hour
Out-of-state tuition: full time: $22,852
Room/board/expenses: $10,710
Full-time enrollment: 1,853
men: 81%; women: 19%; minorities: 7%; international: 61%
Part-time enrollment: 470
men: 82%; women: 18%; minorities: 10%; international: 34%
Acceptance rate: 33%
GRE requirement: Yes
Avg. GRE: quantitative: 751
TOEFL requirement: Yes
Minimum TOEFL score: 550
Fellowships: 248
Teaching assistantships: 392
Research assistantships: 1,426
Students specializing in: aerospace: 10%; agriculture: 4%; biomedical: 4%; chemical: 5%; civil: 11%; computer: 6%; computer science: 5%; electrical: 21%; environmental: 2%; industrial: 6%; materials: 2%; mechanical: 16%; nuclear: 2%; other: 9%

University of Notre Dame
257 Fitzpatrick Hall of Engineering
Notre Dame, IN 46556
http://www.nd.edu
Private
Admissions: (574) 631-7706
E-mail: gradad@nd.edu
Financial aid: (574) 631-7706
Application deadline: 02/01
Tuition: full time: $35,040; part time: $1,922/credit hour
Room/board/expenses: $15,400
Full-time enrollment: 394
men: 75%; women: 25%; minorities: 6%; international: 42%
Part-time enrollment: 7
men: 86%; women: 14%; minorities: 0%; international: 14%
Acceptance rate: 21%
GRE requirement: Yes
Avg. GRE: quantitative: 763
TOEFL requirement: Yes
Minimum TOEFL score: N/A
Fellowships: 37
Teaching assistantships: 48
Research assistantships: 151
Students specializing in: chemical: 15%; civil: 13%; computer: 18%; electrical: 24%; mechanical: 29%

IOWA

Iowa State University
104 Marston Hall
Ames, IA 50011-2151
http://www.eng.iastate.edu/
Public
Admissions: (800) 262-3810
E-mail: grad_admissions@iastate.edu
Financial aid: (800) 478-2998
Application deadline: rolling
In-state tuition: full time: $7,272; part time: $694/credit hour
Out-of-state tuition: full time: $17,932
Room/board/expenses: $9,123
Full-time enrollment: 956
men: 82%; women: 18%; minorities: 6%; international: 49%
Part-time enrollment: N/A
men: N/A; women: N/A; minorities: N/A; international: N/A
Acceptance rate: 22%
GRE requirement: Yes
Avg. GRE: quantitative: 759
TOEFL requirement: Yes

Minimum TOEFL score: 550
Fellowships: 59
Teaching assistantships: 138
Research assistantships: 454
Students specializing in: aerospace: 7%; agriculture: 8%; chemical: 6%; civil: 12%; computer: 15%; electrical: 15%; industrial: 14%; materials: 8%; mechanical: 15%

University of Iowa
3100 Seamans Center
Iowa City, IA 52242-1527
http://www.uiowa.edu/admissions/graduate/index.html
Public
Admissions: (319) 335-1525
E-mail: admissions@uiowa.edu
Financial aid: (319) 335-1450
Application deadline: 07/15
In-state tuition: full time: $7,380; part time: N/A
Out-of-state tuition: full time: $19,366
Room/board/expenses: $14,350
Full-time enrollment: 435
men: 70%; women: 30%; minorities: 8%; international: 49%
Part-time enrollment: N/A
men: N/A; women: N/A; minorities: N/A; international: N/A
Acceptance rate: 28%
GRE requirement: Yes
Avg. GRE: quantitative: 739
TOEFL requirement: Yes
Minimum TOEFL score: 550
Fellowships: 26
Teaching assistantships: 125
Research assistantships: 259
Students specializing in: biomedical: 13%; chemical: 11%; civil: 18%; computer science: 22%; electrical: 15%; industrial: 8%; mechanical: 12%

KANSAS

Kansas State University
1046 Rathbone Hall
Manhattan, KS 66506-5201
http://www.engg.ksu.edu/
Public
Admissions: (785) 532-6191
E-mail: gradschool@ksu.edu
Financial aid: (785) 532-6420
Application deadline: rolling
In-state tuition: full time: $255/credit hour; part time: $255/credit hour
Out-of-state tuition: full time: $586/credit hour
Room/board/expenses: $10,004
Full-time enrollment: 317
men: 75%; women: 25%; minorities: 4%; international: 62%
Part-time enrollment: 168
men: 82%; women: 18%; minorities: 11%; international: 20%
Acceptance rate: 48%
GRE requirement: Yes
Avg. GRE: quantitative: 749
TOEFL requirement: Yes
Minimum TOEFL score: 550
Fellowships: 0
Teaching assistantships: 42
Research assistantships: 169
Students specializing in: agriculture: 6%; architectural: 4%; chemical: 6%; civil: 13%; computer science: 27%; electrical: 18%; industrial: 13%; mechanical: 10%; nuclear: 4%

University of Kansas
1 Eaton Hall, 1520 W. 15th Street
Lawrence, KS 66045-7621
http://www.engr.ku.edu
Public
Admissions: (785) 864-2980
E-mail: kuengr@ku.edu
Financial aid: (785) 864-5491
Application deadline: rolling
In-state tuition: full time: $241/credit hour; part time: $241/credit hour
Out-of-state tuition: full time: $575/credit hour
Room/board/expenses: $10,302
Full-time enrollment: 300
men: 77%; women: 23%; minorities: 1%; international: 60%
Part-time enrollment: 374
men: 81%; women: 19%; minorities: 6%; international: 21%
Acceptance rate: 61%
GRE requirement: Yes
Avg. GRE: quantitative: N/A
TOEFL requirement: Yes
Minimum TOEFL score: 530
Fellowships: 65
Teaching assistantships: 71
Research assistantships: 139
Students specializing in: aerospace: 6%; architectural: 2%; biomedical: 2%; chemical: 7%; civil: 13%; computer: 3%; computer science: 17%; electrical: 14%; management: 24%; environmental: 5%; mechanical: 7%; petroleum: 0%

Wichita State University
1845 N. Fairmount
Wichita, KS 67260-0044
http://www.engr.wichita.edu/
Public
Admissions: (316) 978-3095
E-mail: gradinqu@wichita.edu
Financial aid: (316) 978-3430
Application deadline: rolling
In-state tuition: full time: $208/credit hour; part time: $208/credit hour
Out-of-state tuition: full time: $560/credit hour
Room/board/expenses: $9,200
Full-time enrollment: 252
men: 93%; women: 7%; minorities: N/A; international: N/A
Part-time enrollment: 299
men: 94%; women: 6%; minorities: N/A; international: N/A
Acceptance rate: 35%
GRE requirement: Yes
Avg. GRE: quantitative: N/A
TOEFL requirement: Yes
Minimum TOEFL score: 550
Students specializing in: aerospace: 16%; electrical: 45%; management: 3%; industrial: 21%; mechanical: 15%

KENTUCKY

University of Kentucky
351 Ralph G. Anderson Building
Lexington, KY 40506-0503
http://www.engr.uky.edu
Public
Admissions: (859) 257-4905
E-mail: grad.webmaster@email.uky.edu
Financial aid: (859) 257-3172
Application deadline: 07/26
In-state tuition: full time: $8,470; part time: $401/credit hour
Out-of-state tuition: full time: $16,958
Room/board/expenses: $9,670
Full-time enrollment: 483
men: 77%; women: 23%; minorities: 4%; international: 65%
Part-time enrollment: 132
men: 77%; women: 23%; minorities: 8%; international: 50%
Acceptance rate: 45%
GRE requirement: Yes
Avg. GRE: quantitative: 749
TOEFL requirement: Yes
Minimum TOEFL score: 550
Fellowships: 65
Teaching assistantships: 70
Research assistantships: 255
Students specializing in: agriculture: 5%; biomedical: 4%; chemical: 6%; civil: 11%; computer science: 24%; electrical: 28%; industrial: 5%; materials: 3%; mechanical: 12%; mining: 2%

University of Louisville (Speed)
2301 S. Third Street
Louisville, KY 40292
http://www.louisville.edu/speed
Public
Admissions: (502) 852-6531
E-mail: admitme@gwise.louisville.edu
Financial aid: (502) 852-5511
Application deadline: rolling
In-state tuition: full time: $7,578; part time: $419/credit hour
Out-of-state tuition: full time: $18,140
Room/board/expenses: $12,812
Full-time enrollment: 321
men: 75%; women: 25%; minorities: 6%; international: 54%
Part-time enrollment: 192
men: 88%; women: 12%; minorities: 9%; international: 28%
Acceptance rate: 89%
GRE requirement: Yes
Avg. GRE: quantitative: 703
TOEFL requirement: Yes
Minimum TOEFL score: 550
Fellowships: 25
Teaching assistantships: 45
Research assistantships: 69
Students specializing in: chemical: 7%; civil: 11%; computer: 11%; computer science: 7%; electrical: 19%; management: 11%; industrial: 10%; mechanical: 18%; other: 6%

LOUISIANA

Louisiana State University–Baton Rouge
3304 CEBA Building
Baton Rouge, LA 70803
http://www.eng.lsu.edu
Public
Admissions: (225) 578-1641
E-mail: graddeanoffice@lsu.edu
Financial aid: (225) 578-3103
Application deadline: 05/15
In-state tuition: full time: $4,432; part time: $2,765
Out-of-state tuition: full time: $12,732
Room/board/expenses: $11,020
Full-time enrollment: 470
men: 79%; women: 21%; minorities: 5%; international: 80%
Part-time enrollment: 106
men: 78%; women: 22%; minorities: 16%; international: 43%
Acceptance rate: 39%
GRE requirement: Yes
Avg. GRE: quantitative: 737
TOEFL requirement: Yes
Minimum TOEFL score: 550
Fellowships: 26
Teaching assistantships: 70
Research assistantships: 194
Students specializing in: agriculture: 3%; chemical: 9%; civil: 17%; computer science: 16%; electrical: 18%; science and physics: 11%; industrial: 3%; mechanical: 18%; petroleum: 5%

Louisiana Tech University
PO Box 10348
Ruston, LA 71272
http://www.latech.edu/tech/engr
Public
Admissions: (318) 257-2924
E-mail: gschool@latech.edu
Financial aid: (318) 257-2641
Application deadline: 08/01
In-state tuition: full time: $5,172; part time: $4,270
Out-of-state tuition: full time: $8,752
Room/board/expenses: $10,868
Full-time enrollment: 318
men: 76%; women: 24%; minorities: 5%; international: 73%
Part-time enrollment: 58
men: 69%; women: 31%; minorities: 3%; international: 72%
Acceptance rate: 62%
GRE requirement: Yes
Avg. GRE: quantitative: 733
TOEFL requirement: Yes
Minimum TOEFL score: 550
Fellowships: 24
Teaching assistantships: 188
Research assistantships: 88
Students specializing in: biomedical: 25%; chemical: 5%; civil: 3%; computer science: 13%; electrical: 27%; management: 7%; industrial: 9%; mechanical: 5%; other: 6%

Tulane University
201 Lindy Boggs Building
New Orleans, LA 70118
http://www.sse.tulane.edu
Private
Admissions: (504) 865-5764
E-mail: segrad@tulane.edu
Financial aid: (504) 865-5764
Application deadline: 02/01
Tuition: full time: $36,840; part time: $1,983/credit hour
Room/board/expenses: $15,600
Full-time enrollment: 56
men: 59%; women: 41%; minorities: 4%; international: 50%
Part-time enrollment: 3
men: 67%; women: 33%; minorities: 67%; international: 0%
Acceptance rate: 34%
GRE requirement: Yes
Avg. GRE: quantitative: 741
TOEFL requirement: Yes
Minimum TOEFL score: 600
Fellowships: 11
Teaching assistantships: 19
Research assistantships: 17
Students specializing in: biomedical: 41%; chemical: 59%

University of Louisiana–Lafayette
PO Box 42251
Lafayette, LA 70504
http://engineering.louisiana.edu/
Public
Admissions: (337) 482-6467
E-mail: gradschool@louisiana.edu
Financial aid: (337) 482-6506
Application deadline: rolling
In-state tuition: full time: $3,266; part time: $93/credit hour
Out-of-state tuition: full time: $9,446
Room/board/expenses: $8,192
Full-time enrollment: 277
men: 81%; women: 19%; minorities: 4%; international: 83%
Part-time enrollment: 69
men: 80%; women: 20%; minorities: 3%; international: 55%
Acceptance rate: 39%
GRE requirement: Yes
Avg. GRE: quantitative: 721
TOEFL requirement: Yes
Minimum TOEFL score: 550
Fellowships: 7
Teaching assistantships: 11
Research assistantships: 61
Students specializing in: chemical: 9%; civil: 5%; computer: 12%; computer science: 46%; management: 3%; mechanical: 5%; petroleum: 10%; other: 10%

University of New Orleans
2000 Lakeshore Drive
New Orleans, LA 70148
http://www.uno.edu
Public
Admissions: (504) 280-6595
E-mail: admissions@uno.edu
Financial aid: (504) 280-6603
Application deadline: 07/02
In-state tuition: full time: $3,984; part time: $183/credit hour
Out-of-state tuition: full time: $11,028
Room/board/expenses: $9,107
Full-time enrollment: 94
men: 79%; women: 21%; minorities: 16%; international: 53%
Part-time enrollment: 105
men: 78%; women: 22%; minorities: 19%; international: 10%
Acceptance rate: 59%
GRE requirement: Yes
Avg. GRE: quantitative: 678
TOEFL requirement: Yes
Minimum TOEFL score: 550
Students specializing in: civil: 2%; management: 18%; other: 81%

MAINE

University of Maine
Barrows Hall
Orono, ME 04469
http://www.engineering.umaine.edu/
Public
Admissions: (207) 581-3218
E-mail: graduate@maine.maine.edu
Financial aid: (207) 581-1324
Application deadline: rolling
In-state tuition: full time: $325/credit hour; part time: $325/credit hour
Out-of-state tuition: full time: $936/credit hour
Room/board/expenses: $11,530
Full-time enrollment: 113
men: 81%; women: 19%; minorities: 2%; international: 33%
Part-time enrollment: 41
men: 83%; women: 17%; minorities: 15%; international: 24%
Acceptance rate: 42%
GRE requirement: Yes
Avg. GRE: quantitative: 693
TOEFL requirement: Yes
Minimum TOEFL score: 550
Teaching assistantships: 8
Students specializing in: biomedical: 2%; chemical: 15%; civil: 23%; computer: 2%; computer science: 9%; electrical: 16%; science and physics: 1%; mechanical: 13%; other: 18%

MARYLAND

Johns Hopkins University (Whiting)
3400 N. Charles Street
Baltimore, MD 21218
http://engineering.jhu.edu
Private
Admissions: (410) 516-8174
E-mail: graduateadmissions@jhu.edu
Financial aid: (410) 516-8028
Application deadline: N/A
Tuition: full time: $36,400; part time: $619/credit hour
Room/board/expenses: $15,200
Full-time enrollment: 757
men: 70%; women: 30%; minorities: 11%; international: 49%
Part-time enrollment: 1,904
men: 78%; women: 22%; minorities: 22%; international: 2%
Acceptance rate: 24%
GRE requirement: Yes
Avg. GRE: quantitative: 768
TOEFL requirement: Yes
Minimum TOEFL score: 600
Fellowships: 92
Teaching assistantships: 119
Research assistantships: 342
Students specializing in: biomedical: 7%; chemical: 3%; civil: 1%; computer science: 24%; electrical: 18%; environmental: 4%; materials: 2%; mechanical: 6%; other: 35%

Morgan State University (Mitchell)
1700 E. Coldspring Lane
Baltimore, MD 21251
http://www.morgan.edu
Public
Admissions: (443) 885-1810
E-mail: jwaller@moac.morgan.edu
Financial aid: (443) 885-3185
Application deadline: rolling
In-state tuition: full time: N/A; part time: N/A
Out-of-state tuition: full time: N/A

Room/board/expenses: N/A
Full-time enrollment: 48
men: 65%; women: 35%;
minorities: 63%; international: 31%
Part-time enrollment: 42
men: 69%; women: 31%;
minorities: 81%; international: 17%
GRE requirement: Yes
Avg. GRE: quantitative: N/A
TOEFL requirement: Yes
Minimum TOEFL score: 550
Students specializing in: N/A

University of Maryland–Baltimore County
1000 Hilltop Circle
Baltimore, MD 21250
http://www.umbc.edu/gradschool/
Public
Admissions: (410) 455-2537
E-mail: umbcgrad@umbc.edu
Financial aid: (410) 455-2387
Application deadline: 11/01
In-state tuition: full time: $412/credit
hour; part time: $412/credit hour
Out-of-state tuition: full time:
$681/credit hour
Room/board/expenses: $11,892
Full-time enrollment: 240
men: 78%; women: 23%;
minorities: 10%; international: 58%
Part-time enrollment: 153
men: 78%; women: 22%;
minorities: 22%; international: 20%
Acceptance rate: 38%
GRE requirement: Yes
Avg. GRE: quantitative: 750
TOEFL requirement: Yes
Minimum TOEFL score: 550
Fellowships: 11
Teaching assistantships: 65
Research assistantships: 88
Students specializing in: chemical:
10%; civil: 3%; computer: 7%;
computer science: 32%; electrical:
19%; management: 8%;
mechanical: 20%

University of Maryland–College Park (Clark)
3110 Jeong H. Kim Engineering
Building
College Park, MD 20742-2831
http://www.eng.umd.edu
Public
Admissions: (301) 405-0376
E-mail: gradschool@umd.edu
Financial aid: (301) 314-9000
Application deadline: 12/15
In-state tuition: full time: $8,766;
part time: $427/credit hour
Out-of-state tuition: full time:
$17,658
Room/board/expenses: $16,285
Full-time enrollment: 1,277
men: 78%; women: 22%;
minorities: 9%; international: 62%
Part-time enrollment: 585
men: 79%; women: 21%;
minorities: 28%; international: 13%
Acceptance rate: 22%
GRE requirement: Yes
Avg. GRE: quantitative: 758
TOEFL requirement: Yes
Minimum TOEFL score: 575
Fellowships: 123
Teaching assistantships: 281
Research assistantships: 1,066
Students specializing in: aerospace:
7%; biomedical: 3%; chemical: 3%;
civil: 9%; computer science: 12%;
electrical: 20%; materials: 3%;
mechanical: 12%; nuclear: 1%;
other: 31%

Boston University
44 Cummington Street
Boston, MA 02215
http://www.bu.edu/eng
Private
Admissions: (617) 353-9760

E-mail: enggrad@bu.edu
Financial aid: (617) 353-9760
Application deadline: 01/15
Tuition: full time: $35,310; part
time: $1,092/credit hour
Room/board/expenses: $16,543
Full-time enrollment: 595
men: 76%; women: 24%;
minorities: 8%; international: 47%
Part-time enrollment: 69
men: 78%; women: 22%;
minorities: 22%; international: 12%
Acceptance rate: 26%
GRE requirement: Yes
Avg. GRE: quantitative: 763
TOEFL requirement: Yes
Minimum TOEFL score: 550
Fellowships: 57
Teaching assistantships: 77
Research assistantships: 331
Students specializing in: aerospace:
2%; biomedical: 20%; computer:
9%; computer science: 11%;
electrical: 20%; industrial: 8%;
mechanical: 8%; other: 23%

Harvard University
29 Oxford Street
Room 217A, Pierce Hall
Cambridge, MA 02138
http://www.gsas.harvard.edu
Private
Admissions: (617) 495-5315
E-mail: admiss@fas.harvard.edu
Financial aid: (617) 495-5396
Application deadline: 01/02
Tuition: full time: $34,244; part
time: $10,652
Room/board/expenses: $21,320
Full-time enrollment: 341
men: 75%; women: 25%;
minorities: 19%; international: 42%
Part-time enrollment: 14
men: 86%; women: 14%;
minorities: 14%; international: 7%
Acceptance rate: 13%
GRE requirement: Yes
Avg. GRE: quantitative: 775
TOEFL requirement: Yes
Minimum TOEFL score: 550
Fellowships: 130
Teaching assistantships: 45
Research assistantships: 213
Students specializing in: biomedical:
10%; computer science: 23%;
electrical: 19%; environmental: 6%;
materials: 20%; mechanical: 6%;
other: 17%

Massachusetts Institute of Technology
77 Massachusetts Avenue
Room 1-206
Cambridge, MA 02139-4307
http://web.mit.edu/admissions/
Private
Admissions: (617) 253-2917
E-mail: mitgrad@mit.edu
Financial aid: (617) 253-4971
Application deadline: N/A
Tuition: full time: $34,986; part
time: N/A
Room/board/expenses: $23,090
Full-time enrollment: 2,627
men: 75%; women: 25%;
minorities: 16%; international: 42%
Part-time enrollment: 9
men: 89%; women: 11%;
minorities: 44%; international: 11%
Acceptance rate: 23%
GRE requirement: Yes
Avg. GRE: quantitative: 777
TOEFL requirement: No
Minimum TOEFL score: N/A
Fellowships: 560
Teaching assistantships: 240
Research assistantships: 1,425
Students specializing in: aerospace:
9%; biomedical: 5%; chemical: 9%;
civil: 4%; computer science: 15%;
electrical: 17%; management: 10%;
environmental: 3%; materials: 8%;
mechanical: 17%; nuclear: 4%;
other: 1%

Northeastern University
130 Snell Engineering Center
Boston, MA 02115-5000
http://www.coe.neu.edu/gse
Private
Admissions: (617) 373-2711
E-mail: grad-eng@coe.neu.edu
Financial aid: (617) 373-3190
Application deadline:
Tuition: full time: $1,050/credit
hour; part time: $1,050/credit hour
Room/board/expenses: $14,000
Full-time enrollment: 710
men: 75%; women: 25%;
minorities: 3%; international: 79%
Part-time enrollment: 309
men: 83%; women: 17%;
minorities: 4%; international: 4%
Acceptance rate: 50%
GRE requirement: Yes
Avg. GRE: quantitative: 756
TOEFL requirement: Yes
Minimum TOEFL score: 550
Fellowships: 10
Teaching assistantships: 126
Research assistantships: 129
Students specializing in: chemical:
4%; civil: 7%; computer: 4%;
electrical: 32%; management: 8%;
industrial: 10%; mechanical: 12%;
other: 22%

Tufts University
Anderson Hall
Medford, MA 02155
http://gs.as.tufts.edu
Private
Admissions: (617) 627-3395
E-mail: gradschool@ase.tufts.edu
Financial aid: (617) 627-2000
Application deadline: 01/15
Tuition: full time: $37,965; part
time: $3,504/credit hour
Room/board/expenses: $20,323
Full-time enrollment: 346
men: 64%; women: 36%;
minorities: 7%; international: 32%
Part-time enrollment: 171
men: 77%; women: 23%;
minorities: 14%; international: 11%
Acceptance rate: 54%
GRE requirement: Yes
Avg. GRE: quantitative: N/A
TOEFL requirement: Yes
Minimum TOEFL score: 550
Fellowships: 15
Teaching assistantships: 70
Research assistantships: 118
Students specializing in: biomedical:
14%; chemical: 9%; civil: 16%;
computer science: 11%; electrical:
13%; management: 21%;
mechanical: 14%; other: 1%

University of Massachusetts–Amherst
Room 125, Marston Hall
Amherst, MA 01003
http://www.ecs.umass.edu
Public
Admissions: (413) 545-0721
E-mail: gradinfo@resgs.umass.edu
Financial aid: (413) 577-0555
Application deadline: 02/01
In-state tuition: full time: $12,201;
part time: $110/credit hour
Out-of-state tuition: full time:
$19,498
Room/board/expenses: $10,478
Full-time enrollment: 661
men: 76%; women: 24%;
minorities: 5%; international: 57%
Part-time enrollment: 4
men: 50%; women: 50%;
minorities: 0%; international: 0%
Acceptance rate: 22%
GRE requirement: Yes
Avg. GRE: quantitative: 760
TOEFL requirement: Yes
Minimum TOEFL score: 550
Fellowships: 19
Teaching assistantships: 51
Research assistantships: 426

Worcester Polytechnic Institute
100 Institute Road
Worcester, MA 01609-2280
http://www.wpi.edu/
Private
Admissions: (508) 831-5301
E-mail: gse@wpi.edu
Financial aid: (508) 831-5469
Application deadline: rolling
Tuition: full time: $18,796; part time:
$1,042/credit hour
Room/board/expenses: $20,094
Full-time enrollment: 357
men: 75%; women: 25%;
minorities: 7%; international: 49%

Students specializing in: chemical:
9%; civil: 7%; computer science:
29%; electrical: 27%; environmental: 2%; industrial: 3%; materials:
14%; mechanical: 9%

University of Massachusetts–Dartmouth
285 Old Westport Road
North Dartmouth, MA 02747-2300
http://www.umassd.edu/graduate
Public
Admissions: (508) 999-8604
E-mail: graduate@umassd.edu
Financial aid: (508) 999-8632
Application deadline: N/A
In-state tuition: full time: $9,728;
part time: $405/credit hour
Out-of-state tuition: full time:
$18,174
Room/board/expenses: $11,106
Full-time enrollment: 110
men: 79%; women: 21%;
minorities: 2%; international: 81%
Part-time enrollment: 112
men: 80%; women: 20%;
minorities: 2%; international: 63%
Acceptance rate: 71%
GRE requirement: Yes
Avg. GRE: quantitative: 728
TOEFL requirement: Yes
Minimum TOEFL score: 550
Teaching assistantships: 42
Research assistantships: 66
Students specializing in: biomedical:
3%; civil: 6%; computer: 16%;
computer science: 27%;
electrical: 29%; materials: 6%;
mechanical: 12%

University of Massachusetts–Lowell (Francis)
1 University Avenue
Lowell, MA 01854
http://www.uml.edu/grad
Public
Admissions: (978) 934-2390
E-mail: graduate_school@uml.edu
Financial aid: (978) 934-4226
Application deadline: rolling
In-state tuition: full time: $10,976;
part time: $91/credit hour
Out-of-state tuition: full time:
$17,359
Room/board/expenses: $9,803
Full-time enrollment: 234
men: 69%; women: 31%;
minorities: 9%; international: 55%
Part-time enrollment: 164
men: 76%; women: 24%;
minorities: 16%; international: 16%
Acceptance rate: 75%
GRE requirement: Yes
Avg. GRE: quantitative: N/A
TOEFL requirement: Yes
Minimum TOEFL score: 500
Fellowships: 0
Teaching assistantships: 66
Research assistantships: 102
Students specializing in: chemical:
6%; civil: 7%; computer: 9%; elec-
trical: 31%; environmental: 4%;
mechanical: 16%; nuclear: 3%;
other: 25%

Part-time enrollment: 196
men: 82%; women: 18%;
minorities: 12%; international: 11%
Acceptance rate: 63%
GRE requirement: Yes
Avg. GRE: quantitative: 758
TOEFL requirement: Yes
Minimum TOEFL score: 550
Fellowships: 19
Teaching assistantships: 78
Research assistantships: 81
Students specializing in: biomedical:
8%; chemical: 3%; civil: 7%; com-
puter: 15%; computer science:
19%; electrical: 9%; environmental:
3%; industrial: 3%; materials: 4%;
mechanical: 16%; other: 13%

Lawrence Technological University
21000 W. Ten Mile Road
Southfield, MI 48075
http://www.ltu.edu
Private
Admissions: (248) 204-3160
E-mail: admissions@ltu.edu
Financial aid: (248) 204-2126
Application deadline: 08/01
Tuition: full time: $10,441; part time:
$6,060
Room/board/expenses: $12,719
Full-time enrollment: 7
men: 71%; women: 29%;
minorities: 86%; international: 14%
Part-time enrollment: 454
men: 87%; women: 13%;
minorities: 31%; international: 10%
Acceptance rate: 67%
GRE requirement: No
Avg. GRE: quantitative: N/A
TOEFL requirement: Yes
Minimum TOEFL score: 550
Fellowships: 1
Teaching assistantships: 2
Research assistantships: 21
Students specializing in: civil: 13%;
electrical: 12%; management: 18%;
industrial: 11%; mechanical: 45%

Michigan State University
3410 ENG Building
East Lansing, MI 48824
http://www.egr.msu.edu
Public
Admissions: (517) 353-5221
E-mail: egrgrad@egr.msu.edu
Financial aid: (517) 353-3220
Application deadline: 12/31
In-state tuition: full time:
$379/credit hour; part time:
$379/credit hour
Out-of-state tuition: full time:
$800/credit hour
Room/board/expenses: $11,862
Full-time enrollment: 583
men: 80%; women: 20%;
minorities: 9%; international: 61%
Part-time enrollment: N/A
men: N/A; women: N/A;
minorities: N/A; international: N/A
Acceptance rate: 12%
GRE requirement: Yes
Avg. GRE: quantitative: 742
TOEFL requirement: Yes
Minimum TOEFL score: 600
Fellowships: 70
Teaching assistantships: 125
Research assistantships: 271
Students specializing in: agriculture:
3%; chemical: 10%; civil: 9%;
computer science: 19%; electrical:
27%; environmental: 7%; materials:
5%; mechanical: 21%

Michigan Technological University
1400 Townsend Drive
Houghton, MI 49931-1295
http://www.gradschool.mtu.edu/
Public
Admissions: (906) 487-2327

E-mail: gradadms@mtu.edu
Financial aid: (906) 487-2622
Application deadline: rolling
In-state tuition: full time: $10,399;
part time: $535/credit hour
Out-of-state tuition: full time:
$10,399
Room/board/expenses: $11,642
Full-time enrollment: 423
men: 77%; women: 23%;
minorities: 3%; international: 52%
Part-time enrollment: 79
men: 76%; women: 24%;
minorities: 10%; international: 24%
Acceptance rate: 38%
GRE requirement: Yes
Avg. GRE: quantitative: 733
TOEFL requirement: Yes
Minimum TOEFL score: 550
Fellowships: 41
Teaching assistantships: 84
Research assistantships: 149
Students specializing in: biomedical:
2%; chemical: 5%; civil: 10%; computer science: 7%; electrical: 21%;
environmental: 11%; materials: 3%;
mechanical: 32%; mining: 0%;
other: 9%

Oakland University
2200 Squirrel Road
Rochester, MI 48309
http://www2.oakland.edu/secs/
Public
Admissions: (248) 370-3167
E-mail: applygrad@oakland.edu
Financial aid: (248) 370-2550
Application deadline: 08/01
In-state tuition: full time:
$473/credit hour; part time:
$473/credit hour
Out-of-state tuition: full time:
$815/credit hour
Room/board/expenses: $9,220
Full-time enrollment: 221
men: 75%; women: 25%;
minorities: 5%; international: 49%
Part-time enrollment: 302
men: 80%; women: 20%;
minorities: 3%; international: 15%
Acceptance rate: 81%
GRE requirement: Yes
Avg. GRE: quantitative: N/A
TOEFL requirement: Yes
Minimum TOEFL score: 550
Fellowships: 0
Teaching assistantships: 42
Research assistantships: 43
Students specializing in: computer
science: 10%; electrical: 14%; management: 11%; mechanical: 32%;
other: 32%

University of Detroit Mercy
4001 W. McNichols
Detroit, MI 48221-3038
http://www.udmercy.edu
Private
Admissions: (313) 993-1592
E-mail: coddinsm@udmercy.edu
Financial aid: (313) 993-3350
Application deadline: rolling
Tuition: full time: $955/credit hour;
part time: $955/credit hour
Room/board/expenses: $16,595
Full-time enrollment: 108
men: 85%; women: 15%;
minorities: 6%; international: 75%
Part-time enrollment: 60
men: 73%; women: 27%;
minorities: 12%; international: 27%
Avg. GRE: quantitative: N/A
TOEFL requirement: No
Minimum TOEFL score: N/A
Students specializing in: civil: 8%;
computer science: 19%;
electrical: 28%; management: 18%;
mechanical: 28%

University of Michigan–Ann Arbor
Robert H. Lurie Engineering Center
Ann Arbor, MI 48109-2102
http://www.engin.umich.edu/
students/prospective/graduate/
Public
Admissions: (734) 647-7090
E-mail: grad-ed@engin.umich.edu
Financial aid: (734) 647-7090
Application deadline: rolling
In-state tuition: full time: $17,913;
part time: $1,293/credit hour
Out-of-state tuition: full time:
$33,561
Room/board/expenses: $15,980
Full-time enrollment: 2,136
men: 79%; women: 21%;
minorities: 13%; international: 54%
Part-time enrollment: 280
men: 82%; women: 18%;
minorities: 13%; international: 40%
Acceptance rate: 36%
GRE requirement: Yes
Avg. GRE: quantitative: 770
TOEFL requirement: Yes
Minimum TOEFL score: 560
Teaching assistantships: 222
Research assistantships: 828
Students specializing in: aerospace:
6%; biomedical: 8%; chemical: 4%;
civil: 4%; computer: 3%; computer
science: 5%; electrical: 16%; environmental: 2%; industrial: 7%;
materials: 3%; mechanical: 20%;
nuclear: 3%; other: 21%

Wayne State University
5050 Anthony Wayne Drive
Detroit, MI 48202
http://www.eng.wayne.edu
Public
Admissions: (313) 577-2170
E-mail: admissions@wayne.edu
Financial aid: (313) 577-3378
Application deadline: 07/01
In-state tuition: full time:
$468/credit hour; part time:
$468/credit hour
Out-of-state tuition: full time:
$955/credit hour
Room/board/expenses: $11,457
Full-time enrollment: 651
men: 81%; women: 19%;
minorities: 6%; international: 77%
Part-time enrollment: 410
men: 75%; women: 25%;
minorities: 14%; international: 38%
Acceptance rate: 59%
GRE requirement: Yes
Avg. GRE: quantitative: N/A
TOEFL requirement: Yes
Minimum TOEFL score: 550
Fellowships: 11
Teaching assistantships: 52
Research assistantships: 48
Students specializing in: biomedical:
15%; chemical: 3%; civil: 9%; computer: 6%; computer science: 14%;
electrical: 15%; management: 5%;
industrial: 10%; materials: 7%;
mechanical: 17%; other: 7%

Western Michigan University
1903 W. Michigan Avenue
Kalamazoo, MI 49008-5314
http://www.wmich.edu/engineer/
Public
Admissions: (269) 387-2000
E-mail: ask-wmu@wmich.edu
Financial aid: (269) 387-6000
Application deadline: 12/03
In-state tuition: full time: $345/credit hour; part time: $345/credit hour
Out-of-state tuition: full time:
$730/credit hour
Room/board/expenses: $11,807
Full-time enrollment: 283
men: 79%; women: 21%;
minorities: 5%; international: 72%
Part-time enrollment: 86
men: 87%; women: 13%;
minorities: 6%; international: 29%
Acceptance rate: 62%
GRE requirement: Yes
Avg. GRE: quantitative: 669

TOEFL requirement: Yes
Minimum TOEFL score: 550
Fellowships: 0
Teaching assistantships: 68
Research assistantships: 24
Students specializing in: civil: 4%;
computer: 4%; computer science:
27%; electrical: 18%; management:
14%; industrial: 11%; materials: 0%;
mechanical: 13%; other: 8%

University of Minnesota–Twin Cities
117 Pleasant Street SE
Minneapolis, MN 55455
http://www.it.umn.edu
Public
Admissions: (612) 625-3014
E-mail: gsadmit@umn.edu
Financial aid: (612) 624-1665
Application deadline: 06/15
In-state tuition: full time: $13,040;
part time: $812/credit hour
Out-of-state tuition: full time:
$20,138
Room/board/expenses: $12,884
Full-time enrollment: 1,242
men: 81%; women: 19%;
minorities: 9%; international: 57%
Part-time enrollment: 548
men: 83%; women: 17%;
minorities: 14%; international: 16%
Acceptance rate: 33%
GRE requirement: Yes
Avg. GRE: quantitative: 766
TOEFL requirement: Yes
Minimum TOEFL score: 550
Fellowships: 137
Teaching assistantships: 250
Research assistantships: 600
Students specializing in: aerospace:
7%; biomedical: 7%; chemical: 9%;
civil: 10%; computer science: 27%;
electrical: 3%; management: 5%;
industrial: 3%; materials: 5%;
mechanical: 17%; other: 6%

Mississippi State University (Bagley)
PO Box 9544
Mississippi State, MS 39762
http://www.engr.msstate.edu/
Public
Admissions: (662) 325-7393
E-mail: grad@grad.msstate.edu
Financial aid: (662) 325-2450
Application deadline: N/A
In-state tuition: full time: $6,573;
part time: $274/credit hour
Out-of-state tuition: full time:
$15,228
Room/board/expenses: $12,455
Full-time enrollment: 376
men: 79%; women: 21%;
minorities: 9%; international: 59%
Part-time enrollment: 170
men: 82%; women: 18%;
minorities: 14%; international: 16%
Acceptance rate: 36%
GRE requirement: Yes
Avg. GRE: quantitative: 732
TOEFL requirement: Yes
Minimum TOEFL score: 550
Fellowships: 41
Teaching assistantships: 35
Research assistantships: 217
Students specializing in: aerospace:
6%; biomedical: 5%; chemical: 7%;
civil: 9%; computer: 7%; computer
science: 13%; electrical: 19%; science and physics: 6%; industrial:
11%; mechanical: 11%; other: 6%

University of Mississippi
Carrier Hall, Room 101
University, MS 38677-1848
http://www.olemiss.edu/depts/
engineering_school
Public
Admissions: (662) 915-7474
E-mail: gschool@olemiss.edu

Financial aid: (800) 891-4596
Application deadline: 04/01
In-state tuition: full time: $5,626;
part time: $4,092
Out-of-state tuition: full time:
$11,589
Room/board/expenses: $8,191
Full-time enrollment: 129
men: 77%; women: 23%;
minorities: 25%; international: 75%
Part-time enrollment: 52
men: 77%; women: 23%;
minorities: 54%; international: 46%
Acceptance rate: 26%
GRE requirement: Yes
Avg. GRE: quantitative: N/A
TOEFL requirement: Yes
Minimum TOEFL score: 523
Fellowships: 1
Teaching assistantships: 75
Research assistantships: 47
Students specializing in: chemical:
4%; civil: 9%; computer science:
31%; electrical: 29%; environmental: 4%; materials: 3%; mechanical:
7%; other: 14%

Missouri University of Science & Technology
1870 Miner Circle, 101 ERL
Rolla, MO 65409-0840
http://www.mst.edu
Public
Admissions: (800) 522-0938
E-mail: admissions@mst.edu
Financial aid: (573) 341-4282
Application deadline: 07/15
In-state tuition: full time: $7,001;
part time: $339/credit hour
Out-of-state tuition: full time:
$15,172
Room/board/expenses: $9,816
Full-time enrollment: 539
men: 79%; women: 21%;
minorities: 7%; international: 57%
Part-time enrollment: 361
men: 78%; women: 22%;
minorities: 16%; international: 20%
Acceptance rate: 44%
GRE requirement: Yes
Avg. GRE: quantitative: 738
TOEFL requirement: Yes
Minimum TOEFL score: 550
Fellowships: 26
Teaching assistantships: 130
Research assistantships: 326
Students specializing in: aerospace:
3%; chemical: 4%; civil: 9%; computer: 6%; computer science: 8%;
electrical: 17%; management: 22%;
environmental: 1%; materials: 7%;
mechanical: 12%; mining: 3%;
nuclear: 1%; petroleum: 1%;
other: 6%

St. Louis University (Parks)
3450 Lindell Boulevard
St. Louis, MO 63103
http://parks.slu.edu/index.php
Private
Admissions: (314) 977-2240
E-mail: grequest@slu.edu
Financial aid: (314) 977-2350
Application deadline: 08/01
Tuition: full time: $845/credit hour;
part time: $845/credit hour
Room/board/expenses: $12,553
Full-time enrollment: 6
men: 50%; women: 50%;
minorities: 0%; international: 17%
Part-time enrollment: 4
men: 100%; women: 0%;
minorities: 25%; international: 0%
Acceptance rate: 46%
GRE requirement: Yes
Avg. GRE: quantitative: N/A
TOEFL requirement: Yes
Minimum TOEFL score: 550
Fellowships: 0
Teaching assistantships: 0
Research assistantships: 0
Students specializing in: N/A

University of Missouri–Columbia
W1025 Thomas and
Nell Lafferre Hall
Columbia, MO 65211
http://www.missouri.edu/
Public
Admissions: (573) 882-7786
E-mail: gradadmin@missouri.edu
Financial aid: (573) 882-7506
Application deadline: 02/15
In-state tuition: full time:
$339/credit hour; part time:
$339/credit hour
Out-of-state tuition: full time:
$792/credit hour
Room/board/expenses: $9,040
Full-time enrollment: 476
men: 79%; women: 21%;
minorities: 7%; international: 59%
Part-time enrollment: N/A
men: N/A; women: N/A;
minorities: N/A; international: N/A
Acceptance rate: 38%
GRE requirement: Yes
Avg. GRE: quantitative: 748
TOEFL requirement: Yes
Minimum TOEFL score: 500
Fellowships: 49
Teaching assistantships: 87
Research assistantships: 222
Students specializing in: biomedical:
11%; chemical: 3%; civil: 13%; computer science: 17%; electrical: 27%;
industrial: 6%; mechanical: 12%;
nuclear: 11%; other: 0%

University of Missouri–Kansas City
534 R. H. Flarsheim Hall
5100 Rockhill Road
Kansas City, MO 64110-2499
http://www.umkc.edu/sce
Public
Admissions: (816) 235-1111
E-mail: graduate@umkc.edu
Financial aid: (816) 235-1154
Application deadline: 06/01
In-state tuition: full time: $7,279;
part time: $4,983
Out-of-state tuition: full time:
$16,357
Room/board/expenses: $12,000
Full-time enrollment: 255
men: 76%; women: 24%;
minorities: 2%; international: 92%
Part-time enrollment: 118
men: 86%; women: 14%;
minorities: 10%; international: 45%
Acceptance rate: 65%
GRE requirement: Yes
Avg. GRE: quantitative: 742
TOEFL requirement: Yes
Minimum TOEFL score: 550
Fellowships: 1
Teaching assistantships: 26
Research assistantships: 46
Students specializing in: civil: 9%;
computer: 50%; computer
science: 34%; electrical: 50%;
mechanical: 7%

Washington University in St. Louis (Sever)
1 Brookings Drive
Campus Box 1163
St. Louis, MO 63130
http://www.seas.wustl.edu
Private
Admissions: (314) 935-7974
E-mail:
gradengineering@seas.wustl.edu
Financial aid: (314) 935-5900
Application deadline: 01/15
Tuition: full time: $35,179; part time:
$1,438/credit hour
Room/board/expenses: $16,600
Full-time enrollment: 387
men: 75%; women: 25%;
minorities: 8%; international: 50%
Part-time enrollment: 372
men: 78%; women: 22%;
minorities: 17%; international: 3%
Acceptance rate: 15%
GRE requirement: Yes
Avg. GRE: quantitative: 768

TOEFL requirement: Yes
Minimum TOEFL score: 550
Fellowships: 31
Teaching assistantships: 13
Research assistantships: 229
Students specializing in: aerospace: 3%; biomedical: 14%; chemical: 3%; civil: 4%; computer: 5%; computer science: 20%; electrical: 10%; management: 11%; environmental: 5%; mechanical: 8%; other: 18%

MONTANA

Montana State University
212 Roberts Hall
PO Box 173820
Bozeman, MT 59717-3820
http://www.coe.montana.edu
Public
Admissions: (406) 994-4145
E-mail: engrinfo@coe.montana.edu
Financial aid: (406) 994-2845
Application deadline: N/A
In-state tuition: full time: $8,468; part time: $324/credit hour
Out-of-state tuition: full time: $18,988
Room/board/expenses: $10,580
Full-time enrollment: 78
men: 83%; women: 17%;
minorities: 0%; international: 0%
Part-time enrollment: 89
men: 81%; women: 19%;
minorities: 0%; international: 0%
Acceptance rate: 42%
GRE requirement: Yes
Avg. GRE: quantitative: 714
TOEFL requirement: Yes
Minimum TOEFL score: 550
Fellowships: 17
Teaching assistantships: 42
Research assistantships: 90
Students specializing in: chemical: 12%; civil: 15%; computer: 4%; computer science: 21%; management: 2%; environmental: 3%; industrial: 8%; materials: 1%; mechanical: 12%

NEBRASKA

University of Nebraska–Lincoln
114 Othmer Hall
Lincoln, NE 68588-0642
http://www.nuengr.unl.edu/grad/index.shtml
Public
Admissions: (402) 472-2878
E-mail: graduate@unl.edu
Financial aid: (402) 472-2030
Application deadline: 02/01
In-state tuition: full time: $224/credit hour; part time: $224/credit hour
Out-of-state tuition: full time: $604/credit hour
Room/board/expenses: $11,753
Full-time enrollment: 339
men: 77%; women: 23%;
minorities: 38%; international: 66%
Part-time enrollment: 156
men: 75%; women: 25%;
minorities: 39%; international: 47%
Acceptance rate: 30%
GRE requirement: Yes
Avg. GRE: quantitative: 745
TOEFL requirement: Yes
Minimum TOEFL score: 500
Fellowships: 3
Teaching assistantships: 84
Research assistantships: 232
Students specializing in: agriculture: 4%; architectural: 7%; biomedical: 1%; chemical: 4%; civil: 9%; computer: 0%; computer science: 18%; electrical: 10%; management: 9%; environmental: 2%; industrial: 8%; materials: 6%; mechanical: 8%; other: 12%

NEVADA

University of Nevada–Las Vegas (Hughes)
4505 Maryland Parkway
Box 544005
Las Vegas, NV 89154-4005
http://www.unlv.edu
Public
Admissions: (702) 895-3320
E-mail: gradcollege@ccmail.nevada.edu
Financial aid: (702) 895-3697
Application deadline: rolling
In-state tuition: full time: $3,646; part time: $176/credit hour
Out-of-state tuition: full time: $14,457
Room/board/expenses: $12,738
Full-time enrollment: 91
men: 80%; women: 20%;
minorities: 11%; international: 48%
Part-time enrollment: 164
men: 74%; women: 26%;
minorities: 13%; international: 34%
Acceptance rate: 54%
GRE requirement: Yes
Avg. GRE: quantitative: N/A
TOEFL requirement: Yes
Minimum TOEFL score: 550
Fellowships: 0
Teaching assistantships: 34
Research assistantships: 112
Students specializing in: aerospace: 0%; biomedical: 1%; civil: 22%; computer science: 21%; electrical: 19%; materials: 1%; mechanical: 29%; nuclear: 2%; other: 5%

University of Nevada–Reno
Mail Stop 0256
Reno, NV 89557-0256
http://www.unr.edu
Public
Admissions: (775) 784-4700
E-mail: asknevada@unr.edu
Financial aid: (775) 784-4666
Application deadline: 03/05
In-state tuition: full time: $176/credit hour; part time: $176/credit hour
Out-of-state tuition: full time: $772/credit hour
Room/board/expenses: $13,424
Full-time enrollment: 106
men: 77%; women: 23%;
minorities: 11%; international: 57%
Part-time enrollment: 147
men: 79%; women: 21%;
minorities: 17%; international: 41%
Acceptance rate: 58%
GRE requirement: Yes
Avg. GRE: quantitative: 715
TOEFL requirement: Yes
Minimum TOEFL score: 500
Fellowships: 12
Teaching assistantships: 37
Research assistantships: 109
Students specializing in: biomedical: 4%; chemical: 4%; civil: 23%; computer: 11%; computer science: 18%; electrical: 14%; materials: 9%; mechanical: 17%

NEW HAMPSHIRE

Dartmouth College (Thayer)
8000 Cummings Hall
Hanover, NH 03755
http://engineering.dartmouth.edu
Private
Admissions: (603) 646-2606
E-mail: engineering.admissions@dartmouth.edu
Financial aid: (603) 646-3844
Application deadline: 01/01
Tuition: full time: $35,010; part time: $4,662/credit hour
Room/board/expenses: $20,286
Full-time enrollment: 212
men: 74%; women: 26%;
minorities: 6%; international: 50%
Part-time enrollment: N/A
men: N/A; women: N/A;
minorities: N/A; international: N/A

Acceptance rate: 22%
GRE requirement: Yes
Avg. GRE: quantitative: 766
TOEFL requirement: Yes
Minimum TOEFL score: 600
Fellowships: 10
Teaching assistantships: 30
Research assistantships: 106
Students specializing in: computer science: 26%; other: 74%

University of New Hampshire
Kingsbury Hall, 33 College Road
Durham, NH 03824
http://www.gradschool.unh.edu/
Public
Admissions: (603) 862-3000
E-mail: grad.school@unh.edu
Financial aid: (603) 862-3600
Application deadline: 04/01
In-state tuition: full time: $10,516; part time: $506/credit hour
Out-of-state tuition: full time: $23,476
Room/board/expenses: $12,700
Full-time enrollment: 116
men: 79%; women: 21%;
minorities: 1%; international: 49%
Part-time enrollment: 134
men: 79%; women: 21%;
minorities: 5%; international: 21%
Acceptance rate: 72%
GRE requirement: Yes
Avg. GRE: quantitative: 746
TOEFL requirement: Yes
Minimum TOEFL score: 600
Fellowships: 9
Teaching assistantships: 54
Research assistantships: 74
Students specializing in: chemical: 5%; civil: 23%; computer science: 20%; electrical: 27%; materials: 6%; mechanical: 15%; other: 5%

NEW JERSEY

New Jersey Institute of Technology
University Heights
Newark, NJ 07102-1982
http://www.njit.edu/
Public
Admissions: (973) 596-3300
E-mail: admissions@njit.edu
Financial aid: (973) 596-3479
Application deadline: N/A
In-state tuition: full time: $14,354; part time: $694/credit hour
Out-of-state tuition: full time: $19,714
Room/board/expenses: $11,600
Full-time enrollment: 756
men: 73%; women: 27%;
minorities: 5%; international: 74%
Part-time enrollment: 480
men: 78%; women: 23%;
minorities: 21%; international: 16%
Acceptance rate: 66%
GRE requirement: Yes
Avg. GRE: quantitative: 707
TOEFL requirement: Yes
Minimum TOEFL score: 550
Fellowships: 24
Teaching assistantships: 95
Research assistantships: 127
Students specializing in: N/A

Princeton University
C230 Engineering Quadrangle
Princeton, NJ 08544-5263
http://engineering.princeton.edu
Private
Admissions: (609) 258-3034
E-mail: gsadmit@princeton.edu
Financial aid: (609) 258-3037
Application deadline: 12/15
Tuition: full time: $34,050; part time: N/A
Room/board/expenses: $14,625
Full-time enrollment: 519
men: 73%; women: 27%;
minorities: 13%; international: 53%
Part-time enrollment: N/A
men: N/A; women: N/A;
minorities: N/A; international: N/A

Acceptance rate: 17%
GRE requirement: Yes
Avg. GRE: quantitative: 783
TOEFL requirement: Yes
Minimum TOEFL score: 600
Fellowships: 164
Teaching assistantships: 83
Research assistantships: 202
Students specializing in: chemical: 16%; civil: 10%; computer science: 18%; electrical: 33%; mechanical: 14%; other: 8%

Rutgers, the State University of New Jersey–New Brunswick
98 Brett Road
Piscataway, NJ 08854-8058
http://gradstudy.rutgers.edu
Public
Admissions: (732) 932-7711
E-mail: gradadm@rci.rutgers.edu
Financial aid: (732) 932-7057
Application deadline: rolling
In-state tuition: full time: $13,836; part time: $516/credit hour
Out-of-state tuition: full time: $19,862
Room/board/expenses: $15,106
Full-time enrollment: 569
men: 70%; women: 30%;
minorities: 11%; international: 65%
Part-time enrollment: 314
men: 74%; women: 26%;
minorities: 20%; international: 44%
Acceptance rate: 27%
GRE requirement: Yes
Avg. GRE: quantitative: N/A
TOEFL requirement: Yes
Minimum TOEFL score: 550
Fellowships: 103
Teaching assistantships: 78
Research assistantships: 131
Students specializing in: biomedical: 10%; chemical: 21%; civil: 8%; computer science: 17%; electrical: 25%; industrial: 5%; materials: 5%; mechanical: 9%

Stevens Institute of Technology (Schaefer)
Castle Point on Hudson
Hoboken, NJ 07030
http://www.stevens.edu/ses/index.php
Private
Admissions: (201) 216-5197
E-mail: gradadmissions@stevens.edu
Financial aid: (201) 216-5555
Application deadline: rolling
Tuition: full time: $995/credit hour; part time: $995/credit hour
Room/board/expenses: $12,875
Full-time enrollment: 581
men: 78%; women: 22%;
minorities: 4%; international: 87%
Part-time enrollment: 1,183
men: 81%; women: 19%;
minorities: 21%; international: 10%
Acceptance rate: 61%
GRE requirement: Yes
Avg. GRE: quantitative: N/A
TOEFL requirement: Yes
Minimum TOEFL score: 550
Fellowships: 12
Teaching assistantships: 111
Research assistantships: 136
Students specializing in: biomedical: 0%; chemical: 3%; civil: 5%; computer: 4%; computer science: 25%; electrical: 10%; management: 24%; science and physics: 1%; environmental: 2%; materials: 1%; mechanical: 10%; other: 17%

NEW MEXICO

New Mexico Institute of Mining and Technology
801 Leroy Place
Socorro, NM 87801
http://www.nmt.edu
Public

Admissions: (505) 835-5513
E-mail: graduate@nmt.edu
Financial aid: (505) 835-5333
Application deadline: 04/01
In-state tuition: full time: $4,261; part time: $206/credit hour
Out-of-state tuition: full time: $12,462
Room/board/expenses: $9,294
Full-time enrollment: 103
men: 83%; women: 17%;
minorities: 5%; international: 67%
Part-time enrollment: 75
men: 77%; women: 23%;
minorities: 23%; international: 7%
Acceptance rate: 48%
GRE requirement: Yes
Avg. GRE: quantitative: N/A
TOEFL requirement: Yes
Minimum TOEFL score: 540
Fellowships: 1
Teaching assistantships: 40
Research assistantships: 56
Students specializing in: computer science: 31%; electrical: 6%; management: 15%; environmental: 2%; materials: 16%; mechanical: 14%; mining: 10%; petroleum: 8%

New Mexico State University
PO Box 30001, Department 3449
Las Cruces, NM 88003
http://engr.nmsu.edu
Public
Admissions: (505) 646-2834
E-mail: dcourt@nmsu.edu
Financial aid: (505) 646-4490
Application deadline: 08/01
In-state tuition: full time: $4,641; part time: $189/credit hour
Out-of-state tuition: full time: $14,271
Room/board/expenses: $7,850
Full-time enrollment: 229
men: 76%; women: 24%;
minorities: 15%; international: 70%
Part-time enrollment: 163
men: 79%; women: 21%;
minorities: 29%; international: 32%
Acceptance rate: 75%
GRE requirement: Yes
Avg. GRE: quantitative: 739
TOEFL requirement: Yes
Minimum TOEFL score: 530
Fellowships: 24
Teaching assistantships: 60
Research assistantships: 70
Students specializing in: chemical: 5%; civil: 16%; electrical: 43%; environmental: 3%; industrial: 24%; mechanical: 9%

University of New Mexico
MSC 01 1140
1 University of New Mexico
Albuquerque, NM 87131
http://www.soe.unm.edu
Public
Admissions: (505) 277-2447
E-mail: grad@unm.edu
Financial aid: (505) 277-6062
Application deadline: rolling
In-state tuition: full time: $5,023; part time: $209/credit hour
Out-of-state tuition: full time: $15,361
Room/board/expenses: $12,981
Full-time enrollment: 601
men: 82%; women: 18%;
minorities: 17%; international: 34%
Part-time enrollment: N/A
men: N/A; women: N/A;
minorities: N/A; international: N/A
Acceptance rate: 53%
GRE requirement: Yes
Avg. GRE: quantitative: 723
TOEFL requirement: Yes
Minimum TOEFL score: 550
Fellowships: 14
Teaching assistantships: 23
Research assistantships: 208
Students specializing in: chemical: 9%; civil: 10%; computer: 7%; computer science: 18%; electrical: 27%; industrial: 2%; mechanical: 12%; nuclear: 8%; other: 5%

NEW YORK

Alfred University–New York State College of Ceramics (Inamori)
2 Pine Street
Alfred, NY 14802-1296
http://nyscc.alfred.edu
Public
Admissions: (800) 541-9229
E-mail: admwww@alfred.edu
Financial aid: (607) 871-2159
Application deadline: rolling
In-state tuition: full time: $19,080; part time: $654/credit hour
Out-of-state tuition: full time: $19,080
Room/board/expenses: $12,500
Full-time enrollment: 41
men: 80%; women: 20%; minorities: 29%; international: 27%
Part-time enrollment: 7
men: 86%; women: 14%; minorities: 0%; international: 14%
Acceptance rate: 44%
GRE requirement: No
Avg. GRE: quantitative: N/A
TOEFL requirement: Yes
Minimum TOEFL score: 590
Fellowships: 2
Teaching assistantships: 12
Research assistantships: 19
Students specializing in: electrical: 2%; materials: 92%; mechanical: 6%

Clarkson University
PO Box 5625
Potsdam, NY 13699-5625
http://www.clarkson.edu/engineering/index.html
Private
Admissions: (315) 268-7929
E-mail: enggrad@clarkson.edu
Financial aid: (315) 268-6413
Application deadline: 04/15
Tuition: full time: $949/credit hour; part time: $949/credit hour
Room/board/expenses: $9,142
Full-time enrollment: 206
men: 78%; women: 22%; minorities: 1%; international: 64%
Part-time enrollment: 3
men: 67%; women: 33%; minorities: 0%; international: 0%
Acceptance rate: 51%
GRE requirement: Yes
Avg. GRE: quantitative: 720
TOEFL requirement: Yes
Minimum TOEFL score: 550
Fellowships: 8
Teaching assistantships: 34
Research assistantships: 104
Students specializing in: chemical: 14%; civil: 21%; electrical: 23%; science and physics: 3%; environmental: 8%; mechanical: 31%

Columbia University (Fu Foundation)
500 W. 120th Street
Room 510 Mudd
New York, NY 10027
http://www.engineering.columbia.edu
Private
Admissions: (212) 854-6438
E-mail: seasgradmit@columbia.edu
Financial aid: (212) 854-6438
Application deadline: 12/01
Tuition: full time: $38,383; part time: $1,184/credit hour
Room/board/expenses: $22,071
Full-time enrollment: 1,016
men: 76%; women: 24%; minorities: 8%; international: 67%
Part-time enrollment: 417
men: 80%; women: 20%; minorities: 15%; international: 32%
Acceptance rate: 28%
GRE requirement: Yes
Avg. GRE: quantitative: 775
TOEFL requirement: Yes
Minimum TOEFL score: 560
Fellowships: 93
Teaching assistantships: 139
Research assistantships: 333
Students specializing in: biomedical: 8%; chemical: 5%; civil: 7%; computer: 1%; computer science: 25%; electrical: 17%; management: 3%; science and physics: 3%; environmental: 3%; industrial: 1%; materials: 2%; mechanical: 6%; other: 18%

Cornell University
242 Carpenter Hall
Ithaca, NY 14853
http://www.engineering.cornell.edu
Private
Admissions: (607) 255-5820
E-mail: ah33@cornell.edu
Financial aid: (607) 255-5820
Application deadline: N/A
Tuition: full time: $32,868; part time: N/A
Room/board/expenses: $15,144
Full-time enrollment: 1,378
men: 74%; women: 26%; minorities: 16%; international: 47%
Part-time enrollment: N/A
men: N/A; women: N/A; minorities: N/A; international: N/A
Acceptance rate: 20%
GRE requirement: Yes
Avg. GRE: quantitative: 775
TOEFL requirement: Yes
Minimum TOEFL score: 550
Fellowships: 335
Teaching assistantships: 215
Research assistantships: 566
Students specializing in: aerospace: 3%; agriculture: 4%; biomedical: 6%; chemical: 7%; civil: 7%; computer science: 17%; electrical: 18%; management: 2%; science and physics: 6%; industrial: 11%; materials: 3%; mechanical: 8%; other: 7%

CUNY–City College (Grove)
Convent Avenue at 138th Street
New York, NY 10031
http://www1.ccny.cuny.edu/prospective/engineering
Public
Admissions: (212) 650-6853
E-mail: admissions@ccny.cuny.edu
Financial aid: (212) 817-7460
Application deadline: 05/01
In-state tuition: full time: $7,691; part time: $315/credit hour
Out-of-state tuition: full time: $555/credit hour
Room/board/expenses: $15,950
Full-time enrollment: 238
men: 76%; women: 24%; minorities: 19%; international: 70%
Part-time enrollment: 480
men: 80%; women: 20%; minorities: 30%; international: 64%
Acceptance rate: 61%
GRE requirement: Yes
Avg. GRE: quantitative: 701
TOEFL requirement: Yes
Minimum TOEFL score: 500
Fellowships: 47
Teaching assistantships: 32
Research assistantships: 185
Students specializing in: biomedical: 7%; chemical: 9%; civil: 14%; computer science: 24%; electrical: 34%; mechanical: 13%

Polytechnic University
6 MetroTech Center
Brooklyn, NY 11201
http://www.poly.edu
Private
Admissions: (718) 260-3200
E-mail: gradinfo@poly.edu
Financial aid: (718) 260-3300
Application deadline: 12/29
Tuition: full time: $1,027/credit hour; part time: $1,027/credit hour
Room/board/expenses: $13,353
Full-time enrollment: 662
men: 79%; women: 21%; minorities: 5%; international: 83%
Part-time enrollment: 507
men: 83%; women: 17%; minorities: 24%; international: 20%
Acceptance rate: 69%
GRE requirement: No
Avg. GRE: quantitative: N/A
TOEFL requirement: Yes
Minimum TOEFL score: 550
Fellowships: 132
Teaching assistantships: 0
Research assistantships: 5
Students specializing in: biomedical: 5%; chemical: 3%; civil: 12%; computer: 3%; computer science: 23%; electrical: 47%; environmental: 1%; industrial: 2%; mechanical: 4%

Rensselaer Polytechnic Institute
Jonsson Engineering Center 3004
Troy, NY 12180-3590
http://www.rpi.edu
Private
Admissions: (518) 276-6216
E-mail: admissions@rpi.edu
Financial aid: (518) 276-6813
Application deadline: 01/01
Tuition: full time: $36,702; part time: $1,454/credit hour
Room/board/expenses: $10,802
Full-time enrollment: 602
men: 79%; women: 21%; minorities: 8%; international: 56%
Part-time enrollment: 450
men: 83%; women: 17%; minorities: 23%; international: 3%
Acceptance rate: 31%
GRE requirement: Yes
Avg. GRE: quantitative: 752
TOEFL requirement: Yes
Minimum TOEFL score: 570
Fellowships: 41
Teaching assistantships: 160
Research assistantships: 303
Students specializing in: aerospace: 2%; biomedical: 2%; chemical: 7%; civil: 4%; computer: 5%; computer science: 16%; electrical: 18%; management: 2%; science and physics: 12%; environmental: 1%; industrial: 3%; materials: 5%; mechanical: 22%; nuclear: 2%

Rochester Institute of Technology (Gleason)
77 Lomb Memorial Drive
Rochester, NY 14623
http://www.rit.edu
Private
Admissions: (585) 475-2229
E-mail: gradinfo@rit.edu
Financial aid: (585) 475-5520
Application deadline: rolling
Tuition: full time: $28,692; part time: $800/credit hour
Room/board/expenses: $10,979
Full-time enrollment: 206
men: 77%; women: 23%; minorities: 7%; international: 71%
Part-time enrollment: 225
men: 81%; women: 19%; minorities: 13%; international: 11%
Acceptance rate: 53%
GRE requirement: No
Avg. GRE: quantitative: N/A
TOEFL requirement: Yes
Minimum TOEFL score: 550
Fellowships: 0
Teaching assistantships: 64
Research assistantships: 53
Students specializing in: N/A

SUNY–Binghamton (Watson)
PO Box 6000
Binghamton, NY 13902-6000
http://watson.binghamton.edu
Public
Admissions: (607) 777-2151
E-mail: gradsch@binghamton.edu
Financial aid: (607) 777-2428
Application deadline: rolling
In-state tuition: full time: $7,919; part time: $288/credit hour
Out-of-state tuition: full time: $11,939
Room/board/expenses: $13,886
Full-time enrollment: 388
men: 78%; women: 22%; minorities: 4%; international: 85%
Part-time enrollment: 297
men: 78%; women: 22%; minorities: 13%; international: 39%
Acceptance rate: 55%
GRE requirement: Yes
Avg. GRE: quantitative: 741
TOEFL requirement: Yes
Minimum TOEFL score: 550
Fellowships: 4
Teaching assistantships: 78
Research assistantships: 123
Students specializing in: computer: 1%; computer science: 41%; electrical: 21%; industrial: 24%; materials: 2%; mechanical: 10%

SUNY College of Environmental Science and Forestry
227 Bray Hall
Syracuse, NY 13210
http://www.esf.edu
Public
Admissions: (315) 470-6599
E-mail: esfgrad@esf.edu
Financial aid: (315) 470-6706
Application deadline: rolling
In-state tuition: full time: $7,655; part time: $288/credit hour
Out-of-state tuition: full time: $11,675
Room/board/expenses: $13,570
Full-time enrollment: 38
men: 61%; women: 39%; minorities: 3%; international: 58%
Part-time enrollment: 37
men: 76%; women: 24%; minorities: 11%; international: 24%
Acceptance rate: 57%
GRE requirement: Yes
Avg. GRE: quantitative: 712
TOEFL requirement: Yes
Minimum TOEFL score: 550
Fellowships: 4
Teaching assistantships: 26
Research assistantships: 22
Students specializing in: environmental: 100%

SUNY–Stony Brook
Engineering Room 100
Stony Brook, NY 11794-2200
http://www.grad.sunysb.edu
Public
Admissions: (631) 632-4723
E-mail: graduate.school@sunysb.edu
Financial aid: (631) 632-6840
Application deadline: 01/15
In-state tuition: full time: $8,729; part time: $288/credit hour
Out-of-state tuition: full time: $12,749
Room/board/expenses: $11,282
Full-time enrollment: 725
men: 72%; women: 28%; minorities: 11%; international: 74%
Part-time enrollment: 183
men: 66%; women: 34%; minorities: 15%; international: 44%
Acceptance rate: 36%
GRE requirement: Yes
Avg. GRE: quantitative: 759
TOEFL requirement: Yes
Minimum TOEFL score: 550
Fellowships: 27
Teaching assistantships: 136
Research assistantships: 206
Students specializing in: biomedical: 8%; computer science: 30%; electrical: 16%; materials: 8%; mechanical: 8%; other: 30%

Syracuse University
223 Link Hall
Syracuse, NY 13244-1240
http://www.lcs.syr.edu/
Private
Admissions: (315) 443-4492
Financial aid: (315) 443-2545
Application deadline: rolling
Tuition: full time: $1,012/credit hour; part time: $1,012/credit hour
Room/board/expenses: $17,110
Full-time enrollment: 554
men: 78%; women: 22%; minorities: 3%; international: 97%
Part-time enrollment: 85
men: 75%; women: 25%; minorities: 18%; international: 82%
Acceptance rate: 46%
GRE requirement: Yes
Avg. GRE: quantitative: N/A
TOEFL requirement: Yes
Minimum TOEFL score: 550
Fellowships: 12
Teaching assistantships: 78
Research assistantships: 79
Students specializing in: aerospace: 13%; biomedical: 5%; chemical: 3%; civil: 6%; computer: 28%; computer science: 23%; electrical: 29%; management: 14%; environmental: 2%; industrial: 0%; mechanical: 1%

University at Buffalo–SUNY
412 Bonner Hall
Buffalo, NY 14260-1900
http://www.eng.buffalo.edu
Public
Admissions: (716) 645-2771
E-mail: seasgrad@eng.buffalo.edu
Financial aid: (716) 645-2450
Application deadline: rolling
In-state tuition: full time: $8,289; part time: $394/credit hour
Out-of-state tuition: full time: $12,309
Room/board/expenses: $14,890
Full-time enrollment: 858
men: 81%; women: 19%; minorities: 3%; international: 82%
Part-time enrollment: 157
men: 86%; women: 14%; minorities: 10%; international: 0%
Acceptance rate: 30%
GRE requirement: Yes
Avg. GRE: quantitative: 760
TOEFL requirement: Yes
Minimum TOEFL score: 550
Fellowships: 53
Teaching assistantships: 182
Research assistantships: 152
Students specializing in: aerospace: 4%; chemical: 8%; civil: 11%; computer science: 26%; electrical: 23%; science and physics: 0%; industrial: 13%; mechanical: 16%

University of Rochester
Lattimore Hall, Box 270076
Rochester, NY 14627-0076
http://www.seas.rochester.edu/SEAS/
Private
Admissions: (585) 275-4153
E-mail: gradstudies@mail.rochester.edu
Financial aid: (585) 275-3226
Application deadline: N/A
Tuition: full time: $34,596; part time: $1,075/credit hour
Room/board/expenses: $16,405
Full-time enrollment: 412
men: 73%; women: 27%; minorities: 5%; international: 60%
Part-time enrollment: 39
men: 74%; women: 26%; minorities: 3%; international: 31%
Acceptance rate: 15%
GRE requirement: Yes
Avg. GRE: quantitative: 769
TOEFL requirement: Yes
Minimum TOEFL score: 620
Fellowships: 64
Teaching assistantships: 94
Research assistantships: 219
Students specializing in: biomedical: 13%; chemical: 10%; computer science: 10%; electrical: 32%; materials: 5%; mechanical: 8%; other: 22%

NORTH CAROLINA

Duke University
305 Teer Building
Durham, NC 27708-0271
http://www.pratt.duke.edu
Private
Admissions: (919) 684-3913
E-mail: grad-admissions@duke.edu
Financial aid: (919) 681-1552
Application deadline: 12/15
Tuition: full time: $37,395; part
time: $1,223/credit hour
Room/board/expenses: $16,790
Full-time enrollment: 639
men: 72%; women: 28%;
minorities: 12%; international: 55%
Part-time enrollment: 9
men: 67%; women: 33%;
minorities: 22%; international: 0%
Acceptance rate: 34%
GRE requirement: Yes
Avg. GRE: quantitative: 767
TOEFL requirement: Yes
Minimum TOEFL score: 550
Fellowships: 214
Teaching assistantships: 27
Research assistantships: 162
Students specializing in: biomedical:
27%; civil: 6%; computer science:
13%; electrical: 21%; management:
24%; mechanical: 9%

North Carolina A&T State University[1]
1601 E. Market Street
651 McNair Hall
Greensboro, NC 27411
http://www.eng.ncat.edu
Public
Admissions: (336) 334-7920
E-mail: gradsch@ncat.edu
Financial aid: (336) 334-7973
Tuition: N/A
Room/board/expenses: N/A
Enrollment: N/A

North Carolina State University
PO Box 7901
Raleigh, NC 27695
http://www.engr.ncsu.edu/
Public
Admissions: (919) 515-2872
Financial aid: (919) 515-2421
Application deadline: 06/25
In-state tuition: full time: $7,094;
part time: $4,659
Out-of-state tuition: full time:
$19,142
Room/board/expenses: $15,694
Full-time enrollment: 1,613
men: 79%; women: 21%;
minorities: 7%; international: 62%
Part-time enrollment: 512
men: 81%; women: 19%;
minorities: 14%; international: 20%
Acceptance rate: 27%
GRE requirement: Yes
Avg. GRE: quantitative: 756
TOEFL requirement: Yes
Minimum TOEFL score: 550
Fellowships: 130
Teaching assistantships: 291
Research assistantships: 616
Students specializing in: aerospace:
3%; agriculture: 2%; biomedical:
4%; chemical: 5%; civil: 12%; com-
puter: 7%; computer science: 22%;
electrical: 18%; industrial: 7%;
materials: 3%; mechanical: 8%;
nuclear: 3%; other: 5%

University of North Carolina– Chapel Hill
CB #7431, 106 Rosenau Hall
Chapel Hill, NC 27599-7431
http://www.sph.unc.edu/envr
Public
Admissions: (919) 966-3844
E-mail: jack_whaley@unc.edu
Financial aid: (919) 966-3844
Application deadline: 01/01

In-state tuition: full time: $7,097;
part time: $342/credit hour
Out-of-state tuition: full time:
$20,338
Room/board/expenses: $17,300
Full-time enrollment: 117
men: 49%; women: 51%;
minorities: 16%; international: 16%
Part-time enrollment: 5
men: 20%; women: 80%;
minorities: 20%; international: 0%
Acceptance rate: 36%
GRE requirement: Yes
Avg. GRE: quantitative: 701
TOEFL requirement: Yes
Minimum TOEFL score: 550
Fellowships: 21
Teaching assistantships: 13
Research assistantships: 73
Students specializing in:
environmental: 100%

University of North Carolina– Charlotte (Lee)
Engineering Building
9201 University Boulevard
Charlotte, NC 28223-0001
http://www.coe.uncc.edu
Public
Admissions: (704) 687-3366
E-mail: gradadm@email.uncc.edu
Financial aid: (704) 687-2461
Application deadline: 05/01
In-state tuition: full time: $4,547;
part time: $3,120
Out-of-state tuition: full time:
$14,754
Room/board/expenses: $9,450
Full-time enrollment: 193
men: 80%; women: 20%;
minorities: 5%; international: 76%
Part-time enrollment: 149
men: 77%; women: 23%;
minorities: 9%; international: 44%
Acceptance rate: 57%
GRE requirement: Yes
Avg. GRE: quantitative: 712
TOEFL requirement: Yes
Minimum TOEFL score: 550
Fellowships: 0
Teaching assistantships: 123
Research assistantships: 82
Students specializing in: civil: 14%;
electrical: 46%; management: 7%;
environmental: 8%; mechanical:
23%; other: 1%

NORTH DAKOTA

North Dakota State University
University Station, PO Box 5285
Fargo, ND 58105-5285
http://www.ndsu.nodak.edu/
ndsuj/cea/
Public
Admissions: (701) 231-7033
E-mail: ndsu.grad.school@
ndsu.nodak.edu
Financial aid: (701) 231-7533
Application deadline: rolling
In-state tuition: full time:
$264/credit hour; part time:
$264/credit hour
Out-of-state tuition: full time:
$638/credit hour
Room/board/expenses: $8,420
Full-time enrollment: 48
men: 75%; women: 25%;
minorities: 2%; international: 52%
Part-time enrollment: 97
men: 85%; women: 15%;
minorities: 3%; international: 39%
Acceptance rate: 44%
GRE requirement: Yes
Avg. GRE: quantitative: N/A
TOEFL requirement: Yes
Minimum TOEFL score: 550
Fellowships: 3
Teaching assistantships: 59
Research assistantships: 39
Students specializing in: agriculture:
6%; civil: 30%; electrical: 23%;
environmental: 4%; industrial: 15%;
mechanical: 21%; other: 1%

University of North Dakota
PO Box 8155
Grand Forks, ND 58202
http://www.und.nodak.edu/
dept/grad
Public
Admissions: (701) 777-2945
E-mail:
gradschool@mail.und.nodak.edu
Financial aid: (701) 777-3121
Application deadline: rolling
In-state tuition: full time:
$225/credit hour; part time:
$225/credit hour
Out-of-state tuition: full time:
$601/credit hour
Room/board/expenses: $13,600
Full-time enrollment: 34
men: 85%; women: 15%;
minorities: 35%; international: 44%
Part-time enrollment: 49
men: 90%; women: 10%;
minorities: 45%; international: 51%
Acceptance rate: 18%
GRE requirement: Yes
Avg. GRE: quantitative: 717
TOEFL requirement: Yes
Minimum TOEFL score: 550
Teaching assistantships: 32
Research assistantships: 27
Students specializing in: chemical:
29%; civil: 11%; electrical: 18%;
environmental: 5%; mechanical:
22%; other: 15%

OHIO

Air Force Institute of Technology[1]
AFIT/RRA, 2950 P Street
WPAFB, OH 45433-7765
http://www.afit.edu
Public
Admissions: (800) 211-5097
E-mail: counselors@afit.edu
Financial aid: N/A
Tuition: N/A
Room/board/expenses: N/A
Enrollment: N/A

Case Western Reserve University
500 Nord Hall
10900 Euclid Avenue
Cleveland, OH 44106-7220
http://www.engineering.case.edu/
Private
Admissions: (216) 368-4390
E-mail: gradadmit@cwru.edu
Financial aid: (216) 368-4530
Application deadline: rolling
Tuition: full time: $22,356; part
time: $1,242/credit hour
Room/board/expenses: N/A
Full-time enrollment: 359
men: 75%; women: 25%;
minorities: 9%; international: 56%
Part-time enrollment: 253
men: 84%; women: 16%;
minorities: 8%; international: 32%
Acceptance rate: 34%
GRE requirement: Yes
Avg. GRE: quantitative: 732
TOEFL requirement: Yes
Minimum TOEFL score: 550
Fellowships: 106
Teaching assistantships: 50
Research assistantships: 288
Students specializing in: aerospace:
2%; biomedical: 21%; chemical:
16%; civil: 2%; computer: 7%; com-
puter science: 11%; electrical: 17%;
management: 7%; materials: 7%;
mechanical: 8%; other: 4%

Cleveland State University (Fenn)
2121 Euclid Avenue, SH 104
Cleveland, OH 44115-2425
http://www.csuohio.edu/
engineering/
Public
Admissions: (216) 687-5599

E-mail:
graduate.admissions@csuohio.edu
Financial aid: (216) 687-3764
Application deadline: rolling
In-state tuition: full time:
$439/credit hour; part time:
$439/credit hour
Out-of-state tuition: full time:
$834/credit hour
Room/board/expenses: $10,324
Full-time enrollment: 135
men: 76%; women: 24%;
minorities: 2%; international: 76%
Part-time enrollment: 313
men: 83%; women: 17%;
minorities: 5%; international: 66%
Acceptance rate: 49%
GRE requirement: Yes
Avg. GRE: quantitative: 740
TOEFL requirement: Yes
Minimum TOEFL score: 525
Fellowships: 0
Teaching assistantships: 17
Research assistantships: 57
Students specializing in: biomedical:
7%; chemical: 10%; civil: 9%; com-
puter: 5%; electrical: 40%; envi-
ronmental: 3%; industrial: 10%;
mechanical: 15%; other: 0%

Ohio State University
2070 Neil Avenue
Columbus, OH 43210-1278
http://www.eng.ohio-state.edu
Public
Admissions: (614) 292-9444
E-mail: gradadmissions@osu.edu
Financial aid: (614) 292-0300
Application deadline: rolling
In-state tuition: full time: $11,007;
part time: $387/credit hour
Out-of-state tuition: full time:
$25,161
Room/board/expenses: $16,144
Full-time enrollment: 1,168
men: 79%; women: 21%;
minorities: 4%; international: 64%
Part-time enrollment: 179
men: 74%; women: 26%;
minorities: 6%; international: 39%
Acceptance rate: 37%
GRE requirement: Yes
Avg. GRE: quantitative: 762
TOEFL requirement: Yes
Minimum TOEFL score: 550
Fellowships: 112
Teaching assistantships: 128
Research assistantships: 588
Students specializing in: aerospace:
2%; agriculture: 3%; biomedical:
3%; chemical: 7%; civil: 7%; com-
puter science: 16%; electrical: 21%;
industrial: 13%; materials: 7%;
mechanical: 18%; nuclear: 2%

Ohio University (Russ)
150 Stocker Center
Athens, OH 45701
http://www.ent.ohiou.edu
Public
Admissions: (740) 593-2800
E-mail: graduate@ohio.edu
Financial aid: (740) 593-4141
Application deadline: rolling
In-state tuition: full time: $9,378;
part time: $314/credit hour
Out-of-state tuition: full time:
$17,370
Room/board/expenses: $17,450
Full-time enrollment: 225
men: 85%; women: 15%;
minorities: 1%; international: 66%
Part-time enrollment: 87
men: 79%; women: 21%;
minorities: 7%; international: 43%
Acceptance rate: 62%
GRE requirement: Yes
Avg. GRE: quantitative: 713
TOEFL requirement: Yes
Minimum TOEFL score: 550
Fellowships: 25
Teaching assistantships: 37
Research assistantships: 125
Students specializing in: biomedical:
1%; chemical: 15%; civil: 6%; com-
puter science: 9%; electrical: 35%;
industrial: 17%; mechanical: 11%;
other: 6%

University of Akron
201 ASEC
Akron, OH 44325-3901
http://www.uakron.edu/gradsch/
Public
Admissions: (330) 972-7663
E-mail: gradschool@uakron.edu
Financial aid: (330) 972-7663
Application deadline: rolling
In-state tuition: full time: $6,970;
part time: $342/credit hour
Out-of-state tuition: full time:
$11,381
Room/board/expenses: $12,785
Full-time enrollment: 202
men: 74%; women: 26%;
minorities: 3%; international: 75%
Part-time enrollment: 77
men: 81%; women: 19%;
minorities: 3%; international: 43%
Acceptance rate: 39%
GRE requirement: Yes
Avg. GRE: quantitative: 746
TOEFL requirement: Yes
Minimum TOEFL score: 550
Fellowships: 3
Teaching assistantships: 106
Research assistantships: 42
Students specializing in: biomedical:
17%; chemical: 16%; civil: 19%;
electrical: 16%; management: 3%;
mechanical: 26%; other: 4%

University of Cincinnati
PO Box 210077
Cincinnati, OH 45221-0077
http://www.eng.uc.edu
Public
Admissions: (513) 556-6347
E-mail: engrgrad@uc.edu
Financial aid: (513) 556-3647
Application deadline: 03/31
In-state tuition: full time: $13,347;
part time: $404/credit hour
Out-of-state tuition: full time:
$23,181
Room/board/expenses: $12,567
Full-time enrollment: 899
men: 78%; women: 22%;
minorities: 5%; international: 72%
Part-time enrollment: 35
men: 77%; women: 23%;
minorities: 20%; international: 9%
Acceptance rate: 27%
GRE requirement: Yes
Avg. GRE: quantitative: 751
TOEFL requirement: Yes
Minimum TOEFL score: 550
Fellowships: 19
Teaching assistantships: 51
Research assistantships: 609
Students specializing in: aerospace:
7%; biomedical: 6%; chemical: 5%;
civil: 6%; computer: 9%; computer
science: 9%; electrical: 18%;
environmental: 9%; industrial: 4%;
materials: 6%; mechanical: 18%;
nuclear: 2%; other: 1%

University of Dayton
300 College Park
Dayton, OH 45469-0228
http://www.udayton.edu/
~gradsch/main.htm
Private
Admissions: (937) 229-2390
E-mail:
jonesgas@notes.udayton.edu
Financial aid: (937) 229-2751
Application deadline: rolling
Tuition: full time: $637/credit hour;
part time: $637/credit hour
Room/board/expenses: $16,100
Full-time enrollment: 254
men: 76%; women: 24%;
minorities: 9%; international: 30%
Part-time enrollment: 151
men: 81%; women: 19%;
minorities: 9%; international: 6%
Acceptance rate: 35%
GRE requirement: No
Avg. GRE: quantitative: N/A
TOEFL requirement: Yes
Minimum TOEFL score: 550
Fellowships: 5
Teaching assistantships: 9
Research assistantships: 72

Students specializing in: chemical: 3%; civil: 5%; electrical: 19%; management: 21%; science and physics: 10%; materials: 14%; mechanical: 21%; other: 8%

University of Toledo
2801 W. Bancroft
Toledo, OH 43606
http://www.eng.utoledo.edu/grad_studies/
Public
Admissions: (419) 530-4723
E-mail: gradoff@eng.utoledo.edu
Financial aid: (419) 530-8700
Application deadline: rolling
In-state tuition: full time: $7,371; part time: $410/credit hour
Out-of-state tuition: full time: $13,979
Room/board/expenses: $10,829
Full-time enrollment: 212
men: 79%; women: 21%;
minorities: 1%; international: 82%
Part-time enrollment: 98
men: 80%; women: 20%;
minorities: 1%; international: 51%
Acceptance rate: 64%
GRE requirement: Yes
Avg. GRE: quantitative: 755
TOEFL requirement: Yes
Minimum TOEFL score: 550
Fellowships: 2
Teaching assistantships: 84
Research assistantships: 72
Students specializing in: biomedical: 17%; chemical: 14%; civil: 14%; computer science: 13%; electrical: 17%; industrial: 1%; mechanical: 17%; other: 7%

Wright State University
3640 Colonel Glenn Highway
Dayton, OH 45435
http://www.wright.edu/sogs/
Public
Admissions: (937) 775-2976
E-mail: wsugrad@wright.edu
Financial aid: (937) 775-5721
Application deadline: 08/01
In-state tuition: full time: $9,720; part time: $298/credit hour
Out-of-state tuition: full time: $16,446
Room/board/expenses: $14,727
Full-time enrollment: 427
men: 73%; women: 27%;
minorities: 11%; international: 64%
Part-time enrollment: 153
men: 81%; women: 19%;
minorities: 14%; international: 23%
Acceptance rate: 58%
GRE requirement: Yes
Avg. GRE: quantitative: 690
TOEFL requirement: Yes
Minimum TOEFL score: 550
Fellowships: 33
Teaching assistantships: 25
Research assistantships: 85
Students specializing in: biomedical: 18%; computer: 9%; computer science: 17%; electrical: 68%; industrial: 11%; materials: 2%; mechanical: 16%

OKLAHOMA

Oklahoma State University
201 ATRC
Stillwater, OK 74078-0535
http://gradcollege.okstate.edu
Public
Admissions: (405) 744-6368
E-mail: grad-i@okstate.edu
Financial aid: (405) 744-6604
Application deadline: 02/15
In-state tuition: full time: $148/credit hour; part time: $148/credit hour
Out-of-state tuition: full time: $555/credit hour
Room/board/expenses: $12,730
Full-time enrollment: 316
men: 81%; women: 19%;
minorities: 2%; international: 81%

Part-time enrollment: 454
men: 83%; women: 17%;
minorities: 10%; international: 42%
Acceptance rate: 46%
GRE requirement: Yes
Avg. GRE: quantitative: 731
TOEFL requirement: Yes
Minimum TOEFL score: 550
Fellowships: 19
Teaching assistantships: 141
Research assistantships: 184
Students specializing in: agriculture: 6%; architectural: 0%; chemical: 5%; civil: 5%; computer: 15%; electrical: 19%; environmental: 1%; industrial: 32%; mechanical: 18%

University of Oklahoma
202 W. Boyd, CEC 107
Norman, OK 73019
http://www.coe.ou.edu
Public
Admissions: (405) 325-2252
E-mail: admrec@ou.edu
Financial aid: (405) 325-5505
Application deadline: 04/01
In-state tuition: full time: $5,376; part time: $144/credit hour
Out-of-state tuition: full time: $14,357
Room/board/expenses: $15,554
Full-time enrollment: 325
men: 79%; women: 21%;
minorities: 10%; international: 57%
Part-time enrollment: 188
men: 80%; women: 20%;
minorities: 11%; international: 43%
Acceptance rate: 70%
GRE requirement: Yes
Avg. GRE: quantitative: 731
TOEFL requirement: Yes
Minimum TOEFL score: 550
Fellowships: 34
Teaching assistantships: 95
Research assistantships: 231
Students specializing in: aerospace: 3%; biomedical: 6%; chemical: 8%; civil: 7%; computer science: 14%; electrical: 20%; science and physics: 1%; environmental: 6%; industrial: 9%; mechanical: 12%; petroleum: 10%; other: 4%

University of Tulsa
800 S. Tucker Drive
Tulsa, OK 74104-3189
http://www.utulsa.edu
Private
Admissions: (918) 631-2336
E-mail: grad@utulsa.edu
Financial aid: (918) 631-2526
Application deadline: rolling
Tuition: full time: $778/credit hour; part time: $778/credit hour
Room/board/expenses: $10,900
Full-time enrollment: 178
men: 78%; women: 22%;
minorities: 2%; international: 69%
Part-time enrollment: 26
men: 77%; women: 23%;
minorities: 15%; international: 15%
Acceptance rate: 48%
GRE requirement: Yes
Avg. GRE: quantitative: 721
TOEFL requirement: Yes
Minimum TOEFL score: 550
Fellowships: 5
Teaching assistantships: 36
Research assistantships: 82
Students specializing in: chemical: 10%; computer science: 38%; electrical: 9%; mechanical: 12%; petroleum: 27%; other: 3%

OREGON

OGI School of Science and Engineering–Oregon Health and Science University
20000 N.W. Walker Road
Beaverton, OR 97006-8921
http://www.ogi.edu/graduate_edu/
Private
Admissions: (503) 748-1027
E-mail: admissions@admin.ogi.edu

Financial aid: (503) 494-5117
Application deadline: rolling
Tuition: full time: $22,950; part time: $625/credit hour
Room/board/expenses: N/A
Full-time enrollment: 64
men: 59%; women: 41%;
minorities: 50%; international: 6%
Part-time enrollment: 218
men: 61%; women: 39%;
minorities: 28%; international: 4%
Acceptance rate: 51%
GRE requirement: Yes
Avg. GRE: quantitative: 729
TOEFL requirement: Yes
Minimum TOEFL score: 650
Fellowships: 12
Teaching assistantships: 2
Research assistantships: 28
Students specializing in: biomedical: 17%; computer science: 25%; management: 38%; environmental: 21%

Oregon State University
101 Covell Hall
Corvallis, OR 97331-2409
http://engr.oregonstate.edu/
Public
Admissions: (541) 737-4411
E-mail: osuadmit@orst.edu
Financial aid: (541) 737-2241
Application deadline: 01/01
In-state tuition: full time: $11,902; part time: $338/credit hour
Out-of-state tuition: full time: $17,572
Room/board/expenses: $11,454
Full-time enrollment: 419
men: 80%; women: 20%;
minorities: 5%; international: 45%
Part-time enrollment: 145
men: 83%; women: 17%;
minorities: 6%; international: 27%
Acceptance rate: 38%
GRE requirement: Yes
Avg. GRE: quantitative: 736
TOEFL requirement: Yes
Minimum TOEFL score: 550
Fellowships: 30
Teaching assistantships: 158
Research assistantships: 202
Students specializing in: biomedical: 1%; chemical: 8%; civil: 15%; computer science: 18%; electrical: 25%; industrial: 5%; materials: 4%; mechanical: 9%; nuclear: 4%; other: 10%

Portland State University (Maseeh)
PO Box 751
Portland, OR 97207
http://www.cecs.pdx.edu
Public
Admissions: (503) 725-3511
E-mail: fischerm@cecs.pdx.edu
Financial aid: (503) 725-3461
Application deadline: rolling
In-state tuition: full time: $8,432; part time: $173/credit hour
Out-of-state tuition: full time: $12,563
Room/board/expenses: $13,155
Full-time enrollment: 269
men: 72%; women: 28%;
minorities: 6%; international: 69%
Part-time enrollment: 281
men: 76%; women: 24%;
minorities: 21%; international: 33%
Acceptance rate: 65%
GRE requirement: Yes
Avg. GRE: quantitative: 716
TOEFL requirement: Yes
Minimum TOEFL score: 550
Teaching assistantships: 46
Research assistantships: 74
Students specializing in: civil: 9%; computer: 32%; computer science: 25%; management: 23%; mechanical: 10%; other: 1%

PENNSYLVANIA

Carnegie Mellon University
5000 Forbes Avenue
Pittsburgh, PA 15213
http://www.cit.cmu.edu/
Private
Admissions: (412) 268-2478
Financial aid: (412) 268-2482
Application deadline: N/A
Tuition: full time: $34,300; part time: $1,416/credit hour
Room/board/expenses: $23,000
Full-time enrollment: 1,505
men: 77%; women: 23%;
minorities: 9%; international: 59%
Part-time enrollment: 193
men: 79%; women: 21%;
minorities: 11%; international: 53%
Acceptance rate: 22%
GRE requirement: Yes
Avg. GRE: quantitative: 765
TOEFL requirement: Yes
Minimum TOEFL score: N/A
Fellowships: 291
Teaching assistantships: 83
Research assistantships: 773
Students specializing in: biomedical: 2%; chemical: 6%; civil: 5%; computer: 20%; computer science: 41%; materials: 5%; mechanical: 6%; other: 14%

Drexel University
3141 Chestnut Street
Philadelphia, PA 19104
http://www.drexel.edu/coe
Private
Admissions: (215) 895-6700
E-mail: admissions@drexel.edu
Financial aid: (215) 895-2964
Application deadline: 01/01
Tuition: full time: $23,175; part time: $835/credit hour
Room/board/expenses: $19,550
Full-time enrollment: 646
men: 74%; women: 26%;
minorities: 8%; international: 44%
Part-time enrollment: 504
men: 69%; women: 31%;
minorities: 7%; international: 6%
Acceptance rate: 33%
GRE requirement: Yes
Avg. GRE: quantitative: 758
TOEFL requirement: Yes
Minimum TOEFL score: 600
Fellowships: 55
Teaching assistantships: 70
Research assistantships: 207
Students specializing in: architectural: 1%; biomedical: 17%; chemical: 5%; civil: 4%; computer: 2%; computer science: 7%; electrical: 15%; management: 13%; environmental: 3%; materials: 6%; mechanical: 10%; other: 17%

Lehigh University (Rossin)
19 Memorial Drive W
Bethlehem, PA 18015
http://www3.lehigh.edu/engineering
Private
Admissions: (610) 758-6310
E-mail: ineas@lehigh.edu
Financial aid: (610) 758-3181
Application deadline: 01/15
Tuition: full time: $990/credit hour; part time: $990/credit hour
Room/board/expenses: $12,030
Full-time enrollment: 466
men: 78%; women: 22%;
minorities: 3%; international: 65%
Part-time enrollment: 102
men: 79%; women: 21%;
minorities: 17%; international: 2%
Acceptance rate: 22%
GRE requirement: Yes
Avg. GRE: quantitative: 767
TOEFL requirement: Yes
Minimum TOEFL score: 550
Fellowships: 35
Teaching assistantships: 58
Research assistantships: 227

Students specializing in: chemical: 14%; civil: 7%; computer: 6%; computer science: 8%; electrical: 15%; management: 3%; environmental: 3%; industrial: 23%; materials: 7%; mechanical: 16%

Pennsylvania State University–University Park
101 Hammond Building
University Park, PA 16802
http://www.engr.psu.edu
Public
Admissions: (814) 865-1795
E-mail: gadm@psu.edu
Financial aid: (814) 865-2514
Application deadline: rolling
In-state tuition: full time: $15,298; part time: $614/credit hour
Out-of-state tuition: full time: $26,610
Room/board/expenses: $10,878
Full-time enrollment: 1,559
men: 78%; women: 22%;
minorities: 5%; international: 60%
Part-time enrollment: 161
men: 91%; women: 9%;
minorities: 11%; international: 34%
Acceptance rate: 32%
GRE requirement: Yes
Avg. GRE: quantitative: 752
TOEFL requirement: Yes
Minimum TOEFL score: 550
Fellowships: 55
Teaching assistantships: 348
Research assistantships: 656
Students specializing in: aerospace: 7%; agriculture: 2%; architectural: 3%; biomedical: 2%; chemical: 4%; civil: 5%; computer: 14%; electrical: 16%; science and physics: 6%; environmental: 2%; industrial: 11%; materials: 5%; mechanical: 16%; mining: 0%; nuclear: 3%; petroleum: 3%

Temple University
1947 N. 12th Street
Philadelphia, PA 19122
http://www.temple.edu/engineering/graduate/index.html
Public
Admissions: (215) 204-7800
E-mail: gradengr@temple.edu
Financial aid: (215) 204-2244
Application deadline: 08/01
In-state tuition: full time: $541/credit hour; part time: $541/credit hour
Out-of-state tuition: full time: $790/credit hour
Room/board/expenses: $15,912
Full-time enrollment: 90
men: 76%; women: 24%;
minorities: 8%; international: 76%
Part-time enrollment: 63
men: 70%; women: 30%;
minorities: 13%; international: 46%
Acceptance rate: 76%
GRE requirement: Yes
Avg. GRE: quantitative: 723
TOEFL requirement: Yes
Minimum TOEFL score: 550
Fellowships: 11
Teaching assistantships: 46
Research assistantships: 29
Students specializing in: biomedical: 5%; civil: 12%; computer science: 33%; electrical: 29%; mechanical: 9%; other: 12%

University of Pennsylvania
107 Towne Building
Philadelphia, PA 19104
http://www.seas.upenn.edu/grad
Private
Admissions: (215) 898-4542
E-mail: engstats@seas.upenn.edu
Financial aid: (215) 898-1988
Application deadline: 01/02
Tuition: full time: $36,654; part time: $4,582/credit hour
Room/board/expenses: $22,126

Full-time enrollment: 775
men: 71%; women: 29%;
minorities: 7%; international: 59%
Part-time enrollment: 336
men: 73%; women: 27%;
minorities: 14%; international: 26%
Acceptance rate: 35%
GRE requirement: Yes
Avg. GRE: quantitative: 759
TOEFL requirement: Yes
Minimum TOEFL score: 600
Fellowships: 1
Teaching assistantships: 1
Research assistantships: 303
Students specializing in: biomedical:
24%; chemical: 6%; computer
science: 24%; electrical: 15%;
management: 11%; industrial: 0%;
materials: 7%; mechanical: 8%;
other: 6%

University of Pittsburgh

240 Benedum Hall
Pittsburgh, PA 15261
http://www.engr.pitt.edu
Public
Admissions: (412) 624-9800
E-mail: admin@engr.pitt.edu
Financial aid: (412) 624-7488
Application deadline: 03/01
In-state tuition: full time: $17,730;
part time: $813/credit hour
Out-of-state tuition: full time:
$31,558
Room/board/expenses: $13,960
Full-time enrollment: 446
men: 72%; women: 28%;
minorities: 8%; international: 53%
Part-time enrollment: 195
men: 85%; women: 15%;
minorities: 8%; international: 3%
Acceptance rate: 36%
GRE requirement: Yes
Avg. GRE: quantitative: 731
TOEFL requirement: Yes
Minimum TOEFL score: 550
Fellowships: 28
Teaching assistantships: 137
Research assistantships: 181
Students specializing in: biomedical:
22%; chemical: 7%; civil: 12%;
computer: 1%; computer science:
12%; electrical: 13%; industrial:
12%; materials: 5%; mechanical:
16%

RHODE ISLAND

Brown University

Box D
Providence, RI 02912
http://gradschool.brown.edu/
go/admission/
Private
Admissions: (401) 863-2600
E-mail: gswebmaster@brown.edu
Financial aid: (401) 863-2721
Application deadline: rolling
Tuition: full time: $36,236; part
time: $9,548
Room/board/expenses: $13,058
Full-time enrollment: 246
men: 78%; women: 22%;
minorities: 6%; international: 61%
Part-time enrollment: 15
men: 100%; women: 0%;
minorities: 0%; international: 7%
Acceptance rate: 13%
GRE requirement: No
Avg. GRE: quantitative: N/A
TOEFL requirement: Yes
Minimum TOEFL score: 500
Fellowships: 45
Teaching assistantships: 24
Research assistantships: 139
Students specializing in: computer:
39%; other: 61%

University of Rhode Island

102 Bliss Hall
Kingston, RI 02881
http://www.egr.uri.edu/
Public
Admissions: (401) 874-2872

E-mail: tpj101@uriacc.uri.edu
Financial aid: (401) 874-2314
Application deadline: rolling
In-state tuition: full time: $9,367;
part time: $385/credit hour
Out-of-state tuition: full time:
$21,475
Room/board/expenses: $10,650
Full-time enrollment: 85
men: 74%; women: 26%;
minorities: 1%; international: 55%
Part-time enrollment: 77
men: 77%; women: 23%;
minorities: 5%; international: 19%
Acceptance rate: 65%
GRE requirement: No
Avg. GRE: quantitative: N/A
TOEFL requirement: Yes
Minimum TOEFL score: 550
Teaching assistantships: 29
Research assistantships: 27
Students specializing in: chemical:
10%; civil: 23%; electrical: 22%;
industrial: 10%; mechanical: 20%;
other: 15%

SOUTH CAROLINA

Clemson University

Room 109, Riggs Hall
Clemson, SC 29634-0901
http://www.ces.clemson.edu/
Public
Admissions: (864) 656-2287
E-mail:
cuadmissions@clemson.edu
Financial aid: (864) 656-2280
Application deadline: rolling
In-state tuition: full time: $7,835;
part time: $440/credit hour
Out-of-state tuition: full time:
$15,123
Room/board/expenses: $11,314
Full-time enrollment: 645
men: 76%; women: 24%;
minorities: 5%; international: 60%
Part-time enrollment: 104
men: 76%; women: 24%;
minorities: 4%; international: 20%
Acceptance rate: 47%
GRE requirement: Yes
Avg. GRE: quantitative: 685
TOEFL requirement: Yes
Minimum TOEFL score: 500
Fellowships: 22
Teaching assistantships: 223
Research assistantships: 345
Students specializing in: agriculture:
2%; biomedical: 10%; chemical:
5%; civil: 10%; computer: 3%; com-
puter science: 12%; electrical: 14%;
environmental: 7%; industrial: 7%;
materials: 7%; mechanical: 22%

University of South Carolina

Swearingen Engineering Center
Columbia, SC 29208
http://www.engr.sc.edu
Public
Admissions: (803) 777-4177
E-mail: info@engr.sc.edu
Financial aid: (803) 777-8134
Application deadline: 07/01
In-state tuition: full time: $9,190;
part time: $440/credit hour
Out-of-state tuition: full time:
$19,482
Room/board/expenses: $12,340
Full-time enrollment: 246
men: 78%; women: 22%;
minorities: 11%; international: 54%
Part-time enrollment: 182
men: 90%; women: 10%;
minorities: 13%; international: 23%
GRE requirement: Yes
Avg. GRE: quantitative: N/A
TOEFL requirement: Yes
Minimum TOEFL score: 570
Fellowships: 13
Teaching assistantships: 47
Research assistantships: 167
Students specializing in: biomedical:
1%; chemical: 13%; civil: 12%; com-
puter science: 24%; electrical:
29%; mechanical: 14%; nuclear: 7%

SOUTH DAKOTA

South Dakota School of Mines and Technology

501 E. St. Joseph Street
Rapid City, SD 57701-3995
http://www.sdsmt.edu/
Public
Admissions: (605) 394-2341
E-mail:
graduate.admissions@sdsmt.edu
Financial aid: (605) 394-2400
Application deadline: 07/01
In-state tuition: full time: $125/credit
hour; part time: $125/credit hour
Out-of-state tuition: full time:
$369/credit hour
Room/board/expenses: $9,200
Full-time enrollment: 111
men: 75%; women: 25%;
minorities: 2%; international: 46%
Part-time enrollment: 47
men: 85%; women: 15%;
minorities: 6%; international: 36%
Acceptance rate: 100%
GRE requirement: Yes
Avg. GRE: quantitative: 644
TOEFL requirement: Yes
Minimum TOEFL score: 520
Fellowships: 10
Teaching assistantships: 14
Research assistantships: 24
Students specializing in: biomedical:
6%; chemical: 4%; civil: 19%; com-
puter science: 6%; electrical: 14%;
materials: 25%; mechanical: 8%;
other: 18%

South Dakota State University

CEH 201, Box 2219
Brookings, SD 57007-0096
http://www3.sdstate.edu/
Public
Admissions: (605) 688-4181
E-mail: gradschl@adm.sdstate.edu
Financial aid: (605) 688-4695
Application deadline: 06/16
In-state tuition: full time: $125/credit
hour; part time: $125/credit hour
Out-of-state tuition: full time:
$369/credit hour
Room/board/expenses: $5,881
Full-time enrollment: 170
men: 81%; women: 19%;
minorities: 6%; international: 53%
Part-time enrollment: N/A
men: N/A; women: N/A;
minorities: N/A; international: N/A
Acceptance rate: 51%
GRE requirement: No
Avg. GRE: quantitative: N/A
TOEFL requirement: Yes
Minimum TOEFL score: 550
Fellowships: 0
Teaching assistantships: 57
Research assistantships: 53
Students specializing in: agriculture:
5%; civil: 21%; computer science:
22%; electrical: 22%; science
and physics: 1%; industrial: 18%;
mechanical: 12%

TENNESSEE

Tennessee State University

3500 John Merritt Boulevard
Nashville, TN 37209-1651
http://www.tnstate.edu/
interior.asp?ptid=1&mid=284
Public
Admissions: (615) 963-5107
E-mail: jcade@tnstate.edu
Financial aid: (615) 963-5772
Application deadline: 07/01
In-state tuition: full time: $7,102;
part time: $490/credit hour
Out-of-state tuition: full time:
$17,378
Room/board/expenses: $10,782
Full-time enrollment: 43
men: 67%; women: 33%;
minorities: 35%; international: 44%

Part-time enrollment: 35
men: 77%; women: 23%;
minorities: 37%; international: 20%
Acceptance rate: 62%
GRE requirement: No
Avg. GRE: quantitative: N/A
TOEFL requirement: Yes
Minimum TOEFL score: 500
Fellowships: 0
Teaching assistantships: 3
Research assistantships: 33
Students specializing in: biomedical:
4%; civil: 19%; electrical: 59%;
industrial: 18%

Tennessee Technological University

N. Dixie Avenue
Cookeville, TN 38505
http://www.tntech.edu/engineering
Public
Admissions: (931) 372-3233
E-mail: g_admissions@tntech.edu
Financial aid: (931) 372-3073
Application deadline: 08/01
In-state tuition: full time: $6,595;
part time: $347/credit hour
Out-of-state tuition: full time:
$14,945
Room/board/expenses: $11,280
Full-time enrollment: 99
men: 75%; women: 25%;
minorities: 8%; international: 65%
Part-time enrollment: 59
men: 88%; women: 12%;
minorities: 8%; international: 49%
Acceptance rate: 43%
GRE requirement: Yes
Avg. GRE: quantitative: 717
TOEFL requirement: Yes
Minimum TOEFL score: 550
Fellowships: 6
Teaching assistantships: 29
Research assistantships: 85
Students specializing in: chemical:
16%; civil: 11%; computer science:
7%; electrical: 38%; mechanical:
27%

University of Memphis

Herff College of Engineering
Memphis, TN 38152
http://www.engr.memphis.edu/
Public
Admissions: (901) 678-2111
E-mail: recruitment@memphis.edu
Financial aid: (901) 678-4825
Application deadline: 07/01
In-state tuition: full time: $6,059;
part time: $333/credit hour
Out-of-state tuition: full time:
$16,887
Room/board/expenses: $11,406
Full-time enrollment: 161
men: 70%; women: 30%;
minorities: 2%; international: 71%
Part-time enrollment: 56
men: 82%; women: 18%;
minorities: 13%; international: 23%
Acceptance rate: 79%
GRE requirement: Yes
Avg. GRE: quantitative: 684
TOEFL requirement: Yes
Minimum TOEFL score: 550
Fellowships: 35
Teaching assistantships: 12
Research assistantships: 47
Students specializing in: biomedical:
15%; civil: 9%; computer science:
31%; electrical: 16%; mechanical:
9%; other: 21%

University of Tennessee–Knoxville

124 Perkins Hall
Knoxville, TN 37996-2000
http://admissions.utk.edu/
graduate/
Public
Admissions: (865) 974-3251
E-mail:
graduateadmissions@utk.edu
Financial aid: (865) 974-3131
Application deadline: 02/01

In-state tuition: full time: $6,720;
part time: $329/credit hour
Out-of-state tuition: full time:
$18,962
Room/board/expenses: $15,894
Full-time enrollment: 402
men: 77%; women: 23%;
minorities: 8%; international: 48%
Part-time enrollment: 442
men: 84%; women: 16%;
minorities: 7%; international: 25%
Acceptance rate: 53%
GRE requirement: Yes
Avg. GRE: quantitative: 723
TOEFL requirement: Yes
Minimum TOEFL score: 550
Fellowships: 27
Teaching assistantships: 92
Research assistantships: 349
Students specializing in: aerospace:
4%; agriculture: 1%; biomedical:
2%; chemical: 3%; civil: 11%; computer: 3%; computer science: 10%;
electrical: 17%; science and
physics: 3%; environmental: 4%;
industrial: 8%; materials: 9%;
mechanical: 11%; nuclear: 8%;
other: 7%

Vanderbilt University

VU Station B 351826
2301 Vanderbilt Place
Nashville, TN 37235
http://www.vuse.vanderbilt.edu
Private
Admissions: (615) 322-2651
E-mail: vandygrad@vanderbilt.edu
Financial aid: (615) 322-3591
Application deadline: 01/15
Tuition: full time: $1,434/credit
hour; part time: $1,434/credit hour
Room/board/expenses: $20,100
Full-time enrollment: 389
men: 73%; women: 27%;
minorities: 26%; international: 43%
Part-time enrollment: 17
men: 76%; women: 24%;
minorities: 0%; international: 0%
Acceptance rate: 12%
GRE requirement: Yes
Avg. GRE: quantitative: 754
TOEFL requirement: Yes
Minimum TOEFL score: 550
Fellowships: 43
Teaching assistantships: 88
Research assistantships: 218
Students specializing in: biomedical:
16%; chemical: 8%; civil: 13%;
computer science: 16%; electrical:
25%; environmental: 4%;
materials: 8%; mechanical: 11%

TEXAS

Lamar University

4400 Martin Luther King Parkway
Beaumont, TX 77710
http://www.lamar.edu/lamar/
colleges/engineering/index.html
Public
Admissions: (409) 880-8888
E-mail: admissions@hal.lamar.edu
Financial aid: (409) 880-8450
Application deadline: N/A
In-state tuition: full time: $6,075;
part time: $179/credit hour
Out-of-state tuition: full time:
$13,303
Room/board/expenses: $11,460
Full-time enrollment: 303
men: 83%; women: 17%;
minorities: 3%; international: 95%
Part-time enrollment: 83
men: 88%; women: 12%;
minorities: 2%; international: 93%
Acceptance rate: 39%
GRE requirement: Yes
Avg. GRE: quantitative: 712
TOEFL requirement: Yes
Minimum TOEFL score: 525
Fellowships: 18
Teaching assistantships: 16
Research assistantships: 22
Students specializing in: chemical:
25%; civil: 21%; electrical: 25%;
industrial: 10%; mechanical: 20%

Prairie View A&M University
PO Box 397
Prairie View, TX 77446
http://www.pvamu.edu
Private
Admissions: (936) 261-3500
E-mail: gradadmissions@pvamu.edu
Financial aid: (936) 261-1000
Application deadline: 01/07
Tuition: full time: $175/credit hour; part time: $175/credit hour
Room/board/expenses: $11,712
Full-time enrollment: 52
men: 65%; women: 35%; minorities: 44%; international: 46%
Part-time enrollment: 30
men: 70%; women: 30%; minorities: 73%; international: 7%
Acceptance rate: 84%
GRE requirement: Yes
Avg. GRE: quantitative: 681
TOEFL requirement: Yes
Minimum TOEFL score: 550
Fellowships: 6
Teaching assistantships: 12
Research assistantships: 12
Students specializing in: computer science: 20%; electrical: 43%; other: 38%

Rice University (Brown)
6100 Main Street, MS 364
Houston, TX 77005
http://engr.rice.edu
Private
Admissions: (713) 348-4002
E-mail: grbsoe@rice.edu
Financial aid: (713) 348-4958
Application deadline: N/A
Tuition: full time: $25,128; part time: $1,352/credit hour
Room/board/expenses: $13,200
Full-time enrollment: 505
men: 75%; women: 25%; minorities: 14%; international: 48%
Part-time enrollment: 16
men: 88%; women: 13%; minorities: 38%; international: 25%
Acceptance rate: 15%
GRE requirement: Yes
Avg. GRE: quantitative: 768
TOEFL requirement: Yes
Minimum TOEFL score: 600
Fellowships: 204
Teaching assistantships: 18
Research assistantships: 217
Students specializing in: biomedical: 21%; chemical: 11%; civil: 7%; computer science: 12%; electrical: 19%; environmental: 7%; materials: 14%; mechanical: 14%; other: 15%

Southern Methodist University
3145 Dyer Street
Dallas, TX 75275-0335
http://www.engr.smu.edu
Private
Admissions: (214) 768-3484
E-mail: valerin@engr.smu.edu
Financial aid: (214) 768-3484
Application deadline: 07/01
Tuition: full time: $870/credit hour; part time: $870/credit hour
Room/board/expenses: $14,360
Full-time enrollment: 253
men: 81%; women: 19%; minorities: 8%; international: 76%
Part-time enrollment: 733
men: 79%; women: 21%; minorities: 36%; international: 6%
Acceptance rate: 54%
GRE requirement: Yes
Avg. GRE: quantitative: 724
TOEFL requirement: Yes
Minimum TOEFL score: 550
Fellowships: 0
Teaching assistantships: 33
Research assistantships: 35
Students specializing in: civil: 1%; computer: 3%; computer science: 21%; electrical: 24%; management: 17%; environmental: 2%; industrial: 3%; mechanical: 5%; other: 26%

Texas A&M University–College Station (Look)
301 Wisenbaker Research Center
3126 TAMU
College Station, TX 77843
http://www.tamu.edu/admissions
Public
Admissions: (979) 845-7200
E-mail: essap@tamu.edu
Financial aid: (979) 845-3236
Application deadline: rolling
In-state tuition: full time: $5,678; part time: $3,824
Out-of-state tuition: full time: $10,682
Room/board/expenses: $13,170
Full-time enrollment: 2,069
men: 81%; women: 19%; minorities: 7%; international: 72%
Part-time enrollment: 359
men: 85%; women: 15%; minorities: 16%; international: 39%
Acceptance rate: 37%
GRE requirement: Yes
Avg. GRE: quantitative: 756
TOEFL requirement: Yes
Minimum TOEFL score: 550
Fellowships: 577
Teaching assistantships: 225
Research assistantships: 863
Students specializing in: aerospace: 4%; agriculture: 2%; biomedical: 3%; chemical: 6%; civil: 14%; computer science: 12%; electrical: 20%; industrial: 8%; mechanical: 15%; nuclear: 4%; petroleum: 10%; other: 1%

Texas A&M University–Kingsville (Dotterweich)[1]
MSC 188
Kingsville, TX 78363
http://www.engineer.tamuk.edu
Public
Admissions: (361) 593-2315
Financial aid: (361) 593-3911
Tuition: N/A
Room/board/expenses: N/A
Enrollment: N/A

Texas Tech University
Box 43103
Lubbock, TX 79409-3103
http://www.depts.ttu.edu/coe/
Public
Admissions: (806) 742-2787
E-mail: gradschool@ttu.edu
Financial aid: (806) 742-3681
Application deadline: 05/01
In-state tuition: full time: $194/credit hour; part time: $194/credit hour
Out-of-state tuition: full time: $472/credit hour
Room/board/expenses: $11,631
Full-time enrollment: 481
men: 81%; women: 19%; minorities: 8%; international: 56%
Part-time enrollment: 172
men: 82%; women: 18%; minorities: 10%; international: 28%
Acceptance rate: 39%
GRE requirement: Yes
Avg. GRE: quantitative: 725
TOEFL requirement: Yes
Minimum TOEFL score: 550
Fellowships: 28
Teaching assistantships: 114
Research assistantships: 163
Students specializing in: chemical: 6%; civil: 14%; computer science: 19%; electrical: 19%; environmental: 2%; industrial: 15%; mechanical: 20%; petroleum: 1%; other: 3%

University of Houston (Cullen)
E421 Engineering Building 2
Houston, TX 77204-4007
http://www.egr.uh.edu
Public
Admissions: (713) 743-4200
E-mail: grad-admit@egr.uh.edu
Financial aid: (713) 743-9090
Application deadline: rolling
In-state tuition: full time: $262/credit hour; part time: $262/credit hour
Out-of-state tuition: full time: $540/credit hour
Room/board/expenses: $13,639
Full-time enrollment: 646
men: 76%; women: 24%; minorities: 6%; international: 87%
Part-time enrollment: 232
men: 75%; women: 25%; minorities: 27%; international: 34%
Acceptance rate: 64%
GRE requirement: Yes
Avg. GRE: quantitative: 747
TOEFL requirement: Yes
Minimum TOEFL score: 550
Fellowships: 381
Teaching assistantships: 35
Research assistantships: 235
Students specializing in: aerospace: 1%; biomedical: 0%; chemical: 10%; civil: 8%; computer: 0%; computer science: 26%; electrical: 23%; environmental: 3%; industrial: 11%; materials: 2%; mechanical: 8%; petroleum: 7%

University of Texas–Arlington
PO Box 19019
Arlington, TX 76019
http://www.uta.edu/engineering/
Public
Admissions: (817) 272-2688
E-mail: graduate.school@uta.edu
Financial aid: (817) 272-3561
Application deadline: 06/05
In-state tuition: full time: $6,384; part time: N/A
Out-of-state tuition: full time: $11,388
Room/board/expenses: $10,696
Full-time enrollment: 994
men: 80%; women: 20%; minorities: 8%; international: 89%
Part-time enrollment: 541
men: 79%; women: 21%; minorities: 37%; international: 40%
Acceptance rate: 60%
GRE requirement: Yes
Avg. GRE: quantitative: 719
TOEFL requirement: Yes
Minimum TOEFL score: 550
Fellowships: 380
Teaching assistantships: 190
Research assistantships: 193
Students specializing in: biomedical: 10%; civil: 11%; computer: 22%; electrical: 26%; industrial: 14%; materials: 5%; mechanical: 12%

University of Texas–Austin (Cockrell)
1 University Station, C2100
Austin, TX 78712-0284
http://www.engr.utexas.edu/
Public
Admissions: (512) 475-7390
E-mail: adgrd@utxdp.its.utexas.edu
Financial aid: (512) 475-6282
Application deadline: rolling
In-state tuition: full time: $7,240; part time: N/A
Out-of-state tuition: full time: $13,898
Room/board/expenses: $13,275
Full-time enrollment: 1,641
men: 80%; women: 20%; minorities: 11%; international: 55%
Part-time enrollment: 459
men: 84%; women: 16%; minorities: 26%; international: 30%
Acceptance rate: 23%
GRE requirement: Yes
Avg. GRE: quantitative: 759
TOEFL requirement: Yes
Minimum TOEFL score: 550
Fellowships: 475
Teaching assistantships: 417
Research assistantships: 862
Students specializing in: aerospace: 7%; architectural: 1%; biomedical: 5%; chemical: 9%; civil: 16%; computer: 19%; electrical: 17%; management: 3%; environmental: 2%; industrial: 3%; materials: 2%; mechanical: 11%; petroleum: 6%

University of Texas–Dallas (Jonsson)
PO Box 830688, Mail Station EC32
Richardson, TX 75083-0688
http://www.utdallas.edu
Public
Admissions: (972) 883-2270
E-mail: interest@utdallas.edu
Financial aid: (972) 883-2941
Application deadline: 07/01
In-state tuition: full time: $7,052; part time: N/A
Out-of-state tuition: full time: $12,632
Room/board/expenses: $9,756
Full-time enrollment: 692
men: 76%; women: 24%; minorities: 6%; international: 81%
Part-time enrollment: 357
men: 78%; women: 22%; minorities: 18%; international: 52%
Acceptance rate: 53%
GRE requirement: Yes
Avg. GRE: quantitative: 742
TOEFL requirement: Yes
Minimum TOEFL score: 550
Fellowships: 28
Teaching assistantships: 83
Research assistantships: 268
Students specializing in: computer: 6%; computer science: 54%; electrical: 39%; materials: 2%

University of Texas–El Paso
College of Engineering
El Paso, TX 79968
http://www.utep.edu/graduate
Public
Admissions: (915) 747-5491
E-mail: gradschool@utep.edu
Financial aid: (915) 747-5204
Application deadline: rolling
In-state tuition: full time: N/A; part time: N/A
Out-of-state tuition: full time: N/A
Room/board/expenses: N/A
Full-time enrollment: 245
men: 72%; women: 28%; minorities: 27%; international: 67%
Part-time enrollment: 229
men: 79%; women: 21%; minorities: 40%; international: 53%
Acceptance rate: 58%
GRE requirement: Yes
Avg. GRE: quantitative: 620
TOEFL requirement: Yes
Minimum TOEFL score: 550
Students specializing in: civil: 12%; computer: 25%; computer science: 21%; environmental: 9%; industrial: 8%; materials: 9%; mechanical: 15%; other: 1%

University of Texas–San Antonio
1 UTSA Circle
San Antonio, TX 78249-0670
http://www.utsa.edu/graduate
Public
Admissions: (210) 458-4330
E-mail: gradstudies@utsa.edu
Financial aid: (210) 458-8000
Application deadline: 07/01
In-state tuition: full time: $201/credit hour; part time: $201/credit hour
Out-of-state tuition: full time: $757/credit hour
Room/board/expenses: $12,080
Full-time enrollment: 200
men: 71%; women: 30%; minorities: 12%; international: 73%
Part-time enrollment: 183
men: 75%; women: 25%; minorities: 34%; international: 16%
Acceptance rate: 79%
GRE requirement: Yes
Avg. GRE: quantitative: 686
TOEFL requirement: Yes
Minimum TOEFL score: 500
Fellowships: 18
Teaching assistantships: 45
Research assistantships: 43
Students specializing in: biomedical: 8%; civil: 8%; computer: 4%; computer science: 22%; electrical: 40%; environmental: 8%; mechanical: 9%

UTAH

Brigham Young University (Fulton)
270 CB
Provo, UT 84602
http://www.byu.edu/gradstudies
Private
Admissions: (801) 422-4091
E-mail: gradstudies@byu.edu
Financial aid: (801) 378-4104
Application deadline: 01/15
Tuition: full time: $4,860; part time: $270/credit hour
Room/board/expenses: $12,182
Full-time enrollment: 427
men: 92%; women: 8%; minorities: 16%; international: 19%
Part-time enrollment: N/A
men: N/A; women: N/A; minorities: N/A; international: N/A
Acceptance rate: 58%
GRE requirement: Yes
Avg. GRE: quantitative: 709
TOEFL requirement: Yes
Minimum TOEFL score: 580
Fellowships: 8
Teaching assistantships: 112
Research assistantships: 271
Students specializing in: chemical: 11%; civil: 17%; computer: 7%; computer science: 27%; electrical: 16%; mechanical: 23%

University of Utah
72 S. Central Campus Drive
650 WEB
Salt Lake City, UT 84112-9200
http://www.utah.edu
Public
Admissions: (801) 581-7281
E-mail: admissions@sa.utah.edu
Financial aid: (801) 581-6211
Application deadline: 04/01
In-state tuition: full time: $4,083; part time: $2,955
Out-of-state tuition: full time: $12,811
Room/board/expenses: $15,264
Full-time enrollment: 584
men: 83%; women: 17%; minorities: 5%; international: 50%
Part-time enrollment: 273
men: 84%; women: 16%; minorities: 12%; international: 28%
Acceptance rate: 46%
GRE requirement: Yes
Avg. GRE: quantitative: 743
TOEFL requirement: Yes
Minimum TOEFL score: 500
Fellowships: 27
Teaching assistantships: 133
Research assistantships: 409
Students specializing in: biomedical: 13%; chemical: 6%; civil: 12%; computer: 5%; computer science: 14%; electrical: 16%; materials: 5%; mechanical: 21%; mining: 8%; nuclear: 1%

Utah State University
4100 Old Main Hill
Logan, UT 84322-4100
http://www.engineering.usu.edu/
Public
Admissions: (435) 797-1189
E-mail: gradsch@cc.usu.edu
Financial aid: (435) 797-0173
Application deadline: rolling
In-state tuition: full time: $4,200; part time: $3,171
Out-of-state tuition: full time: $12,225
Room/board/expenses: $8,190
Full-time enrollment: 310
men: 87%; women: 13%; minorities: 0%; international: 44%
Part-time enrollment: N/A
men: N/A; women: N/A; minorities: N/A; international: N/A
Acceptance rate: 49%

GRE requirement: Yes
Avg. GRE: quantitative: 708
TOEFL requirement: Yes
Minimum TOEFL score: 550
Fellowships: 11
Teaching assistantships: 24
Research assistantships: 150
Students specializing in: N/A

VERMONT

University of Vermont
109 Votey Building
Burlington, VT 05405
http://www.cems.uvm.edu
Public
Admissions: (802) 656-1340
E-mail:
graduate.admissions@uvm.edu
Financial aid: (802) 656-2699
Application deadline: N/A
In-state tuition: full time:
$434/credit hour; part time:
$410/credit hour
Out-of-state tuition: full time:
$1,096/credit hour
Room/board/expenses: $10,096
Full-time enrollment: 39
men: 79%; women: 21%;
minorities: 0%; international: 41%
Part-time enrollment: 88
men: 73%; women: 27%;
minorities: 2%; international: 33%
Acceptance rate: 57%
GRE requirement: Yes
Avg. GRE: quantitative: 716
TOEFL requirement: Yes
Minimum TOEFL score: 550
Fellowships: 22
Research assistantships: 45
Students specializing in: biomedical:
5%; civil: 17%; computer science:
23%; electrical: 27%; materials:
10%; mechanical: 18%

VIRGINIA

George Mason University (Volgenau)
4400 University Drive, MS4A3
Fairfax, VA 22030-4444
http://volgenau.gmu.edu/
Public
Admissions: (703) 993-1512
E-mail: itegrad@gmu.edu
Financial aid: (703) 993-2353
Application deadline: 03/15
In-state tuition: full time: $10,488;
part time: $437/credit hour
Out-of-state tuition: full time:
$20,280
Room/board/expenses: $9,395
Full-time enrollment: 310
men: 71%; women: 29%;
minorities: 7%; international: 75%
Part-time enrollment: 1,201
men: 79%; women: 21%;
minorities: 22%; international: 21%
Acceptance rate: 63%
GRE requirement: Yes
Avg. GRE: quantitative: 716
TOEFL requirement: Yes
Minimum TOEFL score: 575
Fellowships: 50
Teaching assistantships: 115
Research assistantships: 80
Students specializing in: civil: 2%;
computer: 4%; computer science:
49%; electrical: 23%; industrial:
3%; other: 19%

Old Dominion University
102 Kaufman Hall
Norfolk, VA 23529
http://www.admissions.odu.edu
Public
Admissions: (757) 683-3685
E-mail: gradadmit@odu.edu
Financial aid: (757) 683-3689
Application deadline: 06/01
In-state tuition: full time:
$304/credit hour; part time:
$304/credit hour
Out-of-state tuition: full time:
$761/credit hour

Room/board/expenses: $9,284
Full-time enrollment: 157
men: 75%; women: 25%;
minorities: 32%; international: 38%
Part-time enrollment: 640
men: 83%; women: 18%;
minorities: 17%; international: 16%
Acceptance rate: 66%
GRE requirement: Yes
Avg. GRE: quantitative: 696
TOEFL requirement: Yes
Minimum TOEFL score: 550
Fellowships: 5
Teaching assistantships: 61
Research assistantships: 71
Students specializing in: aerospace:
4%; civil: 6%; computer: 2%; elec-
trical: 17%; management: 47%; en-
vironmental: 4%; mechanical: 9%;
other: 11%

University of Virginia
Thornton Hall
Charlottesville, VA 22904-4246
http://www.seas.virginia.edu/
Public
Admissions: (434) 924-3897
E-mail:
seas-grad-admission@virginia.edu
Financial aid: (434) 924-3897
Application deadline: rolling
In-state tuition: full time: $11,428;
part time: $380/credit hour
Out-of-state tuition: full time:
$21,193
Room/board/expenses: $18,584
Full-time enrollment: 648
men: 75%; women: 25%;
minorities: 10%; international: 39%
Part-time enrollment: 89
men: 81%; women: 19%;
minorities: 12%; international: 0%
Acceptance rate: 19%
GRE requirement: Yes
Avg. GRE: quantitative: 749
TOEFL requirement: Yes
Minimum TOEFL score: 600
Fellowships: 251
Teaching assistantships: 106
Research assistantships: 455
Students specializing in: biomedical:
11%; chemical: 7%; civil: 8%; com-
puter: 2%; computer science: 11%;
electrical: 16%; science and
physics: 8%; materials: 8%;
mechanical: 13%; other: 17%

Virginia Commonwealth University
PO Box 843068
Richmond, VA 23284-3068
http://www.egr.vcu.edu/
Public
Admissions: (804) 828-8308
E-mail: rhobson@vcu.edu
Financial aid: (804) 828-3925
Application deadline: 07/01
In-state tuition: full time: $8,904;
part time: $401/credit hour
Out-of-state tuition: full time:
$17,584
Room/board/expenses: $16,298
Full-time enrollment: 145
men: 70%; women: 30%;
minorities: 13%; international: 57%
Part-time enrollment: 88
men: 73%; women: 27%;
minorities: 22%; international: 11%
Acceptance rate: 66%
GRE requirement: Yes
Avg. GRE: quantitative: 709
TOEFL requirement: Yes
Minimum TOEFL score: 600
Teaching assistantships: 40
Research assistantships: 53
Students specializing in: biomedical:
26%; computer science: 19%;
other: 55%

Virginia Tech
302 Whittemore Hall
Blacksburg, VA 24061-0217
http://www.grads.vt.edu
Public
Admissions: (540) 231-8636

E-mail: gradappl@vt.edu
Financial aid: (540) 231-5179
Application deadline: rolling
In-state tuition: full time: $9,156;
part time: $410/credit hour
Out-of-state tuition: full time:
$15,351
Room/board/expenses: $12,939
Full-time enrollment: 1,462
men: 79%; women: 21%;
minorities: 14%; international: 44%
Part-time enrollment: 345
men: 85%; women: 15%;
minorities: 16%; international: 18%
Acceptance rate: 22%
GRE requirement: Yes
Avg. GRE: quantitative: 749
TOEFL requirement: Yes
Minimum TOEFL score: 550
Fellowships: 100
Teaching assistantships: 320
Research assistantships: 663
Students specializing in: aerospace:
7%; agriculture: 3%; biomedical:
3%; chemical: 2%; civil: 16%;
computer: 7%; computer science:
12%; electrical: 19%; science and
physics: 4%; industrial: 12%;
materials: 3%; mechanical: 12%;
mining: 1%

WASHINGTON

University of Washington
371 Loew Hall, Box 352180
Seattle, WA 98195-2180
http://www.engr.washington.edu
Public
Admissions: (206) 543-5929
E-mail:
uwgrad2@grad.washington.edu
Financial aid: (206) 543-6101
Application deadline: 12/15
In-state tuition: full time: $9,417;
part time: $449/credit hour
Out-of-state tuition: full time:
$21,464
Room/board/expenses: $16,626
Full-time enrollment: 1,105
men: 74%; women: 26%;
minorities: 13%; international: 31%
Part-time enrollment: 318
men: 79%; women: 21%;
minorities: 18%; international: 18%
Acceptance rate: 29%
GRE requirement: Yes
Avg. GRE: quantitative: 736
TOEFL requirement: Yes
Minimum TOEFL score: 500
Fellowships: 153
Teaching assistantships: 203
Research assistantships: 544
Students specializing in: aerospace:
8%; biomedical: 9%; chemical: 4%;
civil: 14%; computer: 21%; electri-
cal: 20%; industrial: 2%; materials:
5%; mechanical: 12%; other: 5%

Washington State University
PO Box 642714
Pullman, WA 99164-2714
http://www.cea.wsu.edu
Public
Admissions: (509) 335-6424
E-mail: gradsch@wsu.edu
Financial aid: (509) 335-9711
Application deadline: 01/10
In-state tuition: full time: $8,076;
part time: $378/credit hour
Out-of-state tuition: full time:
$18,924
Room/board/expenses: $13,532
Full-time enrollment: 310
men: 74%; women: 26%;
minorities: 3%; international: 58%
Part-time enrollment: 166
men: 80%; women: 20%;
minorities: 13%; international: 14%
Acceptance rate: 19%
GRE requirement: Yes
Avg. GRE: quantitative: 738
TOEFL requirement: Yes
Minimum TOEFL score: 550
Fellowships: 83
Teaching assistantships: 94
Research assistantships: 234

Students specializing in: agriculture:
3%; chemical: 5%; civil: 14%; computer: 2%; computer science: 13%;
electrical: 12%; management: 22%;
science and physics: 6%; environmental: 3%; materials: 8%;
mechanical: 11%

WEST VIRGINIA

West Virginia University
PO Box 6070
Morgantown, WV 26506-6070
http://www.cemr.wvu.edu
Public
Admissions: (304) 293-4821
E-mail: info@cemr.wvu.edu
Financial aid: (304) 293-5242
Application deadline: rolling
In-state tuition: full time: $5,796;
part time: $382/credit hour
Out-of-state tuition: full time:
$15,664
Room/board/expenses: $13,030
Full-time enrollment: 489
men: 77%; women: 23%;
minorities: 4%; international: 59%
Part-time enrollment: 200
men: 80%; women: 20%;
minorities: 7%; international: 32%
Acceptance rate: 46%
GRE requirement: Yes
Avg. GRE: quantitative: 728
TOEFL requirement: Yes
Minimum TOEFL score: 550
Fellowships: 15
Teaching assistantships: 62
Research assistantships: 294
Students specializing in: aerospace:
5%; chemical: 5%; civil: 9%; com-
puter: 0%; computer science: 10%;
electrical: 21%; industrial: 7%;
mechanical: 16%; mining: 3%;
petroleum: 4%; other: 19%

WISCONSIN

Marquette University
PO Box 1881
Milwaukee, WI 53201-1881
http://www.grad.marquette.edu
Private
Admissions: (414) 288-7137
E-mail: mugs@mu.edu
Financial aid: (414) 288-5325
Application deadline: rolling
Tuition: full time: $800/credit hour;
part time: $800/credit hour
Room/board/expenses: $14,210
Full-time enrollment: 107
men: 64%; women: 36%;
minorities: 5%; international: 54%
Part-time enrollment: 127
men: 76%; women: 24%;
minorities: 5%; international: 19%
Acceptance rate: 51%
GRE requirement: Yes
Avg. GRE: quantitative: 707
TOEFL requirement: Yes
Minimum TOEFL score: 590
Fellowships: 2
Teaching assistantships: 67
Research assistantships: 53
Students specializing in: biomedical:
38%; civil: 9%; electrical: 21%;
management: 8%; mechanical:
19%; other: 6%

University of Wisconsin–Madison
2610 Engineering Hall
Madison, WI 53706
http://www.engr.wisc.edu/
Public
Admissions: (608) 262-2433
E-mail:
gradadmiss@bascom.wisc.edu
Financial aid: (608) 262-3060
Application deadline: N/A
In-state tuition: full time: $10,500;
part time: $604/credit hour
Out-of-state tuition: full time:
$25,770
Room/board/expenses: $13,350

Full-time enrollment: 1,180
men: 81%; women: 19%;
minorities: 8%; international: 47%
Part-time enrollment: 344
men: 86%; women: 14%;
minorities: 12%; international: 25%
Acceptance rate: 24%
GRE requirement: Yes
Avg. GRE: quantitative: 781
TOEFL requirement: Yes
Minimum TOEFL score: 580
Fellowships: 73
Teaching assistantships: 183
Research assistantships: 762
Students specializing in: biomedical:
5%; chemical: 8%; civil: 9%;
computer science: 13%; electrical:
19%; industrial: 10%; materials: 7%;
mechanical: 13%; nuclear: 5%;
other: 12%

University of Wisconsin–Milwaukee[1]
PO Box 784
Milwaukee, WI 53201-0784
http://www.uwm.edu/CEAS
Public
Admissions: (414) 229-6169
E-mail: bwarras@uwm.edu
Financial aid: (414) 229-4541
Tuition: N/A
Room/board/expenses: N/A
Enrollment: N/A

WYOMING

University of Wyoming
1000 E. University Avenue
Department 3295
Laramie, WY 82071
http://wwweng.uwyo.edu
Public
Admissions: (307) 766-2287
E-mail: uwgrad@uwyo.edu
Financial aid: (307) 766-2118
Application deadline: rolling
In-state tuition: full time: $164/credit
hour; part time: $164/credit hour
Out-of-state tuition: full time:
$470/credit hour
Room/board/expenses: $13,529
Full-time enrollment: 126
men: 73%; women: 27%;
minorities: 1%; international: 52%
Part-time enrollment: 66
men: 85%; women: 15%;
minorities: 3%; international: 29%
Acceptance rate: 49%
GRE requirement: Yes
Avg. GRE: quantitative: 732
TOEFL requirement: Yes
Minimum TOEFL score: 540
Fellowships: 2
Teaching assistantships: 47
Research assistantships: 92
Students specializing in: chemical:
7%; civil: 17%; computer science:
18%; electrical: 24%; environ-
mental: 4%; mechanical: 14%;
petroleum: 6%; other: 11%

LAW

The law school directory lists the 195 American Bar Association-accredited law schools as published in the 2008 edition of the *Official Guide to ABA-Approved Law Schools,* produced by the Law School Admission Council and the American Bar Association. All of these schools offer the J.D. degree. There were 190 schools that responded to the *U.S. News* survey conducted in fall 2007 and early 2008, and their data are reported below. Schools that did not respond have abbreviated entries.

TERMINOLOGY

1 A school whose name is footnoted with the numeral 1 did not return the *U.S. News* statistical survey; limited data appear in its entry.

N/A. Not available from the school or not applicable.

Admissions. The admissions office phone number.

E-mail. The electronic address of the admissions office. If, instead of an E-mail address, a website is listed, the website will automatically present an E-mail screen programmed to reach the admissions office.

Financial aid. The financial aid office phone number.

Application deadline. For fall 2009 enrollment. "Rolling" means there is no application deadline; the school acts on applications as they are received. "Varies" means deadlines vary according to department or whether applicants are U.S. citizens or foreign nationals.

Tuition. For the 2007–2008 academic year. Includes fees.

Credit hour. The cost per credit hour for the 2007–2008 academic year.

Room/board/expenses. For the 2007–2008 academic year.

Median grant. The median value of grants to full-time students enrolled in 2006–2007. This is calculated for all full-time students, not just those in the first year, who received grants and scholarships from internal sources.

Average law school indebtedness. For 2007 graduates, the average law school debt for borrowing at least one educational loan while in law school.

Enrollment. Full and part time, fall 2007. Gender figure is full and part time.

Minorities. For fall 2007, full- and part-time students who are Asian-American, African-American, Hispanic, or American Indian. (When the U.S. Department of Education calculates minority enrollment percentages, these are the demographic groups it uses.)

Acceptance rate. Percentage of applicants who were accepted for the fall 2007 full-time J.D. program.

Midrange Law School Admission Test (LSAT) score. For full-time students who entered in fall 2007. The first number is the 25th percentile test score for the class, the second the 75th percentile.

Midrange undergraduate grade-point average. For full-time students who entered in fall 2007. The first number is the 25th percentile GPA for the class; the second is the 75th percentile.

Midrange of full-time private-sector starting salaries. For the 2006 graduating class, the starting salary is for those employed full time in the private sector in law firms, business, industry, or other private-sector jobs. The first number is the starting salary at the 25th percentile of the graduating class; the second number is the starting salary at the 75th percentile. When a school has the same salary at the 25th and 75th percentiles, it means that the starting salaries for private-sector jobs were at the same level for a large proportion of the class.

Job classifications. For the 2006 graduating class, the breakdown for the following types of employment: law firms, business and industry (legal and nonlegal), government, public interest, judicial clerkship, academia, and unknown. Numbers may not add up to 100 because of rounding.

Employment locations. For the 2006 graduating class. Abbreviations: **Intl.** international; **N.E.** New England (Conn., Maine, Mass., N.H., R.I., Vt.); **M.A.** Middle Atlantic (N.J., N.Y., Pa.); **S.A.** South Atlantic (Del., D.C., Fla., Ga., Md., N.C., S.C., Va., W.Va.); **E.N.C.** East North Central (Ill., Ind., Mich., Ohio, Wis.); **W.N.C.** West North Central (Iowa, Kan., Minn., Mo., Neb., N.D., S.D.); **E.S.C.** East South Central (Ala., Ky., Miss., Tenn.); **W.S.C.** West South Central (Ark., La., Okla., Texas); **Mt.** Mountain (Ariz., Colo., Idaho, Mont., Nev., N.M., Utah, Wyo.); **Pac.** Pacific (Alaska, Calif., Hawaii, Ore., Wash.).

ALABAMA

Faulkner University (Jones)
5345 Atlanta Highway
Montgomery, AL 36109
http://www.faulkner.edu/admissions/jonesLaw.asp
Private
Admissions: (334) 386-7210
E-mail: law@faulkner.edu
Financial aid: (800) 879-9816
Application deadline: 06/15
Tuition: full time: $22,000; part time: $16,500
Room/board/expenses: $18,900
Percent receiving grants: 26%
Median grant: $7,500
Average student indebtedness at graduation: $62,400
Enrollment: full time: 228; part time: 63
men: 55%; women: 45%; minorities: 10%
Acceptance rate (full-time): 50%
Midrange LSAT (full-time): 148-153
Midrange undergraduate GPA (full-time): 2.77-3.36
Midrange of full-time private-sector salaries of 2006 grads: N/A-N/A
2006 grads employed in: law firms: 54%; business and industry: 6%; government: 28%; public interest: 2%; judicial clerk: 10%; academia: 0%; unknown: 0%
Employment location for 2006 class: Intl. 0%; N.E. 0%; M.A. 0%; E.N.C. 0%; W.N.C. 0%; S.A. 4%; E.S.C. 94%; W.S.C. 2%; Mt. 0%; Pac. 0%; unknown 0%

Samford University (Cumberland)
800 Lakeshore Drive
Birmingham, AL 35229
http://cumberland.samford.edu
Private
Admissions: (205) 726-2702
E-mail: law.admissions@samford.edu
Financial aid: (205) 726-2905
Application deadline: 05/01
Tuition: full time: $27,892; part time: $16,740
Room/board/expenses: $19,700
Percent receiving grants: 36%
Median grant: $18,000
Average student indebtedness at graduation: $94,263
Enrollment: full time: 495; part time: N/A
men: 54%; women: 46%; minorities: 11%
Acceptance rate (full-time): 40%
Midrange LSAT (full-time): 155-159
Midrange undergraduate GPA (full-time): 3.07-3.52
Midrange of full-time private-sector salaries of 2006 grads: $50,000-$82,500
2006 grads employed in: law firms: 67%; business and industry: 9%; government: 14%; public interest: 3%; judicial clerk: 7%; academia: 0%; unknown: 0%
Employment location for 2006 class: Intl. 0%; N.E. 0%; M.A. 1%; E.N.C. 0%; W.N.C. 0%; S.A. 32%; E.S.C. 65%; W.S.C. 1%; Mt. 0%; Pac. 1%; unknown 0%

University of Alabama
Box 870382
Tuscaloosa, AL 35487
http://www.law.ua.edu
Public
Admissions: (205) 348-5440
E-mail: admissions@law.ua.edu
Financial aid: (205) 348-6756
Application deadline: 03/01
In-state tuition: full time: $11,190; part time: N/A
Out-of-state tuition: full time: $22,170
Room/board/expenses: $14,954
Percent receiving grants: 45%
Median grant: $6,603
Average student indebtedness at graduation: $37,611
Enrollment: full time: 492; part time: 23
men: 61%; women: 39%; minorities: 13%
Acceptance rate (full-time): 29%
Midrange LSAT (full-time): 160-165
Midrange undergraduate GPA (full-time): 3.31-3.84
Midrange of full-time private-sector salaries of 2006 grads: $45,000-$95,000
2006 grads employed in: law firms: 69%; business and industry: 7%; government: 9%; public interest: 4%; judicial clerk: 8%; academia: 1%; unknown: 0%
Employment location for 2006 class: Intl. 0%; N.E. 0%; M.A. 0%; E.N.C. 2%; W.N.C. 0%; S.A. 17%; E.S.C. 73%; W.S.C. 6%; Mt. 2%; Pac. N/A; unknown 0%

ARIZONA

Arizona State University (O'Connor)
1100 S. McAllister Avenue
Tempe, AZ 85287-7906
http://www.law.asu.edu
Public
Admissions: (480) 965-1474
E-mail: law.admissions@asu.edu
Financial aid: (480) 965-1474
Application deadline: 02/01
In-state tuition: full time: $14,628; part time: N/A
Out-of-state tuition: full time: $26,320
Room/board/expenses: $19,200
Percent receiving grants: 48%
Median grant: $5,000
Average student indebtedness at graduation: $58,964
Enrollment: full time: 595; part time: N/A
men: 57%; women: 43%; minorities: 26%
Acceptance rate (full-time): 24%
Midrange LSAT (full-time): 156-162
Midrange undergraduate GPA (full-time): 3.30-3.81
Midrange of full-time private-sector salaries of 2006 grads: $65,000-$100,000
2006 grads employed in: law firms: 57%; business and industry: 11%; government: 15%; public interest: 5%; judicial clerk: 8%; academia: 2%; unknown: 2%

Employment location for 2006 class: Intl. 0%; N.E. 0%; M.A. 1%; E.N.C. 2%; W.N.C. 1%; S.A. 5%; E.S.C. 0%; W.S.C. 3%; Mt. 80%; Pac. 7%; unknown 0%

Phoenix School of Law
4041 N. Central Avenue
Suite 100
Phoenix, AZ 85012
http://www.phoenixlaw.edu
Private
Admissions: (602) 682-6800
E-mail: admissions@phoenixlaw.edu
Financial aid: (602) 682-6800
Application deadline: rolling
Tuition: full time: $28,640; part time: $21,800
Room/board/expenses: N/A
Percent receiving grants: 37%
Median grant: $8,995
Enrollment: full time: 103; part time: 91
men: 49%; women: 51%; minorities: 19%
Acceptance rate (full-time): 62%
Midrange LSAT (full-time): 148-157
Midrange undergraduate GPA (full-time): 2.93-3.48
Midrange of full-time private-sector salaries of 2006 grads: N/A-N/A
2006 grads employed in: law firms: N/A; business and industry: N/A; government: N/A; public interest: N/A; judicial clerk: N/A; academia: N/A; unknown: N/A
Employment location for 2006 class: Intl. N/A; N.E. N/A; M.A. N/A; E.N.C. N/A; W.N.C. N/A; S.A. N/A; E.S.C. N/A; W.S.C. N/A; Mt. N/A; Pac. N/A; unknown N/A

University of Arizona (Rogers)
PO Box 210176
Tucson, AZ 85721-0176
http://www.law.arizona.edu
Public
Admissions: (520) 621-3477
E-mail: admissions@law.arizona.edu
Financial aid: (520) 626-8101
Application deadline: 02/15
In-state tuition: full time: $17,768; part time: N/A
Out-of-state tuition: full time: $28,574
Room/board/expenses: $17,706
Percent receiving grants: 79%
Median grant: $7,000
Average student indebtedness at graduation: $61,912
Enrollment: full time: 453; part time: N/A
men: 49%; women: 51%; minorities: 27%
Acceptance rate (full-time): 31%
Midrange LSAT (full-time): 157-164
Midrange undergraduate GPA (full-time): 3.23-3.73
Midrange of full-time private-sector salaries of 2006 grads: $65,000-$110,000
2006 grads employed in: law firms: 41%; business and industry: 13%; government: 16%; public interest: 3%; judicial clerk: 23%; academia: 4%; unknown: 1%
Employment location for 2006 class: Intl. 3%; N.E. 0%; M.A. 4%; E.N.C. 1%; W.N.C. 3%; S.A. 4%; E.S.C. 1%; W.S.C. 2%; Mt. 73%; Pac. 10%; unknown 2%

ARKANSAS

University of Arkansas–Fayetteville
Robert A. Leflar Law Center
Fayetteville, AR 72701
http://law.uark.edu/
Public
Admissions: (479) 575-3102
E-mail: jkmiller@uark.edu
Financial aid: (479) 575-3806
Application deadline: 07/01
In-state tuition: full time: $338/credit hour; part time: N/A
Out-of-state tuition: full time: $677/credit hour
Room/board/expenses: $14,314
Percent receiving grants: 39%
Median grant: $6,000
Average student indebtedness at graduation: $50,031
Enrollment: full time: 407; part time: N/A
men: 61%; women: 39%; minorities: 24%
Acceptance rate (full-time): 30%
Midrange LSAT (full-time): 151-159
Midrange undergraduate GPA (full-time): 3.17-3.70
Midrange of full-time private-sector salaries of 2006 grads: $44,500-$62,000
2006 grads employed in: law firms: 60%; business and industry: 14%; government: 12%; public interest: 8%; judicial clerk: 5%; academia: 1%; unknown: 0%
Employment location for 2006 class: Intl. 0%; N.E. N/A; M.A. 2%; E.N.C. N/A; W.N.C. 6%; S.A. 7%; E.S.C. 3%; W.S.C. 79%; Mt. 2%; Pac. 1%; unknown 0%

University of Arkansas–Little Rock (Bowen)
1201 McMath Avenue
Little Rock, AR 72202-5142
http://www.law.ualr.edu/
Public
Admissions: (501) 324-9439
E-mail: lawadm@ualr.edu
Financial aid: (501) 569-3035
Application deadline: 04/15
In-state tuition: full time: $10,201; part time: $7,135
Out-of-state tuition: full time: $20,524
Room/board/expenses: $12,212
Percent receiving grants: 34%
Median grant: $3,500
Average student indebtedness at graduation: $49,730
Enrollment: full time: 292; part time: 150
men: 52%; women: 48%; minorities: 20%
Acceptance rate (full-time): 26%
Midrange LSAT (full-time): 151-156
Midrange undergraduate GPA (full-time): 2.94-3.68
Midrange of full-time private-sector salaries of 2006 grads: $45,000-$58,000
2006 grads employed in: law firms: 57%; business and industry: 12%; government: 15%; public interest: 2%; judicial clerk: 8%; academia: 2%; unknown: 4%
Employment location for 2006 class: Intl. 0%; N.E. 0%; M.A. 1%; E.N.C. 1%; W.N.C. 0%; S.A. 2%; E.S.C. 6%; W.S.C. 89%; Mt. 1%; Pac. 1%; unknown 0%

CALIFORNIA

California Western School of Law
225 Cedar Street
San Diego, CA 92101-3090
http://www.cwsl.edu
Private
Admissions: (619) 525-1401
E-mail: admissions@cwsl.edu
Financial aid: (619) 525-7060
Application deadline: 04/01
Tuition: full time: $34,300; part time: $24,220
Room/board/expenses: $20,082
Percent receiving grants: 34%
Median grant: $16,140
Average student indebtedness at graduation: $104,338
Enrollment: full time: 755; part time: 92
men: 48%; women: 52%; minorities: 28%
Acceptance rate (full-time): 55%
Midrange LSAT (full-time): 150-156
Midrange undergraduate GPA (full-time): 3.00-3.53
Midrange of full-time private-sector salaries of 2006 grads: $60,000-$70,000
2006 grads employed in: law firms: 63%; business and industry: 15%; government: 10%; public interest: 5%; judicial clerk: 5%; academia: 2%; unknown: 0%
Employment location for 2006 class: Intl. 1%; N.E. 3%; M.A. 4%; E.N.C. 2%; W.N.C. 1%; S.A. 2%; E.S.C. 0%; W.S.C. 1%; Mt. 10%; Pac. 76%; unknown 0%

Chapman University
1 University Drive
Orange, CA 92866
http://www.chapman.edu/law
Private
Admissions: (714) 628-2500
E-mail: lawadm@chapman.edu
Financial aid: (714) 628-2510
Application deadline: 04/15
Tuition: full time: $34,250; part time: $29,468
Room/board/expenses: $21,120
Percent receiving grants: 44%
Median grant: $19,222
Average student indebtedness at graduation: $94,397
Enrollment: full time: 474; part time: 71
men: 54%; women: 46%; minorities: 24%
Acceptance rate (full-time): 32%
Midrange LSAT (full-time): 154-159
Midrange undergraduate GPA (full-time): 3.10-3.61
Midrange of full-time private-sector salaries of 2006 grads: $62,500-$75,000
2006 grads employed in: law firms: 55%; business and industry: 21%; government: 7%; public interest: 2%; judicial clerk: 2%; academia: 9%; unknown: 4%
Employment location for 2006 class: Intl. 0%; N.E. 0%; M.A. 1%; E.N.C. 1%; W.N.C. 0%; S.A. 1%; E.S.C. 0%; W.S.C. 0%; Mt. 6%; Pac. 92%; unknown 0%

Golden Gate University
536 Mission Street
San Francisco, CA 94105
http://www.ggu.edu/law/
Private
Admissions: (415) 442-6630
E-mail: lawadmit@ggu.edu
Financial aid: (415) 442-6635
Application deadline: 04/01
Tuition: full time: $32,940; part time: $23,130
Room/board/expenses: $21,315

Percent receiving grants: 43%
Median grant: $7,500
Average student indebtedness at graduation: $112,477
Enrollment: full time: 538; part time: 150
men: 44%; women: 56%; minorities: 28%
Acceptance rate (full-time): 63%
Midrange LSAT (full-time): 150-154
Midrange undergraduate GPA (full-time): 2.82-3.37
Midrange of full-time private-sector salaries of 2006 grads: $52,000-$75,000
2006 grads employed in: law firms: 53%; business and industry: 25%; government: 12%; public interest: 3%; judicial clerk: 2%; academia: 5%; unknown: 1%
Employment location for 2006 class: Intl. 0%; N.E. 0%; M.A. 2%; E.N.C. 1%; W.N.C. 0%; S.A. 3%; E.S.C. 0%; W.S.C. 0%; Mt. 2%; Pac. 92%; unknown 0%

Loyola Marymount University
919 Albany Street
Los Angeles, CA 90015-1211
http://www.lls.edu
Private
Admissions: (213) 736-1074
E-mail: Admissions@lls.edu
Financial aid: (213) 736-1140
Application deadline: 02/02
Tuition: full time: $36,058; part time: $24,188
Room/board/expenses: $20,220
Percent receiving grants: 25%
Median grant: $26,900
Average student indebtedness at graduation: $101,800
Enrollment: full time: 1,003; part time: 291
men: 51%; women: 49%; minorities: 39%
Acceptance rate (full-time): 30%
Midrange LSAT (full-time): 159-163
Midrange undergraduate GPA (full-time): 3.22-3.65
Midrange of full-time private-sector salaries of 2006 grads: $67,650-$125,000
2006 grads employed in: law firms: 59%; business and industry: 21%; government: 8%; public interest: 8%; judicial clerk: 3%; academia: 2%; unknown: 0%
Employment location for 2006 class: Intl. 2%; N.E. N/A; M.A. 1%; E.N.C. 1%; W.N.C. N/A; S.A. 0%; E.S.C. N/A; W.S.C. 0%; Mt. 1%; Pac. 95%; unknown 0%

Pepperdine University
24255 Pacific Coast Highway
Malibu, CA 90263
http://law.pepperdine.edu
Private
Admissions: (310) 506-4631
E-mail: soladmis@pepperdine.edu
Financial aid: (310) 506-4633
Application deadline: 02/01
Tuition: full time: $35,520; part time: N/A
Room/board/expenses: $20,610
Percent receiving grants: 76%
Median grant: $6,000
Average student indebtedness at graduation: $111,173
Enrollment: full time: 633; part time: N/A
men: 50%; women: 50%; minorities: 17%
Acceptance rate (full-time): 32%
Midrange LSAT (full-time): 158-162
Midrange undergraduate GPA (full-time): 3.42-3.73
Midrange of full-time private-sector salaries of 2006 grads: $65,000-$135,000

2006 grads employed in: law firms: 57%; business and industry: 18%; government: 15%; public interest: 2%; judicial clerk: 5%; academia: 2%; unknown: 1%
Employment location for 2006 class: Intl. 2%; N.E. 2%; M.A. 1%; E.N.C. 1%; W.N.C. 1%; S.A. 4%; E.S.C. 1%; W.S.C. 4%; Mt. 4%; Pac. 78%; unknown 2%

Santa Clara University
500 El Camino Real
Santa Clara, CA 95053-0421
http://www.scu.edu/law
Private
Admissions: (408) 554-4800
E-mail: lawadmissions@scu.edu
Financial aid: (408) 554-4447
Application deadline: 02/01
Tuition: full time: $1,175/credit hour; part time: $1,175/credit hour
Room/board/expenses: $19,578
Percent receiving grants: 40%
Median grant: $10,000
Average student indebtedness at graduation: $98,307
Enrollment: full time: 728; part time: 217
men: 54%; women: 46%; minorities: 41%
Acceptance rate (full-time): 51%
Midrange LSAT (full-time): 156-161
Midrange undergraduate GPA (full-time): 3.16-3.59
Midrange of full-time private-sector salaries of 2006 grads: $70,000-$135,000
2006 grads employed in: law firms: 52%; business and industry: 27%; government: 9%; public interest: 3%; judicial clerk: 1%; academia: 1%; unknown: 7%
Employment location for 2006 class: Intl. 1%; N.E. 0%; M.A. 0%; E.N.C. 0%; W.N.C. 0%; S.A. 2%; E.S.C. 0%; W.S.C. 0%; Mt. 2%; Pac. 95%; unknown 0%

Southwestern Law School
3050 Wilshire Boulevard
Los Angeles, CA 90010-1106
http://www.swlaw.edu
Private
Admissions: (213) 738-6717
E-mail: admissions@swlaw.edu
Financial aid: (213) 738-6719
Application deadline: 04/01
Tuition: full time: $33,410; part time: $20,126
Room/board/expenses: $21,050
Percent receiving grants: 29%
Median grant: $10,000
Average student indebtedness at graduation: $105,029
Enrollment: full time: 698; part time: 274
men: 49%; women: 51%; minorities: 35%
Acceptance rate (full-time): 33%
Midrange LSAT (full-time): 153-157
Midrange undergraduate GPA (full-time): 3.06-3.58
Midrange of full-time private-sector salaries of 2006 grads: $65,000-$87,500
2006 grads employed in: law firms: 57%; business and industry: 14%; government: 13%; public interest: 1%; judicial clerk: 4%; academia: 2%; unknown: 9%
Employment location for 2006 class: Intl. 1%; N.E. 0%; M.A. 0%; E.N.C. 1%; W.N.C. 1%; S.A. 1%; E.S.C. 1%; W.S.C. 1%; Mt. 2%; Pac. 93%; unknown 1%

Stanford University
Crown Quadrangle
559 Nathan Abbott Way
Stanford, CA 94305-8610
http://www.law.stanford.edu/
Private
Admissions: (650) 723-4985
E-mail: admissions@law.stanford.edu
Financial aid: (650) 723-9247
Application deadline: 02/02
Tuition: full time: $39,916; part time: N/A
Room/board/expenses: $20,700
Percent receiving grants: 41%
Median grant: $16,613
Average student indebtedness at graduation: $101,379
Enrollment: full time: 538; part time: N/A
men: 54%; women: 46%; minorities: 33%
Acceptance rate (full-time): 9%
Midrange LSAT (full-time): 167-172
Midrange undergraduate GPA (full-time): 3.74-3.95
Midrange of full-time private-sector salaries of 2006 grads: $135,000-$145,000
2006 grads employed in: law firms: 66%; business and industry: 2%; government: 2%; public interest: 2%; judicial clerk: 27%; academia: 1%; unknown: 0%
Employment location for 2006 class: Intl. 2%; N.E. 2%; M.A. 21%; E.N.C. 2%; W.N.C. 1%; S.A. 15%; E.S.C. 1%; W.S.C. 3%; Mt. 4%; Pac. 48%; unknown 0%

Thomas Jefferson School of Law
2121 San Diego Avenue
San Diego, CA 92110
http://www.tjsl.edu
Private
Admissions: (619) 297-9700
E-mail: info@tjsl.edu
Financial aid: (619) 297-9700
Application deadline: 06/01
Tuition: full time: $31,770; part time: $20,010
Room/board/expenses: $24,566
Percent receiving grants: 45%
Median grant: $12,000
Average student indebtedness at graduation: $92,397
Enrollment: full time: 581; part time: 196
men: 53%; women: 47%; minorities: 31%
Acceptance rate (full-time): 45%
Midrange LSAT (full-time): 148-151
Midrange undergraduate GPA (full-time): 2.75-3.23
Midrange of full-time private-sector salaries of 2006 grads: $40,000-$65,000
2006 grads employed in: law firms: 50%; business and industry: 24%; government: 11%; public interest: 6%; judicial clerk: 2%; academia: 3%; unknown: 4%
Employment location for 2006 class: Intl. 2%; N.E. 1%; M.A. 3%; E.N.C. 4%; W.N.C. 2%; S.A. 5%; E.S.C. 0%; W.S.C. 4%; Mt. 10%; Pac. 67%; unknown 2%

University of California–Berkeley
Boalt Hall
Berkeley, CA 94720-7200
http://www.law.berkeley.edu
Public
Admissions: (510) 642-2274
E-mail: admissions@law.berkeley.edu
Financial aid: (510) 642-1563
Application deadline: 02/01
In-state tuition: full time: $26,896; part time: N/A
Out-of-state tuition: full time: $39,141
Room/board/expenses: $21,507
Percent receiving grants: 69%
Median grant: $8,300
Average student indebtedness at graduation: $74,802
Enrollment: full time: 864; part time: N/A
men: 45%; women: 55%; minorities: 32%
Acceptance rate (full-time): 12%
Midrange LSAT (full-time): 163-170
Midrange undergraduate GPA (full-time): 3.64-3.90
Midrange of full-time private-sector salaries of 2006 grads: $135,000-$135,000
2006 grads employed in: law firms: 67%; business and industry: 3%; government: 5%; public interest: 11%; judicial clerk: 14%; academia: 0%; unknown: 0%
Employment location for 2006 class: Intl. 2%; N.E. 1%; M.A. 11%; E.N.C. 1%; W.N.C. 0%; S.A. 9%; E.S.C. 0%; W.S.C. 2%; Mt. 3%; Pac. 71%; unknown 0%

University of California–Davis
400 Mrak Hall Drive
Davis, CA 95616-5201
http://www.law.ucdavis.edu
Public
Admissions: (530) 752-6477
E-mail: admissions@law.ucdavis.edu
Financial aid: (530) 752-6573
Application deadline: 02/01
In-state tuition: full time: $25,489; part time: N/A
Out-of-state tuition: full time: $37,734
Room/board/expenses: $15,903
Percent receiving grants: 69%
Median grant: $8,300
Average student indebtedness at graduation: $62,077
Enrollment: full time: 577; part time: N/A
men: 45%; women: 55%; minorities: 36%
Acceptance rate (full-time): 29%
Midrange LSAT (full-time): 159-165
Midrange undergraduate GPA (full-time): 3.38-3.75
Midrange of full-time private-sector salaries of 2006 grads: $78,500-$135,000
2006 grads employed in: law firms: 63%; business and industry: 14%; government: 6%; public interest: 11%; judicial clerk: 3%; academia: 1%; unknown: 2%
Employment location for 2006 class: Intl. 0%; N.E. 0%; M.A. 3%; E.N.C. 0%; W.N.C. 0%; S.A. 1%; E.S.C. 1%; W.S.C. 1%; Mt. 1%; Pac. 92%; unknown 1%

University of California (Hastings)
200 McAllister Street
San Francisco, CA 94102
http://www.uchastings.edu
Public
Admissions: (415) 565-4623
E-mail: admiss@uchastings.edu
Financial aid: (415) 565-4624
Application deadline: 03/01
In-state tuition: full time: $24,120; part time: N/A
Out-of-state tuition: full time: $35,345
Room/board/expenses: $19,293
Percent receiving grants: 75%
Median grant: $5,500
Average student indebtedness at graduation: $83,000
Enrollment: full time: 1,215; part time: N/A
men: 47%; women: 53%; minorities: 34%
Acceptance rate (full-time): 27%
Midrange LSAT (full-time): 160-165
Midrange undergraduate GPA (full-time): 3.36-3.74
Midrange of full-time private-sector salaries of 2006 grads: $76,500-$135,000
2006 grads employed in: law firms: 68%; business and industry: 8%; government: 8%; public interest: 10%; judicial clerk: 3%; academia: 2%; unknown: 1%
Employment location for 2006 class: Intl. 2%; N.E. 1%; M.A. 4%; E.N.C. 0%; W.N.C. 0%; S.A. 1%; E.S.C. 0%; W.S.C. 1%; Mt. 2%; Pac. 90%; unknown 0%

University of California–Los Angeles
71 Dodd Hall
PO Box 951445
Los Angeles, CA 90095-1445
http://www.law.ucla.edu
Public
Admissions: (310) 825-2080
E-mail: admissions@law.ucla.edu
Financial aid: (310) 825-2459
Application deadline: 02/01
In-state tuition: full time: $26,855; part time: N/A
Out-of-state tuition: full time: $37,648
Room/board/expenses: $19,725
Percent receiving grants: 61%
Median grant: $8,760
Average student indebtedness at graduation: $91,435
Enrollment: full time: 1,025; part time: N/A
men: 51%; women: 49%; minorities: 33%
Acceptance rate (full-time): 18%
Midrange LSAT (full-time): 163-169
Midrange undergraduate GPA (full-time): 3.54-3.85
Midrange of full-time private-sector salaries of 2006 grads: $100,000-$135,000
2006 grads employed in: law firms: 64%; business and industry: 9%; government: 8%; public interest: 6%; judicial clerk: 11%; academia: 1%; unknown: 1%
Employment location for 2006 class: Intl. 1%; N.E. 0%; M.A. 3%; E.N.C. 2%; W.N.C. 0%; S.A. 5%; E.S.C. 0%; W.S.C. 3%; Mt. 3%; Pac. 83%; unknown 1%

University of La Verne
32nd E. D Street
Ontario, CA 91764
http://law.ulv.edu
Private
Admissions: (909) 460-2001
E-mail: lawadm@ulv.edu
Financial aid: (909) 593-3511
Application deadline: rolling
Tuition: full time: $32,370; part time: $24,470
Room/board/expenses: $21,837
Percent receiving grants: 58%
Median grant: $14,000
Average student indebtedness at graduation: $60,875
Enrollment: full time: 205; part time: 105
men: 58%; women: 42%; minorities: 32%
Acceptance rate (full-time): 43%
Midrange LSAT (full-time): 149-155
Midrange undergraduate GPA (full-time): 2.76-3.31
Midrange of full-time private-sector salaries of 2006 grads: N/A-N/A
2006 grads employed in: law firms: 75%; business and industry: 14%; government: 11%; public interest: 0%; judicial clerk: 0%; academia: 0%; unknown: 0%
Employment location for 2006 class: Intl. 0%; N.E. N/A; M.A. 4%; E.N.C. N/A; W.N.C. N/A; S.A. N/A; E.S.C. N/A; W.S.C. N/A; Mt. N/A; Pac. 96%; unknown 0%

University of San Diego
5998 Alcala Park
San Diego, CA 92110-2492
http://www.law.sandiego.edu
Private
Admissions: (619) 260-4528
E-mail: jdinfo@SanDiego.edu
Financial aid: (619) 260-4570
Application deadline: 02/01
Tuition: full time: $37,704; part time: $26,804
Room/board/expenses: $18,596
Percent receiving grants: 44%
Median grant: $18,000
Average student indebtedness at graduation: $93,403
Enrollment: full time: 768; part time: 280
men: 57%; women: 43%; minorities: 29%
Acceptance rate (full-time): 32%
Midrange LSAT (full-time): 160-164
Midrange undergraduate GPA (full-time): 3.10-3.53
Midrange of full-time private-sector salaries of 2006 grads: $57,000-$91,000
2006 grads employed in: law firms: 60%; business and industry: 17%; government: 13%; public interest: 5%; judicial clerk: 2%; academia: 2%; unknown: 1%
Employment location for 2006 class: Intl. 0%; N.E. 1%; M.A. 2%; E.N.C. 1%; W.N.C. 1%; S.A. 2%; E.S.C. 1%; W.S.C. 2%; Mt. 6%; Pac. 82%; unknown 3%

University of San Francisco
2130 Fulton Street
San Francisco, CA 94117-1080
http://www.usfca.edu/law
Private
Admissions: (415) 422-6586
E-mail: lawadmissions@usfca.edu
Financial aid: (415) 422-6210
Application deadline: 02/01
Tuition: full time: $33,870; part time: $24,245
Room/board/expenses: $19,110
Percent receiving grants: 30%
Median grant: $9,633
Average student indebtedness at graduation: $100,140
Enrollment: full time: 556; part time: 156
men: 48%; women: 52%; minorities: 37%
Acceptance rate (full-time): 38%
Midrange LSAT (full-time): 156-161
Midrange undergraduate GPA (full-time): 3.02-3.56
Midrange of full-time private-sector salaries of 2006 grads: $70,000-$135,000
2006 grads employed in: law firms: 65%; business and industry: 11%; government: 13%; public interest: 8%; judicial clerk: 1%; academia: 0%; unknown: 2%
Employment location for 2006 class: Intl. 0%; N.E. N/A; M.A. 1%; E.N.C. N/A; W.N.C. N/A; S.A. 0%; E.S.C. N/A; W.S.C. 1%; Mt. 1%; Pac. 97%; unknown 0%

University of Southern California (Gould)
Los Angeles, CA 90089-0071
http://lawweb.usc.edu
Private
Admissions: (213) 740-2523
E-mail: admissions@law.usc.edu
Financial aid: (213) 740-6314
Application deadline: 02/01
Tuition: full time: $42,640; part time: N/A
Room/board/expenses: $18,666
Percent receiving grants: 58%
Median grant: $10,000
Average student indebtedness at graduation: $107,609
Enrollment: full time: 598; part time: N/A
men: 53%; women: 47%; minorities: 38%
Acceptance rate (full-time): 19%
Midrange LSAT (full-time): 165-167
Midrange undergraduate GPA (full-time): 3.46-3.72
Midrange of full-time private-sector salaries of 2006 grads: $135,000-$135,000
2006 grads employed in: law firms: 68%; business and industry: 10%; government: 8%; public interest: 4%; judicial clerk: 8%; academia: 3%; unknown: 1%
Employment location for 2006 class: Intl. 0%; N.E. 0%; M.A. 2%; E.N.C. 2%; W.N.C. 0%; S.A. 3%; E.S.C. 0%; W.S.C. 1%; Mt. 2%; Pac. 91%; unknown 0%

University of the Pacific (McGeorge)
3200 Fifth Avenue
Sacramento, CA 95817
http://www.mcgeorge.edu
Private
Admissions: (916) 739-7105
E-mail: admissionsmcgeorge@pacific.edu
Financial aid: (916) 739-7158
Application deadline: rolling
Tuition: full time: $34,474; part time: $22,920
Room/board/expenses: $19,371
Percent receiving grants: 45%
Median grant: $10,500
Average student indebtedness at graduation: $106,729
Enrollment: full time: 615; part time: 399
men: 52%; women: 48%; minorities: 26%
Acceptance rate (full-time): 40%
Midrange LSAT (full-time): 155-159
Midrange undergraduate GPA (full-time): 3.13-3.60
Midrange of full-time private-sector salaries of 2006 grads: $60,000-$80,000
2006 grads employed in: law firms: 48%; business and industry: 15%; government: 18%; public interest: 9%; judicial clerk: 3%; academia: 6%; unknown: 1%
Employment location for 2006 class: Intl. 1%; N.E. 0%; M.A. 0%; E.N.C. 1%; W.N.C. 0%; S.A. 1%; E.S.C. 0%; W.S.C. 0%; Mt. 5%; Pac. 92%; unknown 0%

Western State University
1111 N. State College Boulevard
Fullerton, CA 92831
http://www.wsulaw.edu
Private
Admissions: (714) 459-1101
E-mail: adm@wsulaw.edu
Financial aid: (714) 459-1120
Application deadline: rolling

Tuition: full time: $29,770;
part time: $20,070
Room/board/expenses: $22,817
Percent receiving grants: 53%
Median grant: $10,000
Average student indebtedness at
graduation: $89,151
Enrollment: full time: 259;
part time: 129
men: 51%; women: 49%;
minorities: 31%
Acceptance rate (full-time): 45%
Midrange LSAT (full-time): 148-153
Midrange undergraduate GPA
(full-time): 2.90-3.38
Midrange of full-time private-sector
salaries of 2006 grads: $40,000-
$75,000
2006 grads employed in: law firms:
55%; business and industry: 21%;
government: 13%; public interest:
2%; judicial clerk: 0%; academia:
5%; unknown: 4%
Employment location for 2006 class:
Intl. N/A; N.E. N/A; M.A. N/A; E.N.C.
N/A; W.N.C. N/A; S.A. N/A; E.S.C.
N/A; W.S.C. N/A; Mt. N/A; Pac. N/A;
unknown N/A

Whittier Law School

3333 Harbor Boulevard
Costa Mesa, CA 92626-1501
http://www.law.whittier.edu
Private
Admissions: (800) 808-8188
E-mail: info@law.whittier.edu
Financial aid: (714) 444-4141
Application deadline: 03/15
Tuition: full time: $31,750;
part time: $21,180
Room/board/expenses: $17,714
Percent receiving grants: 53%
Median grant: $12,000
Average student indebtedness at
graduation: $98,385
Enrollment: full time: 372;
part time: 220
men: 47%; women: 53%;
minorities: 33%
Acceptance rate (full-time): 62%
Midrange LSAT (full-time): 149-153
Midrange undergraduate GPA
(full-time): 2.56-3.19
Midrange of full-time private-sector
salaries of 2006 grads: $65,000-
$83,000
2006 grads employed in: law firms:
49%; business and industry: 30%;
government: 9%; public interest:
8%; judicial clerk: 1%; academia:
2%; unknown: 0%
Employment location for 2006 class:
Intl. 3%; N.E. 0%; M.A. 1%; E.N.C.
N/A; W.N.C. N/A; S.A. 2%; E.S.C.
N/A; W.S.C. 1%; Mt. 1%; Pac. 92%;
unknown 0%

University of Colorado–Boulder

Box 401
Boulder, CO 80309-0401
http://www.colorado.edu/law/
Public
Admissions: (303) 492-7203
E-mail: lawadmin@colorado.edu
Financial aid: (303) 492-8223
Application deadline: 03/15
In-state tuition: full time: $18,594;
part time: N/A
Out-of-state tuition: full time:
$31,278
Room/board/expenses: $12,920
Percent receiving grants: 36%
Median grant: $2,500
Average student indebtedness at
graduation: $62,485

Enrollment: full time: 530;
part time: N/A
men: 52%; women: 48%;
minorities: 22%
Acceptance rate (full-time): 25%
Midrange LSAT (full-time): 160-165
Midrange undergraduate GPA
(full-time): 3.33-3.83
Midrange of full-time private-sector
salaries of 2006 grads: $52,000-
$105,000
2006 grads employed in: law firms:
43%; business and industry: 9%;
government: 18%; public interest:
3%; judicial clerk: 19%; academia:
1%; unknown: 8%
Employment location for 2006 class:
Intl. 1%; N.E. 0%; M.A. 2%; E.N.C.
2%; W.N.C. 0%; S.A. 4%; E.S.C.
0%; W.S.C. 1%; Mt. 84%; Pac. 6%;
unknown 1%

University of Denver (Sturm)

2255 E. Evans Avenue
Denver, CO 80208
http://www.law.du.edu
Private
Admissions: (303) 871-6135
E-mail: admissions@law.du.edu
Financial aid: (303) 871-6136
Application deadline: rolling
Tuition: full time: $32,752;
part time: $24,136
Room/board/expenses: $15,833
Percent receiving grants: 41%
Median grant: $10,000
Average student indebtedness at
graduation: $91,062
Enrollment: full time: 855;
part time: 279
men: 55%; women: 45%;
minorities: 17%
Acceptance rate (full-time): 33%
Midrange LSAT (full-time): 155-160
Midrange undergraduate GPA
(full-time): 3.15-3.66
Midrange of full-time private-sector
salaries of 2006 grads: $52,000-
$95,000
2006 grads employed in: law firms:
46%; business and industry: 12%;
government: 17%; public interest:
4%; judicial clerk: 9%; academia:
1%; unknown: 11%
Employment location for 2006 class:
Intl. 0%; N.E. 1%; M.A. 2%; E.N.C.
1%; W.N.C. 1%; S.A. 5%; E.S.C. 1%;
W.S.C. 2%; Mt. 83%; Pac. 2%;
unknown 2%

Quinnipiac University

275 Mount Carmel Avenue
Hamden, CT 06518
http://law.quinnipiac.edu
Private
Admissions: (203) 582-3400
E-mail: ladm@quinnipiac.edu
Financial aid: (203) 582-3405
Application deadline: rolling
Tuition: full time: $36,240;
part time: $25,440
Room/board/expenses: $17,716
Percent receiving grants: 89%
Median grant: $12,000
Average student indebtedness at
graduation: $77,288
Enrollment: full time: 235;
part time: 153
men: 49%; women: 51%;
minorities: 15%
Acceptance rate (full-time): 28%
Midrange LSAT (full-time): 157-160
Midrange undergraduate GPA
(full-time): 3.01-3.62
Midrange of full-time private-sector
salaries of 2006 grads: $47,500-
$78,000

2006 grads employed in: law firms:
49%; business and industry: 20%;
government: 14%; public interest:
5%; judicial clerk: 5%; academia:
3%; unknown: 3%
Employment location for 2006 class:
Intl. 0%; N.E. 69%; M.A. 19%;
E.N.C. 1%; W.N.C. 2%; S.A. 2%;
E.S.C. 1%; W.S.C. 0%; Mt. 0%; Pac.
1%; unknown 6%

University of Connecticut

55 Elizabeth Street
Hartford, CT 06105-2296
http://www.law.uconn.edu
Public
Admissions: (860) 570-5100
E-mail: admit@law.uconn.edu
Financial aid: (860) 570-5147
Application deadline: 03/01
In-state tuition: full time: $17,520;
part time: $12,220
Out-of-state tuition: full time:
$36,960
Room/board/expenses: $17,200
Percent receiving grants: 73%
Median grant: $9,000
Average student indebtedness at
graduation: $72,421
Enrollment: full time: 484;
part time: 179
men: 52%; women: 48%;
minorities: 18%
Acceptance rate (full-time): 14%
Midrange LSAT (full-time): 160-164
Midrange undergraduate GPA
(full-time): 3.24-3.64
Midrange of full-time private-sector
salaries of 2006 grads: $73,000-
$125,000
2006 grads employed in: law firms:
50%; business and industry: 16%;
government: 12%; public interest:
6%; judicial clerk: 13%; academia:
3%; unknown: 0%
Employment location for 2006 class:
Intl. 0%; N.E. 72%; M.A. 15%; E.N.C.
1%; W.N.C. 1%; S.A. 9%; E.S.C. 1%;
W.S.C. 0%; Mt. 2%; Pac. 1%;
unknown 1%

Yale University

PO Box 208215
New Haven, CT 06520-8215
http://www.law.yale.edu
Private
Admissions: (203) 432-4995
E-mail: admissions.law@yale.edu
Financial aid: (203) 432-1688
Application deadline: 02/16
Tuition: full time: $43,750;
part time: $22,750
Room/board/expenses: $16,100
Percent receiving grants: 50%
Median grant: $19,850
Average student indebtedness at
graduation: $85,789
Enrollment: full time: 586;
part time: 1
men: 52%; women: 48%;
minorities: 28%
Acceptance rate (full-time): 7%
Midrange LSAT (full-time): 170-177
Midrange undergraduate GPA
(full-time): 3.77-3.97
Midrange of full-time private-sector
salaries of 2006 grads: $135,000-
$145,000
2006 grads employed in: law firms:
43%; business and industry: 4%;
government: 3%; public interest:
7%; judicial clerk: 43%; academia:
3%; unknown: 0%
Employment location for 2006 class:
Intl. 3%; N.E. 12%; M.A. 35%;
E.N.C. 3%; W.N.C. 3%; S.A. 20%;
E.S.C. 2%; W.S.C. 5%; Mt. 2%;
Pac. 16%; unknown 0%

Widener University

PO Box 7474
Wilmington, DE 19803-0474
http://www.law.widener.edu
Private
Admissions: (302) 477-2162
E-mail:
law.admissions@law.widener.edu
Financial aid: (302) 477-2272
Application deadline: 05/15
Tuition: full time: $30,870;
part time: $23,130
Room/board/expenses: $15,315
Percent receiving grants: 32%
Median grant: $7,170
Average student indebtedness at
graduation: $87,629
Enrollment: full time: 879;
part time: 497
men: 56%; women: 44%;
minorities: 13%
Acceptance rate (full-time): 51%
Midrange LSAT (full-time): 150-154
Midrange undergraduate GPA
(full-time): 2.88-3.46
Midrange of full-time private-sector
salaries of 2006 grads: $50,000-
$68,500
2006 grads employed in: law firms:
38%; business and industry: 22%;
government: 16%; public interest:
3%; judicial clerk: 19%; academia:
1%; unknown: 1%
Employment location for 2006 class:
Intl. 0%; N.E. 1%; M.A. 75%; E.N.C.
0%; W.N.C. 0%; S.A. 22%; E.S.C.
0%; W.S.C. 1%; Mt. 1%; Pac. 0%;
unknown 0%

American University (Washington)

4801 Massachusetts Avenue NW
Washington, DC 20016-8192
http://www.wcl.american.edu
Private
Admissions: (202) 274-4101
E-mail:
wcladmit@wcl.american.edu
Financial aid: (202) 274-4040
Application deadline: 03/02
Tuition: full time: $37,190;
part time: $26,066
Room/board/expenses: $20,057
Percent receiving grants: 23%
Median grant: $10,000
Average student indebtedness at
graduation: $104,062
Enrollment: full time: 1,246;
part time: 233
men: 46%; women: 54%;
minorities: 32%
Acceptance rate (full-time): 23%
Midrange LSAT (full-time): 161-163
Midrange undergraduate GPA
(full-time): 3.14-3.59
Midrange of full-time private-sector
salaries of 2006 grads: $60,000-
$135,000
2006 grads employed in: law firms:
49%; business and industry: 18%;
government: 13%; public interest:
7%; judicial clerk: 11%; academia:
2%; unknown: 0%
Employment location for 2006 class:
Intl. 2%; N.E. 3%; M.A. 11%; E.N.C.
3%; W.N.C. 1%; S.A. 76%; E.S.C.
0%; W.S.C. 1%; Mt. 1%; Pac. 3%;
unknown 0%

Catholic University of America (Columbus)

3600 John McCormack Road NE
Washington, DC 20064
http://www.law.edu
Private
Admissions: (202) 319-5151
E-mail: admissions@law.edu
Financial aid: (202) 319-5143
Application deadline: 03/13
Tuition: full time: $34,505;
part time: $26,225
Room/board/expenses: $23,824
Percent receiving grants: 29%
Median grant: $10,000
Average student indebtedness at
graduation: $112,589
Enrollment: full time: 607;
part time: 295
men: 52%; women: 48%;
minorities: 18%
Acceptance rate (full-time): 34%
Midrange LSAT (full-time): 156-160
Midrange undergraduate GPA
(full-time): 3.08-3.57
Midrange of full-time private-sector
salaries of 2006 grads: $60,000-
$125,000
2006 grads employed in: law firms:
36%; business and industry: 20%;
government: 26%; public interest:
5%; judicial clerk: 14%; academia:
0%; unknown: 0%
Employment location for 2006 class:
Intl. 1%; N.E. 2%; M.A. 7%; E.N.C.
2%; W.N.C. 0%; S.A. 82%; E.S.C.
0%; W.S.C. 0%; Mt. 1%; Pac. 5%;
unknown 0%

Georgetown University

600 New Jersey Avenue NW
Washington, DC 20001-2075
http://www.law.georgetown.edu
Private
Admissions: (202) 662-9015
E-mail:
admis@law.georgetown.edu
Financial aid: (202) 662-9210
Application deadline: 02/01
Tuition: full time: $39,390;
part time: $34,680
Room/board/expenses: $20,210
Percent receiving grants: 32%
Median grant: $14,550
Average student indebtedness at
graduation: $108,074
Enrollment: full time: 1,605;
part time: 385
men: 57%; women: 43%;
minorities: 24%
Acceptance rate (full-time): 23%
Midrange LSAT (full-time): 167-171
Midrange undergraduate GPA
(full-time): 3.44-3.82
Midrange of full-time private-sector
salaries of 2006 grads: $135,000-
$145,000
2006 grads employed in: law firms:
71%; business and industry: 4%;
government: 8%; public interest:
4%; judicial clerk: 10%; academia:
1%; unknown: 2%
Employment location for 2006 class:
Intl. 2%; N.E. 3%; M.A. 28%; E.N.C.
3%; W.N.C. 1%; S.A. 44%; E.S.C.
1%; W.S.C. 2%; Mt. 2%; Pac. 10%;
unknown 2%

George Washington University

2000 H Street NW
Washington, DC 20052
http://www.law.gwu.edu
Private
Admissions: (202) 739-0648
E-mail: jdadmit@law.gwu.edu
Financial aid: (202) 994-7230
Application deadline: 03/01
Tuition: full time: $38,198;
part time: $26,860

Room/board/expenses: $20,500
Percent receiving grants: 47%
Median grant: $11,000
Average student indebtedness at graduation: $104,468
Enrollment: full time: 1,412; part time: 250
men: 57%; women: 43%; minorities: 25%
Acceptance rate (full-time): 20%
Midrange LSAT (full-time): 163-168
Midrange undergraduate GPA (full-time): 3.40-3.86
Midrange of full-time private-sector salaries of 2006 grads: $115,000-$135,000
2006 grads employed in: law firms: 63%; business and industry: 9%; government: 11%; public interest: 4%; judicial clerk: 11%; academia: 0%; unknown: 3%
Employment location for 2006 class: Intl. 0%; N.E. 3%; M.A. 16%; E.N.C. 2%; W.N.C. 1%; S.A. 64%; E.S.C. 0%; W.S.C. 1%; Mt. 1%; Pac. 7%; unknown 5%

Howard University
2900 Van Ness Street NW
Washington, DC 20008
http://www.law.howard.edu
Private
Admissions: (202) 806-8009
E-mail: admissions@law.howard.edu
Financial aid: (202) 806-8005
Application deadline: 07/31
Tuition: full time: $20,445; part time: N/A
Room/board/expenses: $20,384
Percent receiving grants: 56%
Median grant: $10,000
Average student indebtedness at graduation: $24,705
Enrollment: full time: 428; part time: N/A
men: 41%; women: 59%; minorities: 85%
Acceptance rate (full-time): 23%
Midrange LSAT (full-time): 149-155
Midrange undergraduate GPA (full-time): 2.90-3.50
Midrange of full-time private-sector salaries of 2006 grads: $100,000-$145,000
2006 grads employed in: law firms: 48%; business and industry: 16%; government: 14%; public interest: 7%; judicial clerk: 13%; academia: 2%; unknown 0%
Employment location for 2006 class: Intl. 3%; N.E. 5%; M.A. 25%; E.N.C. 5%; W.N.C. 2%; S.A. 48%; E.S.C. 4%; W.S.C. 3%; Mt. 3%; Pac. 4%; unknown 0%

University of the District of Columbia (Clarke)
4200 Connecticut Avenue NW
Building 38 & 39
Washington, DC 20008
http://www.law.udc.edu
Public
Admissions: (202) 274-7341
E-mail: vcanty@udc.edu
Financial aid: (202) 274-7337
Application deadline: 03/15
In-state tuition: full time: $7,350; part time: N/A
Out-of-state tuition: full time: $14,700
Room/board/expenses: $25,435
Percent receiving grants: 70%
Median grant: $4,000
Average student indebtedness at graduation: $74,536
Enrollment: full time: 237; part time: N/A
men: 40%; women: 60%; minorities: 42%

Acceptance rate (full-time): 19%
Midrange LSAT (full-time): 148-153
Midrange undergraduate GPA (full-time): 2.70-3.40
Midrange of full-time private-sector salaries of 2006 grads: $41,600-$70,000
2006 grads employed in: law firms: 9%; business and industry: 27%; government: 25%; public interest: 18%; judicial clerk: 14%; academia: 5%; unknown: 2%
Employment location for 2006 class: Intl. 0%; N.E. N/A; M.A. N/A; E.N.C. N/A; W.N.C. N/A; S.A. N/A; E.S.C. N/A; W.S.C. N/A; Mt. N/A; Pac. N/A; unknown 2%

FLORIDA

Barry University
6441 E. Colonial Drive
Orlando, FL 32807
http://www.barry.edu/law/
Private
Admissions: (866) 532-2779
E-mail: lawinfo@mail.barry.edu
Financial aid: (321) 206-5621
Application deadline: 04/01
Tuition: full time: $29,300; part time: $22,100
Room/board/expenses: $20,500
Percent receiving grants: 66%
Median grant: $5,000
Average student indebtedness at graduation: $99,832
Enrollment: full time: 536; part time: 156
men: 53%; women: 47%; minorities: 18%
Acceptance rate (full-time): 55%
Midrange LSAT (full-time): 148-152
Midrange undergraduate GPA (full-time): 2.70-3.30
Midrange of full-time private-sector salaries of 2006 grads: $45,000-$55,000
2006 grads employed in: law firms: 43%; business and industry: 8%; government: 24%; public interest: 16%; judicial clerk: 1%; academia: 2%; unknown: 6%
Employment location for 2006 class: Intl. 0%; N.E. 1%; M.A. 1%; E.N.C. N/A; W.N.C. N/A; S.A. 96%; E.S.C. N/A; W.S.C. 2%; Mt. N/A; Pac. N/A; unknown 0%

Florida A&M University
1 N. Orange Avenue
Orlando, FL 32801
http://www.famu.edu/acad/colleges/law
Public
Admissions: (407) 254-3263
E-mail: famulaw.admissions@famu.edu
Financial aid: (850) 599-3730
Application deadline: rolling
In-state tuition: full time: $7,567; part time: $6,344
Out-of-state tuition: full time: $26,828
Room/board/expenses: $17,450
Average student indebtedness at graduation: $18,500
Enrollment: full time: 357; part time: 213
men: 43%; women: 57%; minorities: 68%
Acceptance rate (full-time): 37%
Midrange LSAT (full-time): 143-147
Midrange undergraduate GPA (full-time): 2.66-3.22
Midrange of full-time private-sector salaries of 2006 grads: N/A-N/A
2006 grads employed in: law firms: 32%; business and industry: 13%; government: 6%; public interest: 30%; judicial clerk: 2%; academia: 4%; unknown: 13%

Employment location for 2006 class: Intl. 0%; N.E. 0%; M.A. 0%; E.N.C. 0%; W.N.C. 0%; S.A. 96%; E.S.C. 0%; W.S.C. 0%; Mt. 0%; Pac. 0%; unknown 4%

Florida Coastal School of Law
8787 Baypine Road
Jacksonville, FL 32256
http://www.fcsl.edu
Private
Admissions: (904) 680-7710
E-mail: admissions@fcsl.edu
Financial aid: (904) 680-7717
Application deadline: rolling
Tuition: full time: $28,870; part time: $23,360
Room/board/expenses: $18,120
Percent receiving grants: 48%
Median grant: $5,000
Average student indebtedness at graduation: $91,861
Enrollment: full time: 1,231; part time: 164
men: 52%; women: 48%; minorities: 20%
Acceptance rate (full-time): 55%
Midrange LSAT (full-time): 149-154
Midrange undergraduate GPA (full-time): 2.81-3.47
Midrange of full-time private-sector salaries of 2006 grads: $39,000-$55,000
2006 grads employed in: law firms: 48%; business and industry: 15%; government: 17%; public interest: 12%; judicial clerk: 5%; academia: 1%; unknown: 2%
Employment location for 2006 class: Intl. 0%; N.E. 0%; M.A. 1%; E.N.C. 2%; W.N.C. 1%; S.A. 90%; E.S.C. 3%; W.S.C. 1%; Mt. 0%; Pac. 1%; unknown 0%

Florida International University
University Park
GL 485
Miami, FL 33199
http://www.fiu.edu/law
Public
Admissions: (305) 348-8006
E-mail: lawadmit@fiu.edu
Financial aid: (305) 348-8006
Application deadline: 05/01
In-state tuition: full time: $306/credit hour; part time: $306/credit hour
Out-of-state tuition: full time: $766/credit hour
Room/board/expenses: $14,666
Percent receiving grants: 30%
Median grant: $5,000
Average student indebtedness at graduation: $17,774
Enrollment: full time: 307; part time: 143
men: 56%; women: 44%; minorities: 52%
Acceptance rate (full-time): 25%
Midrange LSAT (full-time): 153-157
Midrange undergraduate GPA (full-time): 2.97-3.58
Midrange of full-time private-sector salaries of 2006 grads: $55,000-$92,000
2006 grads employed in: law firms: 34%; business and industry: 9%; government: 17%; public interest: 4%; judicial clerk: 3%; academia: 0%; unknown: 33%
Employment location for 2006 class: Intl. 1%; N.E. N/A; M.A. N/A; E.N.C. N/A; W.N.C. N/A; S.A. 88%; E.S.C. N/A; W.S.C. N/A; Mt. N/A; Pac. N/A; unknown 11%

Florida State University
425 W. Jefferson Street
Tallahassee, FL 32306-1601
http://www.law.fsu.edu
Public
Admissions: (850) 644-3787
E-mail: admissions@law.fsu.edu
Financial aid: (850) 644-5716
Application deadline: 03/15
In-state tuition: full time: $10,770; part time: N/A
Out-of-state tuition: full time: $30,782
Room/board/expenses: $17,700
Percent receiving grants: 33%
Median grant: $2,000
Average student indebtedness at graduation: $56,270
Enrollment: full time: 764; part time: N/A
men: 60%; women: 40%; minorities: 17%
Acceptance rate (full-time): 24%
Midrange LSAT (full-time): 158-162
Midrange undergraduate GPA (full-time): 3.30-3.77
Midrange of full-time private-sector salaries of 2006 grads: $56,000-$80,000
2006 grads employed in: law firms: 44%; business and industry: 7%; government: 31%; public interest: 9%; judicial clerk: 7%; academia: 1%; unknown: 0%
Employment location for 2006 class: Intl. 0%; N.E. 0%; M.A. 1%; E.N.C. 0%; W.N.C. 0%; S.A. 92%; E.S.C. 0%; W.S.C. 1%; Mt. 1%; Pac. 1%; unknown 2%

Nova Southeastern University (Broad)
3305 College Avenue
Fort Lauderdale, FL 33314-7721
http://www.nsulaw.nova.edu/
Private
Admissions: (954) 262-6117
E-mail: admission@nsu.law.nova.edu
Financial aid: (954) 262-7412
Application deadline: 03/01
Tuition: full time: $29,180; part time: $22,010
Room/board/expenses: $20,973
Percent receiving grants: 10%
Median grant: $15,000
Average student indebtedness at graduation: $93,948
Enrollment: full time: 770; part time: 176
men: 48%; women: 52%; minorities: 26%
Acceptance rate (full-time): 47%
Midrange LSAT (full-time): 147-151
Midrange undergraduate GPA (full-time): 3.00-3.53
Midrange of full-time private-sector salaries of 2006 grads: $50,000-$75,000
2006 grads employed in: law firms: 58%; business and industry: 15%; government: 16%; public interest: 7%; judicial clerk: 3%; academia: 1%; unknown: 0%
Employment location for 2006 class: Intl. 1%; N.E. 1%; M.A. 3%; E.N.C. 0%; W.N.C. 1%; S.A. 89%; E.S.C. 0%; W.S.C. 1%; Mt. 0%; Pac. 1%; unknown 0%

Stetson University
1401 61st Street S
Gulfport, FL 33707
http://www.law.stetson.edu
Private
Admissions: (727) 562-7802
E-mail: lawadmit@law.stetson.edu
Financial aid: (727) 562-7813
Application deadline: 03/15
Tuition: full time: $29,240; part time: $20,260
Room/board/expenses: $14,259

Percent receiving grants: 21%
Median grant: $17,479
Average student indebtedness at graduation: $105,900
Enrollment: full time: 765; part time: 229
men: 47%; women: 53%; minorities: 19%
Acceptance rate (full-time): 31%
Midrange LSAT (full-time): 153-157
Midrange undergraduate GPA (full-time): 3.48-3.71
Midrange of full-time private-sector salaries of 2006 grads: $65,000-$90,000
2006 grads employed in: law firms: 52%; business and industry: 13%; government: 21%; public interest: 7%; judicial clerk: 5%; academia: 2%; unknown: 0%
Employment location for 2006 class: Intl. 0%; N.E. 0%; M.A. 1%; E.N.C. 1%; W.N.C. 0%; S.A. 96%; E.S.C. 1%; W.S.C. 0%; Mt. 0%; Pac. 1%; unknown 0%

St. Thomas University
16401 N.W. 37th Avenue
Miami Gardens, FL 33054
http://www.stu.edu
Private
Admissions: (305) 623-2311
E-mail: admitme@stu.edu
Financial aid: (305) 628-6725
Application deadline: 05/01
Tuition: full time: $27,840; part time: N/A
Room/board/expenses: $19,845
Percent receiving grants: 29%
Median grant: $11,000
Average student indebtedness at graduation: $93,000
Enrollment: full time: 625; part time: N/A
men: 53%; women: 47%; minorities: 44%
Acceptance rate (full-time): 46%
Midrange LSAT (full-time): 147-151
Midrange undergraduate GPA (full-time): 2.75-3.43
Midrange of full-time private-sector salaries of 2006 grads: $40,000-$70,000
2006 grads employed in: law firms: 53%; business and industry: 21%; government: 13%; public interest: 8%; judicial clerk: 2%; academia: 1%; unknown: 2%
Employment location for 2006 class: Intl. 0%; N.E. 1%; M.A. 2%; E.N.C. 3%; W.N.C. 0%; S.A. 90%; E.S.C. 0%; W.S.C. 2%; Mt. 2%; Pac. 2%; unknown 0%

University of Florida (Levin)
PO Box 117620
Gainesville, FL 32611-7620
http://www.law.ufl.edu
Public
Admissions: (352) 273-0890
E-mail: patrick@law.ufl.edu
Financial aid: (352) 273-0628
Application deadline: 01/15
In-state tuition: full time: $10,809; part time: N/A
Out-of-state tuition: full time: $30,174
Room/board/expenses: $13,545
Percent receiving grants: 17%
Median grant: $2,100
Average student indebtedness at graduation: $53,949
Enrollment: full time: 1,290; part time: N/A
men: 53%; women: 47%; minorities: 21%
Acceptance rate (full-time): 34%
Midrange LSAT (full-time): 156-162
Midrange undergraduate GPA (full-time): 3.44-3.83

Midrange of full-time private-sector salaries of 2006 grads: $60,000-$100,000
2006 grads employed in: law firms: 56%; business and industry: 13%; government: 16%; public interest: 9%; judicial clerk: 4%; academia: 1%; unknown: 1%
Employment location for 2006 class: Intl. 0%; N.E. 0%; M.A. 2%; E.N.C. 1%; W.N.C. 0%; S.A. 90%; E.S.C. 1%; W.S.C. 1%; Mt. 1%; Pac. 2%; unknown 3%

University of Miami
PO Box 248087
Coral Gables, FL 33124-8087
http://www.law.miami.edu
Private
Admissions: (305) 284-2795
E-mail: admissions@law.miami.edu
Financial aid: (305) 284-3115
Application deadline: 07/31
Tuition: full time: $34,652; part time: $25,650
Room/board/expenses: $19,252
Percent receiving grants: 35%
Median grant: $16,000
Average student indebtedness at graduation: $90,109
Enrollment: full time: 1,252; part time: 16
men: 56%; women: 44%; minorities: 22%
Acceptance rate (full-time): 51%
Midrange LSAT (full-time): 155-160
Midrange undergraduate GPA (full-time): 3.21-3.63
Midrange of full-time private-sector salaries of 2006 grads: $83,500-$125,000
2006 grads employed in: law firms: 70%; business and industry: 7%; government: 13%; public interest: 5%; judicial clerk: 4%; academia: 1%; unknown: 1%
Employment location for 2006 class: Intl. 0%; N.E. 2%; M.A. 6%; E.N.C. 1%; W.N.C. 0%; S.A. 69%; E.S.C. 1%; W.S.C. 2%; Mt. 3%; Pac. 5%; unknown 11%

GEORGIA

Emory University
1301 Clifton Road
Atlanta, GA 30322-2770
http://www.law.emory.edu
Private
Admissions: (404) 727-6802
E-mail: lawinfo@law.emory.edu
Financial aid: (404) 727-6039
Application deadline: 03/01
Tuition: full time: $38,176; part time: N/A
Room/board/expenses: $21,812
Percent receiving grants: 35%
Median grant: $16,000
Average student indebtedness at graduation: $94,326
Enrollment: full time: 709; part time: N/A
men: 53%; women: 47%; minorities: 28%
Acceptance rate (full-time): 26%
Midrange LSAT (full-time): 162-166
Midrange undergraduate GPA (full-time): 3.28-3.62
Midrange of full-time private-sector salaries of 2006 grads: $75,000-$125,000
2006 grads employed in: law firms: 70%; business and industry: 7%; government: 5%; public interest: 7%; judicial clerk: 11%; academia: 0%; unknown: 1%
Employment location for 2006 class: Intl. 0%; N.E. 2%; M.A. 23%; E.N.C. 2%; W.N.C. 1%; S.A. 61%; E.S.C. 4%; W.S.C. 3%; Mt. 0%; Pac. 4%; unknown 0%

Georgia State University
PO Box 4049
Atlanta, GA 30302-4049
http://law.gsu.edu
Public
Admissions: (404) 651-2048
E-mail: admissions@gsulaw.gsu.edu
Financial aid: (404) 651-2227
Application deadline: 03/15
In-state tuition: full time: $9,530; part time: $8,846
Out-of-state tuition: full time: $27,916
Room/board/expenses: $14,974
Percent receiving grants: 15%
Median grant: $9,350
Average student indebtedness at graduation: $52,245
Enrollment: full time: 473; part time: 192
men: 52%; women: 48%; minorities: 20%
Acceptance rate (full-time): 18%
Midrange LSAT (full-time): 158-162
Midrange undergraduate GPA (full-time): 3.11-3.62
Midrange of full-time private-sector salaries of 2006 grads: $55,500-$115,000
2006 grads employed in: law firms: 62%; business and industry: 12%; government: 14%; public interest: 6%; judicial clerk: 4%; academia: 2%; unknown: 0%
Employment location for 2006 class: Intl. 0%; N.E. 1%; M.A. 1%; E.N.C. 1%; W.N.C. 1%; S.A. 92%; E.S.C. 4%; W.S.C. 1%; Mt. 0%; Pac. 1%; unknown 0%

John Marshall Law School–Atlanta
1422 W. Peachtree Street, NW
Atlanta, GA 30309
http://www.johnmarshall.edu
Private
Admissions: (404) 872-3593
E-mail: admissions@johnmarshall.edu
Financial aid: (404) 872-3593
Application deadline: rolling
Tuition: full time: $930/credit hour; part time: $930/credit hour
Room/board/expenses: $15,890
Percent receiving grants: 0%
Median grant: N/A
Average student indebtedness at graduation: $59,204
Enrollment: full time: 302; part time: 172
men: 50%; women: 50%; minorities: 24%
Acceptance rate (full-time): 34%
Midrange LSAT (full-time): 149-153
Midrange undergraduate GPA (full-time): 2.75-3.39
Midrange of full-time private-sector salaries of 2006 grads: $36,400-$80,000
2006 grads employed in: law firms: 70%; business and industry: 14%; government: 11%; public interest: 3%; judicial clerk: 0%; academia: 3%; unknown: 0%
Employment location for 2006 class: Intl. 0%; N.E. 0%; M.A. 0%; E.N.C. 0%; W.N.C. 0%; S.A. 89%; E.S.C. 5%; W.S.C. 2%; Mt. 2%; Pac. 0%; unknown 3%

Mercer University
1021 Georgia Avenue
Macon, GA 31207-0001
http://www.law.mercer.edu
Private
Admissions: (478) 301-2605
E-mail: martin_sv@mercer.edu
Financial aid: (478) 301-2064
Application deadline: 03/15

Tuition: full time: $32,292; part time: N/A
Room/board/expenses: $14,200
Percent receiving grants: 28%
Median grant: $20,000
Average student indebtedness at graduation: $76,293
Enrollment: full time: 448; part time: N/A
men: 57%; women: 43%; minorities: 17%
Acceptance rate (full-time): 32%
Midrange LSAT (full-time): 155-158
Midrange undergraduate GPA (full-time): 3.20-3.69
Midrange of full-time private-sector salaries of 2006 grads: $52,000-$85,000
2006 grads employed in: law firms: 70%; business and industry: 4%; government: 14%; public interest: 4%; judicial clerk: 5%; academia: 4%; unknown: 0%
Employment location for 2006 class: Intl. 1%; N.E. 0%; M.A. 0%; E.N.C. 1%; W.N.C. 1%; S.A. 87%; E.S.C. 3%; W.S.C. 0%; Mt. 2%; Pac. 0%; unknown 5%

University of Georgia
Herty Drive
Athens, GA 30602
http://www.lawsch.uga.edu
Public
Admissions: (706) 542-7060
E-mail: ugajd@uga.edu
Financial aid: (706) 542-6147
Application deadline: 02/01
In-state tuition: full time: $12,058; part time: N/A
Out-of-state tuition: full time: $29,054
Room/board/expenses: $12,700
Percent receiving grants: 49%
Median grant: $2,000
Average student indebtedness at graduation: $57,545
Enrollment: full time: 642; part time: N/A
men: 54%; women: 46%; minorities: 20%
Acceptance rate (full-time): 25%
Midrange LSAT (full-time): 159-165
Midrange undergraduate GPA (full-time): 3.42-3.86
Midrange of full-time private-sector salaries of 2006 grads: $70,000-$115,000
2006 grads employed in: law firms: 58%; business and industry: 6%; government: 6%; public interest: 9%; judicial clerk: 19%; academia: 1%; unknown: 0%
Employment location for 2006 class: Intl. N/A; N.E. 1%; M.A. 3%; E.N.C. 2%; W.N.C. 0%; S.A. 88%; E.S.C. 3%; W.S.C. 0%; Mt. 2%; Pac. 2%; unknown 0%

HAWAII

University of Hawaii (Richardson)
2515 Dole Street
Honolulu, HI 96822
http://www.hawaii.edu/law
Public
Admissions: (808) 956-3000
E-mail: lawadm@hawaii.edu
Financial aid: (808) 956-7251
Application deadline: 03/01
In-state tuition: full time: $13,656; part time: N/A
Out-of-state tuition: full time: $24,480
Room/board/expenses: $14,997
Percent receiving grants: 40%
Median grant: $6,444
Average student indebtedness at graduation: $51,702

Enrollment: full time: 257; part time: 15
men: 57%; women: 43%; minorities: 63%
Acceptance rate (full-time): 19%
Midrange LSAT (full-time): 155-160
Midrange undergraduate GPA (full-time): 3.09-3.62
Midrange of full-time private-sector salaries of 2006 grads: $63,500-$74,500
2006 grads employed in: law firms: 36%; business and industry: 10%; government: 15%; public interest: 11%; judicial clerk: 24%; academia: 3%; unknown: 1%
Employment location for 2006 class: Intl. 2%; N.E. 2%; M.A. N/A; E.N.C. N/A; W.N.C. N/A; S.A. 8%; E.S.C. 1%; W.S.C. 1%; Mt. N/A; Pac. 85%; unknown 1%

IDAHO

University of Idaho
PO Box 442321
Moscow, ID 83844-2321
http://www.law.uidaho.edu
Public
Admissions: (208) 885-6423
E-mail: lawadmit@uidaho.edu
Financial aid: (208) 885-6312
Application deadline: 02/15
In-state tuition: full time: $10,200; part time: N/A
Out-of-state tuition: full time: $20,280
Room/board/expenses: $13,582
Percent receiving grants: 46%
Median grant: $6,030
Average student indebtedness at graduation: $55,326
Enrollment: full time: 308; part time: N/A
men: 55%; women: 45%; minorities: 14%
Acceptance rate (full-time): 44%
Midrange LSAT (full-time): 151-159
Midrange undergraduate GPA (full-time): 3.03-3.64
Midrange of full-time private-sector salaries of 2006 grads: $40,000-$50,000
2006 grads employed in: law firms: 47%; business and industry: 9%; government: 9%; public interest: 8%; judicial clerk: 24%; academia: 3%; unknown: 0%
Employment location for 2006 class: Intl. 1%; N.E. 1%; M.A. 1%; E.N.C. 0%; W.N.C. 1%; S.A. 1%; E.S.C. 0%; W.S.C. 1%; Mt. 75%; Pac. 19%; unknown 0%

ILLINOIS

DePaul University
25 E. Jackson Boulevard
Chicago, IL 60604
http://www.law.depaul.edu
Private
Admissions: (312) 362-6831
E-mail: lawinfo@depaul.edu
Financial aid: (312) 362-8091
Application deadline: 03/01
Tuition: full time: $33,110; part time: $21,545
Room/board/expenses: $22,904
Percent receiving grants: 60%
Median grant: $12,000
Average student indebtedness at graduation: $104,715
Enrollment: full time: 745; part time: 248
men: 50%; women: 50%; minorities: 22%
Acceptance rate (full-time): 35%
Midrange LSAT (full-time): 159-162
Midrange undergraduate GPA (full-time): 3.10-3.66
Midrange of full-time private-sector salaries of 2006 grads: $50,000-$86,000

2006 grads employed in: law firms: 57%; business and industry: 21%; government: 12%; public interest: 4%; judicial clerk: 3%; academia: 2%; unknown: 1%
Employment location for 2006 class: Intl. 1%; N.E. 1%; M.A. 1%; E.N.C. 89%; W.N.C. 1%; S.A. 3%; E.S.C. 0%; W.S.C. 1%; Mt. 0%; Pac. 2%; unknown 2%

Illinois Institute of Technology (Chicago-Kent)
565 W. Adams Street
Chicago, IL 60661-3691
http://www.kentlaw.edu/
Private
Admissions: (312) 906-5020
E-mail: admit@kentlaw.edu
Financial aid: (312) 906-5180
Application deadline: 03/01
Tuition: full time: $33,879; part time: $24,775
Room/board/expenses: $19,027
Percent receiving grants: 56%
Median grant: $15,000
Average student indebtedness at graduation: $98,981
Enrollment: full time: 751; part time: 224
men: 52%; women: 48%; minorities: 19%
Acceptance rate (full-time): 33%
Midrange LSAT (full-time): 157-164
Midrange undergraduate GPA (full-time): 3.20-3.77
Midrange of full-time private-sector salaries of 2006 grads: $55,000-$135,000
2006 grads employed in: law firms: 56%; business and industry: 18%; government: 14%; public interest: 3%; judicial clerk: 5%; academia: 1%; unknown: 3%
Employment location for 2006 class: Intl. 0%; N.E. 0%; M.A. 1%; E.N.C. 90%; W.N.C. 1%; S.A. 4%; E.S.C. 0%; W.S.C. 1%; Mt. 1%; Pac. 1%; unknown 0%

John Marshall Law School
315 S. Plymouth Court
Chicago, IL 60604
http://www.jmls.edu
Private
Admissions: (800) 537-4280
E-mail: admission@jmls.edu
Financial aid: (800) 537-4280
Application deadline: 03/01
Tuition: full time: $31,460; part time: $22,500
Room/board/expenses: $31,592
Percent receiving grants: 38%
Median grant: $6,000
Average student indebtedness at graduation: $108,022
Enrollment: full time: 1,067; part time: 317
men: 57%; women: 43%; minorities: 19%
Acceptance rate (full-time): 49%
Midrange LSAT (full-time): 151-156
Midrange undergraduate GPA (full-time): 2.85-3.42
Midrange of full-time private-sector salaries of 2006 grads: $51,250-$90,000
2006 grads employed in: law firms: 54%; business and industry: 24%; government: 18%; public interest: 1%; judicial clerk: 2%; academia: 1%; unknown: 0%
Employment location for 2006 class: Intl. 1%; N.E. 0%; M.A. 2%; E.N.C. 90%; W.N.C. 1%; S.A. 3%; E.S.C. 0%; W.S.C. 1%; Mt. 0%; Pac. 3%; unknown 0%

Loyola University Chicago

25 E. Pearson Street
Chicago, IL 60611
http://www.luc.edu/schools/law
Private
Admissions: (312) 915-7170
E-mail: law-admissions@luc.edu
Financial aid: (312) 915-7170
Application deadline: 04/01
Tuition: full time: $33,300;
part time: $25,050
Room/board/expenses: $19,700
Percent receiving grants: 72%
Median grant: $10,000
Average student indebtedness at
graduation: $90,518
Enrollment: full time: 621;
part time: 244
men: 48%; women: 52%;
minorities: 18%
Acceptance rate (full-time): 26%
Midrange LSAT (full-time): 159-163
Midrange undergraduate GPA
(full-time): 3.35-3.75
Midrange of full-time private-sector
salaries of 2006 grads: $70,000-
$135,000
2006 grads employed in: law firms:
54%; business and industry: 23%;
government: 16%; public interest:
1%; judicial clerk: 6%; academia:
0%; unknown: 0%
Employment location for 2006 class:
Intl. 0%; N.E. N/A; M.A. 1%; E.N.C.
91%; W.N.C. 0%; S.A. 3%; E.S.C.
N/A; W.S.C. 1%; Mt. 1%; Pac. 2%;
unknown 0%

Northern Illinois University

De Kalb, IL 60115
http://law.niu.edu
Public
Admissions: (815) 753-9485
E-mail: lawadm@niu.edu
Financial aid: (815) 753-9485
Application deadline: 05/15
In-state tuition: full time: $13,036;
part time: $543/credit hour
Out-of-state tuition: full time:
$23,620
Room/board/expenses: $12,604
Percent receiving grants: 22%
Median grant: $8,910
Average student indebtedness at
graduation: $48,472
Enrollment: full time: 310;
part time: 16
men: 50%; women: 50%;
minorities: 21%
Acceptance rate (full-time): 37%
Midrange LSAT (full-time): 150-157
Midrange undergraduate GPA
(full-time): 3.09-3.66
Midrange of full-time private-sector
salaries of 2006 grads: $42,000-
$60,000
2006 grads employed in: law firms:
51%; business and industry: 14%;
government: 25%; public interest:
9%; judicial clerk: 1%; academia:
0%; unknown: 0%
Employment location for 2006 class:
Intl. 0%; N.E. 0%; M.A. 0%; E.N.C.
91%; W.N.C. 1%; S.A. 3%; E.S.C.
0%; W.S.C. 2%; Mt. 0%; Pac. 2%;
unknown 0%

Northwestern University

357 E. Chicago Avenue
Chicago, IL 60611
http://www.law.northwestern.edu
Private
Admissions: (312) 503-8465
E-mail: admissions@
law.northwestern.edu
Financial aid: (312) 503-8465
Application deadline: 02/15

Tuition: full time: $42,942;
part time: N/A
Room/board/expenses: $21,474
Percent receiving grants: 32%
Median grant: N/A
Average student indebtedness at
graduation: $126,398
Enrollment: full time: 771;
part time: N/A
men: 54%; women: 46%;
minorities: 36%
Acceptance rate (full-time): 18%
Midrange LSAT (full-time): 166-172
Midrange undergraduate GPA
(full-time): 3.40-3.80
Midrange of full-time private-sector
salaries of 2006 grads: $135,000-
$135,000
2006 grads employed in: law firms:
74%; business and industry: 8%;
government: 3%; public interest:
2%; judicial clerk: 11%; academia:
1%; unknown: 1%
Employment location for 2006 class:
Intl. 2%; N.E. 2%; M.A. 15%; E.N.C.
55%; W.N.C. 1%; S.A. 8%; E.S.C.
0%; W.S.C. 2%; Mt. 2%; Pac. 12%;
unknown 1%

Southern Illinois University– Carbondale

Lesar Law Building
Carbondale, IL 62901
http://www.law.siu.edu
Public
Admissions: (800) 739-9187
E-mail: lawadmit@siu.edu
Financial aid: (618) 453-4334
Application deadline: 03/01
In-state tuition: full time: $12,265;
part time: N/A
Out-of-state tuition: full time:
$29,185
Room/board/expenses: $12,385
Percent receiving grants: 53%
Median grant: $6,000
Average student indebtedness at
graduation: $52,167
Enrollment: full time: 352;
part time: 2
men: 63%; women: 37%;
minorities: 9%
Acceptance rate (full-time): 52%
Midrange LSAT (full-time): 151-156
Midrange undergraduate GPA
(full-time): 2.90-3.60
Midrange of full-time private-sector
salaries of 2006 grads: $38,000-
$61,000
2006 grads employed in: law firms:
61%; business and industry: 9%;
government: 20%; public interest:
9%; judicial clerk: 1%; academia:
0%; unknown: 0%
Employment location for 2006 class:
Intl. 0%; N.E. N/A; M.A. N/A; E.N.C.
82%; W.N.C. 6%; S.A. 5%; E.S.C.
6%; W.S.C. N/A; Mt. N/A; Pac. 1%;
unknown 0%

University of Chicago

1111 E. 60th Street
Chicago, IL 60637
http://www.law.uchicago.edu
Private
Admissions: (773) 702-9484
E-mail: admissions@
law.uchicago.edu
Financial aid: (773) 702-9484
Application deadline: 02/01
Tuition: full time: $39,198;
part time: N/A
Room/board/expenses: $22,306
Percent receiving grants: 55%
Median grant: $10,800
Average student indebtedness at
graduation: $121,782
Enrollment: full time: 607;
part time: N/A
men: 55%; women: 45%;
minorities: 26%

Acceptance rate (full-time): 16%
Midrange LSAT (full-time): 169-173
Midrange undergraduate GPA
(full-time): 3.49-3.76
Midrange of full-time private-sector
salaries of 2006 grads: $120,000-
$135,000
2006 grads employed in: law firms:
76%; business and industry: 3%;
government: 6%; public interest:
1%; judicial clerk: 14%; academia:
1%; unknown: 1%
Employment location for 2006 class:
Intl. 1%; N.E. 2%; M.A. 22%; E.N.C.
37%; W.N.C. 1%; S.A. 16%; E.S.C.
0%; W.S.C. 3%; Mt. 3%; Pac. 14%;
unknown 1%

University of Illinois– Urbana-Champaign

504 E. Pennsylvania Avenue
Champaign, IL 61820
http://www.law.uiuc.edu/
Public
Admissions: (217) 244-6415
E-mail: admissions@law.uiuc.edu
Financial aid: (217) 244-6415
Application deadline: 03/15
In-state tuition: full time: $26,056;
part time: N/A
Out-of-state tuition: full time:
$36,056
Room/board/expenses: $14,902
Percent receiving grants: 68%
Median grant: $10,000
Average student indebtedness at
graduation: $68,688
Enrollment: full time: 587;
part time: N/A
men: 60%; women: 40%;
minorities: 26%
Acceptance rate (full-time): 30%
Midrange LSAT (full-time): 160-167
Midrange undergraduate GPA
(full-time): 3.18-3.80
Midrange of full-time private-sector
salaries of 2006 grads: $77,500-
$135,000
2006 grads employed in: law firms:
64%; business and industry: 13%;
government: 10%; public interest:
2%; judicial clerk: 7%; academia:
3%; unknown: 1%
Employment location for 2006 class:
Intl. 0%; N.E. 1%; M.A. 2%; E.N.C.
74%; W.N.C. 2%; S.A. 9%; E.S.C.
0%; W.S.C. 1%; Mt. 2%; Pac. 6%;
unknown 4%

Indiana University– Bloomington

211 S. Indiana Avenue
Bloomington, IN 47405-1001
http://www.law.indiana.edu
Public
Admissions: (812) 855-4765
E-mail: lawadmis@indiana.edu
Financial aid: (812) 855-7746
Application deadline: rolling
In-state tuition: full time: $17,912;
part time: N/A
Out-of-state tuition: full time:
$34,486
Room/board/expenses: $14,788
Percent receiving grants: 74%
Median grant: $7,484
Average student indebtedness at
graduation: $82,400
Enrollment: full time: 619;
part time: 1
men: 61%; women: 39%;
minorities: 18%
Acceptance rate (full-time): 39%
Midrange LSAT (full-time): 158-165
Midrange undergraduate GPA
(full-time): 3.03-3.67
Midrange of full-time private-sector
salaries of 2006 grads: $60,000-
$110,000

2006 grads employed in: law firms:
53%; business and industry: 19%;
government: 11%; public interest:
5%; judicial clerk: 9%; academia:
3%; unknown: 0%
Employment location for 2006 class:
Intl. 0%; N.E. 1%; M.A. 3%; E.N.C.
58%; W.N.C. 5%; S.A. 12%; E.S.C.
3%; W.S.C. 6%; Mt. 3%; Pac. 10%;
unknown 0%

Indiana University– Indianapolis

530 W. New York Street
Indianapolis, IN 46202-3225
http://www.indylaw.indiana.edu
Public
Admissions: (317) 274-2459
E-mail: pkkinney@iupui.edu
Financial aid: (317) 278-2862
Application deadline: 03/01
In-state tuition: full time: $14,638;
part time: $10,926
Out-of-state tuition: full time:
$31,993
Room/board/expenses: $21,924
Percent receiving grants: 47%
Median grant: $5,010
Average student indebtedness at
graduation: $64,571
Enrollment: full time: 647;
part time: 305
men: 52%; women: 48%;
minorities: 13%
Acceptance rate (full-time): 35%
Midrange LSAT (full-time): 151-158
Midrange undergraduate GPA
(full-time): 3.36-3.78
Midrange of full-time private-sector
salaries of 2006 grads: $45,000-
$90,000
2006 grads employed in: law firms:
50%; business and industry: 22%;
government: 22%; public interest:
2%; judicial clerk: 2%; academia:
2%; unknown: 0%
Employment location for 2006 class:
Intl. 1%; N.E. 0%; M.A. 0%; E.N.C.
88%; W.N.C. 1%; S.A. 5%; E.S.C.
1%; W.S.C. 0%; Mt. 2%; Pac. 2%;
unknown 0%

University of Notre Dame

PO Box 780
Notre Dame, IN 46556-0780
http://www.lawadmissions.nd.edu
Private
Admissions: (574) 631-6626
E-mail: lawadmit@nd.edu
Financial aid: (574) 631-6626
Application deadline: 03/01
Tuition: full time: $35,950;
part time: N/A
Room/board/expenses: $15,400
Percent receiving grants: 67%
Median grant: $13,000
Average student indebtedness at
graduation: $87,849
Enrollment: full time: 563;
part time: 1
men: 62%; women: 38%;
minorities: 22%
Acceptance rate (full-time): 19%
Midrange LSAT (full-time): 164-167
Midrange undergraduate GPA
(full-time): 3.40-3.76
Midrange of full-time private-sector
salaries of 2006 grads: $90,000-
$125,000
2006 grads employed in: law firms:
65%; business and industry: 6%;
government: 13%; public interest:
6%; judicial clerk: 10%; academia:
2%; unknown: 0%
Employment location for 2006 class:
Intl. 1%; N.E. 4%; M.A. 16%; E.N.C.
36%; W.N.C. 4%; S.A. 22%; E.S.C.
1%; W.S.C. 4%; Mt. 4%; Pac. 9%;
unknown 0%

Valparaiso University

656 S. Greenwich Street
Wesemann Hall
Valparaiso, IN 46383
http://www.valpo.edu/law
Private
Admissions: (219) 548-7703
E-mail: valpolaw@valpo.edu
Financial aid: (219) 465-7818
Application deadline: 06/01
Tuition: full time: $31,208;
part time: $1,220/credit hour
Room/board/expenses: $11,110
Percent receiving grants: 21%
Median grant: $14,125
Average student indebtedness at
graduation: $80,424
Enrollment: full time: 486;
part time: 56
men: 54%; women: 46%;
minorities: 13%
Acceptance rate (full-time): 27%
Midrange LSAT (full-time): 150-154
Midrange undergraduate GPA
(full-time): 3.23-3.67
Midrange of full-time private-sector
salaries of 2006 grads: $47,500-
$70,000
2006 grads employed in: law firms:
56%; business and industry: 20%;
government: 14%; public interest:
0%; judicial clerk: 6%; academia:
4%; unknown: 0%
Employment location for 2006 class:
Intl. 0%; N.E. 0%; M.A. 3%; E.N.C.
72%; W.N.C. 5%; S.A. 5%; E.S.C.
2%; W.S.C. 1%; Mt. 4%; Pac. 7%;
unknown 0%

Drake University

2507 University Avenue
Des Moines, IA 50311
http://www.law.drake.edu/
Private
Admissions: (515) 271-2782
E-mail: lawadmit@drake.edu
Financial aid: (515) 271-2782
Application deadline: 04/01
Tuition: full time: $27,756;
part time: $950/credit hour
Room/board/expenses: $12,150
Percent receiving grants: 61%
Median grant: $11,000
Average student indebtedness at
graduation: $81,702
Enrollment: full time: 414;
part time: 7
men: 54%; women: 46%;
minorities: 12%
Acceptance rate (full-time): 51%
Midrange LSAT (full-time): 153-158
Midrange undergraduate GPA
(full-time): 3.11-3.72
Midrange of full-time private-sector
salaries of 2006 grads: $43,300-
$66,875
2006 grads employed in: law firms:
59%; business and industry: 17%;
government: 9%; public interest:
5%; judicial clerk: 9%; academia:
1%; unknown: 0%
Employment location for 2006 class:
Intl. 1%; N.E. 1%; M.A. 1%; E.N.C.
7%; W.N.C. 75%; S.A. 5%; E.S.C.
1%; W.S.C. 4%; Mt. 3%; Pac. 1%;
unknown 0%

University of Iowa

320 Melrose Avenue
Iowa City, IA 52242
http://www.law.uiowa.edu
Public
Admissions: (319) 335-9133
E-mail: law-admissions@uiowa.edu
Financial aid: (319) 335-9142
Application deadline: 03/01
In-state tuition: full time: $16,341;
part time: N/A

Out-of-state tuition: full time: $32,589
Room/board/expenses: $15,690
Percent receiving grants: 36%
Median grant: $13,374
Average student indebtedness at graduation: $69,375
Enrollment: full time: 633;
part time: N/A
men: 55%; women: 45%;
minorities: 18%
Acceptance rate (full-time): 35%
Midrange LSAT (full-time): 159-163
Midrange undergraduate GPA (full-time): 3.41-3.86
Midrange of full-time private-sector salaries of 2006 grads: $60,000-$115,000
2006 grads employed in: law firms: 58%; business and industry: 14%; government: 10%; public interest: 9%; judicial clerk: 5%; academia: 5%; unknown: 1%
Employment location for 2006 class: Intl. 0%; N.E. 1%; M.A. 2%; E.N.C. 17%; W.N.C. 43%; S.A. 9%; E.S.C. 1%; W.S.C. 2%; Mt. 11%; Pac. 6%; unknown 8%

KANSAS

University of Kansas
Green Hall
1535 W. 15th Street
Lawrence, KS 66045-7577
http://www.law.ku.edu
Public
Admissions: (866) 220-3654
E-mail: admitlaw@ku.edu
Financial aid: (785) 864-4700
Application deadline: 03/15
In-state tuition: full time: $13,384;
part time: N/A
Out-of-state tuition: full time: $24,085
Room/board/expenses: $14,686
Percent receiving grants: 73%
Median grant: $1,700
Average student indebtedness at graduation: $40,690
Enrollment: full time: 491;
part time: N/A
men: 62%; women: 38%;
minorities: 16%
Acceptance rate (full-time): 37%
Midrange LSAT (full-time): 155-160
Midrange undergraduate GPA (full-time): 3.09-3.77
Midrange of full-time private-sector salaries of 2006 grads: $48,000-$90,000
2006 grads employed in: law firms: 51%; business and industry: 18%; government: 15%; public interest: 4%; judicial clerk: 9%; academia: 3%; unknown: 0%
Employment location for 2006 class: Intl. 1%; N.E. 0%; M.A. 1%; E.N.C. 2%; W.N.C. 71%; S.A. 5%; E.S.C. 1%; W.S.C. 7%; Mt. 8%; Pac. 4%; unknown 0%

Washburn University
1700 S.W. College Avenue
Topeka, KS 66621
http://washburnlaw.edu
Public
Admissions: (785) 670-1185
E-mail: admissions@washburnlaw.edu
Financial aid: (785) 670-1151
Application deadline: 04/01
In-state tuition: full time: $480/credit hour;
part time: N/A
Out-of-state tuition: full time: $750/credit hour
Room/board/expenses: $14,586
Percent receiving grants: 39%
Median grant: $5,000

Average student indebtedness at graduation: $61,200
Enrollment: full time: 445;
part time: N/A
men: 60%; women: 40%;
minorities: 13%
Acceptance rate (full-time): 52%
Midrange LSAT (full-time): 150-156
Midrange undergraduate GPA (full-time): 3.06-3.69
Midrange of full-time private-sector salaries of 2006 grads: $44,000-$65,000
2006 grads employed in: law firms: 49%; business and industry: 18%; government: 15%; public interest: 10%; judicial clerk: 6%; academia: 2%; unknown: 0%
Employment location for 2006 class: Intl. 0%; N.E. 0%; M.A. 1%; E.N.C. 2%; W.N.C. 76%; S.A. 2%; E.S.C. 2%; W.S.C. 6%; Mt. 9%; Pac. 2%; unknown 0%

KENTUCKY

Northern Kentucky University (Chase)
Nunn Hall
Highland Heights, KY 41099-6031
http://www.nku.edu/~chase
Public
Admissions: (859) 572-5841
E-mail: folger@nku.edu
Financial aid: (859) 572-6437
Application deadline: rolling
In-state tuition: full time: $12,168;
part time: $9,126
Out-of-state tuition: full time: $26,544
Room/board/expenses: $10,278
Percent receiving grants: 38%
Median grant: $11,112
Average student indebtedness at graduation: $61,857
Enrollment: full time: 304;
part time: 239
men: 56%; women: 44%;
minorities: 9%
Acceptance rate (full-time): 43%
Midrange LSAT (full-time): 153-156
Midrange undergraduate GPA (full-time): 3.07-3.56
Midrange of full-time private-sector salaries of 2006 grads: $40,000-$63,000
2006 grads employed in: law firms: 53%; business and industry: 21%; government: 10%; public interest: 9%; judicial clerk: 4%; academia: 3%; unknown: 0%
Employment location for 2006 class: Intl. 0%; N.E. 0%; M.A. 1%; E.N.C. 50%; W.N.C. 0%; S.A. 1%; E.S.C. 47%; W.S.C. 0%; Mt. 1%; Pac. 0%; unknown 1%

University of Kentucky
209 Law Building
Lexington, KY 40506-0048
http://www.uky.edu/law
Public
Admissions: (859) 257-6770
E-mail: lawadmissions@email.uky.edu
Financial aid: (859) 257-3172
Application deadline: 03/01
In-state tuition: full time: $13,998;
part time: N/A
Out-of-state tuition: full time: $24,804
Room/board/expenses: $14,502
Percent receiving grants: 56%
Median grant: $5,000
Average student indebtedness at graduation: $57,400
Enrollment: full time: 426;
part time: N/A
men: 57%; women: 43%;
minorities: 9%
Acceptance rate (full-time): 36%

Midrange LSAT (full-time): 156-162
Midrange undergraduate GPA (full-time): 3.36-3.79
Midrange of full-time private-sector salaries of 2006 grads: $40,000-$83,000
2006 grads employed in: law firms: 51%; business and industry: 11%; government: 10%; public interest: 9%; judicial clerk: 18%; academia: 1%; unknown: 0%
Employment location for 2006 class: Intl. 0%; N.E. 1%; M.A. 1%; E.N.C. 3%; W.N.C. 1%; S.A. 7%; E.S.C. 82%; W.S.C. 1%; Mt. 3%; Pac. 1%; unknown 0%

University of Louisville (Brandeis)
Louisville, KY 40292
http://www.louisville.edu/brandeislaw/
Public
Admissions: (502) 852-6365
E-mail: lawadmissions@louisville.edu
Financial aid: (502) 852-6391
Application deadline: 05/15
In-state tuition: full time: $12,610;
part time: $10,520
Out-of-state tuition: full time: $25,956
Room/board/expenses: $16,398
Percent receiving grants: 34%
Median grant: $5,000
Average student indebtedness at graduation: $57,165
Enrollment: full time: 323;
part time: 87
men: 54%; women: 46%;
minorities: 9%
Acceptance rate (full-time): 38%
Midrange LSAT (full-time): 155-159
Midrange undergraduate GPA (full-time): 3.17-3.73
Midrange of full-time private-sector salaries of 2006 grads: $45,000-$83,000
2006 grads employed in: law firms: 56%; business and industry: 15%; government: 8%; public interest: 12%; judicial clerk: 8%; academia: 1%; unknown: 0%
Employment location for 2006 class: Intl. 0%; N.E. 0%; M.A. 1%; E.N.C. 3%; W.N.C. 1%; S.A. 7%; E.S.C. 84%; W.S.C. 1%; Mt. 3%; Pac. 0%; unknown 0%

LOUISIANA

Louisiana State University– Baton Rouge
400 Paul M. Hebert Law Center
Baton Rouge, LA 70803
http://www.law.lsu.edu
Public
Admissions: (225) 578-8646
E-mail: admissions@law.lsu.edu
Financial aid: (225) 578-3103
Application deadline: 07/01
In-state tuition: full time: $12,190;
part time: N/A
Out-of-state tuition: full time: $21,286
Room/board/expenses: $16,516
Percent receiving grants: 51%
Median grant: $2,981
Average student indebtedness at graduation: $59,218
Enrollment: full time: 570;
part time: 13
men: 52%; women: 48%;
minorities: 10%
Acceptance rate (full-time): 37%
Midrange LSAT (full-time): 155-159
Midrange undergraduate GPA (full-time): 3.16-3.70
Midrange of full-time private-sector salaries of 2006 grads: N/A-N/A

2006 grads employed in: law firms: 60%; business and industry: 7%; government: 14%; public interest: 2%; judicial clerk: 14%; academia: 1%; unknown: 2%
Employment location for 2006 class: Intl. 0%; N.E. N/A; M.A. 1%; E.N.C. 0%; W.N.C. 0%; S.A. 8%; E.S.C. 1%; W.S.C. 86%; Mt. 0%; Pac. 2%; unknown 1%

Loyola University New Orleans
7214 St. Charles Avenue
PO Box 901
New Orleans, LA 70118
http://law.loyno.edu/
Private
Admissions: (504) 861-5575
E-mail: ladmit@loyno.edu
Financial aid: (504) 865-3231
Application deadline: rolling
Tuition: full time: $30,456;
part time: $20,596
Room/board/expenses: $19,250
Percent receiving grants: 45%
Median grant: $14,000
Average student indebtedness at graduation: $84,155
Enrollment: full time: 700;
part time: 158
men: 48%; women: 52%;
minorities: 25%
Acceptance rate (full-time): 67%
Midrange LSAT (full-time): 149-155
Midrange undergraduate GPA (full-time): 3.09-3.56
Midrange of full-time private-sector salaries of 2006 grads: N/A-N/A
2006 grads employed in: law firms: 62%; business and industry: 12%; government: 9%; public interest: 6%; judicial clerk: 11%; academia: 0%; unknown: 0%
Employment location for 2006 class: Intl. 0%; N.E. 2%; M.A. 2%; E.N.C. 2%; W.N.C. 1%; S.A. 15%; E.S.C. 6%; W.S.C. 68%; Mt. 2%; Pac. 2%; unknown 0%

Southern University
PO Box 9294
Baton Rouge, LA 70813
http://www.sulc.edu/index.html
Public
Admissions: (225) 771-5340
E-mail: Admission@sulc.edu
Financial aid: (225) 771-2141
Application deadline: 02/28
In-state tuition: full time: $6,611;
part time: $5,494
Out-of-state tuition: full time: $11,211
Room/board/expenses: $12,833
Percent receiving grants: 42%
Median grant: $1,567
Average student indebtedness at graduation: $16,793
Enrollment: full time: 377;
part time: 111
men: 48%; women: 52%;
minorities: 56%
Acceptance rate (full-time): 37%
Midrange LSAT (full-time): 143-149
Midrange undergraduate GPA (full-time): 2.52-3.26
Midrange of full-time private-sector salaries of 2006 grads: $70,000-$135,000
2006 grads employed in: law firms: 45%; business and industry: 9%; government: 26%; public interest: 3%; judicial clerk: 12%; academia: 3%; unknown: 0%
Employment location for 2006 class: Intl. 0%; N.E. 0%; M.A. 2%; E.N.C. 7%; W.N.C. 2%; S.A. 7%; E.S.C. 2%; W.S.C. 80%; Mt. 0%; Pac. 2%; unknown 0%

Tulane University
6329 Freret Street
John Giffen Weinmann Hall
New Orleans, LA 70118-6231
http://www.law.tulane.edu
Private
Admissions: (504) 865-5930
E-mail: admissions@law.tulane.edu
Financial aid: (504) 865-5931
Application deadline: 02/15
Tuition: full time: $36,670;
part time: N/A
Room/board/expenses: $18,720
Percent receiving grants: 66%
Median grant: $10,000
Average student indebtedness at graduation: $102,095
Enrollment: full time: 752;
part time: N/A
men: 60%; women: 40%;
minorities: 16%
Acceptance rate (full-time): 36%
Midrange LSAT (full-time): 158-163
Midrange undergraduate GPA (full-time): 3.37-3.75
Midrange of full-time private-sector salaries of 2006 grads: $85,000-$145,000
2006 grads employed in: law firms: 55%; business and industry: 12%; government: 13%; public interest: 7%; judicial clerk: 9%; academia: 1%; unknown: 3%
Employment location for 2006 class: Intl. 1%; N.E. 3%; M.A. 9%; E.N.C. 4%; W.N.C. 2%; S.A. 23%; E.S.C. 5%; W.S.C. 32%; Mt. 4%; Pac. 11%; unknown 6%

MAINE

University of Maine
246 Deering Avenue
Portland, ME 04102
http://mainelaw.maine.edu/
Public
Admissions: (207) 780-4341
E-mail: mainelaw@usm.maine.edu
Financial aid: (207) 780-5250
Application deadline: 03/01
In-state tuition: full time: $18,210;
part time: N/A
Out-of-state tuition: full time: $28,290
Room/board/expenses: $12,532
Percent receiving grants: 50%
Median grant: $2,300
Average student indebtedness at graduation: $48,965
Enrollment: full time: 254;
part time: N/A
men: 54%; women: 46%;
minorities: 2%
Acceptance rate (full-time): 47%
Midrange LSAT (full-time): 154-159
Midrange undergraduate GPA (full-time): 3.06-3.69
Midrange of full-time private-sector salaries of 2006 grads: $48,000-$68,000
2006 grads employed in: law firms: 37%; business and industry: 25%; government: 12%; public interest: 8%; judicial clerk: 13%; academia: 4%; unknown: 0%
Employment location for 2006 class: Intl. 1%; N.E. 74%; M.A. 4%; E.N.C. 2%; W.N.C. 0%; S.A. 10%; E.S.C. 0%; W.S.C. 1%; Mt. 1%; Pac. 6%; unknown 0%

MARYLAND

University of Baltimore
1420 N. Charles Street
Baltimore, MD 21201-5779
http://law.ubalt.edu
Public
Admissions: (410) 837-4459
E-mail: lwadmiss@ubalt.edu
Financial aid: (410) 837-4763

Application deadline: rolling
In-state tuition: full time: $20,597;
part time: $873/credit hour
Out-of-state tuition: full time:
$32,754
Room/board/expenses: $17,198
Percent receiving grants: 11%
Median grant: $3,000
**Average student indebtedness at
graduation:** $33,928
Enrollment: full time: 657;
part time: 425
men: 48%; women: 52%;
minorities: 16%
Acceptance rate (full-time): 41%
Midrange LSAT (full-time): 153–157
**Midrange undergraduate GPA
(full-time):** 3.00–3.57
**Midrange of full-time private-sector
salaries of 2006 grads:** $50,625–
$95,000
2006 grads employed in: law firms:
36%; business and industry: 18%;
government: 14%; public interest:
5%; judicial clerk: 23%; academia:
3%; unknown: 1%
Employment location for 2006 class:
Intl. 0%; N.E. 0%; M.A. 2%; E.N.C.
1%; W.N.C. 0%; S.A. 87%; E.S.C.
0%; W.S.C. 0%; Mt. 1%; Pac. 1%;
unknown 7%

University of Maryland
500 W. Baltimore Street
Baltimore, MD 21201-1786
http://www.law.umaryland.edu
Public
Admissions: (410) 706-3492
E-mail: admissions@law.
umaryland.edu
Financial aid: (410) 706-0873
Application deadline: 03/01
In-state tuition: full time: $20,535;
part time: $15,568
Out-of-state tuition: full time:
$31,814
Room/board/expenses: $24,398
Percent receiving grants: 67%
Median grant: $5,000
**Average student indebtedness at
graduation:** $63,621
Enrollment: full time: 678;
part time: 153
men: 45%; women: 55%;
minorities: 35%
Acceptance rate (full-time): 16%
Midrange LSAT (full-time): 160–166
**Midrange undergraduate GPA
(full-time):** 3.47–3.84
**Midrange of full-time private-sector
salaries of 2006 grads:** $50,000–
$110,000
2006 grads employed in: law firms:
40%; business and industry: 10%;
government: 15%; public interest:
5%; judicial clerk: 25%; academia:
5%; unknown: 0%
Employment location for 2006 class:
Intl. 1%; N.E. 1%; M.A. 3%; E.N.C.
1%; W.N.C. 0%; S.A. 90%; E.S.C.
0%; W.S.C. 0%; Mt. 1%; Pac. 3%;
unknown 0%

Boston College
885 Centre Street
Newton, MA 02459-1154
http://www.bc.edu/lawschool
Private
Admissions: (617) 552-4351
E-mail: bclawadm@bc.edu
Financial aid: (617) 552-4243
Application deadline: 03/01
Tuition: full time: $36,590;
part time: N/A
Room/board/expenses: $18,390
Percent receiving grants: 57%
Median grant: $12,500
**Average student indebtedness at
graduation:** $80,497

Enrollment: full time: 778;
part time: 5
men: 55%; women: 45%;
minorities: 23%
Acceptance rate (full-time): 20%
Midrange LSAT (full-time): 162–165
**Midrange undergraduate GPA
(full-time):** 3.44–3.78
**Midrange of full-time private-sector
salaries of 2006 grads:** $125,000–
$135,000
2006 grads employed in: law firms:
65%; business and industry: 6%;
government: 9%; public interest:
5%; judicial clerk: 14%; academia:
1%; unknown: 0%
Employment location for 2006 class:
Intl. 1%; N.E. 58%; M.A. 21%; E.N.C.
5%; W.N.C. 1%; S.A. 8%; E.S.C.
0%; W.S.C. 1%; Mt. 1%; Pac. 4%;
unknown 0%

Boston University
765 Commonwealth Avenue
Boston, MA 02215
http://www.bu.edu/law/
Private
Admissions: (617) 353-3100
E-mail: bulawadm@bu.edu
Financial aid: (617) 353-3160
Application deadline: 03/01
Tuition: full time: $36,806;
part time: N/A
Room/board/expenses: $17,059
Percent receiving grants: 57%
Median grant: $15,000
**Average student indebtedness at
graduation:** $89,198
Enrollment: full time: 815;
part time: 19
men: 50%; women: 50%;
minorities: 19%
Acceptance rate (full-time): 27%
Midrange LSAT (full-time): 164–166
**Midrange undergraduate GPA
(full-time):** 3.51–3.81
**Midrange of full-time private-sector
salaries of 2006 grads:** $95,000–
$135,000
2006 grads employed in: law firms:
61%; business and industry: 8%;
government: 6%; public interest:
3%; judicial clerk: 9%; academia:
1%; unknown: 12%
Employment location for 2006 class:
Intl. 1%; N.E. 43%; M.A. 23%;
E.N.C. 3%; W.N.C. 1%; S.A. 7%;
E.S.C. 1%; W.S.C. 2%; Mt. 3%; Pac.
12%; unknown 5%

Harvard University
1563 Massachusetts Avenue
Cambridge, MA 02138
http://www.law.harvard.edu
Private
Admissions: (617) 495-3109
E-mail: jdadmiss@law.harvard.edu
Financial aid: (617) 495-4606
Application deadline: 02/01
Tuition: full time: $39,325;
part time: N/A
Room/board/expenses: $23,075
Percent receiving grants: 41%
Median grant: $16,705
**Average student indebtedness at
graduation:** $105,494
Enrollment: full time: 1,734;
part time: N/A
men: 53%; women: 47%;
minorities: 30%
Acceptance rate (full-time): 12%
Midrange LSAT (full-time): 170–175
**Midrange undergraduate GPA
(full-time):** 3.75–3.95
**Midrange of full-time private-sector
salaries of 2006 grads:** $135,000–
$145,000
2006 grads employed in: law firms:
66%; business and industry: 4%;
government: 2%; public interest:
5%; judicial clerk: 23%; academia:
0%; unknown: 0%

Employment location for 2006 class:
Intl. 2%; N.E. 13%; M.A. 31%; E.N.C.
7%; W.N.C. 1%; S.A. 20%; E.S.C.
1%; W.S.C. 5%; Mt. 3%; Pac. 17%;
unknown 0%

New England School of Law
154 Stuart Street
Boston, MA 02116
http://www.nesl.edu
Private
Admissions: (617) 422-7210
E-mail: admit@admin.nesl.edu
Financial aid: (617) 422-7298
Application deadline: 03/15
Tuition: full time: $28,020;
part time: $21,030
Room/board/expenses: $16,605
Percent receiving grants: 46%
Median grant: $3,000
**Average student indebtedness at
graduation:** $86,346
Enrollment: full time: 715;
part time: 386
men: 45%; women: 55%;
minorities: 10%
Acceptance rate (full-time): 58%
Midrange LSAT (full-time): 150–153
**Midrange undergraduate GPA
(full-time):** 3.02–3.52
**Midrange of full-time private-sector
salaries of 2006 grads:** $40,000–
$70,000
2006 grads employed in: law firms:
45%; business and industry: 20%;
government: 17%; public interest:
5%; judicial clerk: 11%; academia:
2%; unknown: 2%
Employment location for 2006 class:
Intl. 0%; N.E. 67%; M.A. 14%;
E.N.C. 1%; W.N.C. 1%; S.A. 9%;
E.S.C. 0%; W.S.C. 1%; Mt. 1%; Pac.
5%; unknown 0%

Northeastern University
400 Huntington Avenue
Boston, MA 02115
http://www.slaw.neu.edu
Private
Admissions: (617) 373-2395
E-mail:
lawadmissions@nunet.neu.edu
Financial aid: (617) 373-4620
Application deadline: 07/01
Tuition: full time: $36,564;
part time: N/A
Room/board/expenses: $18,325
Percent receiving grants: 84%
Median grant: $8,500
**Average student indebtedness at
graduation:** $93,775
Enrollment: full time: 624;
part time: N/A
men: 41%; women: 59%;
minorities: 27%
Acceptance rate (full-time): 36%
Midrange LSAT (full-time): 156–162
**Midrange undergraduate GPA
(full-time):** 3.14–3.61
**Midrange of full-time private-sector
salaries of 2006 grads:** $52,250–
$135,000
2006 grads employed in: law firms:
40%; business and industry: 18%;
government: 10%; public interest:
16%; judicial clerk: 14%; academia:
1%; unknown: 1%
Employment location for 2006 class:
Intl. 2%; N.E. 65%; M.A. 13%;
E.N.C. 1%; W.N.C. 1%; S.A. 10%;
E.S.C. 1%; W.S.C. 1%; Mt. 1%; Pac.
6%; unknown 0%

Suffolk University
120 Tremont Street
Boston, MA 02108
http://www.law.suffolk.edu/
Private
Admissions: (617) 573-8144
E-mail: lawadm@admin.suffolk.edu
Financial aid: (617) 573-8147
Application deadline: 03/01
Tuition: full time: $36,068;
part time: $27,051
Room/board/expenses: $14,114
Percent receiving grants: 49%
Median grant: $6,500
**Average student indebtedness at
graduation:** $94,360
Enrollment: full time: 1,021;
part time: 604
men: 51%; women: 49%;
minorities: 14%
Acceptance rate (full-time): 50%
Midrange LSAT (full-time): 154–158
**Midrange undergraduate GPA
(full-time):** 3.03–3.49
**Midrange of full-time private-sector
salaries of 2006 grads:** $52,000–
$125,000
2006 grads employed in: law firms:
46%; business and industry: 23%;
government: 13%; public interest:
2%; judicial clerk: 10%; academia:
2%; unknown: 4%
Employment location for 2006 class:
Intl. 0%; N.E. 91%; M.A. 3%; E.N.C.
1%; W.N.C. 0%; S.A. 2%; E.S.C.
0%; W.S.C. 0%; Mt. 1%; Pac. 1%;
unknown 0%

Western New England College
1215 Wilbraham Road
Springfield, MA 01119-2684
http://www.law.wnec.edu
Private
Admissions: (413) 782-1406
E-mail: admissions@law.wnec.edu
Financial aid: (413) 796-2080
Application deadline: rolling
Tuition: full time: $31,048;
part time: $23,286
Room/board/expenses: $19,709
Percent receiving grants: 54%
Median grant: $17,000
**Average student indebtedness at
graduation:** $82,793
Enrollment: full time: 397;
part time: 182
men: 56%; women: 44%;
minorities: 10%
Acceptance rate (full-time): 71%
Midrange LSAT (full-time): 150–156
**Midrange undergraduate GPA
(full-time):** 2.80–3.38
**Midrange of full-time private-sector
salaries of 2006 grads:** $40,000–
$60,000
2006 grads employed in: law firms:
43%; business and industry: 26%;
government: 18%; public interest:
4%; judicial clerk: 7%; academia:
2%; unknown: 0%
Employment location for 2006 class:
Intl. 2%; N.E. 68%; M.A. 16%;
E.N.C. 0%; W.N.C. 1%; S.A. 7%;
E.S.C. 0%; W.S.C. 0%; Mt. 2%;
Pac. 5%; unknown 0%

Ave Maria School of Law
3475 Plymouth Road
Ann Arbor, MI 48105-2550
http://www.avemarialaw.edu
Private
Admissions: (734) 827-8063
E-mail: info@avemarialaw.edu
Financial aid: (734) 827-8051
Application deadline: 04/01

Tuition: full time: $32,302;
part time: N/A
Room/board/expenses: $19,688
Percent receiving grants: 69%
Median grant: $20,000
**Average student indebtedness at
graduation:** $79,211
Enrollment: full time: 331;
part time: 1
men: 65%; women: 35%;
minorities: 17%
Acceptance rate (full-time): 51%
Midrange LSAT (full-time): 147–155
**Midrange undergraduate GPA
(full-time):** 2.93–3.47
**Midrange of full-time private-sector
salaries of 2006 grads:** $48,100–
$90,000
2006 grads employed in: law firms:
40%; business and industry: 24%;
government: 14%; public interest:
3%; judicial clerk: 17%; academia:
2%; unknown: 0%
Employment location for 2006 class:
Intl. 0%; N.E. 3%; M.A. 10%; E.N.C.
33%; W.N.C. 14%; S.A. 18%; E.S.C.
3%; W.S.C. 3%; Mt. 3%; Pac. 6%;
unknown 6%

Michigan State University
368 Law College Building
East Lansing, MI 48824-1300
http://www.law.msu.edu
Private
Admissions: (517) 432-0222
E-mail: law@msu.edu
Financial aid: (517) 432-6810
Application deadline: 03/01
Tuition: full time: $30,124;
part time: $22,907
Room/board/expenses: $12,894
Percent receiving grants: 37%
Median grant: $20,968
**Average student indebtedness at
graduation:** $71,762
Enrollment: full time: 696;
part time: 310
men: 58%; women: 42%;
minorities: 13%
Acceptance rate (full-time): 42%
Midrange LSAT (full-time): 155–161
**Midrange undergraduate GPA
(full-time):** 3.21–3.64
**Midrange of full-time private-sector
salaries of 2006 grads:** $48,000–
$87,000
2006 grads employed in: law firms:
47%; business and industry: 16%;
government: 14%; public interest:
5%; judicial clerk: 5%; academia:
2%; unknown: 9%
Employment location for 2006 class:
Intl. 3%; N.E. 1%; M.A. 5%; E.N.C.
66%; W.N.C. 1%; S.A. 11%; E.S.C.
0%; W.S.C. 1%; Mt. 7%; Pac. 2%;
unknown 3%

Thomas M. Cooley Law School
300 S. Capitol Avenue
PO Box 13038
Lansing, MI 48901
http://www.cooley.edu
Private
Admissions: (517) 371-5140
E-mail: admissions@cooley.edu
Financial aid: (517) 371-5140
Application deadline: 09/01
Tuition: full time: $25,436;
part time: $21,808
Room/board/expenses: $11,160
Percent receiving grants: 86%
Median grant: $7,872
**Average student indebtedness at
graduation:** $85,450
Enrollment: full time: 535;
part time: 3,129
men: 53%; women: 47%;
minorities: 21%
Acceptance rate (full-time): 74%

Midrange LSAT (full-time): 145-154
Midrange undergraduate GPA
(full-time): 2.75-3.35
Midrange of full-time private-sector
salaries of 2006 grads: $40,000-
$67,000
2006 grads employed in: law firms:
48%; business and industry: 20%;
government: 17%; public interest:
5%; judicial clerk: 7%; academia:
2%; unknown: 1%
Employment location for 2006 class:
Intl. 1%; N.E. 1%; M.A. 10%; E.N.C.
44%; W.N.C. 3%; S.A. 19%; E.S.C.
2%; W.S.C. 3%; Mt. 7%; Pac. 4%;
unknown 7%

University of Detroit Mercy
651 E. Jefferson Avenue
Detroit, MI 48226
http://www.law.udmercy.edu
Private
Admissions: (313) 596-0264
E-mail: udmlawao@udmercy.edu
Financial aid: (313) 596-0214
Application deadline: 04/15
Tuition: full time: $28,500;
part time: $950/credit hour
Room/board/expenses: $18,556
Percent receiving grants: 15%
Median grant: $6,270
Average student indebtedness at
graduation: $86,431
Enrollment: full time: 591;
part time: 160
men: 54%; women: 46%;
minorities: 14%
Acceptance rate (full-time): 47%
Midrange LSAT (full-time): 146-154
Midrange undergraduate GPA
(full-time): 2.95-3.36
Midrange of full-time private-sector
salaries of 2006 grads: $55,000-
$100,000
2006 grads employed in: law firms:
59%; business and industry: 24%;
government: 7%; public interest:
3%; judicial clerk: 4%; academia:
1%; unknown: 2%
Employment location for 2006 class:
Intl. 18%; N.E. 1%; M.A. 1%; E.N.C.
75%; W.N.C. 0%; S.A. 3%; E.S.C.
0%; W.S.C. 1%; Mt. 1%; Pac. 0%;
unknown 0%

University of Michigan– Ann Arbor
625 S. State Street
Ann Arbor, MI 48109-1215
http://www.law.umich.edu/
Public
Admissions: (734) 764-0537
E-mail:
law.jd.admissions@umich.edu
Financial aid: (734) 764-5289
Application deadline: 02/15
In-state tuition: full time: $38,949;
part time: N/A
Out-of-state tuition: full time:
$41,949
Room/board/expenses: $15,000
Percent receiving grants: 56%
Median grant: $8,800
Average student indebtedness at
graduation: $91,000
Enrollment: full time: 1,148;
part time: N/A
men: 56%; women: 44%;
minorities: 27%
Acceptance rate (full-time): 21%
Midrange LSAT (full-time): 167-170
Midrange undergraduate GPA
(full-time): 3.49-3.79
Midrange of full-time private-sector
salaries of 2006 grads: $135,000-
$145,000

2006 grads employed in: law firms:
73%; business and industry: 4%;
government: 4%; public interest:
6%; judicial clerk: 13%; academia:
2%; unknown: 0%
Employment location for 2006 class:
Intl. 2%; N.E. 2%; M.A. 23%; E.N.C.
32%; W.N.C. 2%; S.A. 15%; E.S.C.
1%; W.S.C. 2%; Mt. 3%; Pac. 17%;
unknown 2%

Wayne State University
471 W. Palmer Street
Detroit, MI 48202
http://www.law.wayne.edu
Public
Admissions: (313) 577-3937
E-mail: lawinquire@wayne.edu
Financial aid: (313) 577-5142
Application deadline: 03/15
In-state tuition: full time: $21,328;
part time: $11,534
Out-of-state tuition: full time:
$23,305
Room/board/expenses: $22,180
Percent receiving grants: 67%
Median grant: $4,000
Average student indebtedness at
graduation: $60,228
Enrollment: full time: 481;
part time: 134
men: 52%; women: 48%;
minorities: 18%
Acceptance rate (full-time): 52%
Midrange LSAT (full-time): 152-158
Midrange undergraduate GPA
(full-time): 3.29-3.69
Midrange of full-time private-sector
salaries of 2006 grads: $50,000-
$90,000
2006 grads employed in: law firms:
75%; business and industry: 13%;
government: 4%; public interest:
3%; judicial clerk: 3%; academia:
2%; unknown: 0%
Employment location for 2006 class:
Intl. 0%; N.E. 0%; M.A. 1%; E.N.C.
96%; W.N.C. 0%; S.A. 2%; E.S.C.
0%; W.S.C. 0%; Mt. 1%; Pac. 1%;
unknown 0%

Hamline University
1536 Hewitt Avenue
St. Paul, MN 55104-1284
http://www.hamline.edu/law
Private
Admissions: (651) 523-2461
E-mail: lawadm@hamline.edu
Financial aid: (651) 523-3000
Application deadline: 04/01
Tuition: full time: $28,682;
part time: $20,682
Room/board/expenses: $15,553
Percent receiving grants: 50%
Median grant: $20,000
Average student indebtedness at
graduation: $86,882
Enrollment: full time: 489;
part time: 211
men: 48%; women: 52%;
minorities: 13%
Acceptance rate (full-time): 49%
Midrange LSAT (full-time): 152-158
Midrange undergraduate GPA
(full-time): 3.22-3.70
Midrange of full-time private-sector
salaries of 2006 grads: $46,000-
$90,000
2006 grads employed in: law firms:
36%; business and industry: 24%;
government: 15%; public interest:
5%; judicial clerk: 13%; academia:
3%; unknown: 4%
Employment location for 2006 class:
Intl. 1%; N.E. 1%; M.A. 3%; E.N.C.
9%; W.N.C. 76%; S.A. 1%; E.S.C.
0%; W.S.C. 1%; Mt. 2%; Pac. 3%;
unknown 4%

University of Minnesota– Twin Cities
229 19th Avenue S
Minneapolis, MN 55455
http://www.law.umn.edu
Public
Admissions: (612) 625-3487
E-mail: umnlsadm@umn.edu
Financial aid: (612) 625-3487
Application deadline: 03/01
In-state tuition: full time: $22,505;
part time: N/A
Out-of-state tuition: full time:
$32,005
Room/board/expenses: $13,392
Percent receiving grants: 59%
Median grant: $8,000
Average student indebtedness at
graduation: $82,981
Enrollment: full time: 793;
part time: N/A
men: 58%; women: 42%;
minorities: 16%
Acceptance rate (full-time): 25%
Midrange LSAT (full-time): 163-167
Midrange undergraduate GPA
(full-time): 3.28-3.78
Midrange of full-time private-sector
salaries of 2006 grads: $65,000-
$110,000
2006 grads employed in: law firms:
51%; business and industry: 15%;
government: 6%; public interest:
7%; judicial clerk: 19%; academia:
2%; unknown: 1%
Employment location for 2006 class:
Intl. 2%; N.E. 3%; M.A. 6%; E.N.C.
8%; W.N.C. 62%; S.A. 7%; E.S.C.
0%; W.S.C. 1%; Mt. 3%; Pac. 10%;
unknown 1%

University of St. Thomas
MSL 411
1000 LaSalle Avenue
Minneapolis, MN 55403-2015
http://www.stthomas.edu/law
Private
Admissions: (651) 962-4895
E-mail: lawschool@stthomas.edu
Financial aid: (651) 962-4895
Application deadline: 07/01
Tuition: full time: $28,832;
part time: N/A
Room/board/expenses: $16,440
Percent receiving grants: 70%
Median grant: $10,000
Average student indebtedness at
graduation: $75,312
Enrollment: full time: 467;
part time: N/A
men: 55%; women: 45%;
minorities: 15%
Acceptance rate (full-time): 49%
Midrange LSAT (full-time): 154-161
Midrange undergraduate GPA
(full-time): 3.16-3.63
Midrange of full-time private-sector
salaries of 2006 grads: $48,000-
$61,000
2006 grads employed in: law firms:
36%; business and industry: 23%;
government: 9%; public interest:
14%; judicial clerk: 16%; academia:
2%; unknown: 0%
Employment location for 2006 class:
Intl. 1%; N.E. 0%; M.A. 0%; E.N.C.
2%; W.N.C. 85%; S.A. 4%; E.S.C.
0%; W.S.C. 1%; Mt. 4%; Pac. 2%;
unknown 1%

William Mitchell College of Law
875 Summit Avenue
St. Paul, MN 55105-3076
http://www.wmitchell.edu
Private
Admissions: (651) 290-6476
E-mail: admissions@wmitchell.edu
Financial aid: (651) 290-6403
Application deadline: 05/01
Tuition: full time: $29,020;
part time: $21,002
Room/board/expenses: $15,900
Percent receiving grants: 43%
Median grant: $5,000
Average student indebtedness at
graduation: $74,555
Enrollment: full time: 233;
part time: 103
men: 52%; women: 48%;
minorities: 7%
Acceptance rate (full-time): 51%
Midrange LSAT (full-time): 151-157
Midrange undergraduate GPA
(full-time): 3.15-3.63
Midrange of full-time private-sector
salaries of 2006 grads: $50,000-
$100,000
2006 grads employed in: law firms:
45%; business and industry: 25%;
government: 10%; public interest:
5%; judicial clerk: 11%; academia:
1%; unknown: 3%
Employment location for 2006 class:
Intl. 0%; N.E. 0%; M.A. 1%; E.N.C.
4%; W.N.C. 88%; S.A. 2%; E.S.C.
0%; W.S.C. 1%; Mt. 2%; Pac. 1%;
unknown 1%

Mississippi College
151 E. Griffith Street
Jackson, MS 39201
http://www.law.mc.edu
Private
Admissions: (601) 925-7151
E-mail: hweaver@mc.edu
Financial aid: (601) 925-7110
Application deadline: 06/01
Tuition: full time: $23,720;
part time: N/A
Room/board/expenses: $17,200
Percent receiving grants: 28%
Median grant: $7,333
Average student indebtedness at
graduation: $77,716
Enrollment: full time: 528;
part time: 9
men: 58%; women: 42%;
minorities: 9%
Acceptance rate (full-time): 52%
Midrange LSAT (full-time): 148-153
Midrange undergraduate GPA
(full-time): 2.88-3.50
Midrange of full-time private-sector
salaries of 2006 grads: $60,000-
$85,000
2006 grads employed in: law firms:
61%; business and industry: 13%;
government: 11%; public interest:
5%; judicial clerk: 8%; academia:
2%; unknown: 0%
Employment location for 2006 class:
Intl. 0%; N.E. 0%; M.A. 4%; E.N.C.
0%; W.N.C. 2%; S.A. 8%; E.S.C.
81%; W.S.C. 6%; Mt. 1%; Pac. 2%;
unknown 0%

University of Mississippi
PO Box 1848
University, MS 38677
http://www.olemiss.edu/
depts/law_school/
Public
Admissions: (662) 915-6910
E-mail: lawmiss@olemiss.edu
Financial aid: (800) 891-4569
Application deadline: 02/15
In-state tuition: full time: $8,930;
part time: N/A

Out-of-state tuition: full time:
$18,550
Room/board/expenses: $14,858
Percent receiving grants: 39%
Median grant: $4,750
Average student indebtedness at
graduation: $48,400
Enrollment: full time: 517;
part time: N/A
men: 56%; women: 44%;
minorities: 14%
Acceptance rate (full-time): 31%
Midrange LSAT (full-time): 152-157
Midrange undergraduate GPA
(full-time): 3.28-3.79
Midrange of full-time private-sector
salaries of 2006 grads: $45,000-
$81,000
2006 grads employed in: law firms:
58%; business and industry: 6%;
government: 11%; public interest:
4%; judicial clerk: 18%; academia:
2%; unknown: 1%
Employment location for 2006 class:
Intl. 1%; N.E. 0%; M.A. 1%; E.N.C.
0%; W.N.C. 1%; S.A. 11%; E.S.C.
77%; W.S.C. 5%; Mt. 2%; Pac. 2%;
unknown 0%

St. Louis University
3700 Lindell Boulevard
St. Louis, MO 63108
http://law.slu.edu
Private
Admissions: (314) 977-2800
E-mail: admissions@law.slu.edu
Financial aid: (314) 977-3369
Application deadline: rolling
Tuition: full time: $31,750;
part time: $23,135
Room/board/expenses: $18,877
Percent receiving grants: 44%
Median grant: $13,000
Average student indebtedness at
graduation: $89,682
Enrollment: full time: 750;
part time: 218
men: 52%; women: 48%;
minorities: 13%
Acceptance rate (full-time): 52%
Midrange LSAT (full-time): 154-159
Midrange undergraduate GPA
(full-time): 3.24-3.74
Midrange of full-time private-sector
salaries of 2006 grads: $52,000-
$90,000
2006 grads employed in: law firms:
62%; business and industry: 16%;
government: 12%; public interest:
6%; judicial clerk: 3%; academia:
1%; unknown: 0%
Employment location for 2006 class:
Intl. 1%; N.E. 1%; M.A. 17%; E.N.C.
71%; W.N.C. 5%; S.A. 1%; E.S.C.
1%; W.S.C. 1%; Mt. 1%; Pac. 1%;
unknown 0%

University of Missouri–Columbia
203 Hulston Hall
Columbia, MO 65211-4300
http://www.law.missouri.edu
Public
Admissions: (573) 882-6042
E-mail: umclawadmissions@
missouri.edu
Financial aid: (573) 882-6643
Application deadline: 03/01
In-state tuition: full time: $14,854;
part time: N/A
Out-of-state tuition: full time:
$28,336
Room/board/expenses: $14,992
Percent receiving grants: 40%
Median grant: $4,000
Average student indebtedness at
graduation: $60,858

Enrollment: full time: 449;
part time: 6
men: 62%; women: 38%;
minorities: 14%
Acceptance rate (full-time): 36%
Midrange LSAT (full-time): 156-161
Midrange undergraduate GPA
(full-time): 3.26-3.80
Midrange of full-time private-sector
salaries of 2006 grads: $45,000-
$75,000
2006 grads employed in: law firms:
52%; business and industry: 5%;
government: 20%; public interest:
8%; judicial clerk: 13%; academia:
0%; unknown: 3%
Employment location for 2006 class:
Intl. 0%; N.E. 0%; M.A. 0%; E.N.C.
4%; W.N.C. 88%; S.A. 2%; E.S.C.
0%; W.S.C. 3%; Mt. 0%; Pac. 2%;
unknown 2%

University of
Missouri–Kansas City
5100 Rockhill Road
Kansas City, MO 64110
http://www.law.umkc.edu
Public
Admissions: (816) 235-1644
E-mail: law@umkc.edu
Financial aid: (816) 235-1154
Application deadline: rolling
In-state tuition: full time: $13,681;
part time: $9,844
Out-of-state tuition: full time:
$26,188
Room/board/expenses: $19,600
Percent receiving grants: 39%
Median grant: $5,000
Average student indebtedness at
graduation: $73,343
Enrollment: full time: 467;
part time: 26
men: 59%; women: 41%;
minorities: 10%
Acceptance rate (full-time): 50%
Midrange LSAT (full-time): 152-156
Midrange undergraduate GPA
(full-time): 3.03-3.64
Midrange of full-time private-sector
salaries of 2006 grads: $43,000-
$73,000
2006 grads employed in: law firms:
57%; business and industry: 25%;
government: 8%; public interest:
3%; judicial clerk: 6%; academia:
1%; unknown: 1%
Employment location for 2006 class:
Intl. 1%; N.E. N/A; M.A. N/A; E.N.C.
2%; W.N.C. 91%; S.A. 2%; E.S.C.
N/A; W.S.C. 1%; Mt. 2%; Pac. 2%;
unknown 0%

Washington
University
in St. Louis
1 Brookings Drive
Box 1120
St. Louis, MO 63130
http://www.law.wustl.edu/
Private
Admissions: (314) 935-4525
E-mail: admiss@wulaw.wustl.edu
Financial aid: (314) 935-4605
Application deadline: 03/01
Tuition: full time: $38,189;
part time: N/A
Room/board/expenses: $19,600
Percent receiving grants: 56%
Median grant: $15,000
Average student indebtedness at
graduation: $100,220
Enrollment: full time: 801;
part time: 9
men: 55%; women: 45%;
minorities: 18%
Acceptance rate (full-time): 26%
Midrange LSAT (full-time): 163-167
Midrange undergraduate GPA
(full-time): 3.30-3.70

Midrange of full-time private-sector
salaries of 2006 grads: $83,000-
$130,000
2006 grads employed in: law firms:
62%; business and industry: 6%;
government: 17%; public interest:
5%; judicial clerk: 10%; academia:
0%; unknown: 0%
Employment location for 2006 class:
Intl. 2%; N.E. 2%; M.A. 13%; E.N.C.
21%; W.N.C. 28%; S.A. 15%; E.S.C.
3%; W.S.C. 4%; Mt. 5%; Pac. 6%;
unknown 1%

University of Montana
32 Campus Drive
Missoula, MT 59812
http://www.umt.edu/law
Public
Admissions: (406) 243-2698
E-mail:
heidi.fanslow@umontana.edu
Financial aid: (406) 243-5524
Application deadline: 03/01
In-state tuition: full time: $8,973;
part time: N/A
Out-of-state tuition: full time:
$20,239
Room/board/expenses: $11,727
Enrollment: full time: 252;
part time: N/A
men: 49%; women: 51%;
minorities: 7%
Acceptance rate (full-time): 42%
Midrange LSAT (full-time): 151-158
Midrange undergraduate GPA
(full-time): 3.12-3.75
Midrange of full-time private-sector
salaries of 2006 grads: $41,500-
$50,000
2006 grads employed in: law firms:
48%; business and industry: 5%;
government: 6%; public interest:
9%; judicial clerk: 32%; academia:
0%; unknown: 0%
Employment location for 2006 class:
Intl. N/A; N.E. N/A; M.A. N/A; E.N.C.
N/A; W.N.C. N/A; S.A. N/A; E.S.C.
N/A; W.S.C. N/A; Mt. N/A; Pac. N/A;
unknown N/A

Creighton University
2500 California Plaza
Omaha, NE 68178
http://law.creighton.edu/
Private
Admissions: (800) 282-5835
E-mail: lawadmit@creighton.edu
Financial aid: (402) 280-2352
Application deadline: 03/01
Tuition: full time: $25,850;
part time: $15,948
Room/board/expenses: $16,530
Percent receiving grants: 38%
Median grant: $8,000
Average student indebtedness at
graduation: $91,517
Enrollment: full time: 451;
part time: 18
men: 59%; women: 41%;
minorities: 10%
Acceptance rate (full-time): 45%
Midrange LSAT (full-time): 151-156
Midrange undergraduate GPA
(full-time): 3.23-3.68
Midrange of full-time private-sector
salaries of 2006 grads: $50,000-
$78,000
2006 grads employed in: law firms:
47%; business and industry: 23%;
government: 15%; public interest:
5%; judicial clerk: 9%; academia:
1%; unknown: 0%
Employment location for 2006 class:
Intl. 1%; N.E. N/A; M.A. N/A; E.N.C.
9%; W.N.C. 68%; S.A. 2%; E.S.C.
N/A; W.S.C. N/A; Mt. 16%; Pac. 4%;
unknown 0%

University of
Nebraska–Lincoln
PO Box 830902
Lincoln, NE 68583-0902
http://law.unl.edu
Public
Admissions: (402) 472-2161
E-mail: lawadm@unl.edu
Financial aid: (402) 472-2161
Application deadline: 03/01
In-state tuition: full time: $9,018;
part time: N/A
Out-of-state tuition: full time:
$20,935
Room/board/expenses: $11,920
Percent receiving grants: 41%
Median grant: $8,000
Average student indebtedness at
graduation: $44,985
Enrollment: full time: 397;
part time: 1
men: 53%; women: 47%;
minorities: 16%
Acceptance rate (full-time): 37%
Midrange LSAT (full-time): 153-159
Midrange undergraduate GPA
(full-time): 3.50-3.82
Midrange of full-time private-sector
salaries of 2006 grads: $43,125-
$76,250
2006 grads employed in: law firms:
53%; business and industry: 16%;
government: 19%; public interest:
8%; judicial clerk: 6%; academia:
4%; unknown: 0%
Employment location for 2006 class:
Intl. 3%; N.E. 0%; M.A. 2%; E.N.C.
2%; W.N.C. 76%; S.A. 3%; E.S.C.
0%; W.S.C. 2%; Mt. 8%; Pac. 3%;
unknown 1%

University of
Nevada–Las Vegas
(Boyd)
4505 S. Maryland Parkway
PO Box 451003
Las Vegas, NV 89154-1003
http://www.law.unlv.edu/
Public
Admissions: (702) 895-2440
E-mail: request@law.unlv.edu
Financial aid: (702) 895-0630
Application deadline: 03/15
In-state tuition: full time: $10,502;
part time: $6,946
Out-of-state tuition: full time:
$20,302
Room/board/expenses: $14,260
Percent receiving grants: 49%
Median grant: $5,000
Average student indebtedness at
graduation: $49,186
Enrollment: full time: 341;
part time: 122
men: 52%; women: 48%;
minorities: 29%
Acceptance rate (full-time): 23%
Midrange LSAT (full-time): 156-161
Midrange undergraduate GPA
(full-time): 3.20-3.66
Midrange of full-time private-sector
salaries of 2006 grads: $60,000-
$90,000
2006 grads employed in: law firms:
48%; business and industry: 8%;
government: 13%; public interest:
5%; judicial clerk: 21%; academia:
5%; unknown: 0%
Employment location for 2006 class:
Intl. 0%; N.E. 0%; M.A. 0%; E.N.C.
1%; W.N.C. 1%; S.A. 2%; E.S.C. 0%;
W.S.C. 0%; Mt. 94%; Pac. 2%;
unknown 0%

Franklin Pierce
Law Center
2 White Street
Concord, NH 03301
http://www.piercelaw.edu
Private
Admissions: (603) 228-9217
E-mail: admissions@piercelaw.edu
Financial aid: (603) 228-1541
Application deadline: 06/30
Tuition: full time: $30,780;
part time: N/A
Room/board/expenses: $15,550
Percent receiving grants: 65%
Median grant: $3,500
Average student indebtedness at
graduation: $97,592
Enrollment: full time: 400;
part time: N/A
men: 66%; women: 35%;
minorities: 16%
Acceptance rate (full-time): 50%
Midrange LSAT (full-time): 150-155
Midrange undergraduate GPA
(full-time): 3.00-3.50
Midrange of full-time private-sector
salaries of 2006 grads: $60,000-
$125,000
2006 grads employed in: law firms:
58%; business and industry: 14%;
government: 12%; public interest:
4%; judicial clerk: 9%; academia:
1%; unknown: 1%
Employment location for 2006 class:
Intl. 2%; N.E. 41%; M.A. 15%; E.N.C.
6%; W.N.C. 4%; S.A. 23%; E.S.C.
1%; W.S.C. 1%; Mt. 2%; Pac. 5%;
unknown 0%

Rutgers, the
State University
of New Jersey–
Camden
217 N. Fifth Street
Camden, NJ 08102-1203
http://www-camlaw.rutgers.edu
Public
Admissions: (800) 466-7561
E-mail: admissions@
camlaw.rutgers.edu
Financial aid: (856) 225-6039
Application deadline: 03/01
In-state tuition: full time: $21,488;
part time: $17,144
Out-of-state tuition: full time:
$30,492
Room/board/expenses: $13,763
Percent receiving grants: 39%
Median grant: $4,500
Average student indebtedness at
graduation: $71,113
Enrollment: full time: 561;
part time: 229
men: 59%; women: 41%;
minorities: 20%
Acceptance rate (full-time): 22%
Midrange LSAT (full-time): 160-162
Midrange undergraduate GPA
(full-time): 3.09-3.65
Midrange of full-time private-sector
salaries of 2006 grads: $60,001-
$115,000
2006 grads employed in: law firms:
41%; business and industry: 8%;
government: 6%; public interest:
2%; judicial clerk: 40%; academia:
0%; unknown: 3%
Employment location for 2006 class:
Intl. 1%; N.E. 1%; M.A. 82%; E.N.C.
1%; W.N.C. 1%; S.A. 6%; E.S.C. 0%;
W.S.C. 1%; Mt. 1%; Pac. 4%;
unknown 3%

Rutgers, the
State University
of New Jersey–
Newark
123 Washington Street
Newark, NJ 07102
http://law.newark.rutgers.edu
Public
Admissions: (973) 353-5554
E-mail: awalton@
andromeda.rutgers.edu
Financial aid: (973) 353-1702
Application deadline: 03/15
In-state tuition: full time: $21,302;
part time: $13,803
Out-of-state tuition: full time:
$30,307
Room/board/expenses: $13,948
Percent receiving grants: 46%
Median grant: $4,000
Average student indebtedness at
graduation: $64,775
Enrollment: full time: 558;
part time: 260
men: 56%; women: 44%;
minorities: 37%
Acceptance rate (full-time): 30%
Midrange LSAT (full-time): 155-161
Midrange undergraduate GPA
(full-time): 3.08-3.55
Midrange of full-time private-sector
salaries of 2006 grads: $90,000-
$145,000
2006 grads employed in: law firms:
45%; business and industry: 14%;
government: 7%; public interest:
3%; judicial clerk: 28%; academia:
2%; unknown: 0%
Employment location for 2006 class:
Intl. 1%; N.E. 1%; M.A. 93%; E.N.C.
1%; W.N.C. 0%; S.A. 4%; E.S.C.
0%; W.S.C. 0%; Mt. 0%; Pac. 1%;
unknown 0%

Seton Hall University
1 Newark Center
Newark, NJ 07102-5210
http://law.shu.edu
Private
Admissions: (888) 415-7271
E-mail: admitme@shu.edu
Financial aid: (973) 642-8850
Application deadline: 04/01
Tuition: full time: $38,040;
part time: $28,725
Room/board/expenses: $17,290
Percent receiving grants: 42%
Median grant: $17,500
Average student indebtedness at
graduation: $91,500
Enrollment: full time: 722;
part time: 342
men: 56%; women: 44%;
minorities: 14%
Acceptance rate (full-time): 43%
Midrange LSAT (full-time): 157-162
Midrange undergraduate GPA
(full-time): 3.22-3.65
Midrange of full-time private-sector
salaries of 2006 grads: $55,000-
$105,000
2006 grads employed in: law firms:
39%; business and industry: 16%;
government: 7%; public interest:
1%; judicial clerk: 33%; academia:
1%; unknown: 2%
Employment location for 2006 class:
Intl. 0%; N.E. 1%; M.A. 85%; E.N.C.
0%; W.N.C. N/A; S.A. 4%; E.S.C.
N/A; W.S.C. 1%; Mt. 1%; Pac. 0%;
unknown 8%

NEW MEXICO

University of New Mexico
1117 Stanford Drive NE
Albuquerque, NM 87131-1431
http://lawschool.unm.edu
Public
Admissions: (505) 277-0572
E-mail: admissions@law.unm.edu
Financial aid: (505) 277-0572
Application deadline: 02/15
In-state tuition: full time: $10,561;
part time: N/A
Out-of-state tuition: full time:
$24,467
Room/board/expenses: $13,600
Percent receiving grants: 24%
Median grant: $9,565
Average student indebtedness at
graduation: $34,558
Enrollment: full time: 347;
part time: N/A
men: 49%; women: 51%;
minorities: 45%
Acceptance rate (full-time): 22%
Midrange LSAT (full-time): 152-159
Midrange undergraduate GPA
(full-time): 3.09-3.72
Midrange of full-time private-sector
salaries of 2006 grads: $36,000-
$72,000
2006 grads employed in: law firms:
50%; business and industry: 6%;
government: 17%; public interest:
12%; judicial clerk: 9%; academia:
5%; unknown: 1%
Employment location for 2006 class:
Intl. 1%; N.E. 0%; M.A. 1%; E.N.C.
1%; W.N.C. 1%; S.A. 2%; E.S.C. 1%;
W.S.C. 0%; Mt. 87%; Pac. 6%;
unknown 0%

NEW YORK

Albany Law School-Union University
80 New Scotland Avenue
Albany, NY 12208-3494
http://www.albanylaw.edu
Private
Admissions: (518) 445-2326
E-mail: admissions@albanylaw.edu
Financial aid: (518) 445-2357
Application deadline: 03/01
Tuition: full time: $37,550;
part time: $28,200
Room/board/expenses: $17,050
Percent receiving grants: 35%
Median grant: $18,000
Average student indebtedness at
graduation: $85,839
Enrollment: full time: 662;
part time: 22
men: 55%; women: 45%;
minorities: 14%
Acceptance rate (full-time): 45%
Midrange LSAT (full-time): 152-157
Midrange undergraduate GPA
(full-time): 2.92-3.48
Midrange of full-time private-sector
salaries of 2006 grads: $47,000-
$72,000
2006 grads employed in: law firms:
51%; business and industry: 17%;
government: 18%; public interest:
3%; judicial clerk: 9%; academia:
1%; unknown: 1%
Employment location for 2006 class:
Intl. 0%; N.E. 3%; M.A. 91%; E.N.C.
0%; W.N.C. 1%; S.A. 4%; E.S.C.
0%; W.S.C. 0%; Mt. 0%; Pac. 0%;
unknown 1%

Brooklyn Law School
250 Joralemon Street
Brooklyn, NY 11201
http://www.brooklaw.edu
Private
Admissions: (718) 780-7906
E-mail: admitq@brooklaw.edu
Financial aid: (718) 780-7915
Application deadline: rolling
Tuition: full time: $39,625;
part time: $29,807
Room/board/expenses: $20,566
Percent receiving grants: 71%
Median grant: $15,860
Average student indebtedness at
graduation: $92,447
Enrollment: full time: 1,186;
part time: 310
men: 52%; women: 48%;
minorities: 28%
Acceptance rate (full-time): 29%
Midrange LSAT (full-time): 162-165
Midrange undergraduate GPA
(full-time): 3.17-3.63
Midrange of full-time private-sector
salaries of 2006 grads: $65,000-
$145,000
2006 grads employed in: law firms:
56%; business and industry: 19%;
government: 15%; public interest:
4%; judicial clerk: 5%; academia:
0%; unknown: 1%
Employment location for 2006 class:
Intl. 1%; N.E. 2%; M.A. 92%; E.N.C.
0%; W.N.C. 0%; S.A. 2%; E.S.C.
0%; W.S.C. 0%; Mt. 0%; Pac. 3%;
unknown 0%

Columbia University
435 W. 116th Street
New York, NY 10027
http://www.law.columbia.edu
Private
Admissions: (212) 854-2670
E-mail: admissions@
law.columbia.edu
Financial aid: (212) 854-7730
Application deadline: 02/15
Tuition: full time: $43,470;
part time: N/A
Room/board/expenses: $19,598
Percent receiving grants: 44%
Median grant: $10,000
Average student indebtedness at
graduation: $113,540
Enrollment: full time: 1,236;
part time: N/A
men: 56%; women: 44%;
minorities: 29%
Acceptance rate (full-time): 16%
Midrange LSAT (full-time): 169-174
Midrange undergraduate GPA
(full-time): 3.56-3.81
Midrange of full-time private-sector
salaries of 2006 grads: $145,000-
$145,000
2006 grads employed in: law firms:
80%; business and industry: 3%;
government: 2%; public interest:
6%; judicial clerk: 9%; academia:
1%; unknown: 0%
Employment location for 2006 class:
Intl. 4%; N.E. 1%; M.A. 73%; E.N.C.
1%; W.N.C. 0%; S.A. 11%; E.S.C.
0%; W.S.C. 1%; Mt. 0%; Pac. 10%;
unknown 0%

Cornell University
Myron Taylor Hall
Ithaca, NY 14853-4901
http://www.lawschool.cornell.edu
Private
Admissions: (607) 255-5141
E-mail: lawadmit@
postoffice.law.cornell.edu
Financial aid: (607) 255-5141
Application deadline: 02/01
Tuition: full time: $42,683;
part time: N/A
Room/board/expenses: $17,350

Percent receiving grants: 38%
Median grant: $13,000
Average student indebtedness at
graduation: $102,000
Enrollment: full time: 583;
part time: N/A
men: 50%; women: 50%;
minorities: 21%
Acceptance rate (full-time): 22%
Midrange LSAT (full-time): 166-168
Midrange undergraduate GPA
(full-time): 3.54-3.78
Midrange of full-time private-sector
salaries of 2006 grads: $135,000-
$145,000
2006 grads employed in: law firms:
82%; business and industry: 4%;
government: 2%; public interest:
2%; judicial clerk: 9%; academia:
1%; unknown: 0%
Employment location for 2006 class:
Intl. 1%; N.E. 7%; M.A. 58%; E.N.C.
5%; W.N.C. 2%; S.A. 8%; E.S.C.
1%; W.S.C. 2%; Mt. 4%; Pac. 12%;
unknown 0%

CUNY–Queens College
65-21 Main Street
Flushing, NY 11367
http://www.law.cuny.edu/
Public
Admissions: (718) 340-4210
E-mail:
admissions@mail.law.cuny.edu
Financial aid: (718) 340-4284
Application deadline: 03/16
In-state tuition: full time: $10,562;
part time: N/A
Out-of-state tuition: full time:
$16,462
Room/board/expenses: $13,306
Percent receiving grants: 42%
Median grant: $2,290
Average student indebtedness at
graduation: $57,262
Enrollment: full time: 412;
part time: N/A
men: 35%; women: 65%;
minorities: 31%
Acceptance rate (full-time): 25%
Midrange LSAT (full-time): 151-156
Midrange undergraduate GPA
(full-time): 2.92-3.47
Midrange of full-time private-sector
salaries of 2006 grads: $51,003-
$80,000
2006 grads employed in: law firms:
21%; business and industry: 15%;
government: 14%; public interest:
28%; judicial clerk: 17%; academia:
5%; unknown: 0%
Employment location for 2006 class:
Intl. 4%; N.E. 2%; M.A. 86%; E.N.C.
0%; W.N.C. 0%; S.A. 5%; E.S.C.
0%; W.S.C. 1%; Mt. 1%; Pac. 2%;
unknown 0%

Fordham University
140 W. 62nd Street
New York, NY 10023-7485
http://law.fordham.edu
Private
Admissions: (212) 636-6810
E-mail: lawadmissions@
law.fordham.edu
Financial aid: (212) 636-6815
Application deadline: 03/01
Tuition: full time: $39,450;
part time: $29,650
Room/board/expenses: $22,000
Percent receiving grants: 34%
Median grant: $9,600
Average student indebtedness at
graduation: $100,554
Enrollment: full time: 1,191;
part time: 318
men: 53%; women: 47%;
minorities: 24%
Acceptance rate (full-time): 24%
Midrange LSAT (full-time): 163-167
Midrange undergraduate GPA
(full-time): 3.41-3.74

Midrange of full-time private-sector
salaries of 2006 grads: $125,000-
$145,000
2006 grads employed in: law firms:
69%; business and industry: 8%;
government: 8%; public interest:
7%; judicial clerk: 4%; academia:
1%; unknown: 3%
Employment location for 2006 class:
Intl. 1%; N.E. 3%; M.A. 80%; E.N.C.
0%; W.N.C. 0%; S.A. 3%; E.S.C.
0%; W.S.C. 0%; Mt. 0%; Pac. 3%;
unknown 9%

Hofstra University
121 Hofstra University
Hempstead, NY 11549
http://law.hofstra.edu
Private
Admissions: (516) 463-5916
E-mail:
lawadmissions@hofstra.edu
Financial aid: (516) 463-5929
Application deadline: 04/15
Tuition: full time: $37,600;
part time: $1,320/credit hour
Room/board/expenses: $15,676
Percent receiving grants: 50%
Median grant: $13,540
Average student indebtedness at
graduation: $100,915
Enrollment: full time: 870;
part time: 272
men: 53%; women: 47%;
minorities: 24%
Acceptance rate (full-time): 42%
Midrange LSAT (full-time): 154-159
Midrange undergraduate GPA
(full-time): 3.11-3.69
Midrange of full-time private-sector
salaries of 2006 grads: $70,000-
$160,000
2006 grads employed in: law firms:
56%; business and industry: 22%;
government: 11%; public interest:
3%; judicial clerk: 5%; academia:
2%; unknown: 2%
Employment location for 2006 class:
Intl. 0%; N.E. 1%; M.A. 75%; E.N.C.
1%; W.N.C. 0%; S.A. 6%; E.S.C.
0%; W.S.C. 1%; Mt. 1%; Pac. 2%;
unknown 15%

New York Law School
57 Worth Street
New York, NY 10013-2960
http://www.nyls.edu
Private
Admissions: (212) 431-2888
E-mail: admissions@nyls.edu
Financial aid: (212) 431-2828
Application deadline: 04/01
Tuition: full time: $41,950;
part time: $32,250
Room/board/expenses: $20,785
Percent receiving grants: 32%
Median grant: $8,750
Average student indebtedness at
graduation: $105,793
Enrollment: full time: 1,165;
part time: 407
men: 48%; women: 52%;
minorities: 23%
Acceptance rate (full-time): 47%
Midrange LSAT (full-time): 153-157
Midrange undergraduate GPA
(full-time): 3.08-3.57
Midrange of full-time private-sector
salaries of 2006 grads: $65,000-
$145,000
2006 grads employed in: law firms:
52%; business and industry: 18%;
government: 11%; public interest:
4%; judicial clerk: 5%; academia:
2%; unknown: 8%
Employment location for 2006 class:
Intl. 1%; N.E. 2%; M.A. 90%; E.N.C.
0%; W.N.C. 0%; S.A. 4%; E.S.C.
0%; W.S.C. 1%; Mt. 0%; Pac. 2%;
unknown 0%

New York University
40 Washington Square S
New York, NY 10012
http://www.law.nyu.edu
Private
Admissions: (212) 998-6060
E-mail: law.moreinfo@nyu.edu
Financial aid: (212) 998-6050
Application deadline: 02/01
Tuition: full time: $40,890;
part time: N/A
Room/board/expenses: $23,570
Percent receiving grants: 33%
Median grant: $15,000
Average student indebtedness at
graduation: $117,636
Enrollment: full time: 1,424;
part time: N/A
men: 53%; women: 47%;
minorities: 23%
Acceptance rate (full-time): 23%
Midrange LSAT (full-time): 169-173
Midrange undergraduate GPA
(full-time): 3.54-3.86
Midrange of full-time private-sector
salaries of 2006 grads: $135,000-
$145,000
2006 grads employed in: law firms:
69%; business and industry: 2%;
government: 3%; public interest:
13%; judicial clerk: 12%; academia:
0%; unknown: 1%
Employment location for 2006 class:
Intl. 2%; N.E. 4%; M.A. 68%; E.N.C.
3%; W.N.C. 0%; S.A. 8%; E.S.C.
1%; W.S.C. 2%; Mt. 1%; Pac. 12%;
unknown 0%

Pace University
78 N. Broadway
White Plains, NY 10603
http://www.law.pace.edu
Private
Admissions: (914) 422-4210
E-mail: admissions@law.pace.edu
Financial aid: (914) 422-4050
Application deadline: 03/01
Tuition: full time: $37,430;
part time: $28,090
Room/board/expenses: $23,070
Percent receiving grants: 51%
Median grant: $12,000
Average student indebtedness at
graduation: $78,000
Enrollment: full time: 533;
part time: 232
men: 41%; women: 59%;
minorities: 15%
Acceptance rate (full-time): 37%
Midrange LSAT (full-time): 153-157
Midrange undergraduate GPA
(full-time): 3.13-3.59
Midrange of full-time private-sector
salaries of 2006 grads: $54,000-
$95,000
2006 grads employed in: law firms:
51%; business and industry: 27%;
government: 15%; public interest:
2%; judicial clerk: 3%; academia:
1%; unknown: 1%
Employment location for 2006 class:
Intl. 0%; N.E. 5%; M.A. 65%; E.N.C.
1%; W.N.C. 0%; S.A. 6%; E.S.C. 1%;
W.S.C. 0%; Mt. 0%; Pac. 3%;
unknown 19%

St. John's University
8000 Utopia Parkway
Jamaica, NY 11439
http://www.law.stjohns.edu/
Private
Admissions: (718) 990-6474
E-mail: lawinfo@stjohns.edu
Financial aid: (718) 990-1485
Application deadline: 04/01
Tuition: full time: $38,400;
part time: $28,800
Room/board/expenses: $19,210
Percent receiving grants: 42%
Median grant: $20,000

Average student indebtedness at graduation: $93,619
Enrollment: full time: 748;
part time: 166
men: 52%; women: 48%;
minorities: 23%
Acceptance rate (full-time): 34%
Midrange LSAT (full-time): 157-162
Midrange undergraduate GPA (full-time): 3.19-3.74
Midrange of full-time private-sector salaries of 2006 grads: $60,000-$145,000
2006 grads employed in: law firms: 58%; business and industry: 14%; government: 20%; public interest: 3%; judicial clerk: 4%; academia: 1%; unknown: 1%
Employment location for 2006 class: Intl. 0%; N.E. 2%; M.A. 93%; E.N.C. 0%; W.N.C. N/A; S.A. 2%; E.S.C. N/A; W.S.C. N/A; Mt. 1%; Pac. 1%; unknown 1%

Syracuse University
Suite 340
Syracuse, NY 13244-1030
http://www.law.syr.edu
Private
Admissions: (315) 443-1962
E-mail: admissions@law.syr.edu
Financial aid: (315) 443-1963
Application deadline: 04/01
Tuition: full time: $41,694;
part time: $1,800/credit hour
Room/board/expenses: $16,816
Percent receiving grants: 72%
Median grant: $7,600
Average student indebtedness at graduation: $99,886
Enrollment: full time: 659;
part time: 7
men: 55%; women: 45%;
minorities: 19%
Acceptance rate (full-time): 50%
Midrange LSAT (full-time): 152-156
Midrange undergraduate GPA (full-time): 3.09-3.59
Midrange of full-time private-sector salaries of 2006 grads: $45,000-$85,000
2006 grads employed in: law firms: 46%; business and industry: 16%; government: 16%; public interest: 4%; judicial clerk: 15%; academia: 3%; unknown: 0%
Employment location for 2006 class: Intl. 1%; N.E. 5%; M.A. 54%; E.N.C. 4%; W.N.C. 1%; S.A. 24%; E.S.C. 1%; W.S.C. 2%; Mt. 2%; Pac. 6%; unknown 0%

Touro College (Fuchsberg)
225 Eastview Drive
Central Islip, NY 11722
http://www.tourolaw.edu
Private
Admissions: (631) 761-7010
E-mail: admissions@tourolaw.edu
Financial aid: (631) 761-7020
Application deadline: 08/01
Tuition: full time: $33,920;
part time: $25,520
Room/board/expenses: $23,006
Percent receiving grants: 64%
Median grant: $3,628
Average student indebtedness at graduation: $88,249
Enrollment: full time: 513;
part time: 234
men: 53%; women: 47%;
minorities: 21%
Acceptance rate (full-time): 43%
Midrange LSAT (full-time): 150-153
Midrange undergraduate GPA (full-time): 2.81-3.32
Midrange of full-time private-sector salaries of 2006 grads: $48,000-$75,500

2006 grads employed in: law firms: 60%; business and industry: 15%; government: 16%; public interest: 5%; judicial clerk: 3%; academia: 1%; unknown: 0%
Employment location for 2006 class: Intl. 0%; N.E. 0%; M.A. 94%; E.N.C. 1%; W.N.C. 0%; S.A. 3%; E.S.C. 0%; W.S.C. 0%; Mt. 1%; Pac. 1%; unknown 0%

University at Buffalo–SUNY
John Lord O'Brian Hall
Buffalo, NY 14260
http://www.law.buffalo.edu
Public
Admissions: (716) 645-2907
E-mail: law-admissions@buffalo.edu
Financial aid: (716) 645-7324
Application deadline: 03/15
In-state tuition: full time: $14,633;
part time: N/A
Out-of-state tuition: full time: $21,433
Room/board/expenses: $14,444
Percent receiving grants: 72%
Median grant: $5,340
Average student indebtedness at graduation: $54,294
Enrollment: full time: 746;
part time: 5
men: 51%; women: 49%;
minorities: 16%
Acceptance rate (full-time): 39%
Midrange LSAT (full-time): 154-159
Midrange undergraduate GPA (full-time): 3.19-3.65
Midrange of full-time private-sector salaries of 2006 grads: $50,000-$83,000
2006 grads employed in: law firms: 54%; business and industry: 11%; government: 14%; public interest: 11%; judicial clerk: 6%; academia: 2%; unknown: 2%
Employment location for 2006 class: Intl. 2%; N.E. 2%; M.A. 78%; E.N.C. 2%; W.N.C. 0%; S.A. 7%; E.S.C. 1%; W.S.C. 1%; Mt. 2%; Pac. 4%; unknown 1%

Yeshiva University (Cardozo)
55 Fifth Avenue
10th Floor
New York, NY 10003
http://www.cardozo.yu.edu
Private
Admissions: (212) 790-0274
E-mail: lawinfo@yu.edu
Financial aid: (212) 790-0392
Application deadline: 04/01
Tuition: full time: $39,470;
part time: $39,470
Room/board/expenses: $25,680
Percent receiving grants: 60%
Median grant: $12,500
Average student indebtedness at graduation: $100,298
Enrollment: full time: 948;
part time: 127
men: 51%; women: 49%;
minorities: 20%
Acceptance rate (full-time): 27%
Midrange LSAT (full-time): 162-166
Midrange undergraduate GPA (full-time): 3.30-3.70
Midrange of full-time private-sector salaries of 2006 grads: $65,000-$145,000
2006 grads employed in: law firms: 60%; business and industry: 17%; government: 14%; public interest: 5%; judicial clerk: 3%; academia: 1%; unknown: 0%

Employment location for 2006 class: Intl. 1%; N.E. 1%; M.A. 89%; E.N.C. 1%; W.N.C. 1%; S.A. 3%; E.S.C. 0%; W.S.C. 1%; Mt. 2%; Pac. 3%; unknown 0%

NORTH CAROLINA

Campbell University (Wiggins)
PO Box 158
Buies Creek, NC 27506
http://www.law.campbell.edu
Private
Admissions: (910) 893-1754
E-mail: admissions@law.campbell.edu
Financial aid: (910) 893-1310
Application deadline: 05/05
Tuition: full time: $26,800;
part time: N/A
Room/board/expenses: $12,822
Percent receiving grants: 52%
Median grant: $6,600
Average student indebtedness at graduation: $89,500
Enrollment: full time: 339;
part time: N/A
men: 54%; women: 46%;
minorities: 7%
Acceptance rate (full-time): 36%
Midrange LSAT (full-time): 151-157
Midrange undergraduate GPA (full-time): 2.94-3.55
Midrange of full-time private-sector salaries of 2006 grads: $48,000-$75,000
2006 grads employed in: law firms: 69%; business and industry: 9%; government: 12%; public interest: 5%; judicial clerk: 5%; academia: 0%; unknown: 0%
Employment location for 2006 class: Intl. 0%; N.E. N/A; M.A. N/A; E.N.C. 1%; W.N.C. N/A; S.A. 98%; E.S.C. N/A; W.S.C. N/A; Mt. N/A; Pac. 1%; unknown 0%

Duke University
Towerview and Science Drive
Box 90362
Durham, NC 27708-0362
http://www.law.duke.edu
Private
Admissions: (919) 613-7020
E-mail: admissions@law.duke.edu
Financial aid: (919) 613-7026
Application deadline: 02/16
Tuition: full time: $40,748;
part time: N/A
Room/board/expenses: $16,629
Percent receiving grants: 79%
Median grant: $10,000
Average student indebtedness at graduation: $108,596
Enrollment: full time: 583;
part time: 37
men: 56%; women: 44%;
minorities: 17%
Acceptance rate (full-time): 27%
Midrange LSAT (full-time): 167-170
Midrange undergraduate GPA (full-time): 3.61-3.82
Midrange of full-time private-sector salaries of 2006 grads: $115,000-$145,000
2006 grads employed in: law firms: 66%; business and industry: 6%; government: 6%; public interest: 3%; judicial clerk: 19%; academia: 0%; unknown: 0%
Employment location for 2006 class: Intl. 2%; N.E. 7%; M.A. 25%; E.N.C. 1%; W.N.C. 2%; S.A. 42%; E.S.C. 2%; W.S.C. 7%; Mt. 4%; Pac. 8%; unknown 0%

North Carolina Central University
640 Nelson Street
Durham, NC 27707
http://web.nccu.edu/law
Public
Admissions: (919) 530-5243
E-mail: recruiter@nccu.edu
Financial aid: (919) 530-7173
Application deadline: 03/31
In-state tuition: full time: $5,709;
part time: $5,709
Out-of-state tuition: full time: $17,569
Room/board/expenses: $19,736
Percent receiving grants: 27%
Median grant: $3,464
Average student indebtedness at graduation: $19,886
Enrollment: full time: 478;
part time: 126
men: 41%; women: 59%;
minorities: 50%
Acceptance rate (full-time): 22%
Midrange LSAT (full-time): 143-151
Midrange undergraduate GPA (full-time): 2.88-3.45
Midrange of full-time private-sector salaries of 2006 grads: N/A-N/A
2006 grads employed in: law firms: 61%; business and industry: 8%; government: 16%; public interest: 7%; judicial clerk: 5%; academia: 3%; unknown: 0%
Employment location for 2006 class: Intl. 0%; N.E. N/A; M.A. 3%; E.N.C. 2%; W.N.C. N/A; S.A. 92%; E.S.C. 1%; W.S.C. 2%; Mt. N/A; Pac. N/A; unknown 0%

University of North Carolina–Chapel Hill
Van Hecke-Wettach Hall
CB No. 3380
Chapel Hill, NC 27599-3380
http://www.law.unc.edu
Public
Admissions: (919) 962-5109
E-mail: law_admission@unc.edu
Financial aid: (919) 962-8396
Application deadline: 02/01
In-state tuition: full time: $13,004;
part time: N/A
Out-of-state tuition: full time: $25,422
Room/board/expenses: $17,300
Percent receiving grants: 82%
Median grant: $2,200
Average student indebtedness at graduation: $56,740
Enrollment: full time: 699;
part time: N/A
men: 48%; women: 52%;
minorities: 21%
Acceptance rate (full-time): 19%
Midrange LSAT (full-time): 157-164
Midrange undergraduate GPA (full-time): 3.45-3.80
Midrange of full-time private-sector salaries of 2006 grads: $70,000-$115,000
2006 grads employed in: law firms: 58%; business and industry: 5%; government: 11%; public interest: 9%; judicial clerk: 13%; academia: 2%; unknown: 2%
Employment location for 2006 class: Intl. 1%; N.E. 1%; M.A. 8%; E.N.C. 2%; W.N.C. 2%; S.A. 77%; E.S.C. 0%; W.S.C. 1%; Mt. 1%; Pac. 6%; unknown 1%

Wake Forest University
Reynolda Station
PO Box 7206
Winston-Salem, NC 27109
http://www.law.wfu.edu
Private
Admissions: (336) 758-5437
E-mail: lawadmissions@wfu.edu
Financial aid: (336) 758-5437
Application deadline: 03/15
Tuition: full time: $31,500;
part time: N/A
Room/board/expenses: $16,050
Percent receiving grants: 40%
Median grant: $22,125
Average student indebtedness at graduation: $83,265
Enrollment: full time: 452;
part time: 10
men: 59%; women: 41%;
minorities: 12%
Acceptance rate (full-time): 35%
Midrange LSAT (full-time): 159-166
Midrange undergraduate GPA (full-time): 3.17-3.68
Midrange of full-time private-sector salaries of 2006 grads: $58,000-$115,000
2006 grads employed in: law firms: 69%; business and industry: 4%; government: 11%; public interest: 3%; judicial clerk: 11%; academia: 0%; unknown: 2%
Employment location for 2006 class: Intl. 0%; N.E. 3%; M.A. 12%; E.N.C. 2%; W.N.C. 0%; S.A. 69%; E.S.C. 6%; W.S.C. 1%; Mt. 3%; Pac. 3%; unknown 0%

NORTH DAKOTA

University of North Dakota
215 Centennial Drive
Stop 9003
Grand Forks, ND 58202
http://www.law.und.nodak.edu
Public
Admissions: (701) 777-2260
E-mail: hoffman@law.und.edu
Financial aid: (701) 777-6265
Application deadline: 04/01
In-state tuition: full time: $8,774;
part time: N/A
Out-of-state tuition: full time: $18,909
Room/board/expenses: $13,650
Percent receiving grants: 34%
Median grant: $5,780
Average student indebtedness at graduation: $53,367
Enrollment: full time: 249;
part time: N/A
men: 53%; women: 47%;
minorities: 12%
Acceptance rate (full-time): 28%
Midrange LSAT (full-time): 147-154
Midrange undergraduate GPA (full-time): 3.02-3.73
Midrange of full-time private-sector salaries of 2006 grads: $37,000-$45,000
2006 grads employed in: law firms: 44%; business and industry: 4%; government: 13%; public interest: 8%; judicial clerk: 31%; academia: 0%; unknown: 0%
Employment location for 2006 class: Intl. 0%; N.E. N/A; M.A. N/A; E.N.C. N/A; W.N.C. 85%; S.A. 6%; E.S.C. N/A; W.S.C. N/A; Mt. 7%; Pac. 2%; unknown 0%

OHIO

Capital University
303 E. Broad Street
Columbus, OH 43215-3200
http://www.law.capital.edu
Private
Admissions: (614) 236-6310
E-mail:
admissions@law.capital.edu
Financial aid: (614) 236-6350
Application deadline: rolling
Tuition: full time: $975/credit hour;
part time: $975/credit hour
Room/board/expenses: $13,475
Percent receiving grants: 58%
Median grant: $11,000
Average student indebtedness at
graduation: $74,598
Enrollment: full time: 459;
part time: 216
men: 56%; women: 44%;
minorities: 12%
Acceptance rate (full-time): 51%
Midrange LSAT (full-time): 151-156
Midrange undergraduate GPA
(full-time): 2.94-3.54
Midrange of full-time private-sector
salaries of 2006 grads: $50,000-
$85,000
2006 grads employed in: law firms:
47%; business and industry: 19%;
government: 21%; public interest:
6%; judicial clerk: 3%; academia:
4%; unknown: 0%
Employment location for 2006 class:
Intl. 1%; N.E. 0%; M.A. 1%; E.N.C.
90%; W.N.C. 0%; S.A. 4%; E.S.C.
1%; W.S.C. 0%; Mt. 3%; Pac. 0%;
unknown 0%

Case Western Reserve University
11075 E. Boulevard
Cleveland, OH 44106-7148
http://www.law.case.edu
Private
Admissions: (800) 756-0036
E-mail: lawadmissions@case.edu
Financial aid: (877) 889-4279
Application deadline: 04/01
Tuition: full time: $35,220;
part time: $1,446/credit hour
Room/board/expenses: $16,635
Percent receiving grants: 46%
Median grant: $11,000
Average student indebtedness at
graduation: $83,730
Enrollment: full time: 678;
part time: 24
men: 58%; women: 42%;
minorities: 14%
Acceptance rate (full-time): 35%
Midrange LSAT (full-time): 156-160
Midrange undergraduate GPA
(full-time): 3.17-3.60
Midrange of full-time private-sector
salaries of 2006 grads: $70,000-
$110,000
2006 grads employed in: law firms:
50%; business and industry: 20%;
government: 12%; public interest:
9%; judicial clerk: 6%; academia:
2%; unknown: 1%
Employment location for 2006 class:
Intl. 2%; N.E. 3%; M.A. 16%; E.N.C.
52%; W.N.C. 0%; S.A. 15%; E.S.C.
0%; W.S.C. 2%; Mt. 4%; Pac. 5%;
unknown 0%

Cleveland State University (Cleveland-Marshall)
2121 Euclid Avenue
LB 138
Cleveland, OH 44115-2214
http://www.law.csuohio.edu
Public
Admissions: (216) 687-2304
E-mail:
admissions@law.csuohio.edu
Financial aid: (216) 687-2304
Application deadline: 05/01
In-state tuition: full time: $16,478;
part time: $12,675
Out-of-state tuition: full time:
$22,608
Room/board/expenses: $16,262
Percent receiving grants: 35%
Median grant: $3,840
Average student indebtedness at
graduation: $66,118
Enrollment: full time: 503;
part time: 203
men: 53%; women: 47%;
minorities: 14%
Acceptance rate (full-time): 36%
Midrange LSAT (full-time): 153-157
Midrange undergraduate GPA
(full-time): 3.14-3.65
Midrange of full-time private-sector
salaries of 2006 grads: $50,000-
$90,000
2006 grads employed in: law firms:
47%; business and industry: 29%;
government: 14%; public interest:
5%; judicial clerk: 5%; academia:
1%; unknown: 0%
Employment location for 2006 class:
Intl. 1%; N.E. 1%; M.A. 2%; E.N.C.
86%; W.N.C. 1%; S.A. 5%; E.S.C.
1%; W.S.C. 1%; Mt. 1%; Pac. 1%;
unknown 0%

Ohio Northern University (Pettit)
525 S. Main Street
Ada, OH 45810-1599
http://www.law.onu.edu
Private
Admissions: (877) 452-9668
E-mail: law-admissions@onu.edu
Financial aid: (419) 772-2272
Application deadline: 08/01
Tuition: full time: $26,350;
part time: N/A
Room/board/expenses: $12,315
Percent receiving grants: 50%
Median grant: $15,000
Average student indebtedness at
graduation: $85,570
Enrollment: full time: 311;
part time: N/A
men: 53%; women: 47%;
minorities: 11%
Acceptance rate (full-time): 30%
Midrange LSAT (full-time): 148-156
Midrange undergraduate GPA
(full-time): 3.10-3.70
Midrange of full-time private-sector
salaries of 2006 grads: $42,000-
$73,500
2006 grads employed in: law firms:
60%; business and industry: 15%;
government: 17%; public interest:
3%; judicial clerk: 3%; academia:
2%; unknown: N/A
Employment location for 2006 class:
Intl. 0%; N.E. 0%; M.A. 9%; E.N.C.
44%; W.N.C. 4%; S.A. 24%; E.S.C.
7%; W.S.C. 4%; Mt. 5%; Pac. 3%;
unknown 0%

Ohio State University (Moritz)
55 W. 12th Avenue
Columbus, OH 43210
http://www.moritzlaw.osu.edu
Public
Admissions: (614) 292-8810
E-mail: lawadmit@osu.edu
Financial aid: (614) 292-8807
Application deadline: 03/15
In-state tuition: full time: $19,246;
part time: N/A
Out-of-state tuition: full time:
$33,946
Room/board/expenses: $17,870
Percent receiving grants: 84%
Median grant: $4,302
Average student indebtedness at
graduation: $53,525
Enrollment: full time: 669;
part time: N/A
men: 57%; women: 43%;
minorities: 23%
Acceptance rate (full-time): 29%
Midrange LSAT (full-time): 158-164
Midrange undergraduate GPA
(full-time): 3.34-3.81
Midrange of full-time private-sector
salaries of 2006 grads: $63,000-
$105,000
2006 grads employed in: law firms:
48%; business and industry: 18%;
government: 15%; public interest:
6%; judicial clerk: 7%; academia:
4%; unknown: 2%
Employment location for 2006 class:
Intl. 1%; N.E. 1%; M.A. 6%; E.N.C.
66%; W.N.C. 0%; S.A. 13%; E.S.C.
1%; W.S.C. 3%; Mt. 4%; Pac. 3%;
unknown 2%

University of Akron
C. Blake McDowell Law Center
Akron, OH 44325-2901
http://www.uakron.edu/law
Public
Admissions: (800) 425-7668
E-mail: lawadmissions@uakron.edu
Financial aid: (800) 621-3847
Application deadline: 03/01
In-state tuition: full time: $16,497;
part time: $10,506
Out-of-state tuition: full time:
$26,089
Room/board/expenses: $14,402
Percent receiving grants: 55%
Median grant: $12,738
Average student indebtedness at
graduation: $57,669
Enrollment: full time: 308;
part time: 221
men: 57%; women: 43%;
minorities: 13%
Acceptance rate (full-time): 32%
Midrange LSAT (full-time): 156-160
Midrange undergraduate GPA
(full-time): 3.16-3.76
Midrange of full-time private-sector
salaries of 2006 grads: $46,253-
$87,912
2006 grads employed in: law firms:
41%; business and industry: 30%;
government: 16%; public interest:
4%; judicial clerk: 7%; academia:
2%; unknown: N/A
Employment location for 2006 class:
Intl. 0%; N.E. N/A; M.A. 5%; E.N.C.
85%; W.N.C. N/A; S.A. 9%; E.S.C.
N/A; W.S.C. 1%; Mt. 1%; Pac. N/A;
unknown 0%

University of Cincinnati
PO Box 210040
Cincinnati, OH 45221-0040
http://www.law.uc.edu
Public
Admissions: (513) 556-6805
E-mail: admissions@law.uc.edu
Financial aid: (513) 556-6805
Application deadline: 03/01
In-state tuition: full time: $18,982;
part time: N/A
Out-of-state tuition: full time:
$33,102
Room/board/expenses: $15,378
Percent receiving grants: 71%
Median grant: $6,500
Average student indebtedness at
graduation: $53,982
Enrollment: full time: 356;
part time: N/A
men: 54%; women: 46%;
minorities: 17%
Acceptance rate (full-time): 35%
Midrange LSAT (full-time): 157-162
Midrange undergraduate GPA
(full-time): 3.39-3.87
Midrange of full-time private-sector
salaries of 2006 grads: $65,000-
$100,000
2006 grads employed in: law firms:
56%; business and industry: 16%;
government: 9%; public interest:
5%; judicial clerk: 8%; academia:
4%; unknown: 2%
Employment location for 2006 class:
Intl. 0%; N.E. 0%; M.A. 1%; E.N.C.
81%; W.N.C. 1%; S.A. 7%; E.S.C.
3%; W.S.C. 1%; Mt. 3%; Pac. 4%;
unknown 1%

University of Dayton
300 College Park
Dayton, OH 45469-2772
http://law.udayton.edu
Private
Admissions: (937) 229-3555
E-mail: lawinfo@notes.udayton.edu
Financial aid: (937) 229-3555
Application deadline: rolling
Tuition: full time: $910/credit hour;
part time: N/A
Room/board/expenses: $11,700
Percent receiving grants: 62%
Median grant: $11,000
Average student indebtedness at
graduation: $83,575
Enrollment: full time: 424;
part time: N/A
men: 57%; women: 43%;
minorities: 16%
Acceptance rate (full-time): 51%
Midrange LSAT (full-time): 149-154
Midrange undergraduate GPA
(full-time): 2.96-3.50
Midrange of full-time private-sector
salaries of 2006 grads: $45,000-
$60,000
2006 grads employed in: law firms:
61%; business and industry: 15%;
government: 2%; public interest:
11%; judicial clerk: 6%; academia:
3%; unknown: 2%
Employment location for 2006 class:
Intl. 0%; N.E. 1%; M.A. 8%; E.N.C.
67%; W.N.C. 1%; S.A. 14%; E.S.C.
4%; W.S.C. 1%; Mt. 2%; Pac. 1%;
unknown 0%

University of Toledo
2801 W. Bancroft
Toledo, OH 43606
http://www.utlaw.edu
Public
Admissions: (419) 530-4131
E-mail:
law.admissions@utoledo.edu
Financial aid: (419) 530-7929
Application deadline: 08/01

In-state tuition: full time: $15,666;
part time: $12,409
Out-of-state tuition: full time:
$25,910
Room/board/expenses: $13,930
Percent receiving grants: 59%
Median grant: $13,426
Average student indebtedness at
graduation: $65,654
Enrollment: full time: 348;
part time: 195
men: 61%; women: 39%;
minorities: 9%
Acceptance rate (full-time): 27%
Midrange LSAT (full-time): 156-161
Midrange undergraduate GPA
(full-time): 3.10-3.74
Midrange of full-time private-sector
salaries of 2006 grads: $40,000-
$60,000
2006 grads employed in: law firms:
52%; business and industry: 15%;
government: 15%; public interest:
6%; judicial clerk: 4%; academia:
3%; unknown: 5%
Employment location for 2006 class:
Intl. 1%; N.E. 0%; M.A. 2%; E.N.C.
78%; W.N.C. 0%; S.A. 8%; E.S.C.
0%; W.S.C. 3%; Mt. 6%; Pac. 0%;
unknown 2%

OKLAHOMA

Oklahoma City University
2501 N. Blackwelder
Oklahoma City, OK 73106-1493
http://www.okcu.edu/law
Private
Admissions: (866) 529-6281
E-mail: lawquestions@okcu.edu
Financial aid: (800) 633-7242
Application deadline: 08/01
Tuition: full time: $930/credit hour;
part time: $930/credit hour
Room/board/expenses: $16,600
Percent receiving grants: 30%
Median grant: $14,000
Average student indebtedness at
graduation: $96,522
Enrollment: full time: 501;
part time: 97
men: 59%; women: 41%;
minorities: 16%
Acceptance rate (full-time): 57%
Midrange LSAT (full-time): 147-152
Midrange undergraduate GPA
(full-time): 2.87-3.40
Midrange of full-time private-sector
salaries of 2006 grads: $40,000-
$70,000
2006 grads employed in: law firms:
60%; business and industry: 19%;
government: 14%; public interest:
4%; judicial clerk: 0%; academia:
3%; unknown: 0%
Employment location for 2006 class:
Intl. 0%; N.E. 0%; M.A. 2%; E.N.C.
1%; W.N.C. 7%; S.A. 3%; E.S.C. 1%;
W.S.C. 77%; Mt. 3%; Pac. 1%;
unknown 5%

University of Oklahoma
Andrew M. Coats Hall
300 Timberdell Road
Norman, OK 73019-5081
http://www.law.ou.edu
Public
Admissions: (405) 325-4728
E-mail: admissions@ou.edu
Financial aid: (405) 325-4521
Application deadline: 03/15
In-state tuition: full time: $15,025;
part time: N/A
Out-of-state tuition: full time:
$24,953
Room/board/expenses: $15,554
Percent receiving grants: 63%
Median grant: $2,500

Average student indebtedness at graduation: $68,208
Enrollment: full time: 510; part time: N/A
men: 56%; women: 44%; minorities: 23%
Acceptance rate (full-time): 38%
Midrange LSAT (full-time): 154-160
Midrange undergraduate GPA (full-time): 3.35-3.78
Midrange of full-time private-sector salaries of 2006 grads: $52,000-$88,000
2006 grads employed in: law firms: 58%; business and industry: 18%; government: 16%; public interest: 5%; judicial clerk: 3%; academia: 0%; unknown: 0%
Employment location for 2006 class: Intl. 0%; N.E. 1%; M.A. 0%; E.N.C. 1%; W.N.C. 1%; S.A. 3%; E.S.C. 0%; W.S.C. 92%; Mt. 1%; Pac. 1%; unknown 0%

University of Tulsa
3120 E. Fourth Place
Tulsa, OK 74104
http://www.law.utulsa.edu
Private
Admissions: (918) 631-2709
E-mail: lawadmissions@utulsa.edu
Financial aid: (918) 631-2526
Application deadline: 07/31
Tuition: full time: $26,528; part time: $18,572
Room/board/expenses: $13,219
Percent receiving grants: 35%
Median grant: $8,000
Average student indebtedness at graduation: $84,115
Enrollment: full time: 452; part time: 59
men: 62%; women: 38%; minorities: 13%
Acceptance rate (full-time): 51%
Midrange LSAT (full-time): 151-155
Midrange undergraduate GPA (full-time): 2.95-3.50
Midrange of full-time private-sector salaries of 2006 grads: $40,000-$54,000
2006 grads employed in: law firms: 64%; business and industry: 17%; government: 12%; public interest: 3%; judicial clerk: 1%; academia: 2%; unknown: 1%
Employment location for 2006 class: Intl. 0%; N.E. 0%; M.A. 1%; E.N.C. 4%; W.N.C. 1%; S.A. 6%; E.S.C. 1%; W.S.C. 64%; Mt. 11%; Pac. 2%; unknown 0%

Lewis and Clark College (Northwestern)
10015 S.W. Terwilliger Boulevard
Portland, OR 97219
http://law.lclark.edu
Private
Admissions: (503) 768-6613
E-mail: lawadmss@lclark.edu
Financial aid: (503) 768-7090
Application deadline: 03/01
Tuition: full time: $28,984; part time: $21,738
Room/board/expenses: $16,345
Percent receiving grants: 47%
Median grant: $9,000
Average student indebtedness at graduation: $94,341
Enrollment: full time: 537; part time: 188
men: 52%; women: 48%; minorities: 19%
Acceptance rate (full-time): 37%
Midrange LSAT (full-time): 157-163
Midrange undergraduate GPA (full-time): 3.15-3.73

Midrange of full-time private-sector salaries of 2006 grads: $57,000-$95,000
2006 grads employed in: law firms: 47%; business and industry: 17%; government: 16%; public interest: 12%; judicial clerk: 7%; academia: 1%; unknown: 0%
Employment location for 2006 class: Intl. 0%; N.E. N/A; M.A. 4%; E.N.C. 1%; W.N.C. N/A; S.A. 4%; E.S.C. N/A; W.S.C. 2%; Mt. 6%; Pac. 83%; unknown 0%

University of Oregon
1221 University of Oregon
Eugene, OR 97403-1221
http://www.law.uoregon.edu
Public
Admissions: (541) 346-3846
E-mail: admissions@law.uoregon.edu
Financial aid: (800) 760-6953
Application deadline: 03/01
In-state tuition: full time: $19,596; part time: N/A
Out-of-state tuition: full time: $24,396
Room/board/expenses: $11,454
Percent receiving grants: 63%
Median grant: $4,000
Average student indebtedness at graduation: $71,136
Enrollment: full time: 528; part time: N/A
men: 58%; women: 42%; minorities: 18%
Acceptance rate (full-time): 41%
Midrange LSAT (full-time): 156-160
Midrange undergraduate GPA (full-time): 3.27-3.68
Midrange of full-time private-sector salaries of 2006 grads: $48,000-$89,000
2006 grads employed in: law firms: 47%; business and industry: 11%; government: 15%; public interest: 13%; judicial clerk: 12%; academia: 1%; unknown: 1%
Employment location for 2006 class: Intl. 0%; N.E. 1%; M.A. 1%; E.N.C. 1%; W.N.C. 0%; S.A. 3%; E.S.C. 0%; W.S.C. 1%; Mt. 12%; Pac. 81%; unknown 0%

Willamette University (Collins)
245 Winter Street SE
Salem, OR 97301
http://www.willamette.edu/wucl
Private
Admissions: (503) 370-6282
E-mail: law-admission@willamette.edu
Financial aid: (503) 370-6273
Application deadline: 04/01
Tuition: full time: $27,495; part time: N/A
Room/board/expenses: $15,986
Percent receiving grants: 54%
Median grant: $12,000
Average student indebtedness at graduation: $90,196
Enrollment: full time: 395; part time: N/A
men: 54%; women: 46%; minorities: 13%
Acceptance rate (full-time): 45%
Midrange LSAT (full-time): 153-158
Midrange undergraduate GPA (full-time): 2.85-3.52
Midrange of full-time private-sector salaries of 2006 grads: $43,200-$60,000
2006 grads employed in: law firms: 56%; business and industry: 11%; government: 13%; public interest: 7%; judicial clerk: 10%; academia: 0%; unknown: 3%

Employment location for 2006 class: Intl. 1%; N.E. 0%; M.A. 1%; E.N.C. 1%; W.N.C. 1%; S.A. 3%; E.S.C. 1%; W.S.C. 1%; Mt. 9%; Pac. 82%; unknown 0%

Duquesne University
600 Forbes Avenue
Pittsburgh, PA 15282
http://www.duq.edu/law
Private
Admissions: (412) 396-6296
E-mail: ricci@duq.edu
Financial aid: (412) 396-6607
Application deadline: 04/01
Tuition: full time: $27,230; part time: $21,078
Room/board/expenses: $11,058
Percent receiving grants: 37%
Median grant: $8,564
Average student indebtedness at graduation: $75,760
Enrollment: full time: 470; part time: 209
men: 50%; women: 50%; minorities: 7%
Acceptance rate (full-time): 53%
Midrange LSAT (full-time): 151-155
Midrange undergraduate GPA (full-time): 3.28-3.65
Midrange of full-time private-sector salaries of 2006 grads: $50,000-$80,000
2006 grads employed in: law firms: 55%; business and industry: 23%; government: 8%; public interest: 4%; judicial clerk: 8%; academia: 2%; unknown: N/A
Employment location for 2006 class: Intl. 0%; N.E. 2%; M.A. 86%; E.N.C. 2%; W.N.C. N/A; S.A. 8%; E.S.C. N/A; W.S.C. 1%; Mt. 1%; Pac. N/A; unknown 0%

Pennsylvania State University (Dickinson)
100 Beam Building
University Park, PA 16802
http://www.dsl.psu.edu
Public
Admissions: (800) 840-1122
E-mail: dsladmit@psu.edu
Financial aid: (800) 840-1122
Application deadline: 03/01
In-state tuition: full time: $29,674; part time: $27,248
Out-of-state tuition: full time: $29,674
Room/board/expenses: $18,034
Percent receiving grants: 39%
Median grant: $4,800
Average student indebtedness at graduation: $89,529
Enrollment: full time: 573; part time: 82
men: 56%; women: 44%; minorities: 23%
Acceptance rate (full-time): 33%
Midrange LSAT (full-time): 156-159
Midrange undergraduate GPA (full-time): 3.02-3.69
Midrange of full-time private-sector salaries of 2006 grads: $50,000-$100,000
2006 grads employed in: law firms: 50%; business and industry: 14%; government: 12%; public interest: 3%; judicial clerk: 14%; academia: 2%; unknown: 5%
Employment location for 2006 class: Intl. 0%; N.E. 0%; M.A. 66%; E.N.C. 2%; W.N.C. 2%; S.A. 16%; E.S.C. 1%; W.S.C. 1%; Mt. 1%; Pac. 4%; unknown 7%

Temple University (Beasley)
1719 N. Broad Street
Philadelphia, PA 19122
http://www.law.temple.edu
Public
Admissions: (800) 560-1428
E-mail: lawadmis@temple.edu
Financial aid: (800) 560-1428
Application deadline: 03/01
In-state tuition: full time: $15,800; part time: $12,756
Out-of-state tuition: full time: $27,078
Room/board/expenses: $19,208
Percent receiving grants: 44%
Median grant: $6,000
Average student indebtedness at graduation: $72,529
Enrollment: full time: 754; part time: 214
men: 53%; women: 47%; minorities: 21%
Acceptance rate (full-time): 41%
Midrange LSAT (full-time): 160-164
Midrange undergraduate GPA (full-time): 3.27-3.65
Midrange of full-time private-sector salaries of 2006 grads: $57,000-$120,000
2006 grads employed in: law firms: 49%; business and industry: 19%; government: 11%; public interest: 6%; judicial clerk: 12%; academia: 2%; unknown: 1%
Employment location for 2006 class: Intl. 1%; N.E. 1%; M.A. 86%; E.N.C. 0%; W.N.C. 0%; S.A. 8%; E.S.C. 0%; W.S.C. 1%; Mt. 1%; Pac. 1%; unknown 1%

University of Pennsylvania
3400 Chestnut Street
Philadelphia, PA 19104-6204
http://www.law.upenn.edu
Private
Admissions: (215) 898-7400
E-mail: admissions@law.upenn.edu
Financial aid: (215) 898-7400
Application deadline: 02/15
Tuition: full time: $41,960; part time: N/A
Room/board/expenses: $17,700
Percent receiving grants: 33%
Median grant: $14,080
Average student indebtedness at graduation: $100,701
Enrollment: full time: 782; part time: N/A
men: 54%; women: 46%; minorities: 25%
Acceptance rate (full-time): 16%
Midrange LSAT (full-time): 166-171
Midrange undergraduate GPA (full-time): 3.52-3.86
Midrange of full-time private-sector salaries of 2006 grads: $135,000-$145,000
2006 grads employed in: law firms: 80%; business and industry: 5%; government: 1%; public interest: 2%; judicial clerk: 13%; academia: 0%; unknown: 0%
Employment location for 2006 class: Intl. 1%; N.E. 4%; M.A. 65%; E.N.C. 3%; W.N.C. 2%; S.A. 13%; E.S.C. 0%; W.S.C. 2%; Mt. 1%; Pac. 10%; unknown 0%

University of Pittsburgh
3900 Forbes Avenue
Pittsburgh, PA 15260
http://www.law.pitt.edu
Public
Admissions: (412) 648-1415
E-mail: admissions@law.pitt.edu
Financial aid: (412) 648-1415
Application deadline: 03/01

In-state tuition: full time: $22,106; part time: N/A
Out-of-state tuition: full time: $30,362
Room/board/expenses: $17,100
Percent receiving grants: 53%
Median grant: $10,000
Average student indebtedness at graduation: $71,787
Enrollment: full time: 714; part time: N/A
men: 57%; women: 43%; minorities: 15%
Acceptance rate (full-time): 37%
Midrange LSAT (full-time): 158-161
Midrange undergraduate GPA (full-time): 3.11-3.65
Midrange of full-time private-sector salaries of 2006 grads: $53,500-$120,000
2006 grads employed in: law firms: 57%; business and industry: 17%; government: 7%; public interest: 6%; judicial clerk: 11%; academia: 2%; unknown: 0%
Employment location for 2006 class: Intl. 1%; N.E. 1%; M.A. 70%; E.N.C. 6%; W.N.C. 1%; S.A. 14%; E.S.C. 1%; W.S.C. 1%; Mt. 4%; Pac. 3%; unknown 0%

Villanova University
299 N. Spring Mill Road
Villanova, PA 19085
http://www.law.villanova.edu/
Private
Admissions: (610) 519-7010
E-mail: admissions@law.villanova.edu
Financial aid: (610) 519-7015
Application deadline: 07/01
Tuition: full time: $30,890; part time: N/A
Room/board/expenses: $19,274
Percent receiving grants: 20%
Median grant: $10,000
Average student indebtedness at graduation: $108,084
Enrollment: full time: 727; part time: N/A
men: 55%; women: 45%; minorities: 16%
Acceptance rate (full-time): 43%
Midrange LSAT (full-time): 160-163
Midrange undergraduate GPA (full-time): 3.14-3.63
Midrange of full-time private-sector salaries of 2006 grads: $65,000-$120,000
2006 grads employed in: law firms: 59%; business and industry: 14%; government: 8%; public interest: 4%; judicial clerk: 13%; academia: 2%; unknown: 0%
Employment location for 2006 class: Intl. 1%; N.E. 3%; M.A. 78%; E.N.C. 1%; W.N.C. 1%; S.A. 15%; E.S.C. 1%; W.S.C. 1%; Mt. 1%; Pac. 2%; unknown 0%

Catholic University[1]
2250 Avenida Las Americas
Suite 584
Ponce, PR 00717-0777
http://www.pucpr.edu
Private
Admissions: (787) 841-2000
E-mail: admsiones@pucpr.edu
Financial aid: (787) 841-2000
Tuition: N/A
Room/board/expenses: N/A
Enrollment: N/A

Inter-American University[1]

PO Box 70351
San Juan, PR 00936-8351
http://www.metro.inter.edu
Private
Admissions: (787) 765-1270
E-mail: edmendez@inter.edu
Financial aid: (787) 250-1912
Tuition: N/A
Room/board/expenses: N/A
Enrollment: N/A

University of Puerto Rico[1]

PO Box 23303 Estacion
Universidad
Rio Piedras, PR 00931-3302
http://www.upr.edu
Public
Admissions: (787) 764-0000
E-mail: admisiones@upr.edu
Financial aid: (787) 764-0000
Tuition: N/A
Room/board/expenses: N/A
Enrollment: N/A

RHODE ISLAND

Roger Williams University

10 Metacom Avenue
Bristol, RI 02809-5171
http://law.rwu.edu
Private
Admissions: (401) 254-4555
E-mail: Admissions@rwu.edu
Financial aid: (401) 254-4641
Application deadline: 03/15
Tuition: full time: $1,050/credit
hour; part time: N/A
Room/board/expenses: $20,144
Percent receiving grants: 43%
Median grant: $11,000
Average student indebtedness at graduation: $99,573
Enrollment: full time: 556;
part time: 30
men: 52%; women: 48%;
minorities: 12%
Acceptance rate (full-time): 57%
Midrange LSAT (full-time): 151-155
Midrange undergraduate GPA (full-time): 2.90-3.44
Midrange of full-time private-sector salaries of 2006 grads: $45,000-$70,000
2006 grads employed in: law firms: 48%; business and industry: 18%; government: 8%; public interest: 9%; judicial clerk: 12%; academia: 3%; unknown: 2%
Employment location for 2006 class: Intl. 0%; N.E. 69%; M.A. 17%; E.N.C. 1%; W.N.C. 1%; S.A. 5%; E.S.C. 1%; W.S.C. 0%; Mt. 2%; Pac. 3%; unknown 2%

SOUTH CAROLINA

Charleston School of Law

PO Box 535
Charleston, SC 29402
http://www.charlestonlaw.org
Private
Admissions: (843) 329-1000
E-mail: info@charlestonlaw.org
Financial aid: (843) 377-4901
Application deadline: 03/01
Tuition: full time: $30,598;
part time: $23,188
Room/board/expenses: $13,020
Percent receiving grants: 40%
Median grant: $7,500
Average student indebtedness at graduation: $91,015

Enrollment: full time: 394;
part time: 197
men: 58%; women: 42%;
minorities: 6%
Acceptance rate (full-time): 34%
Midrange LSAT (full-time): 153-157
Midrange undergraduate GPA (full-time): 2.96-3.49
Midrange of full-time private-sector salaries of 2006 grads: N/A-N/A
2006 grads employed in: law firms: N/A; business and industry: N/A; government: N/A; public interest: N/A; judicial clerk: N/A; academia: N/A; unknown: N/A
Employment location for 2006 class: Intl. N/A; N.E. N/A; M.A. N/A; E.N.C. N/A; W.N.C. N/A; S.A. N/A; E.S.C. N/A; W.S.C. N/A; Mt. N/A; Pac. N/A; unknown N/A

University of South Carolina

701 S. Main Street
Columbia, SC 29208
http://www.law.sc.edu
Public
Admissions: (803) 777-6605
E-mail: usclaw@law.sc.edu
Financial aid: (803) 777-6605
Application deadline: 04/01
In-state tuition: full time: $16,936;
part time: N/A
Out-of-state tuition: full time: $33,622
Room/board/expenses: $15,760
Percent receiving grants: 32%
Median grant: $7,992
Average student indebtedness at graduation: $65,585
Enrollment: full time: 665;
part time: 2
men: 57%; women: 43%;
minorities: 13%
Acceptance rate (full-time): 31%
Midrange LSAT (full-time): 156-161
Midrange undergraduate GPA (full-time): 3.04-3.69
Midrange of full-time private-sector salaries of 2006 grads: $52,000-$80,000
2006 grads employed in: law firms: 52%; business and industry: 5%; government: 10%; public interest: 6%; judicial clerk: 25%; academia: 2%; unknown: 0%
Employment location for 2006 class: Intl. 0%; N.E. 0%; M.A. 3%; E.N.C. 1%; W.N.C. 1%; S.A. 94%; E.S.C. 1%; W.S.C. 0%; Mt. 1%; Pac. 1%; unknown 0%

SOUTH DAKOTA

University of South Dakota

414 E. Clark Street
Vermillion, SD 57069-2390
http://www.usd.edu/law/
Public
Admissions: (605) 677-5443
E-mail: lawreq@usd.edu
Financial aid: (605) 677-5446
Application deadline: 03/01
In-state tuition: full time: $8,991;
part time: $4,496
Out-of-state tuition: full time: $17,606
Room/board/expenses: $12,456
Percent receiving grants: 33%
Median grant: $1,196
Average student indebtedness at graduation: $46,014
Enrollment: full time: 222;
part time: N/A
men: 55%; women: 45%;
minorities: 4%
Acceptance rate (full-time): 49%
Midrange LSAT (full-time): 150-156

Midrange undergraduate GPA (full-time): 3.21-3.75
Midrange of full-time private-sector salaries of 2006 grads: $38,700-$50,000
2006 grads employed in: law firms: 28%; business and industry: 17%; government: 16%; public interest: 14%; judicial clerk: 21%; academia: 4%; unknown: 0%
Employment location for 2006 class: Intl. 1%; N.E. 0%; M.A. 1%; E.N.C. 3%; W.N.C. 80%; S.A. 1%; E.S.C. 1%; W.S.C. 0%; Mt. 7%; Pac. 5%; unknown 0%

TENNESSEE

University of Memphis (Humphreys)

207 Humphreys Law School
Memphis, TN 38152-3140
http://www.law.memphis.edu
Public
Admissions: (901) 678-5403
E-mail: lawadmissions@mail.law.memphis.edu
Financial aid: (901) 678-3737
Application deadline: 03/01
In-state tuition: full time: $11,412;
part time: $10,756
Out-of-state tuition: full time: $30,598
Room/board/expenses: $13,441
Percent receiving grants: 28%
Median grant: $3,850
Average student indebtedness at graduation: $55,250
Enrollment: full time: 395;
part time: 22
men: 56%; women: 44%;
minorities: 17%
Acceptance rate (full-time): 34%
Midrange LSAT (full-time): 154-158
Midrange undergraduate GPA (full-time): 3.03-3.64
Midrange of full-time private-sector salaries of 2006 grads: $40,000-$72,000
2006 grads employed in: law firms: 56%; business and industry: 21%; government: 5%; public interest: 4%; judicial clerk: 10%; academia: 4%; unknown: N/A
Employment location for 2006 class: Intl. N/A; N.E. 2%; M.A. 1%; E.N.C. N/A; W.N.C. 1%; S.A. 4%; E.S.C. 91%; W.S.C. 1%; Mt. N/A; Pac. 1%; unknown N/A

University of Tennessee–Knoxville

1505 W. Cumberland Avenue
Knoxville, TN 37996-1810
http://www.law.utk.edu
Public
Admissions: (865) 974-4131
E-mail: lawadmit@utk.edu
Financial aid: (865) 974-4131
Application deadline: 03/01
In-state tuition: full time: $11,502;
part time: N/A
Out-of-state tuition: full time: $27,762
Room/board/expenses: $13,844
Percent receiving grants: 46%
Median grant: $5,000
Average student indebtedness at graduation: $53,767
Enrollment: full time: 469;
part time: N/A
men: 52%; women: 48%;
minorities: 16%
Acceptance rate (full-time): 29%
Midrange LSAT (full-time): 157-162
Midrange undergraduate GPA (full-time): 3.35-3.82

Midrange of full-time private-sector salaries of 2006 grads: $55,000-$85,000
2006 grads employed in: law firms: 65%; business and industry: 7%; government: 12%; public interest: 4%; judicial clerk: 11%; academia: 1%; unknown: 0%
Employment location for 2006 class: Intl. 0%; N.E. 0%; M.A. 2%; E.N.C. 1%; W.N.C. 1%; S.A. 20%; E.S.C. 73%; W.S.C. 3%; Mt. 0%; Pac. 0%; unknown 0%

Vanderbilt University

131 21st Avenue S
Nashville, TN 37203-1181
http://www.vanderbilt.edu/law/
Private
Admissions: (615) 322-6452
E-mail: admissions@law.vanderbilt.edu
Financial aid: (615) 322-6452
Application deadline: 03/15
Tuition: full time: $39,838;
part time: N/A
Room/board/expenses: $20,618
Percent receiving grants: 69%
Median grant: $15,000
Average student indebtedness at graduation: $100,891
Enrollment: full time: 601;
part time: N/A
men: 54%; women: 46%;
minorities: 16%
Acceptance rate (full-time): 25%
Midrange LSAT (full-time): 164-168
Midrange undergraduate GPA (full-time): 3.54-3.83
Midrange of full-time private-sector salaries of 2006 grads: $100,000-$135,000
2006 grads employed in: law firms: 71%; business and industry: 8%; government: 7%; public interest: 3%; judicial clerk: 10%; academia: 0%; unknown: 1%
Employment location for 2006 class: Intl. 1%; N.E. 1%; M.A. 13%; E.N.C. 7%; W.N.C. 2%; S.A. 25%; E.S.C. 29%; W.S.C. 7%; Mt. 4%; Pac. 10%; unknown 1%

TEXAS

Baylor University (Umphrey)

1114 S. University Parks Drive
1 Bear Place # 97288
Waco, TX 76798-7288
http://law.baylor.edu
Private
Admissions: (254) 710-1911
E-mail: Becky_Beck@baylor.edu
Financial aid: (254) 710-2611
Application deadline: 03/01
Tuition: full time: $33,294;
part time: $33,294
Room/board/expenses: $16,923
Percent receiving grants: 91%
Median grant: $3,000
Average student indebtedness at graduation: $83,338
Enrollment: full time: 411;
part time: N/A
men: 60%; women: 40%;
minorities: 12%
Acceptance rate (full-time): 30%
Midrange LSAT (full-time): 157-162
Midrange undergraduate GPA (full-time): 3.38-3.78
Midrange of full-time private-sector salaries of 2006 grads: $60,000-$90,000
2006 grads employed in: law firms: 61%; business and industry: 14%; government: 16%; public interest: 1%; judicial clerk: 7%; academia: 1%; unknown: 0%

Employment location for 2006 class: Intl. 0%; N.E. 0%; M.A. 0%; E.N.C. 3%; W.N.C. 1%; S.A. 2%; E.S.C. 0%; W.S.C. 89%; Mt. 4%; Pac. 2%; unknown 0%

Southern Methodist University

PO Box 750116
Dallas, TX 75275-0116
http://www.law.smu.edu
Private
Admissions: (214) 768-2550
E-mail: lawadmit@mail.smu.edu
Financial aid: (214) 768-4119
Application deadline: 02/15
Tuition: full time: $34,576;
part time: $25,932
Room/board/expenses: $19,000
Percent receiving grants: 92%
Median grant: $8,500
Average student indebtedness at graduation: $75,831
Enrollment: full time: 562;
part time: 425
men: 55%; women: 45%;
minorities: 23%
Acceptance rate (full-time): 23%
Midrange LSAT (full-time): 157-165
Midrange undergraduate GPA (full-time): 3.28-3.84
Midrange of full-time private-sector salaries of 2006 grads: $65,000-$135,000
2006 grads employed in: law firms: 69%; business and industry: 16%; government: 7%; public interest: 1%; judicial clerk: 5%; academia: 2%; unknown: 0%
Employment location for 2006 class: Intl. 1%; N.E. 1%; M.A. 1%; E.N.C. 1%; W.N.C. 1%; S.A. 2%; E.S.C. 0%; W.S.C. 91%; Mt. 2%; Pac. 1%; unknown 0%

South Texas College of Law

1303 San Jacinto Street
Houston, TX 77002-7000
http://www.stcl.edu
Private
Admissions: (713) 646-1810
E-mail: admissions@stcl.edu
Financial aid: (713) 646-1820
Application deadline: 02/15
Tuition: full time: $23,610;
part time: $15,940
Room/board/expenses: $16,700
Percent receiving grants: 34%
Median grant: $2,040
Average student indebtedness at graduation: $72,381
Enrollment: full time: 936;
part time: 316
men: 55%; women: 45%;
minorities: 24%
Acceptance rate (full-time): 51%
Midrange LSAT (full-time): 150-155
Midrange undergraduate GPA (full-time): 2.99-3.52
Midrange of full-time private-sector salaries of 2006 grads: $70,000-$135,000
2006 grads employed in: law firms: 63%; business and industry: 16%; government: 11%; public interest: 2%; judicial clerk: 3%; academia: 1%; unknown: 4%
Employment location for 2006 class: Intl. 1%; N.E. N/A; M.A. N/A; E.N.C. 1%; W.N.C. N/A; S.A. 1%; E.S.C. N/A; W.S.C. 95%; Mt. 1%; Pac. N/A; unknown 1%

St. Mary's University

1 Camino Santa Maria
San Antonio, TX 78228-8602
http://law.stmarytx.edu
Private
Admissions: (210) 436-3523
E-mail:
lawadmissions@stmarytx.edu
Financial aid: (210) 431-6743
Application deadline: 03/01
Tuition: full time: $23,440;
part time: $16,040
Room/board/expenses: $14,512
Percent receiving grants: 44%
Median grant: $1,432
**Average student indebtedness at
graduation:** $84,124
Enrollment: full time: 699;
part time: 63
men: 54%; women: 46%;
minorities: 34%
Acceptance rate (full-time): 51%
Midrange LSAT (full-time): 149-156
**Midrange undergraduate GPA
(full-time):** 2.80-3.41
**Midrange of full-time private-sector
salaries of 2006 grads:** $45,000-
$75,000
2006 grads employed in: law firms:
56%; business and industry: 15%;
government: 11%; public interest:
1%; judicial clerk: 4%; academia:
1%; unknown: 12%
Employment location for 2006 class:
Intl. N/A; N.E. N/A; M.A. 1%; E.N.C.
N/A; W.N.C. 1%; S.A. 2%; E.S.C.
N/A; W.S.C. 91%; Mt. 1%; Pac. N/A;
unknown 4%

Texas Southern University (Marshall)

3100 Cleburne Street
Houston, TX 77004
http://www.tsu.edu/academics/
law/index.asp
Public
Admissions: (713) 313-7114
E-mail: lawadmit@tsulaw.edu
Financial aid: (713) 313-7243
Application deadline: 04/01
In-state tuition: full time: $11,528;
part time: N/A
Out-of-state tuition: full time:
$15,278
Room/board/expenses: $12,500
Percent receiving grants: 43%
Median grant: $3,000
**Average student indebtedness at
graduation:** $20,000
Enrollment: full time: 583;
part time: N/A
men: 50%; women: 50%;
minorities: 79%
Acceptance rate (full-time): 36%
Midrange LSAT (full-time): 146-151
**Midrange undergraduate GPA
(full-time):** 2.83-3.29
**Midrange of full-time private-sector
salaries of 2006 grads:** $65,000-
$105,000
2006 grads employed in: law firms:
71%; business and industry: 13%;
government: 10%; public interest:
1%; judicial clerk: 1%; academia:
2%; unknown: 2%
Employment location for 2006 class:
Intl. 1%; N.E. 0%; M.A. 3%; E.N.C.
4%; W.N.C. 1%; S.A. 6%; E.S.C.
2%; W.S.C. 76%; Mt. 4%; Pac. .3%;
unknown 0%

Texas Tech University

1802 Hartford Avenue
Lubbock, TX 79409-0004
http://www.law.ttu.edu
Public
Admissions: (806) 742-3791
E-mail: donna.williams@ttu.edu
Financial aid: (806) 742-3990
Application deadline: 02/01

In-state tuition: full time: $13,654;
part time: N/A
Out-of-state tuition: full time:
$20,759
Room/board/expenses: $12,990
Percent receiving grants: 75%
Median grant: $3,400
**Average student indebtedness at
graduation:** $50,716
Enrollment: full time: 692;
part time: N/A
men: 57%; women: 43%;
minorities: 21%
Acceptance rate (full-time): 43%
Midrange LSAT (full-time): 151-157
**Midrange undergraduate GPA
(full-time):** 3.34-3.75
**Midrange of full-time private-sector
salaries of 2006 grads:** $36,000-
$101,000
2006 grads employed in: law firms:
86%; business and industry: 1%;
government: 8%; public interest:
3%; judicial clerk: 2%; academia:
0%; unknown: 0%
Employment location for 2006 class:
Intl. 0%; N.E. N/A; M.A. 1%; E.N.C.
N/A; W.N.C. N/A; S.A. 1%; E.S.C.
N/A; W.S.C. 96%; Mt. 3%; Pac. 1%;
unknown N/A

Texas Wesleyan University

1515 Commerce Street
Fort Worth, TX 76102
http://www.law.txwes.edu/
Private
Admissions: (817) 212-4040
E-mail:
lawadmissions@law.txwes.edu
Financial aid: (817) 212-4090
Application deadline: 05/15
Tuition: full time: $23,250;
part time: $16,800
Room/board/expenses: $14,295
Percent receiving grants: 37%
Median grant: $7,500
**Average student indebtedness at
graduation:** $57,231
Enrollment: full time: 443;
part time: 314
men: 52%; women: 48%;
minorities: 22%
Acceptance rate (full-time): 46%
Midrange LSAT (full-time): 152-156
**Midrange undergraduate GPA
(full-time):** 2.89-3.40
**Midrange of full-time private-sector
salaries of 2006 grads:** $48,000-
$80,000
2006 grads employed in: law firms:
42%; business and industry: 26%;
government: 12%; public interest:
4%; judicial clerk: 2%; academia:
1%; unknown: 13%
Employment location for 2006 class:
Intl. 0%; N.E. 0%; M.A. 1%; E.N.C.
1%; W.N.C. 0%; S.A. 1%; E.S.C. 1%;
W.S.C. 94%; Mt. 1%; Pac. 1%;
unknown 0%

University of Houston

100 Law Center
Houston, TX 77204-6060
http://www.law.uh.edu
Public
Admissions: (713) 743-2280
E-mail: lawadmissions@uh.edu
Financial aid: (713) 743-2269
Application deadline: 02/15
In-state tuition: full time: $17,192;
part time: $8,901
Out-of-state tuition: full time:
$24,632
Room/board/expenses: $15,536
Percent receiving grants: 75%
Median grant: $3,000
**Average student indebtedness at
graduation:** $62,584

Enrollment: full time: 785;
part time: 170
men: 58%; women: 42%;
minorities: 28%
Acceptance rate (full-time): 29%
Midrange LSAT (full-time): 158-163
**Midrange undergraduate GPA
(full-time):** 3.30-3.79
**Midrange of full-time private-sector
salaries of 2006 grads:** $60,000-
$135,000
2006 grads employed in: law firms:
57%; business and industry: 21%;
government: 8%; public interest:
3%; judicial clerk: 5%; academia:
1%; unknown: 0%
Employment location for 2006 class:
Intl. 1%; N.E. 1%; M.A. 2%; E.N.C.
0%; W.N.C. 0%; S.A. 2%; E.S.C.
1%; W.S.C. 89%; Mt. 2%; Pac. 4%;
unknown 0%

University of Texas–Austin

727 E. Dean Keeton Street
Austin, TX 78705-3299
http://www.utexas.edu/law
Public
Admissions: (512) 232-1200
E-mail:
admissions@law.utexas.edu
Financial aid: (512) 232-1130
Application deadline: 02/01
In-state tuition: full time: $20,632;
part time: N/A
Out-of-state tuition: full time:
$35,130
Room/board/expenses: $13,636
Percent receiving grants: 90%
Median grant: $6,416
**Average student indebtedness at
graduation:** $62,399
Enrollment: full time: 1,291;
part time: N/A
men: 60%; women: 40%;
minorities: 30%
Acceptance rate (full-time): 24%
Midrange LSAT (full-time): 163-168
**Midrange undergraduate GPA
(full-time):** 3.38-3.80
**Midrange of full-time private-sector
salaries of 2006 grads:** $100,000-
$135,000
2006 grads employed in: law firms:
67%; business and industry: 9%;
government: 9%; public interest:
1%; judicial clerk: 11%; academia:
2%; unknown: 2%
Employment location for 2006 class:
Intl. 1%; N.E. 1%; M.A. 5%; E.N.C.
4%; W.N.C. 1%; S.A. 6%; E.S.C. 1%;
W.S.C. 72%; Mt. 2%; Pac. 5%;
unknown 2%

Brigham Young University (Clark)

340 JRCB
Provo, UT 84602-8000
http://www.law.byu.edu
Private
Admissions: (801) 422-4277
E-mail: kucharg@lawgate.byu.edu
Financial aid: (801) 422-6386
Application deadline: 03/01
Tuition: full time: $8,700;
part time: N/A
Room/board/expenses: $12,108
Percent receiving grants: 43%
Median grant: $2,500
**Average student indebtedness at
graduation:** $44,128
Enrollment: full time: 457;
part time: N/A
men: 66%; women: 34%;
minorities: 17%
Acceptance rate (full-time): 29%
Midrange LSAT (full-time): 162-167
**Midrange undergraduate GPA
(full-time):** 3.51-3.85

**Midrange of full-time private-sector
salaries of 2006 grads:** $70,000-
$110,000
2006 grads employed in: law firms:
57%; business and industry: 17%;
government: 11%; public interest:
1%; judicial clerk: 13%; academia:
1%; unknown: 0%
Employment location for 2006 class:
Intl. 1%; N.E. 1%; M.A. 3%; E.N.C.
3%; W.N.C. 1%; S.A. 6%; E.S.C.
2%; W.S.C. 6%; Mt. 60%; Pac.
18%; unknown 0%

University of Utah (Quinney)

332 S 1400 E
Room 101
Salt Lake City, UT 84112
http://www.law.utah.edu
Public
Admissions: (801) 581-7479
E-mail: admissions@law.utah.edu
Financial aid: (801) 581-6211
Application deadline: 02/01
In-state tuition: full time: $11,896;
part time: N/A
Out-of-state tuition: full time:
$26,256
Room/board/expenses: $15,312
Percent receiving grants: 40%
Median grant: $2,000
**Average student indebtedness at
graduation:** $53,839
Enrollment: full time: 397;
part time: N/A
men: 60%; women: 40%;
minorities: 10%
Acceptance rate (full-time): 37%
Midrange LSAT (full-time): 156-162
**Midrange undergraduate GPA
(full-time):** 3.31-3.77
**Midrange of full-time private-sector
salaries of 2006 grads:** $50,750-
$108,500
2006 grads employed in: law firms:
58%; business and industry: 11%;
government: 13%; public interest:
3%; judicial clerk: 14%; academia:
0%; unknown: 0%
Employment location for 2006 class:
Intl. 1%; N.E. 1%; M.A. 2%; E.N.C.
2%; W.N.C. 0%; S.A. 2%; E.S.C.
0%; W.S.C. 0%; Mt. 85%; Pac. 8%;
unknown 0%

Vermont Law School

Chelsea Street
South Royalton, VT 05068-0096
http://www.vermontlaw.edu
Private
Admissions: (888) 277-5985
E-mail: admiss@vermontlaw.edu
Financial aid: (888) 277-5985
Application deadline: 03/01
Tuition: full time: $31,514;
part time: N/A
Room/board/expenses: $18,288
Percent receiving grants: 52%
Median grant: $6,000
**Average student indebtedness at
graduation:** $108,666
Enrollment: full time: 555;
part time: N/A
men: 50%; women: 50%;
minorities: 12%
Acceptance rate (full-time): 59%
Midrange LSAT (full-time): 151-158
**Midrange undergraduate GPA
(full-time):** 2.95-3.54
**Midrange of full-time private-sector
salaries of 2006 grads:** $39,500-
$70,000
2006 grads employed in: law firms:
33%; business and industry: 17%;
government: 13%; public interest:
18%; judicial clerk: 16%; academia:
3%; unknown: 0%

Employment location for 2006 class:
Intl. 1%; N.E. 40%; M.A. 11%; E.N.C.
6%; W.N.C. 1%; S.A. 22%; E.S.C.
1%; W.S.C. 0%; Mt. 3%; Pac. 14%;
unknown 0%

Appalachian School of Law

PO Box 2825
Grundy, VA 24614-2825
http://www.asl.edu
Private
Admissions: (800) 895-7411
E-mail: aslinfo@asl.edu
Financial aid: (800) 895-7411
Application deadline: rolling
Tuition: full time: $24,000;
part time: N/A
Room/board/expenses: $14,920
Percent receiving grants: 28%
Median grant: $11,250
**Average student indebtedness at
graduation:** $78,315
Enrollment: full time: 339;
part time: N/A
men: 65%; women: 35%;
minorities: 5%
Acceptance rate (full-time): 38%
Midrange LSAT (full-time): 147-153
**Midrange undergraduate GPA
(full-time):** 2.75-3.32
**Midrange of full-time private-sector
salaries of 2006 grads:** $36,000-
$62,000
2006 grads employed in: law firms:
44%; business and industry: 15%;
government: 22%; public interest:
7%; judicial clerk: 8%; academia:
0%; unknown: 4%
Employment location for 2006 class:
Intl. 0%; N.E. 3%; M.A. 5%; E.N.C.
2%; W.N.C. N/A; S.A. 67%; E.S.C.
16%; W.S.C. 3%; Mt. 3%; Pac. 2%;
unknown 0%

College of William and Mary (Marshall-Wythe)

PO Box 8795
Williamsburg, VA 23187-8795
http://www.wm.edu/law
Public
Admissions: (757) 221-3785
E-mail: lawadm@wm.edu
Financial aid: (757) 221-2420
Application deadline: 03/01
In-state tuition: full time: $18,336;
part time: N/A
Out-of-state tuition: full time:
$28,536
Room/board/expenses: $10,734
Percent receiving grants: 23%
Median grant: $5,000
**Average student indebtedness at
graduation:** $68,270
Enrollment: full time: 617;
part time: N/A
men: 51%; women: 49%;
minorities: 17%
Acceptance rate (full-time): 27%
Midrange LSAT (full-time): 159-166
**Midrange undergraduate GPA
(full-time):** 3.44-3.82
**Midrange of full-time private-sector
salaries of 2006 grads:** $80,000-
$135,000
2006 grads employed in: law firms:
53%; business and industry: 11%;
government: 15%; public interest:
5%; judicial clerk: 16%; academia:
1%; unknown: 0%
Employment location for 2006 class:
Intl. 1%; N.E. 2%; M.A. 13%; E.N.C.
5%; W.N.C. 0%; S.A. 64%; E.S.C.
2%; W.S.C. 3%; Mt. 3%; Pac. 5%;
unknown 2%

George Mason University

3301 Fairfax Drive
Arlington, VA 22201-4426
http://www.law.gmu.edu
Public
Admissions: (703) 993-8010
E-mail: aprice1@gmu.edu
Financial aid: (703) 993-2353
Application deadline: 04/01
In-state tuition: full time: $16,716;
part time: $597/credit hour
Out-of-state tuition: full time:
$28,532
Room/board/expenses: $21,134
Percent receiving grants: 13%
Median grant: $5,000
**Average student indebtedness at
graduation:** $62,589
Enrollment: full time: 503;
part time: 285
men: 60%; women: 40%;
minorities: 17%
Acceptance rate (full-time): 22%
Midrange LSAT (full-time): 159-166
**Midrange undergraduate GPA
(full-time):** 3.11-3.86
**Midrange of full-time private-sector
salaries of 2006 grads:** $75,000-
$135,000
2006 grads employed in: law firms:
41%; business and industry: 14%;
government: 25%; public interest:
5%; judicial clerk: 12%; academia:
3%; unknown: 0%
Employment location for 2006 class:
Intl. 3%; N.E. 2%; M.A. 3%; E.N.C.
2%; W.N.C. 0%; S.A. 86%; E.S.C.
0%; W.S.C. 2%; Mt. 1%; Pac. 3%;
unknown 0%

Liberty University[1]

1971 University Boulevard
Lynchburg, VA 24502
http://law.liberty.edu
Private
Admissions: (434) 592-5300
E-mail: law@liberty.edu
Financial aid: (434) 592-5300
Tuition: N/A
Room/board/expenses: N/A
Enrollment: N/A

Regent University

1000 Regent University Drive
Virginia Beach, VA 23464-9880
http://www.regent.edu/law/
admissions
Private
Admissions: (757) 226-4584
E-mail: lawschool@regent.edu
Financial aid: (757) 226-4559
Application deadline: 06/01
Tuition: full time: $26,862;
part time: $19,982
Room/board/expenses: $16,492
Percent receiving grants: 78%
Median grant: $6,000
**Average student indebtedness at
graduation:** $90,193
Enrollment: full time: 437;
part time: 22
men: 51%; women: 49%;
minorities: 14%
Acceptance rate (full-time): 53%
Midrange LSAT (full-time): 150-156
**Midrange undergraduate GPA
(full-time):** 2.95-3.66
**Midrange of full-time private-sector
salaries of 2006 grads:** $40,000-
$65,000
2006 grads employed in: law firms:
44%; business and industry: 14%;
government: 23%; public interest:
6%; judicial clerk: 6%; academia:
6%; unknown: 0%
Employment location for 2006 class:
Intl. 0%; N.E. 2%; M.A. 0%; E.N.C.
7%; W.N.C. 2%; S.A. 64%; E.S.C.
9%; W.S.C. 4%; Mt. 9%; Pac. 4%;
unknown 0%

University of Richmond (Williams)

28 Westhampton Way
Richmond, VA 23173
http://law.richmond.edu
Private
Admissions: (804) 289-8189
E-mail: mrahman@richmond.edu
Financial aid: (804) 289-8438
Application deadline: 03/01
Tuition: full time: $30,010;
part time: $1,500/credit hour
Room/board/expenses: $14,270
Percent receiving grants: 51%
Median grant: $7,500
**Average student indebtedness at
graduation:** $84,714
Enrollment: full time: 486;
part time: 1
men: 51%; women: 49%;
minorities: 14%
Acceptance rate (full-time): 35%
Midrange LSAT (full-time): 158-162
**Midrange undergraduate GPA
(full-time):** 3.23-3.66
**Midrange of full-time private-sector
salaries of 2006 grads:** $55,000-
$95,000
2006 grads employed in: law firms:
38%; business and industry: 13%;
government: 22%; public interest:
4%; judicial clerk: 22%; academia:
1%; unknown: 1%
Employment location for 2006 class:
Intl. 1%; N.E. 1%; M.A. 8%; E.N.C.
1%; W.N.C. 1%; S.A. 83%; E.S.C.
0%; W.S.C. 3%; Mt. 0%; Pac. 1%;
unknown 1%

University of Virginia

580 Massie Road
Charlottesville, VA 22903-1738
http://www.law.virginia.edu
Public
Admissions: (434) 924-7351
E-mail: lawadmit@virginia.edu
Financial aid: (434) 924-7805
Application deadline: 03/01
In-state tuition: full time: $33,500;
part time: N/A
Out-of-state tuition: full time:
$38,500
Room/board/expenses: $17,700
Percent receiving grants: 60%
Median grant: $14,000
**Average student indebtedness at
graduation:** $86,600
Enrollment: full time: 1,175;
part time: N/A
men: 61%; women: 39%;
minorities: 16%
Acceptance rate (full-time): 24%
Midrange LSAT (full-time): 167-171
**Midrange undergraduate GPA
(full-time):** 3.51-3.87
**Midrange of full-time private-sector
salaries of 2006 grads:** $115,000-
$160,000
2006 grads employed in: law firms:
71%; business and industry: 4%;
government: 5%; public interest:
4%; judicial clerk: 16%; academia:
1%; unknown: 0%
Employment location for 2006 class:
Intl. 2%; N.E. 3%; M.A. 21%; E.N.C.
5%; W.N.C. 2%; S.A. 51%; E.S.C.
3%; W.S.C. 4%; Mt. 3%; Pac. 7%;
unknown 1%

Washington and Lee University

Sydney Lewis Hall
Lexington, VA 24450-0303
http://law.wlu.edu
Private
Admissions: (540) 458-8504
E-mail: lawadm@wlu.edu
Financial aid: (540) 458-8729
Application deadline: 02/01

Tuition: full time: $33,685;
part time: N/A
Room/board/expenses: $15,695
Percent receiving grants: 66%
Median grant: $11,500
**Average student indebtedness at
graduation:** $92,280
Enrollment: full time: 395;
part time: N/A
men: 62%; women: 38%;
minorities: 15%
Acceptance rate (full-time): 24%
Midrange LSAT (full-time): 161-167
**Midrange undergraduate GPA
(full-time):** 3.25-3.81
**Midrange of full-time private-sector
salaries of 2006 grads:** $70,000-
$125,000
2006 grads employed in: law firms:
56%; business and industry: 11%;
government: 8%; public interest:
5%; judicial clerk: 19%; academia:
0%; unknown: 1%
Employment location for 2006 class:
Intl. 1%; N.E. 2%; M.A. 11%; E.N.C.
1%; W.N.C. 0%; S.A. 71%; E.S.C.
3%; W.S.C. 2%; Mt. 4%; Pac. 4%;
unknown 1%

Gonzaga University

PO Box 3528
Spokane, WA 99220-3528
http://www.law.gonzaga.edu
Private
Admissions: (800) 793-1710
E-mail: admissions@
lawschool.gonzaga.edu
Financial aid: (800) 448-2138
Application deadline: 04/15
Tuition: full time: $29,397;
part time: $17,667
Room/board/expenses: $14,375
Percent receiving grants: 67%
Median grant: $10,000
**Average student indebtedness at
graduation:** $87,458
Enrollment: full time: 549;
part time: 16
men: 58%; women: 42%;
minorities: 9%
Acceptance rate (full-time): 45%
Midrange LSAT (full-time): 153-157
**Midrange undergraduate GPA
(full-time):** 3.06-3.54
**Midrange of full-time private-sector
salaries of 2006 grads:** $45,000-
$68,500
2006 grads employed in: law firms:
48%; business and industry: 13%;
government: 20%; public interest:
6%; judicial clerk: 12%; academia:
1%; unknown: 0%
Employment location for 2006 class:
Intl. 0%; N.E. 0%; M.A. 0%; E.N.C.
1%; W.N.C. 1%; S.A. 4%; E.S.C. 2%;
W.S.C. 3%; Mt. 31%; Pac. 58%;
unknown 0%

Seattle University

901 12th Avenue
Seattle, WA 98122-1090
http://www.law.seattleu.edu
Private
Admissions: (206) 398-4200
E-mail: lawadmin@seattleu.edu
Financial aid: (206) 398-4250
Application deadline: 03/01
Tuition: full time: $29,938;
part time: $19,958
Room/board/expenses: $16,319
Percent receiving grants: 56%
Median grant: $7,000
**Average student indebtedness at
graduation:** $86,253
Enrollment: full time: 845;
part time: 226
men: 48%; women: 52%;
minorities: 25%
Acceptance rate (full-time): 28%
Midrange LSAT (full-time): 155-161

**Midrange undergraduate GPA
(full-time):** 3.17-3.62
**Midrange of full-time private-sector
salaries of 2006 grads:** $45,000-
$90,000
2006 grads employed in: law firms:
43%; business and industry: 30%;
government: 15%; public interest:
7%; judicial clerk: 3%; academia:
2%; unknown: 0%
Employment location for 2006 class:
Intl. 2%; N.E. 1%; M.A. 2%; E.N.C.
1%; W.N.C. 0%; S.A. 2%; E.S.C.
0%; W.S.C. 0%; Mt. 3%; Pac. 90%;
unknown 0%

University of Washington

Campus Box 353020
Seattle, WA 98195-3020
http://www.law.washington.edu
Public
Admissions: (206) 543-4078
E-mail: lawadm@u.washington.edu
Financial aid: (206) 543-4552
Application deadline: 01/15
In-state tuition: full time: $17,847;
part time: N/A
Out-of-state tuition: full time:
$26,231
Room/board/expenses: $16,626
Percent receiving grants: 45%
Median grant: $6,000
**Average student indebtedness at
graduation:** $65,507
Enrollment: full time: 528;
part time: N/A
men: 41%; women: 59%;
minorities: 21%
Acceptance rate (full-time): 23%
Midrange LSAT (full-time): 159-165
**Midrange undergraduate GPA
(full-time):** 3.47-3.82
**Midrange of full-time private-sector
salaries of 2006 grads:** $65,000-
$101,000
2006 grads employed in: law firms:
54%; business and industry: 7%;
government: 14%; public interest:
6%; judicial clerk: 16%; academia:
2%; unknown: 0%
Employment location for 2006 class:
Intl. 4%; N.E. 0%; M.A. 6%; E.N.C.
1%; W.N.C. 1%; S.A. 2%; E.S.C. 0%;
W.S.C. 0%; Mt. 0%; Pac. 88%;
unknown 0%

West Virginia University

PO Box 6130
Morgantown, WV 26506-6130
http://www.wvu.edu/~law
Public
Admissions: (304) 293-5304
E-mail:
wvulaw.admissions@mail.wvu.edu
Financial aid: (304) 293-5302
Application deadline: 02/01
In-state tuition: full time: $9,856;
part time: $551/credit hour
Out-of-state tuition: full time:
$22,432
Room/board/expenses: $12,715
Percent receiving grants: 36%
Median grant: $1,600
**Average student indebtedness at
graduation:** $46,094
Enrollment: full time: 443;
part time: N/A
men: 56%; women: 44%;
minorities: 12%
Acceptance rate (full-time): 37%
Midrange LSAT (full-time): 150-156
**Midrange undergraduate GPA
(full-time):** 3.18-3.75
**Midrange of full-time private-sector
salaries of 2006 grads:** $35,400-
$106,000

2006 grads employed in: law firms:
51%; business and industry: 14%;
government: 7%; public interest:
5%; judicial clerk: 19%; academia:
5%; unknown: 0%
Employment location for 2006 class:
Intl. 0%; N.E. 1%; M.A. 4%; E.N.C.
2%; W.N.C. 0%; S.A. 91%; E.S.C.
1%; W.S.C. 1%; Mt. 2%; Pac. 0%;
unknown 0%

Marquette University

Sensenbrenner Hall
PO Box 1881
Milwaukee, WI 53201-1881
http://law.marquette.edu
Private
Admissions: (414) 288-6767
E-mail: law.admission@
marquette.edu
Financial aid: (414) 288-7390
Application deadline: 07/01
Tuition: full time: $29,410;
part time: $17,625
Room/board/expenses: $16,606
Percent receiving grants: 44%
Median grant: $6,500
**Average student indebtedness at
graduation:** $81,722
Enrollment: full time: 530;
part time: 188
men: 56%; women: 44%;
minorities: 12%
Acceptance rate (full-time): 46%
Midrange LSAT (full-time): 155-159
**Midrange undergraduate GPA
(full-time):** 3.20-3.65
**Midrange of full-time private-sector
salaries of 2006 grads:** $45,000-
$84,000
2006 grads employed in: law firms:
65%; business and industry: 14%;
government: 9%; public interest:
5%; judicial clerk: 5%; academia:
2%; unknown: 0%
Employment location for 2006 class:
Intl. 0%; N.E. 0%; M.A. 1%; E.N.C.
84%; W.N.C. 5%; S.A. 3%; E.S.C.
1%; W.S.C. 0%; Mt. 5%; Pac. 1%;
unknown 0%

University of Wisconsin-Madison

975 Bascom Mall
Madison, WI 53706-1399
http://www.law.wisc.edu
Public
Admissions: (608) 262-5914
E-mail: admissions@law.wisc.edu
Financial aid: (608) 262-5914
Application deadline: 02/01
In-state tuition: full time: $13,708;
part time: $1,146/credit hour
Out-of-state tuition: full time:
$32,774
Room/board/expenses: $14,520
Percent receiving grants: 24%
Median grant: $13,000
**Average student indebtedness at
graduation:** $65,082
Enrollment: full time: 807;
part time: 35
men: 53%; women: 47%;
minorities: 25%
Acceptance rate (full-time): 30%
Midrange LSAT (full-time): 157-163
**Midrange undergraduate GPA
(full-time):** 3.32-3.74
**Midrange of full-time private-sector
salaries of 2006 grads:** $72,000-
$125,000
2006 grads employed in: law firms:
55%; business and industry: 12%;
government: 17%; public interest:
7%; judicial clerk: 7%; academia:
2%; unknown: 0%

Employment location for 2006 class: Intl. 1%; N.E. 2%; M.A. 4%; E.N.C. 64%; W.N.C. 7%; S.A. 7%; E.S.C. 1%; W.S.C. 3%; Mt. 2%; Pac. 9%; unknown 0%

WYOMING

University of Wyoming
Department 3035
1000 E. University Avenue
Laramie, WY 82071
http://www.uwyo.edu/law
Public
Admissions: (307) 766-6416
E-mail: lawadmis@uwyo.edu
Financial aid: (307) 766-2116
Application deadline: 03/02

In-state tuition: full time: $8,491; part time: N/A
Out-of-state tuition: full time: $17,977
Room/board/expenses: $12,637
Percent receiving grants: 75%
Median grant: $1,500
Average student indebtedness at graduation: $39,033
Enrollment: full time: 228; part time: N/A
men: 53%; women: 47%; minorities: 8%
Acceptance rate (full-time): 28%
Midrange LSAT (full-time): 150-156
Midrange undergraduate GPA (full-time): 3.18-3.63
Midrange of full-time private-sector salaries of 2006 grads: $43,250-$57,000

2006 grads employed in: law firms: 53%; business and industry: 5%; government: 15%; public interest: 3%; judicial clerk: 20%; academia: 3%; unknown: 0%
Employment location for 2006 class: Intl. 0%; N.E. 0%; M.A. 3%; E.N.C. 0%; W.N.C. 2%; S.A. 3%; E.S.C. 0%; W.S.C. 2%; Mt. 87%; Pac. 3%; unknown 0%

MEDICINE

The medical school directory lists the 125 schools offering M.D. degrees that are accredited by the Liaison Committee on Medical Education, plus the 20 schools that offer the D.O. degree and are accredited by the American Osteopathic Association. Of those, 111 M.D.-granting schools and 15 D.O.-granting schools responded to the *U.S. News* survey, which was conducted in fall 2007 and early 2008. Their data are reported below. Schools that did not respond have abbreviated entries.

TERMINOLOGY

1 A school whose name is footnoted with the numeral 1 did not return the *U.S. News* statistical survey; limited data appear in its entry.
N/A. Not available from the school or not applicable.
Admissions. The admissions office phone number.
E-mail. The electronic address of the admissions office. If, instead of an E-mail address, a website is listed, the website will automatically present an E-mail screen programmed to reach the admissions office.
Financial aid. The financial aid office phone number.
Application deadline. For fall 2009 enrollment.
Tuition. For the 2007–2008 academic year. Includes fees.
Room/board/expenses. For the 2007–2008 academic year.
Students receiving grants. The percentage of the entire student body during the 2007–2008 academic year that received grants or scholarships.
Average indebtedness. For 2006 graduates who incurred medical school-related debt.
Enrollment. Total doctor of medicine (M.D.) or doctor of osteopathy (D.O.) degree program enrollment for fall 2007.
Minorities. For fall 2007, percentage of students who are Asian-American, African-American, Hispanic, or American Indian. (When the U.S. Department of Education calculates minority enrollment percentages, these are the demographic groupings it uses.)
Underrepresented minorities. For fall 2007, percentage of students who are African-American, Hispanic, or American Indian. (This category is used only for medical schools.)
Acceptance rate. Percentage of applicants who were accepted for fall 2007 to an M.D. or D.O. degree program.
Average Medical College Admission Test (MCAT) score. For M.D. or D.O. students who entered the medical or osteopathic program in the fall of 2007. The average of verbal and physical and biological sciences MCAT scores. (These MCAT scores are reported to test takers on a scale of 1 to 15.)
Average undergraduate grade-point average (GPA). For M.D. or D.O. students who entered in the fall of 2007.
Most popular undergraduate majors. For students who entered in fall 2007. The main areas are biological sciences, which include microbiology; physical sciences, which include chemistry; nonsciences, which include the humanities; and other, which includes double majors, mixed disciplines, and other health professions like nursing and pharmacy.
Graduates entering primary-care specialties. This is the three-year average percentage of all medical or osteopathic school graduates entering primary-care residencies in the fields of family practice, general pediatrics, or general internal medicine during the 2005–2007 period.

INSTITUTIONS THAT GRANT THE DOCTOR OF MEDICINE (M.D.) DEGREE

ALABAMA

University of Alabama–Birmingham
Medical Student Services
VH Suite 100
Birmingham, AL 35294-0019
http://www.uab.edu/uasom/admissions
Public
Admissions: (205) 934-2433
E-mail: medschool@uab.edu
Financial aid: (205) 934-8223
Application deadline: 11/01
In-state tuition: $17,998
Out-of-state tuition: $45,238
Room/board/expenses: $10,879
Percent receiving grants: 23%
Average student indebtedness at graduation: $110,040
Enrollment: 716
men: 60%; women: 40%; minorities: 23%; underrepresented minorities: 10%; in state: 93%
Acceptance rate: 11%
Average MCAT: 10.0
Average GPA: 3.71
Most popular undergraduate majors: biological sciences: 42%; physical sciences: 21%; nonsciences: 9%; other: 29%
Percent of graduates entering primary-care specialties: 38.0%

University of South Alabama[1]
307 University Boulevard
170 CSAB
Mobile, AL 36688
http://southmed.usouthal.edu/
Public
Admissions: (251) 460-7176
E-mail: mscott@usouthal.edu
Financial aid: (251) 460-7918
Tuition: N/A
Room/board/expenses: N/A
Enrollment: N/A

ARIZONA

University of Arizona
1501 N. Campbell Avenue
Tucson, AZ 85724
http://www.medicine.arizona.edu
Public
Admissions: (520) 626-6214
E-mail: admissions@medicine.arizona.edu
Financial aid: (520) 626-7145
Application deadline: 11/01
In-state tuition: $17,736
Out-of-state tuition: N/A
Room/board/expenses: $9,500
Percent receiving grants: 79%
Average student indebtedness at graduation: $104,616
Enrollment: 481
men: 45%; women: 55%; minorities: 27%; underrepresented minorities: 16%; in state: 100%
Acceptance rate: 32%
Average MCAT: 9.8
Average GPA: 3.68

Most popular undergraduate majors: biological sciences: N/A; physical sciences: N/A; nonsciences: N/A; other: N/A
Percent of graduates entering primary-care specialties: 42.5%

ARKANSAS

University of Arkansas for Medical Sciences
4301 W. Markham Street
Slot 551
Little Rock, AR 72205
http://www.uams.edu
Public
Admissions: (501) 686-5354
E-mail: southtomg@uams.edu
Financial aid: (501) 686-5813
Application deadline: N/A
In-state tuition: $16,430
Out-of-state tuition: $31,962
Room/board/expenses: N/A
Percent receiving grants: 45%
Average student indebtedness at graduation: $112,469
Enrollment: 596
men: 59%; women: 41%; minorities: 16%; underrepresented minorities: 5%; in state: 91%
Acceptance rate: 16%
Average MCAT: 9.8
Average GPA: 3.62
Most popular undergraduate majors: biological sciences: 56%; physical sciences: 25%; nonsciences: 15%; other: 4%
Percent of graduates entering primary-care specialties: 53.0%

CALIFORNIA

Loma Linda University[1]
Loma Linda, CA 92350
http://www.llu.edu/
Private
Admissions: (909) 558-4467
E-mail: ledwards@som.llu.edu
Financial aid: (909) 558-4509
Tuition: N/A
Room/board/expenses: N/A
Enrollment: N/A

Stanford University
300 Pasteur Drive
Suite M121
Stanford, CA 94305
http://med.stanford.edu
Private
Admissions: (650) 723-6861
E-mail: mdadmissions@stanford.edu
Financial aid: (650) 723-6958
Application deadline: 10/15
Tuition: $41,760
Room/board/expenses: $20,700
Percent receiving grants: 71%
Average student indebtedness at graduation: $70,235
Enrollment: 472
men: 55%; women: 45%; minorities: 53%; underrepresented minorities: 20%; in state: 40%
Acceptance rate: 3%

Average MCAT: 11.6
Average GPA: 3.76
Most popular undergraduate majors: biological sciences: 30%; physical sciences: 40%; nonsciences: 6%; other: 24%
Percent of graduates entering primary-care specialties: 32.7%

University of California–Davis

1 Shields Avenue
Davis, CA 95616-8661
http://www.ucdmc.ucdavis.edu
Public
Admissions: (916) 734-4800
E-mail: medadmisinfo@ucdavis.edu
Financial aid: (916) 734-4120
Application deadline: N/A
In-state tuition: $25,155
Out-of-state tuition: $37,400
Room/board/expenses: $13,978
Percent receiving grants: 92%
Average student indebtedness at graduation: $100,178
Enrollment: 393
men: 44%; women: 56%; minorities: 55%; underrepresented minorities: 14%; in state: 99%
Acceptance rate: 5%
Average MCAT: 10.3
Average GPA: 3.62
Most popular undergraduate majors: biological sciences: 52%; physical sciences: 21%; nonsciences: 26%; other: 1%
Percent of graduates entering primary-care specialties: 42.5%

University of California–Irvine

252 Irvine Hall
Irvine, CA 92697-3950
http://www.ucihs.uci.edu
Public
Admissions: (949) 824-5388
E-mail: medadmit@uci.edu
Financial aid: (949) 824-6476
Application deadline: 11/01
In-state tuition: $24,328
Out-of-state tuition: $36,573
Room/board/expenses: $13,490
Percent receiving grants: 72%
Average student indebtedness at graduation: $90,597
Enrollment: 408
men: 51%; women: 49%; minorities: 47%; underrepresented minorities: 11%; in state: 100%
Acceptance rate: 6%
Average MCAT: 10.7
Average GPA: 3.65
Most popular undergraduate majors: biological sciences: 60%; physical sciences: 24%; nonsciences: 16%; other: N/A
Percent of graduates entering primary-care specialties: 46.0%

University of California–Los Angeles (Geffen)

12-138 CHS
10833 Le Conte Avenue
Los Angeles, CA 90095-1720
http://www.medsch.ucla.edu
Public
Admissions: (310) 825-6081
E-mail: somadmiss@mednet.ucla.edu
Financial aid: (310) 825-4181
Application deadline: 11/01
In-state tuition: $22,551
Out-of-state tuition: $34,796
Room/board/expenses: $13,780
Percent receiving grants: 98%
Average student indebtedness at graduation: $86,564

Enrollment: 693
men: 49%; women: 51%; minorities: 60%; underrepresented minorities: 21%; in state: 94%
Acceptance rate: 4%
Average MCAT: 11.9
Average GPA: 3.78
Most popular undergraduate majors: biological sciences: 51%; physical sciences: 18%; nonsciences: 15%; other: 16%
Percent of graduates entering primary-care specialties: 44.0%

University of California–San Diego

9500 Gilman Drive
La Jolla, CA 92093-0602
http://meded.ucsd.edu/
Public
Admissions: (858) 534-3880
E-mail: somadmissions@ucsd.edu
Financial aid: (858) 534-4664
Application deadline: 11/01
In-state tuition: $22,959
Out-of-state tuition: $35,204
Room/board/expenses: $12,493
Percent receiving grants: 55%
Average student indebtedness at graduation: $79,562
Enrollment: 521
men: 53%; women: 47%; minorities: 46%; underrepresented minorities: 11%; in state: 92%
Acceptance rate: 6%
Average MCAT: 11.0
Average GPA: 3.75
Most popular undergraduate majors: biological sciences: 53%; physical sciences: 32%; nonsciences: 7%; other: 8%
Percent of graduates entering primary-care specialties: 40.7%

University of California–San Francisco

513 Parnassus Avenue
Room S224
San Francisco, CA 94143-0410
http://medschool.ucsf.edu/
Public
Admissions: (415) 476-4044
E-mail: admissions@medsch.ucsf.edu
Financial aid: (415) 476-4181
Application deadline: 10/15
In-state tuition: $23,438
Out-of-state tuition: $35,683
Room/board/expenses: $18,525
Percent receiving grants: 81%
Average student indebtedness at graduation: $85,020
Enrollment: 594
men: 45%; women: 55%; minorities: 56%; underrepresented minorities: 27%; in state: 94%
Acceptance rate: 4%
Average MCAT: 11.4
Average GPA: 3.73
Most popular undergraduate majors: biological sciences: 33%; physical sciences: 12%; nonsciences: 13%; other: 42%
Percent of graduates entering primary-care specialties: 37.5%

University of Southern California (Keck)

1975 Zonal Avenue, KAM 500
Los Angeles, CA 90033
http://www.usc.edu/keck
Private
Admissions: (323) 442-2552
E-mail: medadmit@usc.edu
Financial aid: (213) 740-5462
Application deadline: 11/01

Tuition: $44,240
Room/board/expenses: $14,610
Percent receiving grants: 40%
Average student indebtedness at graduation: $142,961
Enrollment: 679
men: 51%; women: 49%; minorities: 38%; underrepresented minorities: 15%; in state: 72%
Acceptance rate: 6%
Average MCAT: 11.1
Average GPA: 3.64
Most popular undergraduate majors: biological sciences: 50%; physical sciences: 13%; nonsciences: 18%; other: 19%
Percent of graduates entering primary-care specialties: 41.0%

COLORADO

University of Colorado–Denver

4200 E. Ninth Avenue
PO Box C290
Denver, CO 80262
http://www.uchsc.edu/som/admissions
Public
Admissions: (303) 724-8025
E-mail: somadmin@uchsc.edu
Financial aid: (303) 556-2886
Application deadline: 11/01
In-state tuition: $24,828
Out-of-state tuition: $48,030
Room/board/expenses: $14,500
Percent receiving grants: 73%
Average student indebtedness at graduation: $121,327
Enrollment: 607
men: 52%; women: 48%; minorities: 17%; underrepresented minorities: 10%; in state: 89%
Acceptance rate: 9%
Average MCAT: 11.0
Average GPA: 3.71
Most popular undergraduate majors: biological sciences: 49%; physical sciences: 21%; nonsciences: 12%; other: 19%
Percent of graduates entering primary-care specialties: 47.6%

CONNECTICUT

University of Connecticut

263 Farmington Avenue
Farmington, CT 06030-1905
http://medicine.uchc.edu
Public
Admissions: (860) 679-3874
E-mail: sanford@nso1.uchc.edu
Financial aid: (860) 679-3574
Application deadline: 12/15
In-state tuition: $26,827
Out-of-state tuition: $49,463
Room/board/expenses: N/A
Percent receiving grants: 45%
Average student indebtedness at graduation: $100,000
Enrollment: 320
men: 39%; women: 61%; minorities: 35%; underrepresented minorities: 16%; in state: 94%
Acceptance rate: 6%
Average MCAT: 10.0
Average GPA: 3.65
Most popular undergraduate majors: biological sciences: 53%; physical sciences: 12%; nonsciences: 18%; other: 17%
Percent of graduates entering primary-care specialties: 46.0%

Yale University

333 Cedar Street
PO Box 208055
New Haven, CT 06520-8055
http://info.med.yale.edu/ysm
Private
Admissions: (203) 785-2643
E-mail: medical.admissions@yale.edu
Financial aid: (203) 785-2645
Application deadline: 10/15
Tuition: $40,770
Room/board/expenses: $10,660
Percent receiving grants: 60%
Average student indebtedness at graduation: $114,744
Enrollment: 395
men: 47%; women: 53%; minorities: 37%; underrepresented minorities: 14%; in state: 10%
Acceptance rate: 6%
Average MCAT: 11.3
Average GPA: 3.72
Most popular undergraduate majors: biological sciences: 50%; physical sciences: 37%; nonsciences: 11%; other: 2%
Percent of graduates entering primary-care specialties: 25.4%

DISTRICT OF COLUMBIA

Georgetown University

3900 Reservoir Road NW
Med-Dent Building
Washington, DC 20007
http://som.georgetown.edu/index.html
Private
Admissions: (202) 687-1154
E-mail: medicaladmissions@georgetown.edu
Financial aid: (202) 687-1693
Application deadline: 10/31
Tuition: $42,764
Room/board/expenses: $15,030
Percent receiving grants: 44%
Average student indebtedness at graduation: $146,000
Enrollment: 779
men: 50%; women: 50%; minorities: 25%; underrepresented minorities: 9%; in state: 0%
Acceptance rate: 4%
Average MCAT: 10.6
Average GPA: 3.68
Most popular undergraduate majors: biological sciences: 60%; physical sciences: 16%; nonsciences: 20%; other: 4%
Percent of graduates entering primary-care specialties: 35.0%

George Washington University

2300 Eye Street NW
Room 713W
Washington, DC 20037
http://www.gwumc.edu/
Private
Admissions: (202) 994-3506
E-mail: medadmit@gwu.edu
Financial aid: (202) 994-2960
Application deadline: 12/01
Tuition: $44,615
Room/board/expenses: $20,085
Percent receiving grants: 40%
Average student indebtedness at graduation: $156,752
Enrollment: 700
men: 44%; women: 56%; minorities: 38%; underrepresented minorities: 12%; in state: 0%
Acceptance rate: 3%
Average MCAT: 9.6
Average GPA: 3.55
Most popular undergraduate majors: biological sciences: 35%; physical sciences: 8%; nonsciences: 32%; other: 25%

Percent of graduates entering primary-care specialties: 47.2%

Howard University

520 W Street NW
Washington, DC 20059
http://www.med.howard.edu
Private
Admissions: (202) 806-6279
E-mail: hucmadmissions@howard.edu
Financial aid: (202) 806-6388
Application deadline: 12/15
Tuition: $29,846
Room/board/expenses: $14,340
Percent receiving grants: 69%
Average student indebtedness at graduation: $129,136
Enrollment: 469
men: 49%; women: 51%; minorities: 94%; underrepresented minorities: 84%; in state: 8%
Acceptance rate: 6%
Average MCAT: 8.2
Average GPA: 3.40
Most popular undergraduate majors: biological sciences: 64%; physical sciences: 14%; nonsciences: 11%; other: 11%
Percent of graduates entering primary-care specialties: 33.1%

FLORIDA

Florida State University

1115 W. Call Street
Tallahassee, FL 32306-4300
http://www.med.fsu.edu/
Public
Admissions: (850) 644-7904
E-mail: medadmissions@med.fsu.edu
Financial aid: (850) 645-7270
Application deadline: 12/14
In-state tuition: $19,332
Out-of-state tuition: $52,160
Room/board/expenses: $15,910
Percent receiving grants: 33%
Average student indebtedness at graduation: $114,543
Enrollment: 357
men: 40%; women: 60%; minorities: 34%; underrepresented minorities: 22%; in state: 100%
Acceptance rate: 15%
Average MCAT: 9.4
Average GPA: 3.62
Most popular undergraduate majors: biological sciences: 55%; physical sciences: 23%; nonsciences: 10%; other: 12%
Percent of graduates entering primary-care specialties: 47.7%

University of Florida

Box 100215 UFHSC
Gainesville, FL 32610-0215
http://www.med.ufl.edu
Public
Admissions: (352) 273-7992
E-mail: robyn@dean.med.ufl.edu
Financial aid: (352) 273-7939
Application deadline: 12/01
In-state tuition: $23,170
Out-of-state tuition: $51,018
Room/board/expenses: $9,640
Percent receiving grants: 65%
Average student indebtedness at graduation: $109,907
Enrollment: 509
men: 50%; women: 50%; minorities: 37%; underrepresented minorities: 15%; in state: 97%
Acceptance rate: 8%
Average MCAT: 10.6
Average GPA: 3.70
Most popular undergraduate majors: biological sciences: 47%; physical sciences: 10%; nonsciences: 35%; other: 8%

Percent of graduates entering primary-care specialties: 32.0%

University of Miami (Miller)
1600 N.W. Tenth Avenue
Miami, FL 33136
http://www.miami.edu/medical-admissions
Private
Admissions: (305) 243-6791
E-mail: med.admissions@miami.edu
Financial aid: (305) 243-6211
Application deadline: 12/01
Tuition: $30,048
Room/board/expenses: $22,955
Percent receiving grants: 40%
Average student indebtedness at graduation: $150,607
Enrollment: 681
men: 54%; women: 46%; minorities: 42%; underrepresented minorities: 19%; in state: 76%
Acceptance rate: 8%
Average MCAT: 10.4
Average GPA: 3.68
Most popular undergraduate majors: biological sciences: 60%; physical sciences: 18%; nonsciences: 20%; other: 2%
Percent of graduates entering primary-care specialties: 39.2%

University of South Florida
12901 Bruce B. Downs Boulevard
Box 3
Tampa, FL 33612
http://www.hsc.usf.edu/medicine/mdadmissions
Public
Admissions: (813) 974-2229
E-mail: md-admissions@lyris.hsc.usf.edu
Financial aid: (813) 974-2068
Application deadline: 12/01
In-state tuition: $21,192
Out-of-state tuition: $53,066
Room/board/expenses: $10,200
Percent receiving grants: 40%
Average student indebtedness at graduation: $112,611
Enrollment: 480
men: 47%; women: 53%; minorities: 40%; underrepresented minorities: 18%; in state: 99%
Acceptance rate: 7%
Average MCAT: 9.9
Average GPA: 3.71
Most popular undergraduate majors: biological sciences: 53%; physical sciences: 11%; nonsciences: 15%; other: 21%
Percent of graduates entering primary-care specialties: 37.8%

GEORGIA

Emory University
1648 Pierce Drive
Atlanta, GA 30322-1053
http://www.med.emory.edu
Private
Admissions: (404) 727-5660
E-mail: medadmiss@emory.edu
Financial aid: (404) 727-6039
Application deadline: 10/15
Tuition: $39,976
Room/board/expenses: $22,020
Percent receiving grants: 66%
Average student indebtedness at graduation: $124,138
Enrollment: 480
men: 50%; women: 50%; minorities: 31%; underrepresented minorities: 13%; in state: 31%
Acceptance rate: 8%

Average MCAT: 11.5
Average GPA: 3.70
Most popular undergraduate majors: biological sciences: 33%; physical sciences: 17%; nonsciences: 20%; other: 30%
Percent of graduates entering primary-care specialties: 37.5%

Medical College of Georgia
1120 15th Street
Augusta, GA 30912-4750
http://www.mcg.edu/som/index.html
Public
Admissions: (706) 721-3186
E-mail: stdadmin@mail.mcg.edu
Financial aid: (706) 721-4901
Application deadline: 11/01
In-state tuition: $14,297
Out-of-state tuition: $31,723
Room/board/expenses: $3,611
Percent receiving grants: 41%
Average student indebtedness at graduation: $93,064
Enrollment: 739
men: 56%; women: 44%; minorities: 26%; underrepresented minorities: 8%; in state: 99%
Acceptance rate: 13%
Average MCAT: 10.1
Average GPA: 3.70
Most popular undergraduate majors: biological sciences: 56%; physical sciences: 29%; nonsciences: 7%; other: 8%
Percent of graduates entering primary-care specialties: 35.6%

Mercer University
1550 College Street
Macon, GA 31207
http://medicine.mercer.edu
Private
Admissions: (478) 301-2542
E-mail: admissions@med.mercer.edu
Financial aid: (478) 301-2853
Application deadline: 11/01
Tuition: $35,132
Room/board/expenses: $13,740
Percent receiving grants: 63%
Average student indebtedness at graduation: $147,266
Enrollment: 243
men: 53%; women: 47%; minorities: 13%; underrepresented minorities: 3%; in state: 100%
Acceptance rate: 12%
Average MCAT: 8.5
Average GPA: 3.52
Most popular undergraduate majors: biological sciences: 48%; physical sciences: 19%; nonsciences: 8%; other: 25%
Percent of graduates entering primary-care specialties: 46.0%

Morehouse School of Medicine
720 Westview Drive SW
Atlanta, GA 30310
http://www.msm.edu
Private
Admissions: (404) 752-1650
E-mail: mdadmissions@msm.edu
Financial aid: (404) 752-1655
Application deadline: 12/01
Tuition: $33,681
Room/board/expenses: N/A
Percent receiving grants: 77%
Average student indebtedness at graduation: $134,930
Enrollment: 210
men: 40%; women: 60%; minorities: 86%; underrepresented minorities: 76%; in state: 30%

Acceptance rate: 5%
Most popular undergraduate majors: biological sciences: 66%; physical sciences: 10%; nonsciences: 17%; other: 7%
Percent of graduates entering primary-care specialties: N/A

HAWAII

University of Hawaii–Manoa (Burns)[1]
651 Ilalo Street
Honolulu, HI 96813
http://jabsom.hawaii.edu
Public
Admissions: (808) 692-1000
E-mail: medadmin@hawaii.edu
Financial aid: (808) 956-7251
Tuition: N/A
Room/board/expenses: N/A
Enrollment: N/A

ILLINOIS

Loyola University Chicago (Stritch)
2160 S. First Avenue
Building 120
Maywood, IL 60153
http://www.meddean.lumc.edu
Private
Admissions: (708) 216-3229
Financial aid: (708) 216-3227
Application deadline: 11/15
Tuition: $39,215
Room/board/expenses: $15,725
Percent receiving grants: 73%
Average student indebtedness at graduation: $157,299
Enrollment: 563
men: 49%; women: 51%; minorities: 22%; underrepresented minorities: 9%; in state: 45%
Acceptance rate: 5%
Average MCAT: 9.9
Average GPA: 3.64
Most popular undergraduate majors: biological sciences: 42%; physical sciences: 12%; nonsciences: 16%; other: 30%
Percent of graduates entering primary-care specialties: 52.0%

Northwestern University (Feinberg)
303 E. Chicago Avenue
Morton Building 1-606
Chicago, IL 60611
http://www.feinberg.northwestern.edu
Private
Admissions: (312) 503-8206
E-mail: med-admissions@northwestern.edu
Financial aid: (312) 503-8722
Application deadline: 10/15
Tuition: $43,140
Room/board/expenses: $12,375
Percent receiving grants: 36%
Average student indebtedness at graduation: $150,468
Enrollment: 700
men: 52%; women: 48%; minorities: 48%; underrepresented minorities: 12%; in state: 26%
Acceptance rate: 6%
Average MCAT: 11.4
Average GPA: 3.71
Most popular undergraduate majors: biological sciences: 45%; physical sciences: 23%; nonsciences: 24%; other: 8%
Percent of graduates entering primary-care specialties: 37.0%

Rosalind Franklin University of Medicine and Science
3333 Green Bay Road
North Chicago, IL 60064
http://www.rosalindfranklin.edu
Private
Admissions: (847) 578-3204
E-mail: cms.admissions@rosalindfranklin.edu
Financial aid: (847) 578-3217
Application deadline: 11/01
Tuition: $39,472
Room/board/expenses: $14,400
Percent receiving grants: 47%
Average student indebtedness at graduation: $169,863
Enrollment: 757
men: 54%; women: 46%; minorities: 48%; underrepresented minorities: 6%; in state: 25%
Acceptance rate: 5%
Average MCAT: 9.7
Average GPA: 3.55
Most popular undergraduate majors: biological sciences: 54%; physical sciences: 24%; nonsciences: 12%; other: 10%
Percent of graduates entering primary-care specialties: N/A

Rush University
600 S. Paulina Street
Chicago, IL 60612
http://www.rushu.rush.edu/medcol/
Private
Admissions: N/A
E-mail: RMC_Admissions@rush.edu
Financial aid: (312) 942-6256
Application deadline: 11/01
Tuition: $43,680
Room/board/expenses: $9,340
Percent receiving grants: 59%
Average student indebtedness at graduation: $159,701
Enrollment: 536
men: 48%; women: 52%; minorities: 39%; underrepresented minorities: 6%; in state: 81%
Acceptance rate: 5%
Average MCAT: 10.3
Average GPA: 3.60
Most popular undergraduate majors: biological sciences: 49%; physical sciences: 29%; nonsciences: 13%; other: 9%
Percent of graduates entering primary-care specialties: 44.0%

Southern Illinois University–Springfield
801 N. Rutledge
PO Box 19620
Springfield, IL 62794-9620
http://www.siumed.edu/
Public
Admissions: (217) 545-6013
E-mail: admissions@siumed.edu
Financial aid: (217) 545-2224
Application deadline: 11/15
In-state tuition: $23,856
Out-of-state tuition: $66,160
Room/board/expenses: $7,560
Percent receiving grants: 47%
Average student indebtedness at graduation: $113,724
Enrollment: 291
men: 47%; women: 53%; minorities: 26%; underrepresented minorities: 17%; in state: 100%
Acceptance rate: 11%
Average MCAT: 9.1
Average GPA: 3.52
Most popular undergraduate majors: biological sciences: 63%; physical sciences: 21%; nonsciences: 12%; other: 4%

Percent of graduates entering primary-care specialties: 43.8%

University of Chicago (Pritzker)
5841 S. Maryland Avenue
MC 1000
Chicago, IL 60637-5416
http://pritzker.bsd.uchicago.edu
Private
Admissions: (773) 702-1937
E-mail: pritzkeradmissions@bsd.uchicago.edu
Financial aid: (773) 702-1938
Application deadline: 10/15
Tuition: $38,658
Room/board/expenses: $15,769
Percent receiving grants: 79%
Average student indebtedness at graduation: $162,859
Enrollment: 441
men: 50%; women: 50%; minorities: 38%; underrepresented minorities: 16%; in state: 30%
Acceptance rate: 5%
Average MCAT: 11.6
Average GPA: 3.79
Most popular undergraduate majors: biological sciences: 48%; physical sciences: 21%; nonsciences: 13%; other: 18%
Percent of graduates entering primary-care specialties: 42.0%

University of Illinois–Chicago
1853 W. Polk Street
M/C 784
Chicago, IL 60612
http://www.uic.edu/depts/mcam
Public
Admissions: (312) 996-5635
E-mail: medadmit@uic.edu
Financial aid: (312) 413-0127
Application deadline: 11/17
In-state tuition: $28,572
Out-of-state tuition: $57,468
Room/board/expenses: $12,967
Enrollment: 1,443
men: 52%; women: 48%; minorities: 44%; underrepresented minorities: 22%; in state: 74%
Acceptance rate: 8%
Average MCAT: 10.1
Average GPA: 3.58
Most popular undergraduate majors: biological sciences: 58%; physical sciences: 15%; nonsciences: 25%; other: 2%
Percent of graduates entering primary-care specialties: N/A

INDIANA

Indiana University–Indianapolis
1120 South Drive
Indianapolis, IN 46202
http://www.medicine.iu.edu
Public
Admissions: (317) 274-3772
E-mail: inmedadm@iupui.edu
Financial aid: (317) 274-1967
Application deadline: 12/15
In-state tuition: $25,904
Out-of-state tuition: $42,894
Room/board/expenses: $15,168
Percent receiving grants: 34%
Average student indebtedness at graduation: $142,859
Enrollment: 1,175
men: 57%; women: 43%; minorities: 24%; underrepresented minorities: 12%; in state: 88%
Acceptance rate: 13%
Average MCAT: 10.3
Average GPA: 3.73

Most popular undergraduate majors: biological sciences: 51%; physical sciences: 19%; nonsciences: 10%; other: 20%
Percent of graduates entering primary-care specialties: 39.5%

IOWA

University of Iowa (Carver)
200 CMAB
Iowa City, IA 52242-1101
http://www.medicine.uiowa.edu
Public
Admissions: (319) 335-8052
E-mail: medical-admissions@uiowa.edu
Financial aid: (319) 335-8059
Application deadline: 11/01
In-state tuition: $25,689
Out-of-state tuition: $41,719
Room/board/expenses: $9,270
Percent receiving grants: 60%
Average student indebtedness at graduation: $100,000
Enrollment: 576
men: 53%; women: 47%; minorities: 19%; underrepresented minorities: 12%; in state: 71%
Acceptance rate: 10%
Average MCAT: 10.5
Average GPA: 3.71
Most popular undergraduate majors: biological sciences: 56%; physical sciences: 17%; nonsciences: 16%; other: 11%
Percent of graduates entering primary-care specialties: 45.0%

KANSAS

University of Kansas Medical Center
3901 Rainbow Boulevard
Kansas City, KS 66160
http://www.kumc.edu/som/som.html
Public
Admissions: (913) 588-5245
E-mail: premedinfo@kumc.edu
Financial aid: (913) 588-5170
Application deadline: 10/15
In-state tuition: $25,476
Out-of-state tuition: $42,867
Room/board/expenses: $18,981
Percent receiving grants: 74%
Average student indebtedness at graduation: $110,840
Enrollment: 712
men: 52%; women: 48%; minorities: 22%; underrepresented minorities: 11%; in state: 84%
Acceptance rate: 12%
Average MCAT: 9.5
Average GPA: 3.69
Most popular undergraduate majors: biological sciences: 58%; physical sciences: 19%; nonsciences: 9%; other: 15%
Percent of graduates entering primary-care specialties: 48.1%

KENTUCKY

University of Kentucky
Chandler Medical Center
800 Rose Street
Lexington, KY 40536
http://www.mc.uky.edu/medicine/
Public
Admissions: (859) 323-6161
E-mail: kymedap@uky.edu
Financial aid: (859) 323-5261
Application deadline: 11/01
In-state tuition: $23,910
Out-of-state tuition: $45,313
Room/board/expenses: $12,370

Percent receiving grants: 52%
Average student indebtedness at graduation: $107,110
Enrollment: 413
men: 60%; women: 40%; minorities: 17%; underrepresented minorities: 6%; in state: 84%
Acceptance rate: 9%
Average MCAT: 10.1
Average GPA: 3.65
Most popular undergraduate majors: biological sciences: 49%; physical sciences: 23%; nonsciences: 13%; other: 15%
Percent of graduates entering primary-care specialties: 45.0%

University of Louisville
Abell Administration Center, H.S.C.
Louisville, KY 40202
http://www.louisville.edu
Public
Admissions: (502) 852-5193
E-mail: medadm@louisville.edu
Financial aid: (502) 852-5187
Application deadline: 10/15
In-state tuition: $23,079
Out-of-state tuition: $43,425
Room/board/expenses: $6,618
Percent receiving grants: 34%
Average student indebtedness at graduation: $124,604
Enrollment: 595
men: 58%; women: 42%; minorities: 19%; underrepresented minorities: 7%; in state: 83%
Acceptance rate: 11%
Average MCAT: 9.7
Average GPA: 3.65
Most popular undergraduate majors: biological sciences: 57%; physical sciences: 22%; nonsciences: 14%; other: 7%
Percent of graduates entering primary-care specialties: 44.0%

LOUISIANA

LSU School of Medicine–New Orleans[1]
Admissions Office
1901 Perdido Street
New Orleans, LA 70112-1393
http://www.medschool.lsumc.edu
Public
Admissions: (504) 568-6262
E-mail: ms-admissions@lsumc.edu
Financial aid: (504) 568-4820
Tuition: N/A
Room/board/expenses: N/A
Enrollment: N/A

LSU School of Medicine–Shreveport[1]
PO Box 33932
Shreveport, LA 71130-3932
http://www.sh.lsumc.edu
Public
Admissions: (318) 675-5190
E-mail: shvadm@lsumc.edu
Financial aid: (318) 675-5561
Tuition: N/A
Room/board/expenses: N/A
Enrollment: N/A

Tulane University
1430 Tulane Avenue, SL67
New Orleans, LA 70112-2699
http://www.mcl.tulane.edu
Private
Admissions: (504) 988-5331
E-mail: medsch@tulane.edu
Financial aid: (504) 988-6135
Application deadline: 01/15
Tuition: $45,080
Room/board/expenses: $12,890

Percent receiving grants: 38%
Average student indebtedness at graduation: $175,598
Enrollment: 652
men: 57%; women: 43%; minorities: 19%; underrepresented minorities: 7%; in state: 33%
Acceptance rate: 5%
Average MCAT: 10.0
Average GPA: 3.60
Most popular undergraduate majors: biological sciences: 30%; physical sciences: 31%; nonsciences: 18%; other: 21%
Percent of graduates entering primary-care specialties: 37.0%

MARYLAND

Johns Hopkins University
733 N. Broadway
Baltimore, MD 21205
http://www.hopkinsmedicine.org
Private
Admissions: (410) 955-3182
E-mail: somadmiss@jhmi.edu
Financial aid: (410) 955-1324
Application deadline: 10/15
Tuition: $40,669
Room/board/expenses: $14,906
Percent receiving grants: 57%
Average student indebtedness at graduation: $93,753
Enrollment: 460
men: 52%; women: 48%; minorities: 48%; underrepresented minorities: 13%; in state: 23%
Acceptance rate: 6%
Average MCAT: 11.8
Average GPA: 3.85
Most popular undergraduate majors: biological sciences: 57%; physical sciences: 24%; nonsciences: 11%; other: 8%
Percent of graduates entering primary-care specialties: 34.9%

Uniformed Services University of the Health Sciences (Hebert)
4301 Jones Bridge Road
Bethesda, MD 20814
http://www.usuhs.mil
Public
Admissions: (800) 772-1743
E-mail: admissions@usuhs.mil
Financial aid: N/A
Application deadline: 11/15
In-state tuition: N/A
Out-of-state tuition: N/A
Room/board/expenses: N/A
Percent receiving grants: 0%
Average student indebtedness at graduation: $0
Enrollment: 670
men: 70%; women: 30%; minorities: 21%; underrepresented minorities: 7%; in state: 6%
Acceptance rate: 15%
Average MCAT: 9.8
Average GPA: 3.51
Most popular undergraduate majors: biological sciences: 41%; physical sciences: 32%; nonsciences: 11%; other: 16%
Percent of graduates entering primary-care specialties: 34.0%

University of Maryland
655 W. Baltimore Street
Room 14-029
Baltimore, MD 21201-1559
http://medschool.umaryland.edu
Public
Admissions: (410) 706-7478

E-mail: mfoxwell@som.umaryland.edu
Financial aid: (410) 706-7347
Application deadline: 11/01
In-state tuition: $22,316
Out-of-state tuition: $41,101
Room/board/expenses: $18,490
Percent receiving grants: 70%
Average student indebtedness at graduation: $112,440
Enrollment: 621
men: 42%; women: 58%; minorities: 37%; underrepresented minorities: 15%; in state: 81%
Acceptance rate: 7%
Average MCAT: 10.4
Average GPA: 3.67
Most popular undergraduate majors: biological sciences: 52%; physical sciences: 20%; nonsciences: 19%; other: 9%
Percent of graduates entering primary-care specialties: 43.0%

MASSACHUSETTS

Boston University
715 Albany Street, L-103
Boston, MA 02118
http://www.bumc.bu.edu
Private
Admissions: (617) 638-4630
E-mail: medadms@bu.edu
Financial aid: (617) 638-5130
Application deadline: 11/01
Tuition: $43,234
Room/board/expenses: $11,933
Percent receiving grants: 31%
Average student indebtedness at graduation: $158,478
Enrollment: 674
men: 45%; women: 55%; minorities: 47%; underrepresented minorities: 20%; in state: 16%
Acceptance rate: 4%
Average MCAT: 10.0
Average GPA: 3.56
Most popular undergraduate majors: biological sciences: 45%; physical sciences: 21%; nonsciences: 12%; other: 22%
Percent of graduates entering primary-care specialties: 35.0%

Harvard University
25 Shattuck Street
Boston, MA 02115-6092
http://hms.harvard.edu
Private
Admissions: (617) 432-1550
E-mail: admissions_office@hms.harvard.edu
Financial aid: (617) 432-1575
Application deadline: N/A
Tuition: $41,861
Room/board/expenses: $11,434
Percent receiving grants: 54%
Average student indebtedness at graduation: $106,344
Enrollment: 758
men: 50%; women: 50%; minorities: 47%; underrepresented minorities: 21%; in state: N/A
Acceptance rate: 4%
Average MCAT: 11.9
Average GPA: 3.81
Most popular undergraduate majors: biological sciences: 56%; physical sciences: 11%; nonsciences: 26%; other: 7%
Percent of graduates entering primary-care specialties: 44.0%

Tufts University
136 Harrison Avenue
Boston, MA 02111
http://www.tufts.edu/med
Private
Admissions: (617) 636-6571
E-mail: med-admissions@tufts.edu

Financial aid: (617) 636-6574
Application deadline: 11/01
Tuition: $47,116
Room/board/expenses: $11,088
Percent receiving grants: 20%
Average student indebtedness at graduation: $171,686
Enrollment: 705
men: 54%; women: 46%; minorities: 34%; underrepresented minorities: 9%; in state: 38%
Acceptance rate: 7%
Average MCAT: 10.6
Average GPA: 3.60
Most popular undergraduate majors: biological sciences: 50%; physical sciences: 19%; nonsciences: 26%; other: 5%
Percent of graduates entering primary-care specialties: 47.0%

University of Massachusetts–Worcester
55 Lake Avenue N
Worcester, MA 01655
http://www.umassmed.edu
Public
Admissions: (508) 856-2323
E-mail: admissions@umassmed.edu
Financial aid: (508) 856-2265
Application deadline: 11/01
In-state tuition: $14,087
Out-of-state tuition: N/A
Room/board/expenses: $12,347
Percent receiving grants: 29%
Average student indebtedness at graduation: $110,722
Enrollment: 435
men: 45%; women: 55%; minorities: 20%; underrepresented minorities: 7%; in state: 98%
Acceptance rate: 23%
Average MCAT: 10.5
Average GPA: 3.59
Most popular undergraduate majors: biological sciences: 29%; physical sciences: 23%; nonsciences: 38%; other: 10%
Percent of graduates entering primary-care specialties: 49.5%

MICHIGAN

Michigan State University
A110 E. Fee Hall
East Lansing, MI 48824
http://humanmedicine.msu.edu
Public
Admissions: (517) 353-9620
E-mail: MDadmissions@msu.edu
Financial aid: (517) 353-5940
Application deadline: 11/15
In-state tuition: $28,010
Out-of-state tuition: $60,890
Room/board/expenses: $12,456
Percent receiving grants: 64%
Average student indebtedness at graduation: $163,390
Enrollment: 494
men: 45%; women: 55%; minorities: 33%; underrepresented minorities: 15%; in state: 74%
Acceptance rate: 6%
Average MCAT: 9.5
Average GPA: 3.51
Most popular undergraduate majors: biological sciences: 65%; physical sciences: 18%; nonsciences: 13%; other: 4%
Percent of graduates entering primary-care specialties: 47.8%

University of Michigan–Ann Arbor
1301 Catherine Road
Ann Arbor, MI 48109-0624
http://www.med.umich.edu/
medschool/
Public
Admissions: (734) 764-6317
E-mail:
umichmedadmiss@umich.edu
Financial aid: (734) 763-4147
Application deadline: 11/15
In-state tuition: $24,755
Out-of-state tuition: $39,119
Room/board/expenses: $20,052
Percent receiving grants: 61%
Average student indebtedness at graduation: $100,373
Enrollment: 671
men: 51%; women: 49%; minorities: 41%; underrepresented minorities: 15%; in state: 45%
Acceptance rate: 7%
Average MCAT: 11.7
Average GPA: 3.74
Most popular undergraduate majors: biological sciences: 41%; physical sciences: 29%; nonsciences: 9%; other: 22%
Percent of graduates entering primary-care specialties: 36.0%

Wayne State University
540 E. Canfield
Detroit, MI 48201
http://www.med.wayne.edu/
Admissions
Public
Admissions: (313) 577-1466
E-mail:
admissions@med.wayne.edu
Financial aid: (313) 577-1039
Application deadline: 12/15
In-state tuition: $28,668
Out-of-state tuition: $56,656
Room/board/expenses: $13,450
Percent receiving grants: 38%
Average student indebtedness at graduation: $129,245
Enrollment: 1,161
men: 53%; women: 47%; minorities: 31%; underrepresented minorities: 14%; in state: 90%
Acceptance rate: 14%
Average MCAT: 10.1
Average GPA: 3.57
Most popular undergraduate majors: biological sciences: 52%; physical sciences: 16%; nonsciences: 8%; other: 24%
Percent of graduates entering primary-care specialties: 30.0%

Mayo Medical School
200 First Street SW
Rochester, MN 55905
http://www.mayo.edu/mms/
Private
Admissions: (507) 284-3671
E-mail:
medschooladmissions@mayo.edu
Financial aid: (507) 284-4839
Application deadline: 11/03
Tuition: $29,700
Room/board/expenses: $12,375
Percent receiving grants: 100%
Average student indebtedness at graduation: $84,422
Enrollment: 160
men: 49%; women: 51%; minorities: 33%; underrepresented minorities: 22%; in state: 22%
Acceptance rate: 1%
Average MCAT: 11.0
Average GPA: 3.81

Most popular undergraduate majors: biological sciences: 36%; physical sciences: 32%; nonsciences: 10%; other: 22%
Percent of graduates entering primary-care specialties: 36.0%

University of Minnesota Medical School
420 Delaware Street SE, MMC 293
Minneapolis, MN 55455
http://www.med.umn.edu
Public
Admissions: (612) 625-7977
E-mail: meded@umn.edu
Financial aid: (612) 625-4998
Application deadline: 11/15
In-state tuition: $33,109
Out-of-state tuition: $40,423
Room/board/expenses: $11,448
Percent receiving grants: 65%
Average student indebtedness at graduation: $134,493
Enrollment: 944
men: 50%; women: 50%; minorities: 19%; underrepresented minorities: 9%; in state: 80%
Acceptance rate: 9%
Average MCAT: 10.4
Average GPA: 3.69
Most popular undergraduate majors: biological sciences: 47%; physical sciences: 25%; nonsciences: 12%; other: 16%
Percent of graduates entering primary-care specialties: 45.9%

University of Mississippi[1]
2500 N. State Street
Jackson, MS 39216-4505
http://www.umc.edu
Public
Admissions: (601) 984-5010
Financial aid: (601) 984-1117
Tuition: N/A
Room/board/expenses: N/A
Enrollment: N/A

St. Louis University
1402 S. Grand Boulevard
St. Louis, MO 63104
http://medschool.slu.edu
Private
Admissions: (314) 977-9870
E-mail: slumd@slu.edu
Financial aid: (314) 977-9840
Application deadline: 12/15
Tuition: $42,783
Room/board/expenses: $11,988
Percent receiving grants: 25%
Average student indebtedness at graduation: $156,722
Enrollment: 698
men: 57%; women: 43%; minorities: 25%; underrepresented minorities: 6%; in state: 50%
Acceptance rate: 9%
Average MCAT: 10.4
Average GPA: 3.76
Most popular undergraduate majors: biological sciences: 57%; physical sciences: 14%; nonsciences: 10%; other: 19%
Percent of graduates entering primary-care specialties: 43.7%

University of Missouri–Columbia
1 Hospital Drive
Columbia, MO 65212
http://som.missouri.edu
Public
Admissions: (573) 882-8047
E-mail:
eastonm@health.missouri.edu
Financial aid: (573) 882-2923
Application deadline: 11/01
In-state tuition: $23,848
Out-of-state tuition: $47,492
Room/board/expenses: $9,000
Percent receiving grants: 80%
Average student indebtedness at graduation: $136,108
Enrollment: 387
men: 51%; women: 49%; minorities: 14%; underrepresented minorities: 5%; in state: 98%
Acceptance rate: 13%
Average MCAT: 10.3
Average GPA: 3.77
Most popular undergraduate majors: biological sciences: 43%; physical sciences: 26%; nonsciences: 14%; other: 17%
Percent of graduates entering primary-care specialties: 46.0%

University of Missouri–Kansas City
2411 Holmes
Kansas City, MO 64108
http://www.med.umkc.edu
Public
Admissions: (816) 235-1208
E-mail: dehaemersj@umkc.edu
Financial aid: (816) 235-1242
Application deadline: 11/15
In-state tuition: $28,142
Out-of-state tuition: $55,075
Room/board/expenses: $8,000
Average student indebtedness at graduation: $107,185
Enrollment: 401
men: 42%; women: 58%; minorities: 47%; underrepresented minorities: 9%; in state: 81%
Acceptance rate: 23%
Most popular undergraduate majors: biological sciences: N/A; physical sciences: N/A; nonsciences: N/A; other: N/A
Percent of graduates entering primary-care specialties: 41.9%

Washington University in St. Louis
660 S. Euclid Avenue
St. Louis, MO 63110
http://medschool.wustl.edu
Private
Admissions: (314) 362-6858
E-mail: wumscoa@wustl.edu
Financial aid: (314) 362-6862
Application deadline: 12/01
Tuition: $43,380
Room/board/expenses: $9,428
Percent receiving grants: 73%
Average student indebtedness at graduation: $100,975
Enrollment: 591
men: 53%; women: 47%; minorities: 36%; underrepresented minorities: 9%; in state: 8%
Acceptance rate: 11%
Average MCAT: 12.5
Average GPA: 3.88
Most popular undergraduate majors: biological sciences: 40%; physical sciences: 40%; nonsciences: 15%; other: 5%
Percent of graduates entering primary-care specialties: 39.8%

Creighton University
2500 California Plaza
Omaha, NE 68178
http://medicine.creighton.edu
Private
Admissions: (402) 280-2799
E-mail: medschadm@creighton.edu
Financial aid: (402) 280-2666
Application deadline: 11/01
Tuition: $41,778
Room/board/expenses: $13,500
Percent receiving grants: 27%
Average student indebtedness at graduation: $155,871
Enrollment: 500
men: 53%; women: 47%; minorities: 17%; underrepresented minorities: 9%; in state: 13%
Acceptance rate: 6%
Average MCAT: 10.0
Average GPA: 3.67
Most popular undergraduate majors: biological sciences: 56%; physical sciences: 20%; nonsciences: 18%; other: 7%
Percent of graduates entering primary-care specialties: 39.0%

University of Nebraska College of Medicine
986585 Nebraska Medical Center
Omaha, NE 68198-6585
http://www.unmc.edu/UNCOM/
Public
Admissions: (402) 559-2259
E-mail: grrogers@unmc.edu
Financial aid: (402) 559-4199
Application deadline: 11/01
In-state tuition: $24,338
Out-of-state tuition: $53,910
Room/board/expenses: $14,400
Percent receiving grants: 60%
Average student indebtedness at graduation: $118,669
Enrollment: 476
men: 57%; women: 43%; minorities: 11%; underrepresented minorities: 6%; in state: 86%
Acceptance rate: 12%
Average MCAT: 9.7
Average GPA: 3.73
Most popular undergraduate majors: biological sciences: 50%; physical sciences: 23%; nonsciences: 5%; other: 22%
Percent of graduates entering primary-care specialties: 60.0%

University of Nevada–Reno
Pennington Building, Mailstop 357
Reno, NV 89557-0357
http://www.medicine.nevada.edu
Public
Admissions: (775) 784-6063
E-mail: asa@med.unr.edu
Financial aid: (775) 784-4666
Application deadline: 11/01
In-state tuition: $15,077
Out-of-state tuition: $34,933
Room/board/expenses: $9,540
Percent receiving grants: 81%
Average student indebtedness at graduation: $114,760
Enrollment: 224
men: 51%; women: 49%; minorities: 28%; underrepresented minorities: N/A; in state: 90%
Acceptance rate: 8%
Average MCAT: 10.1
Average GPA: 3.63
Most popular undergraduate majors: biological sciences: 53%; physical sciences: 26%; nonsciences: 1%; other: 20%

Percent of graduates entering primary-care specialties: 43.0%

Dartmouth Medical School
3 Rope Ferry Road
Hanover, NH 03755-1404
http://dms.dartmouth.edu
Private
Admissions: (603) 650-1505
E-mail: dms.admissions@
dartmouth.edu
Financial aid: (603) 650-1919
Application deadline: 11/01
Tuition: $40,675
Room/board/expenses: $9,750
Percent receiving grants: 52%
Average student indebtedness at graduation: $110,343
Enrollment: 316
men: 48%; women: 52%; minorities: 24%; underrepresented minorities: 6%; in state: 8%
Acceptance rate: 6%
Average MCAT: 11.1
Average GPA: 3.74
Most popular undergraduate majors: biological sciences: 56%; physical sciences: 19%; nonsciences: 11%; other: 14%
Percent of graduates entering primary-care specialties: 43.1%

UMDNJ–New Jersey Medical School[1]
185 S. Orange Avenue
PO Box 1709
Newark, NJ 07101-1709
http://www.njms.umdnj.edu
Public
Admissions: (973) 972-4631
E-mail: njmsadmiss@umdnj.edu
Financial aid: (973) 972-7030
Tuition: N/A
Room/board/expenses: N/A
Enrollment: N/A

UMDNJ–Robert Wood Johnson Medical School
125 Paterson Street
New Brunswick, NJ 08903-0019
http://rwjms.umdnj.edu
Public
Admissions: (732) 235-4576
E-mail: rwjapadm@umdnj.edu
Financial aid: (732) 235-4689
Application deadline: 12/01
In-state tuition: $26,128
Out-of-state tuition: $39,195
Room/board/expenses: $12,294
Percent receiving grants: 47%
Average student indebtedness at graduation: $121,096
Enrollment: 674
men: 45%; women: 55%; minorities: 50%; underrepresented minorities: 15%; in state: 99%
Acceptance rate: 10%
Average MCAT: 10.2
Average GPA: 3.63
Most popular undergraduate majors: biological sciences: 48%; physical sciences: 15%; nonsciences: 26%; other: 11%
Percent of graduates entering primary-care specialties: 45.2%

NEW MEXICO

University of New Mexico

Basic Medical Sciences Building
Room 107
Albuquerque, NM 87131
http://hsc.unm.edu/som/
Public
Admissions: (505) 272-4766
E-mail:
somadmissions@salud.unm.edu
Financial aid: (505) 272-8008
Application deadline: 11/15
In-state tuition: $16,754
Out-of-state tuition: $42,910
Room/board/expenses: $10,810
Percent receiving grants: 62%
Average student indebtedness at graduation: $94,639
Enrollment: 315
men: 47%; women: 53%; minorities: 40%; underrepresented minorities: 33%; in state: 79%
Acceptance rate: 9%
Average MCAT: 9.2
Average GPA: 3.61
Most popular undergraduate majors: biological sciences: 36%; physical sciences: 20%; nonsciences: 15%; other: 29%
Percent of graduates entering primary-care specialties: 46.0%

NEW YORK

Albany Medical College

47 New Scotland Avenue
Albany, NY 12208
http://www.amc.edu
Private
Admissions: (518) 262-5521
E-mail: admissions@mail.amc.edu
Financial aid: (518) 262-5435
Application deadline: 11/15
Tuition: $42,873
Room/board/expenses: N/A
Percent receiving grants: 33%
Average student indebtedness at graduation: $162,151
Enrollment: 566
men: 43%; women: 57%; minorities: 36%; underrepresented minorities: 7%; in state: 42%
Average MCAT: 10.0
Average GPA: 3.60
Most popular undergraduate majors: biological sciences: N/A; physical sciences: N/A; nonsciences: N/A; other: N/A
Percent of graduates entering primary-care specialties: N/A

Columbia University College of Physicians and Surgeons

630 W. 168th Street
New York, NY 10032
http://www.cumc.columbia.edu/dept/ps
Private
Admissions: (212) 305-3595
E-mail:
psadmissions@columbia.edu
Financial aid: (212) 305-4100
Application deadline: 10/15
Tuition: $45,213
Room/board/expenses: $11,890
Percent receiving grants: 54%
Average student indebtedness at graduation: $120,050
Enrollment: 645
men: 47%; women: 53%; minorities: 39%; underrepresented minorities: 20%; in state: 31%
Acceptance rate: 4%
Average MCAT: 11.8
Average GPA: 3.78

Most popular undergraduate majors: biological sciences: 37%; physical sciences: 25%; nonsciences: 26%; other: 12%
Percent of graduates entering primary-care specialties: 30.0%

Cornell University (Weill)

525 E. 68th Street
New York, NY 10021
http://www.med.cornell.edu
Private
Admissions: (212) 746-1067
E-mail: cumc-admissions@med.cornell.edu
Financial aid: (212) 746-1066
Application deadline: 10/15
Tuition: $40,890
Room/board/expenses: $10,709
Percent receiving grants: 57%
Average student indebtedness at graduation: $98,144
Enrollment: 410
men: 50%; women: 50%; minorities: 41%; underrepresented minorities: 20%; in state: 53%
Acceptance rate: 4%
Average MCAT: 11.5
Average GPA: 3.70
Most popular undergraduate majors: biological sciences: 30%; physical sciences: 25%; nonsciences: 23%; other: 22%
Percent of graduates entering primary-care specialties: 32.6%

Mount Sinai School of Medicine

1 Gustave L. Levy Place
PO Box 1475
New York, NY 10029
http://www.mssm.edu
Private
Admissions: (212) 241-6696
E-mail: admissions@mssm.edu
Financial aid: (212) 241-5245
Application deadline: 11/01
Tuition: $38,528
Room/board/expenses: $15,000
Percent receiving grants: 37%
Average student indebtedness at graduation: $136,338
Enrollment: 506
men: 48%; women: 52%; minorities: 44%; underrepresented minorities: 24%; in state: 33%
Acceptance rate: 6%
Average MCAT: 11.3
Average GPA: 3.64
Most popular undergraduate majors: biological sciences: 44%; physical sciences: 19%; nonsciences: 37%; other: N/A
Percent of graduates entering primary-care specialties: 35.6%

New York Medical College

Administration Building
Valhalla, NY 10595
http://www.nymc.edu
Private
Admissions: (914) 594-4507
E-mail: mdadmit@nymc.edu
Financial aid: (914) 594-4491
Application deadline: 12/15
Tuition: $43,696
Room/board/expenses: $18,798
Percent receiving grants: 18%
Average student indebtedness at graduation: $168,000
Enrollment: 786
men: 47%; women: 53%; minorities: 40%; underrepresented minorities: 3%; in state: 32%
Acceptance rate: 8%
Average MCAT: 10.3

Average GPA: 3.60
Most popular undergraduate majors: biological sciences: 48%; physical sciences: 15%; nonsciences: 14%; other: 23%
Percent of graduates entering primary-care specialties: 44.3%

New York University

550 First Avenue
New York, NY 10016
http://www.med.nyu.edu/medicaldegree
Private
Admissions: (212) 263-5290
E-mail: admissions@med.nyu.edu
Financial aid: (212) 263-5286
Application deadline: 10/15
Tuition: $43,919
Room/board/expenses: $10,000
Percent receiving grants: 47%
Average student indebtedness at graduation: $112,839
Enrollment: 670
men: 51%; women: 49%; minorities: 35%; underrepresented minorities: 12%; in state: 46%
Acceptance rate: 6%
Average MCAT: 11.2
Average GPA: 3.63
Most popular undergraduate majors: biological sciences: 57%; physical sciences: 23%; nonsciences: 16%; other: 4%
Percent of graduates entering primary-care specialties: 35.4%

Stony Brook University

Office of Admissions
Health Science Center, L4
Stony Brook, NY 11794-8434
http://www.stonybrookmedicalcenter.org/education/som_admissions.cfm
Public
Admissions: (631) 444-2113
E-mail: somadmissions@stonybrook.edu
Financial aid: (631) 444-2341
Application deadline: 12/15
In-state tuition: $19,890
Out-of-state tuition: $34,590
Room/board/expenses: $22,800
Percent receiving grants: 32%
Average student indebtedness at graduation: $130,513
Enrollment: 449
men: 49%; women: 51%; minorities: 50%; underrepresented minorities: 14%; in state: 96%
Acceptance rate: 8%
Average MCAT: 10.7
Average GPA: 3.60
Most popular undergraduate majors: biological sciences: 45%; physical sciences: 30%; nonsciences: 25%; other: N/A
Percent of graduates entering primary-care specialties: 42.2%

SUNY–Downstate Medical Center[1]

450 Clarkson Avenue, Box 60
Brooklyn, NY 11203
http://www.hscbklyn.edu
Public
Admissions: (718) 270-2446
E-mail: admissions@downstate.edu
Financial aid: (718) 270-2488
Tuition: N/A
Room/board/expenses: N/A
Enrollment: N/A

SUNY–Syracuse

766 Irving Avenue
Syracuse, NY 13210
http://www.upstate.edu
Public
Admissions: (315) 464-4570
E-mail: admiss@upstate.edu
Financial aid: (315) 464-4329
Application deadline: 11/01
In-state tuition: $20,850
Out-of-state tuition: $35,550
Room/board/expenses: $10,450
Percent receiving grants: 38%
Average student indebtedness at graduation: $120,442
Enrollment: 623
men: 49%; women: 51%; minorities: 29%; underrepresented minorities: 11%; in state: 86%
Acceptance rate: 9%
Average MCAT: 10.1
Average GPA: 3.63
Most popular undergraduate majors: biological sciences: N/A; physical sciences: N/A; nonsciences: N/A; other: N/A
Percent of graduates entering primary-care specialties: 38.0%

University at Buffalo–SUNY

155 Biomedical Education Building
Buffalo, NY 14214
http://www.smbs.buffalo.edu/ome
Public
Admissions: (716) 829-3466
E-mail: jjrosso@buffalo.edu
Financial aid: (716) 645-2450
Application deadline: 11/15
In-state tuition: $20,218
Out-of-state tuition: $34,918
Room/board/expenses: $10,707
Percent receiving grants: 24%
Average student indebtedness at graduation: $97,027
Enrollment: 571
men: 47%; women: 53%; minorities: 33%; underrepresented minorities: 5%; in state: 100%
Acceptance rate: 8%
Average MCAT: 10.1
Average GPA: 3.62
Most popular undergraduate majors: biological sciences: 28%; physical sciences: 23%; nonsciences: 31%; other: 18%
Percent of graduates entering primary-care specialties: 31.2%

University of Rochester

601 Elmwood Avenue, Box 706
Rochester, NY 14642
http://www.urmc.rochester.edu/smd/
Private
Admissions: (585) 275-4542
E-mail:
mdadmish@urmc.rochester.edu
Financial aid: (585) 275-4523
Application deadline: 10/15
Tuition: $40,384
Room/board/expenses: $16,000
Percent receiving grants: 45%
Average student indebtedness at graduation: $131,881
Enrollment: 414
men: 48%; women: 52%; minorities: 33%; underrepresented minorities: 12%; in state: 43%
Acceptance rate: 8%
Average MCAT: 10.6
Average GPA: 3.63
Most popular undergraduate majors: biological sciences: 43%; physical sciences: 18%; nonsciences: 8%; other: 31%
Percent of graduates entering primary-care specialties: 35.8%

Yeshiva University (Einstein)

1300 Morris Park Avenue
Bronx, NY 10461
http://www.aecom.yu.edu
Private
Admissions: (718) 430-2106
E-mail: admissions@aecom.yu.edu
Financial aid: (718) 430-2336
Application deadline: 11/01
Tuition: $43,370
Room/board/expenses: $15,200
Percent receiving grants: 47%
Average student indebtedness at graduation: $112,000
Enrollment: 753
men: 48%; women: 52%; minorities: 31%; underrepresented minorities: 10%; in state: 44%
Acceptance rate: 7%
Average MCAT: 10.8
Average GPA: 3.73
Most popular undergraduate majors: biological sciences: 45%; physical sciences: 21%; nonsciences: 26%; other: 8%
Percent of graduates entering primary-care specialties: 55.0%

NORTH CAROLINA

Duke University

DUMC
Durham, NC 27710
http://dukemed.duke.edu
Private
Admissions: (919) 684-2985
E-mail: medadm@mc.duke.edu
Financial aid: (919) 684-6649
Application deadline: 01/12
Tuition: $41,817
Room/board/expenses: $12,240
Percent receiving grants: 73%
Average student indebtedness at graduation: $89,335
Enrollment: 404
men: 52%; women: 48%; minorities: 50%; underrepresented minorities: 22%; in state: 13%
Acceptance rate: 4%
Average MCAT: 11.5
Average GPA: 3.74
Most popular undergraduate majors: biological sciences: 46%; physical sciences: 31%; nonsciences: 16%; other: 7%
Percent of graduates entering primary-care specialties: 41.2%

East Carolina University (Brody)

600 Moye Boulevard
Greenville, NC 27834
http://www.ecu.edu/bsomadmissions
Public
Admissions: (252) 744-2202
E-mail: somadmissions@ecu.edu
Financial aid: (252) 744-2278
Application deadline: 11/15
In-state tuition: $11,056
Out-of-state tuition: $36,075
Room/board/expenses: $11,019
Percent receiving grants: 48%
Average student indebtedness at graduation: $81,212
Enrollment: 293
men: 52%; women: 48%; minorities: 29%; underrepresented minorities: 22%; in state: 100%
Acceptance rate: 13%
Average MCAT: 9.1
Average GPA: 3.50
Most popular undergraduate majors: biological sciences: 29%; physical sciences: 18%; nonsciences: 12%; other: 41%
Percent of graduates entering primary-care specialties: 60.0%

University of North Carolina–Chapel Hill

CB #7000
4030 Bondurant Hall
Chapel Hill, NC 27599-7000
http://www.med.unc.edu/admit/
Public
Admissions: (919) 962-8331
E-mail: admissions@med.unc.edu
Financial aid: (919) 962-6117
Application deadline: 11/15
In-state tuition: $11,919
Out-of-state tuition: $35,585
Room/board/expenses: $27,052
Percent receiving grants: 82%
Average student indebtedness at graduation: $83,475
Enrollment: 736
men: 52%; women: 48%; minorities: 31%; underrepresented minorities: 15%; in state: 76%
Acceptance rate: 6%
Average MCAT: 11.0
Average GPA: 3.73
Most popular undergraduate majors: biological sciences: 44%; physical sciences: 23%; nonsciences: 22%; other: 11%
Percent of graduates entering primary-care specialties: 52.0%

Wake Forest University

Medical Center Boulevard
Winston-Salem, NC 27157
http://www.wfubmc.edu
Private
Admissions: (336) 716-4264
E-mail: medadmit@wfubmc.edu
Financial aid: (336) 716-2889
Application deadline: 11/01
Tuition: $37,134
Room/board/expenses: $19,326
Percent receiving grants: 68%
Average student indebtedness at graduation: $125,852
Enrollment: 454
men: 54%; women: 46%; minorities: 27%; underrepresented minorities: 15%; in state: 37%
Acceptance rate: 4%
Average MCAT: 10.3
Average GPA: 3.64
Most popular undergraduate majors: biological sciences: 59%; physical sciences: 23%; nonsciences: 10%; other: 8%
Percent of graduates entering primary-care specialties: 50.0%

NORTH DAKOTA

University of North Dakota

501 N. Columbia Road, Stop 9037
Grand Forks, ND 58202-9037
http://www.med.und.nodak.edu
Public
Admissions: (701) 777-4221
E-mail: jdheit@medicine.nodak.edu
Financial aid: (701) 777-2849
Application deadline: 11/01
In-state tuition: $22,873
Out-of-state tuition: $41,120
Room/board/expenses: $9,104
Percent receiving grants: 62%
Average student indebtedness at graduation: $129,975
Enrollment: 248
men: 54%; women: 46%; minorities: 13%; underrepresented minorities: 11%; in state: 82%
Acceptance rate: 29%
Average MCAT: 9.0
Average GPA: 3.70
Most popular undergraduate majors: biological sciences: 50%; physical sciences: 16%; nonsciences: 21%; other: 13%

Percent of graduates entering primary-care specialties: 43.4%

OHIO

Case Western Reserve University

10900 Euclid Avenue
Cleveland, OH 44106
http://casemed.case.edu/
Private
Admissions: (216) 368-3450
E-mail: lina.mehta@case.edu
Financial aid: (216) 368-3666
Application deadline: 11/01
Tuition: $43,206
Room/board/expenses: $17,930
Percent receiving grants: 57%
Average student indebtedness at graduation: $134,100
Enrollment: 711
men: 55%; women: 45%; minorities: 38%; underrepresented minorities: 11%; in state: 41%
Acceptance rate: 8%
Average MCAT: 11.2
Average GPA: 3.62
Most popular undergraduate majors: biological sciences: 0%; physical sciences: 1%; nonsciences: 0%; other: 100%
Percent of graduates entering primary-care specialties: 36.0%

Northeastern Ohio Universities College of Medicine

4209 State Route 44
PO Box 95
Rootstown, OH 44272-0095
http://www.neoucom.edu
Public
Admissions: (330) 325-6270
E-mail: admission@neoucom.edu
Financial aid: (330) 325-6481
Application deadline: 11/01
In-state tuition: $28,794
Out-of-state tuition: $55,599
Room/board/expenses: $10,000
Percent receiving grants: 33%
Average student indebtedness at graduation: $112,043
Enrollment: 455
men: 49%; women: 51%; minorities: 40%; underrepresented minorities: 7%; in state: 98%
Acceptance rate: 11%
Average MCAT: 9.5
Average GPA: 3.71
Most popular undergraduate majors: biological sciences: 81%; physical sciences: 5%; nonsciences: 3%; other: 11%
Percent of graduates entering primary-care specialties: 37.0%

Ohio State University

200 Meiling Hall
370 W. Ninth Avenue
Columbus, OH 43210-1238
http://medicine.osu.edu
Public
Admissions: (614) 292-7137
E-mail: medicine@osu.edu
Financial aid: (614) 688-4955
Application deadline: 11/01
In-state tuition: $27,234
Out-of-state tuition: $33,322
Room/board/expenses: $8,320
Percent receiving grants: 62%
Average student indebtedness at graduation: $125,322
Enrollment: 819
men: 60%; women: 40%; minorities: 31%; underrepresented minorities: 10%; in state: 88%
Acceptance rate: 9%
Average MCAT: 11.2

Average GPA: 3.74
Most popular undergraduate majors: biological sciences: 43%; physical sciences: 20%; nonsciences: 12%; other: 24%
Percent of graduates entering primary-care specialties: 44.5%

University of Cincinnati

231 Albert Sabin Way
Cincinnati, OH 45267-0552
http://www.med.uc.edu
Public
Admissions: (513) 558-7314
E-mail: comadmis@ucmail.uc.edu
Financial aid: (513) 558-6797
Application deadline: 11/15
In-state tuition: $28,542
Out-of-state tuition: $47,639
Room/board/expenses: $18,888
Percent receiving grants: 40%
Average student indebtedness at graduation: $139,091
Enrollment: 634
men: 57%; women: 43%; minorities: 29%; underrepresented minorities: 9%; in state: 94%
Acceptance rate: 8%
Average MCAT: 10.6
Average GPA: 3.67
Most popular undergraduate majors: biological sciences: 56%; physical sciences: 27%; nonsciences: 13%; other: 4%
Percent of graduates entering primary-care specialties: 33.3%

University of Toledo

3000 Arlington Avenue
Toledo, OH 43614
http://hsc.utoledo.edu
Public
Admissions: (419) 383-4229
E-mail: medadmissions@utnet.utoledo.edu
Financial aid: (419) 383-4232
Application deadline: 11/01
In-state tuition: $24,850
Out-of-state tuition: $53,590
Room/board/expenses: N/A
Percent receiving grants: 24%
Average student indebtedness at graduation: $128,346
Enrollment: 614
men: 56%; women: 44%; minorities: 25%; underrepresented minorities: 7%; in state: 90%
Acceptance rate: 9%
Average MCAT: 10.0
Average GPA: 3.58
Most popular undergraduate majors: biological sciences: 63%; physical sciences: 12%; nonsciences: 13%; other: 12%
Percent of graduates entering primary-care specialties: 42.0%

Wright State University

PO Box 1751
Dayton, OH 45401-1751
http://www.med.wright.edu
Public
Admissions: (937) 775-2934
E-mail: som_saa@wright.edu
Financial aid: (937) 775-2934
Application deadline: 11/15
In-state tuition: $26,393
Out-of-state tuition: $36,461
Room/board/expenses: $11,946
Percent receiving grants: 40%
Average student indebtedness at graduation: $135,749
Enrollment: 409
men: 43%; women: 57%; minorities: 24%; underrepresented minorities: 8%; in state: 98%
Acceptance rate: 7%
Average MCAT: 9.4
Average GPA: 3.58

biological sciences: 49%; physical sciences: 18%; nonsciences: 14%; other: 19%
Percent of graduates entering primary-care specialties: 50.0%

OKLAHOMA

University of Oklahoma

PO Box 26901, BMSB 357
Oklahoma City, OK 73190
http://www.medicine.ouhsc.edu
Public
Admissions: (405) 271-2331
E-mail: adminmed@ouhsc.edu
Financial aid: (405) 271-2118
Application deadline: 10/15
In-state tuition: $20,450
Out-of-state tuition: $42,535
Room/board/expenses: $20,116
Percent receiving grants: 53%
Average student indebtedness at graduation: $120,000
Enrollment: 623
men: 60%; women: 40%; minorities: 25%; underrepresented minorities: 11%; in state: 92%
Acceptance rate: 17%
Average MCAT: 9.7
Average GPA: 3.69
Most popular undergraduate majors: biological sciences: 62%; physical sciences: 18%; nonsciences: 12%; other: 8%
Percent of graduates entering primary-care specialties: 38.4%

OREGON

Oregon Health and Science University

3181 S.W. Sam Jackson Park Road
L102
Portland, OR 97239-3098
http://www.ohsu.edu/som
Public
Admissions: (503) 494-2998
Financial aid: (503) 494-7800
Application deadline: 10/15
In-state tuition: $31,538
Out-of-state tuition: $42,353
Room/board/expenses: $17,500
Percent receiving grants: 80%
Average student indebtedness at graduation: $145,576
Enrollment: 512
men: 45%; women: 55%; minorities: 17%; underrepresented minorities: 4%; in state: 59%
Acceptance rate: 5%
Average MCAT: 10.2
Average GPA: 3.61
Most popular undergraduate majors: biological sciences: 40%; physical sciences: 9%; nonsciences: 24%; other: 27%
Percent of graduates entering primary-care specialties: 48.0%

PENNSYLVANIA

Drexel University

2900 Queen Lane
Philadelphia, PA 19129
http://www.drexelmed.edu
Private
Admissions: (215) 991-8202
E-mail: Medadmis@drexel.edu
Financial aid: (215) 991-8210
Application deadline: 12/15
Tuition: $42,030
Room/board/expenses: $14,960
Percent receiving grants: 23%
Average student indebtedness at graduation: $182,684
Enrollment: 1,070
men: 51%; women: 49%; minorities: 43%; underrepresented minorities: 8%; in state: 30%

Acceptance rate: 9%
Average MCAT: 10.3
Average GPA: 3.53
Most popular undergraduate majors: biological sciences: N/A; physical sciences: N/A; nonsciences: N/A; other: N/A
Percent of graduates entering primary-care specialties: 39.0%

Jefferson Medical College

1025 Walnut Street, Room 100
Philadelphia, PA 19107-5083
http://www.tju.edu
Private
Admissions: (215) 955-6983
E-mail: jmc.admissions@jefferson.edu
Financial aid: (215) 955-2867
Application deadline: 11/15
Tuition: $41,101
Room/board/expenses: $15,609
Percent receiving grants: 46%
Average student indebtedness at graduation: $153,198
Enrollment: 999
men: 50%; women: 50%; minorities: 32%; underrepresented minorities: 7%; in state: 50%
Acceptance rate: 6%
Average MCAT: 10.4
Average GPA: 3.62
Most popular undergraduate majors: biological sciences: 34%; physical sciences: 12%; nonsciences: 14%; other: 40%
Percent of graduates entering primary-care specialties: 39.0%

Pennsylvania State University College of Medicine[1]

500 University Drive
Hershey, PA 17033
http://www.hmc.psu.edu
Public
Admissions: (717) 531-8755
E-mail: StudentAffairs@hmc.psu.edu
Financial aid: (717) 531-4103
Tuition: N/A
Room/board/expenses: N/A
Enrollment: N/A

Temple University

3420 N. Broad Street, MRB 102
Philadelphia, PA 19140
http://www.temple.edu/medicine
Private
Admissions: (215) 707-3656
E-mail: medadmissions@temple.edu
Financial aid: (215) 707-2667
Application deadline: 12/15
Tuition: $38,502
Room/board/expenses: $10,320
Percent receiving grants: 33%
Average student indebtedness at graduation: $150,614
Enrollment: 707
men: 53%; women: 47%; minorities: 39%; underrepresented minorities: 16%; in state: 51%
Acceptance rate: 5%
Average MCAT: 10.2
Average GPA: 3.64
Most popular undergraduate majors: biological sciences: 40%; physical sciences: 18%; nonsciences: 20%; other: 22%
Percent of graduates entering primary-care specialties: 47.0%

University of Pennsylvania

237 John Morgan Building
3620 Hamilton Walk
Philadelphia, PA 19104-6055
http://www.med.upenn.edu
Private
Admissions: (215) 898-8001
E-mail:
admiss@mail.med.upenn.edu
Financial aid: (215) 573-3423
Application deadline: 10/15
Tuition: $42,706
Room/board/expenses: $17,260
Percent receiving grants: 60%
Average student indebtedness at
graduation: $116,700
Enrollment: 585
men: 50%; women: 50%; minorities: 34%; underrepresented
minorities: 17%; in state: 38%
Acceptance rate: 4%
Average MCAT: 11.6
Average GPA: 3.79
Most popular undergraduate majors:
biological sciences: 51%; physical
sciences: 13%; nonsciences: 28%;
other: 8%
Percent of graduates entering
primary-care specialties: 37.0%

University of Pittsburgh

401 Scaife Hall
Pittsburgh, PA 15261
http://www.medschool.pitt.edu
Public
Admissions: (412) 648-9891
E-mail:
admissions@medschool.pitt.edu
Financial aid: (412) 648-9891
Application deadline: 11/15
In-state tuition: $35,990
Out-of-state tuition: $39,856
Room/board/expenses: $14,500
Percent receiving grants: 60%
Average student indebtedness at
graduation: $135,254
Enrollment: 582
men: 53%; women: 47%; minorities: 48%; underrepresented
minorities: 15%; in state: 30%
Acceptance rate: 8%
Average MCAT: 11.4
Average GPA: 3.70
Most popular undergraduate majors:
biological sciences: 45%; physical
sciences: 24%; nonsciences: 22%;
other: 9%
Percent of graduates entering
primary-care specialties: 38.7%

PUERTO RICO

Ponce School of Medicine

PO Box 7004
Ponce, PR 00732
http://www.psm.edu
Private
Admissions: (787) 840-2575
E-mail: admissions@psm.edu
Financial aid: (787) 840-2575
Application deadline: 12/15
Tuition: $21,389
Room/board/expenses: $11,000
Percent receiving grants: 6%
Average student indebtedness at
graduation: $128,230
Enrollment: 279
men: 49%; women: 51%; minorities: 100%; underrepresented
minorities: N/A; in state: 99%
Acceptance rate: 30%
Average MCAT: 7.0
Average GPA: 3.35

Most popular undergraduate majors:
biological sciences: 73%; physical
sciences: 4%; nonsciences: 21%;
other: 2%
Percent of graduates entering
primary-care specialties: 33.0%

Universidad Central del Caribe[1]

PO Box 60-327
Bayamon, PR 00960-6032
http://www.uccaribe.edu
Private
Admissions: (787) 740-1611
E-mail: icordero@uccaribe.edu
Financial aid: (787) 740-1611
Tuition: N/A
Room/board/expenses: N/A
Enrollment: N/A

University of Puerto Rico School of Medicine[1]

PO Box 365067
San Juan, PR 00936-5067
http://medweb.rcm.upr.edu/
Public
Admissions: (787) 758-2525
E-mail: marrivera@rcm.upr.edu
Financial aid: (787) 758-2525
Tuition: N/A
Room/board/expenses: N/A
Enrollment: N/A

RHODE ISLAND

Brown University (Alpert)

97 Waterman Street, Box G-A213
Providence, RI 02912-9706
http://med.brown.edu
Private
Admissions: (401) 863-2149
E-mail: medschool_admissions@
brown.edu
Financial aid: (401) 863-1142
Application deadline: 11/01
Tuition: $41,184
Room/board/expenses: $16,796
Percent receiving grants: 45%
Average student indebtedness at
graduation: $112,062
Enrollment: 372
men: 45%; women: 55%; minorities: 43%; underrepresented
minorities: 14%; in state: 13%
Acceptance rate: 3%
Average MCAT: 11.7
Average GPA: 3.66
Most popular undergraduate majors:
biological sciences: 33%; physical
sciences: 17%; nonsciences: 42%;
other: 9%
Percent of graduates entering
primary-care specialties: 44.5%

SOUTH CAROLINA

Medical University of South Carolina

171 Ashley Avenue
Charleston, SC 29425
http://www2.musc.edu/COM/
COM1.shtml
Public
Admissions: (843) 792-2055
E-mail: taylorwl@musc.edu
Financial aid: (843) 792-2536
Application deadline: 12/01
In-state tuition: $24,713
Out-of-state tuition: $67,243
Room/board/expenses: $10,770
Percent receiving grants: 25%
Average student indebtedness at
graduation: $130,000

Enrollment: 620
men: 57%; women: 43%; minorities: 21%; underrepresented
minorities: 14%; in state: 93%
Acceptance rate: 14%
Average MCAT: 9.7
Average GPA: 3.57
Most popular undergraduate majors:
biological sciences: 56%; physical
sciences: 19%; nonsciences: 14%;
other: 11%
Percent of graduates entering
primary-care specialties: 58.7%

University of South Carolina

Columbia, SC 29208
http://www.med.sc.edu
Public
Admissions: (803) 733-3325
E-mail: jeanette@gw.sc.edu
Financial aid: (803) 733-3135
Application deadline: 12/01
In-state tuition: $23,094
Out-of-state tuition: $60,410
Room/board/expenses: $12,210
Percent receiving grants: 42%
Average student indebtedness at
graduation: $108,000
Enrollment: 315
men: 53%; women: 47%; minorities: 17%; underrepresented
minorities: 5%; in state: 94%
Acceptance rate: 8%
Average MCAT: 9.5
Average GPA: 3.66
Most popular undergraduate majors:
biological sciences: 60%; physical
sciences: 20%; nonsciences: 4%;
other: 17%
Percent of graduates entering
primary-care specialties: 46.8%

SOUTH DAKOTA

University of South Dakota (Sanford)

1400 W. 22nd Street
Sioux Falls, SD 57105
http://www.usd.edu/med/md
Public
Admissions: (605) 677-6886
E-mail: usdsmsa@usd.edu
Financial aid: (605) 677-5112
Application deadline: 11/15
In-state tuition: $18,436
Out-of-state tuition: $38,409
Room/board/expenses: $20,030
Percent receiving grants: 82%
Average student indebtedness at
graduation: $118,438
Enrollment: 210
men: 52%; women: 48%; minorities: 4%; underrepresented
minorities: 2%; in state: 98%
Acceptance rate: 10%
Average MCAT: 9.6
Average GPA: 3.77
Most popular undergraduate majors:
biological sciences: 56%; physical
sciences: 17%; nonsciences: 9%;
other: 18%
Percent of graduates entering
primary-care specialties: 29.2%

TENNESSEE

East Tennessee State University (Quillen)

PO Box 70694
Johnson City, TN 37614
http://com.etsu.edu
Public
Admissions: (423) 439-2033
E-mail: sacom@etsu.edu
Financial aid: (423) 439-2035
Application deadline: 11/15

In-state tuition: $21,043
Out-of-state tuition: $41,993
Room/board/expenses: $12,325
Percent receiving grants: 40%
Average student indebtedness at
graduation: $108,073
Enrollment: 240
men: 50%; women: 50%; minorities: 14%; underrepresented
minorities: 8%; in state: 91%
Acceptance rate: 9%
Average MCAT: 9.4
Average GPA: 3.64
Most popular undergraduate majors:
biological sciences: 48%; physical
sciences: 27%; nonsciences: 15%;
other: 10%
Percent of graduates entering
primary-care specialties: 41.7%

Meharry Medical College[1]

1005 D. B. Todd Jr. Boulevard
Nashville, TN 37208
http://www.mmc.edu
Private
Admissions: (615) 327-6223
E-mail: amosley@mmc.edu
Financial aid: (615) 327-6826
Tuition: N/A
Room/board/expenses: N/A
Enrollment: N/A

University of Tennessee Health Science Center

62 S. Dunlap, Suite 400
Memphis, TN 38163
http://www.utmem.edu/Medicine/
Public
Admissions: (901) 448-5559
E-mail: diharris@utmem.edu
Financial aid: (901) 448-5568
Application deadline: 11/15
In-state tuition: $21,095
Out-of-state tuition: $38,935
Room/board/expenses: $13,251
Percent receiving grants: 43%
Average student indebtedness at
graduation: $116,936
Enrollment: 605
men: 62%; women: 38%; minorities: 24%; underrepresented
minorities: 13%; in state: 97%
Acceptance rate: 17%
Average MCAT: 10.0
Average GPA: 3.62
Most popular undergraduate majors:
biological sciences: 33%; physical
sciences: 23%; nonsciences: 13%;
other: 31%
Percent of graduates entering
primary-care specialties: 50.3%

Vanderbilt University

21st Avenue S and Garland Avenue
Nashville, TN 37232-2104
http://www.mc.vanderbilt.edu/
medschool/
Private
Admissions: (615) 322-2145
Financial aid: (615) 343-6310
Application deadline: 01/31
Tuition: $39,511
Room/board/expenses: $10,260
Percent receiving grants: 59%
Average student indebtedness at
graduation: $110,200
Enrollment: 417
men: 56%; women: 44%; minorities: 27%; underrepresented
minorities: 10%; in state: 17%
Acceptance rate: 6%
Average MCAT: 11.5
Average GPA: 3.80
Most popular undergraduate majors:
biological sciences: 51%; physical
sciences: 35%; nonsciences: 13%;
other: 1%

Percent of graduates entering
primary-care specialties: 30.0%

TEXAS

Baylor College of Medicine

1 Baylor Plaza
Houston, TX 77030
http://www.bcm.edu
Private
Admissions: (713) 798-4842
E-mail: admissions@bcm.tmc.edu
Financial aid: (713) 798-4603
Application deadline: 11/01
Tuition: $12,848
Room/board/expenses: $19,718
Percent receiving grants: 47%
Average student indebtedness at
graduation: $81,329
Enrollment: 681
men: 52%; women: 48%; minorities: 55%; underrepresented
minorities: 24%; in state: 86%
Acceptance rate: 6%
Average MCAT: 11.6
Average GPA: 3.82
Most popular undergraduate majors:
biological sciences: 42%; physical
sciences: 28%; nonsciences: 10%;
other: 20%
Percent of graduates entering
primary-care specialties: 43.1%

Texas A&M Health Science Center

147 Joe H. Reynolds Medical
Building
College Station, TX 77843-1114
http://medicine.tamhsc.edu
Public
Admissions: (979) 845-7743
E-mail:
admissions@medicine.tamhsc.edu
Financial aid: (979) 845-8854
Application deadline: 10/01
In-state tuition: $10,682
Out-of-state tuition: $23,782
Room/board/expenses: $13,000
Percent receiving grants: 74%
Average student indebtedness at
graduation: $87,961
Enrollment: 353
men: 46%; women: 54%; minorities: 47%; underrepresented
minorities: 14%; in state: 92%
Acceptance rate: 14%
Average MCAT: 9.7
Average GPA: 3.76
Most popular undergraduate majors:
biological sciences: 68%; physical
sciences: 10%; nonsciences: 7%;
other: 15%
Percent of graduates entering
primary-care specialties: 37.8%

Texas Tech University Health Sciences Center

3601 Fourth Street
Lubbock, TX 79430
http://www.ttuhsc.edu/SOM/
Public
Admissions: (806) 743-2297
E-mail: somadm@ttuhsc.edu
Financial aid: (806) 743-3025
Application deadline: N/A
In-state tuition: $11,914
Out-of-state tuition: $25,014
Room/board/expenses: $10,831
Percent receiving grants: 56%
Average student indebtedness at
graduation: $122,818
Enrollment: 571
men: 57%; women: 43%; minorities: 41%; underrepresented
minorities: 16%; in state: 96%
Acceptance rate: 10%
Average MCAT: 9.8
Average GPA: 3.62

Most popular undergraduate majors: biological sciences: 64%; physical sciences: 8%; nonsciences: 17%; other: 11%
Percent of graduates entering primary-care specialties: 40.0%

University of Texas Health Science Center–Houston

6431 Fannin Street
MSB G. 420
Houston, TX 77030
http://www.med.uth.tmc.edu
Public
Admissions: (713) 500-5116
E-mail:
msadmissions@uth.tmc.edu
Financial aid: (713) 500-3860
Application deadline: 10/01
In-state tuition: $12,193
Out-of-state tuition: $25,293
Room/board/expenses: $13,910
Percent receiving grants: 44%
Average student indebtedness at graduation: $111,834
Enrollment: 877
men: 55%; women: 45%; minorities: 29%; underrepresented minorities: 17%; in state: 97%
Acceptance rate: 11%
Average MCAT: 10.0
Average GPA: 3.70
Most popular undergraduate majors: biological sciences: 41%; physical sciences: 26%; nonsciences: 13%; other: 20%
Percent of graduates entering primary-care specialties: 33.0%

University of Texas Health Science Center–San Antonio[1]

7703 Floyd Curl Drive
San Antonio, TX 78229-3900
http://www.uthscsa.edu
Public
Admissions: (210) 567-6080
E-mail: msprospect@uthscsa.edu
Financial aid: (210) 567-2635
Tuition: N/A
Room/board/expenses: N/A
Enrollment: N/A

University of Texas Medical Branch–Galveston

301 University Boulevard
Galveston, TX 77555-0133
http://www.utmb.edu/
somstudentaffairs
Public
Admissions: (409) 772-6958
E-mail: lauthoma@utmb.edu
Financial aid: (409) 772-4955
Application deadline: 10/01
In-state tuition: $12,230
Out-of-state tuition: $25,330
Room/board/expenses: $17,694
Percent receiving grants: 49%
Average student indebtedness at graduation: $123,960
Enrollment: 882
men: 51%; women: 49%; minorities: 42%; underrepresented minorities: 26%; in state: 94%
Acceptance rate: 15%
Average MCAT: 9.7
Average GPA: 3.78
Most popular undergraduate majors: biological sciences: 56%; physical sciences: 20%; nonsciences: 14%; other: 10%
Percent of graduates entering primary-care specialties: 38.6%

University of Texas Southwestern Medical Center–Dallas

5323 Harry Hines Boulevard
Dallas, TX 75390
http://www.utsouthwestern.edu/
Public
Admissions: (214) 648-5617
E-mail: admissions@
utsouthwestern.edu
Financial aid: (214) 648-3611
Application deadline: 10/01
In-state tuition: $12,594
Out-of-state tuition: $25,694
Room/board/expenses: $16,208
Percent receiving grants: 65%
Average student indebtedness at graduation: $90,000
Enrollment: 909
men: 54%; women: 46%; minorities: 50%; underrepresented minorities: 20%; in state: 87%
Acceptance rate: 12%
Average MCAT: 10.8
Average GPA: 3.68
Most popular undergraduate majors: biological sciences: 40%; physical sciences: 25%; nonsciences: 10%; other: 26%
Percent of graduates entering primary-care specialties: 42.0%

University of Utah

30 N. 1900 E
Salt Lake City, UT 84132-2101
http://medicine.utah.edu
Public
Admissions: (801) 581-7498
E-mail:
deans.admissions@hsc.utah.edu
Financial aid: (801) 581-6474
Application deadline: 11/01
In-state tuition: $20,693
Out-of-state tuition: $38,529
Room/board/expenses: $8,964
Percent receiving grants: 73%
Average student indebtedness at graduation: $123,335
Enrollment: 411
men: 63%; women: 37%; minorities: 17%; underrepresented minorities: 6%; in state: 87%
Acceptance rate: 11%
Average MCAT: 9.7
Average GPA: 3.64
Most popular undergraduate majors: biological sciences: 45%; physical sciences: 14%; nonsciences: 16%; other: 25%
Percent of graduates entering primary-care specialties: 39.1%

University of Vermont

E-126 Given Building
89 Beaumont Avenue
Burlington, VT 05405
https://www.med.uvm.edu/
admissions
Public
Admissions: (802) 656-2154
E-mail: medadmissions@uvm.edu
Financial aid: (802) 656-8293
Application deadline: 11/01
In-state tuition: $27,143
Out-of-state tuition: $46,243
Room/board/expenses: $10,564
Percent receiving grants: 58%
Average student indebtedness at graduation: $145,409
Enrollment: 431
men: 42%; women: 58%; minorities: 19%; underrepresented minorities: 3%; in state: 32%
Acceptance rate: 3%
Average MCAT: 10.2
Average GPA: 3.70

Most popular undergraduate majors: biological sciences: 36%; physical sciences: 21%; nonsciences: 30%; other: 13%
Percent of graduates entering primary-care specialties: 58.6%

Eastern Virginia Medical School

721 Fairfax Avenue
PO Box 1980
Norfolk, VA 23501-1980
http://www.evms.edu
Public
Admissions: (757) 446-5812
E-mail: nanezkf@evms.edu
Financial aid: (757) 446-5814
Application deadline: N/A
Tuition: $24,204
Room/board/expenses: N/A
Percent receiving grants: 66%
Average student indebtedness at graduation: $134,179
Enrollment: 447
men: 50%; women: 50%; minorities: 6%; underrepresented minorities: 6%; in state: 67%
Acceptance rate: 6%
Average GPA: 3.49
Most popular undergraduate majors: biological sciences: 19%; physical sciences: 48%; nonsciences: 33%; other: N/A
Percent of graduates entering primary-care specialties: 49.6%

University of Virginia

PO Box 800793
McKim Hall
Charlottesville, VA 22908-0793
http://www.healthsystem.
virginia.edu/internet/SOM/
Public
Admissions: (434) 924-5571
E-mail: medsch-adm@virginia.edu
Financial aid: (434) 924-0033
Application deadline: 11/01
In-state tuition: $31,305
Out-of-state tuition: $41,070
Room/board/expenses: $18,730
Percent receiving grants: 67%
Average student indebtedness at graduation: $112,634
Enrollment: 558
men: 55%; women: 45%; minorities: 26%; underrepresented minorities: 7%; in state: 59%
Acceptance rate: 13%
Average MCAT: 11.1
Average GPA: 3.70
Most popular undergraduate majors: biological sciences: 44%; physical sciences: 30%; nonsciences: 22%; other: 4%
Percent of graduates entering primary-care specialties: 39.0%

Virginia Commonwealth University

PO Box 980565
Richmond, VA 23298-0565
http://www.medschool.vcu.edu
Public
Admissions: (804) 828-9629
E-mail: somume@hsc.vcu.edu
Financial aid: (804) 828-4006
Application deadline: 10/15
In-state tuition: $27,502
Out-of-state tuition: $41,004
Room/board/expenses: $13,400
Percent receiving grants: 41%
Average student indebtedness at graduation: $121,056

Enrollment: 734
men: 52%; women: 48%; minorities: 34%; underrepresented minorities: 9%; in state: 59%
Acceptance rate: 7%
Average MCAT: 9.8
Average GPA: 3.60
Most popular undergraduate majors: biological sciences: 45%; physical sciences: 18%; nonsciences: 28%; other: 9%
Percent of graduates entering primary-care specialties: 42.6%

University of Washington

PO Box 356340
Seattle, WA 98195
http://www.uwmedicine.org
Public
Admissions: (206) 543-7212
E-mail:
askuwsom@u.washington.edu
Financial aid: (206) 685-9229
Application deadline: 11/01
In-state tuition: $17,900
Out-of-state tuition: $41,904
Room/board/expenses: $14,007
Percent receiving grants: 65%
Average student indebtedness at graduation: $97,604
Enrollment: 826
men: 46%; women: 54%; minorities: 23%; underrepresented minorities: 8%; in state: 88%
Acceptance rate: 5%
Average MCAT: 10.5
Average GPA: 3.68
Most popular undergraduate majors: biological sciences: 60%; physical sciences: 14%; nonsciences: 17%; other: 9%
Percent of graduates entering primary-care specialties: 45.0%

Marshall University (Edwards)[1]

1600 Medical Center Drive
Huntington, WV 25701-3655
http://musom.marshall.edu
Public
Admissions: (800) 544-8514
E-mail: warren@marshall.edu
Financial aid: (304) 696-3162
Tuition: N/A
Room/board/expenses: N/A
Enrollment: N/A

West Virginia University

1 Medical Center Drive
Morgantown, WV 26506-9111
http://www.hsc.wvu.edu/som/
students
Public
Admissions: (304) 293-2408
E-mail:
medadmissions@hsc.wvu.edu
Financial aid: (304) 293-3706
Application deadline: 11/01
In-state tuition: $19,204
Out-of-state tuition: $41,866
Room/board/expenses: $9,080
Percent receiving grants: 57%
Average student indebtedness at graduation: $118,962
Enrollment: 421
men: 59%; women: 41%; minorities: 15%; underrepresented minorities: 3%; in state: 70%
Acceptance rate: 6%
Average MCAT: 9.5
Average GPA: 3.69

Most popular undergraduate majors: biological sciences: 54%; physical sciences: 30%; nonsciences: 7%; other: 9%
Percent of graduates entering primary-care specialties: 48.0%

Medical College of Wisconsin

8701 Watertown Plank Road
Milwaukee, WI 53226
http://www.mcw.edu/acad/
admission
Private
Admissions: (414) 456-8246
E-mail: medschool@mcw.edu
Financial aid: (414) 456-8208
Application deadline: 11/01
Tuition: $32,515
Room/board/expenses: $8,000
Percent receiving grants: 62%
Average student indebtedness at graduation: $143,605
Enrollment: 795
men: 51%; women: 49%; minorities: 24%; underrepresented minorities: 10%; in state: 44%
Acceptance rate: 7%
Average MCAT: 9.9
Average GPA: 3.74
Most popular undergraduate majors: biological sciences: 45%; physical sciences: 17%; nonsciences: 10%; other: 29%
Percent of graduates entering primary-care specialties: 39.0%

University of Wisconsin–Madison

750 Highland Avenue
Madison, WI 53705-2221
http://www.med.wisc.edu/
Education
Public
Admissions: (608) 265-6344
E-mail: eamenzer@wisc.edu
Financial aid: (608) 262-3060
Application deadline: 11/01
In-state tuition: $22,722
Out-of-state tuition: $33,846
Room/board/expenses: $15,330
Percent receiving grants: 37%
Average student indebtedness at graduation: $124,950
Enrollment: 614
men: 47%; women: 53%; minorities: 23%; underrepresented minorities: 8%; in state: 83%
Acceptance rate: 8%
Average MCAT: 10.4
Average GPA: 3.76
Most popular undergraduate majors: biological sciences: 37%; physical sciences: 33%; nonsciences: 17%; other: 13%
Percent of graduates entering primary-care specialties: 41.3%

INSTITUTIONS THAT GRANT THE DOCTOR OF OSTEOPATHY (D.O.) DEGREE

ARIZONA

Arizona College of Osteopathic Medicine (Midwestern University)[1]
19555 N. 59th Avenue
Glendale, AZ 85308
http://www.midwestern.edu
Private
Admissions: (623) 572-3275
E-mail: admissaz@midwestern.edu
Financial aid: (623) 572-3321
Tuition: N/A
Room/board/expenses: N/A
Enrollment: N/A

CALIFORNIA

College of Osteopathic Medicine of the Pacific (Western University)
309 E. Second Street
Pomona, CA 91766-1854
http://www.westernu.edu/comp/home.xml
Private
Admissions: (909) 469-5335
E-mail: admissions@westernu.edu
Financial aid: (909) 469-5350
Application deadline: N/A
Tuition: $39,275
Room/board/expenses: $11,190
Percent receiving grants: 13%
Average student indebtedness at graduation: $164,315
Enrollment: 829
men: 50%; women: 50%; minorities: 45%; underrepresented minorities: 6%; in state: 61%
Acceptance rate: 16%
Average MCAT: 9.0
Average GPA: 3.50
Most popular undergraduate majors: biological sciences: 50%; physical sciences: 15%; nonsciences: 13%; other: 22%
Percent of graduates entering primary-care specialties: N/A

Touro University College of Osteopathic Medicine
1310 Johnson Lane
Vallejo, CA 94592
http://www.tu.edu
Private
Admissions: (707) 638-5270
E-mail: haight@touro.edu
Financial aid: (707) 638-5280
Application deadline: 04/01
Tuition: $35,800
Room/board/expenses: $14,798
Percent receiving grants: 18%
Average student indebtedness at graduation: $145,200
Enrollment: 540
men: N/A; women: N/A; minorities: N/A; underrepresented minorities: N/A; in state: N/A
Acceptance rate: 7%
Average MCAT: 9.0
Average GPA: 3.35
Most popular undergraduate majors: biological sciences: 66%; physical sciences: 29%; nonsciences: 5%; other: N/A
Percent of graduates entering primary-care specialties: 55.0%

FLORIDA

Nova Southeastern University College of Osteopathic Medicine
3200 S. University Drive
Fort Lauderdale, FL 33328
http://medicine.nova.edu
Private
Admissions: (954) 262-1101
E-mail: rachwein@nsu.nova.edu
Financial aid: (954) 262-3380
Application deadline: 01/15
Tuition: $28,580
Room/board/expenses: $17,050
Average student indebtedness at graduation: $154,676
Enrollment: 916
men: 50%; women: 50%; minorities: 33%; underrepresented minorities: 18%; in state: 49%
Acceptance rate: 17%
Average MCAT: 8.3
Average GPA: 3.48
Most popular undergraduate majors: biological sciences: 25%; physical sciences: 12%; nonsciences: 13%; other: 51%
Percent of graduates entering primary-care specialties: 60.0%

ILLINOIS

Chicago College of Osteopathic Medicine[1]
555 31st Street
Downers Grove, IL 60515
http://www.midwestern.edu
Private
Admissions: (630) 515-7200
E-mail: admissil@midwestern.edu
Financial aid: (630) 515-6035
Tuition: N/A
Room/board/expenses: N/A
Enrollment: N/A

IOWA

Des Moines University Osteopathic Medical Center[1]
3200 Grand Avenue
Des Moines, IA 50312
http://www.dmu.edu
Private
Admissions: (515) 271-1450
E-mail: doadmit@dmu.edu
Financial aid: (515) 271-1470
Tuition: N/A
Room/board/expenses: N/A
Enrollment: N/A

KENTUCKY

Pikeville College School of Osteopathic Medicine
147 Sycamore Street
Pikeville, KY 41501
http://www.pc.edu
Private
Admissions: (606) 218-5400
E-mail: ahamilto@pc.edu
Financial aid: (606) 218-5407
Application deadline: 02/01
Tuition: $31,745
Room/board/expenses: N/A
Percent receiving grants: 72%
Average student indebtedness at graduation: $136,000

Enrollment: 301
men: 56%; women: 44%; minorities: 10%; underrepresented minorities: 4%; in state: 51%
Acceptance rate: 15%
Average MCAT: 7.3
Average GPA: 3.30
Most popular undergraduate majors: biological sciences: 59%; physical sciences: 9%; nonsciences: 9%; other: 23%
Percent of graduates entering primary-care specialties: 77.0%

MAINE

University of New England College of Osteopathic Medicine
11 Hills Beach Road
Biddeford, ME 04005
http://www.une.edu/com/
Private
Admissions: (800) 477-4863
E-mail: unecomadmissions@une.edu
Financial aid: (207) 283-0171
Application deadline: 02/01
Tuition: $39,520
Room/board/expenses: $11,500
Percent receiving grants: 29%
Average student indebtedness at graduation: $180,730
Enrollment: 501
men: 45%; women: 55%; minorities: 13%; underrepresented minorities: 4%; in state: 20%
Acceptance rate: 7%
Average MCAT: 8.5
Average GPA: 3.41
Most popular undergraduate majors: biological sciences: 51%; physical sciences: 14%; nonsciences: 21%; other: 14%
Percent of graduates entering primary-care specialties: 65.0%

MICHIGAN

Michigan State University College of Osteopathic Medicine
A308 E. Fee Hall
East Lansing, MI 48824
http://www.com.msu.edu
Public
Admissions: (517) 353-7740
E-mail: comadm@com.msu.edu
Financial aid: (517) 353-5188
Application deadline: 12/01
In-state tuition: $28,025
Out-of-state tuition: $60,905
Room/board/expenses: $14,484
Percent receiving grants: 72%
Average student indebtedness at graduation: $156,045
Enrollment: 787
men: 48%; women: 52%; minorities: 19%; underrepresented minorities: 6%; in state: 90%
Acceptance rate: 11%
Average MCAT: 8.7
Average GPA: 3.55
Most popular undergraduate majors: biological sciences: 58%; physical sciences: 4%; nonsciences: 11%; other: 27%
Percent of graduates entering primary-care specialties: 83.3%

MISSOURI

A.T. Still University of Health Sciences (Kirksville)
800 W. Jefferson Street
Kirksville, MO 63501
http://www.atsu.edu
Private
Admissions: (866) 626-2878
E-mail: admissions@atsu.edu
Financial aid: (660) 626-2529
Application deadline: 08/02
Tuition: $38,000
Room/board/expenses: $10,593
Percent receiving grants: 16%
Average student indebtedness at graduation: $152,713
Enrollment: 697
men: 60%; women: 40%; minorities: 17%; underrepresented minorities: 4%; in state: 21%
Acceptance rate: 12%
Average MCAT: 8.7
Average GPA: 3.42
Most popular undergraduate majors: biological sciences: 47%; physical sciences: 18%; nonsciences: 17%; other: 18%
Percent of graduates entering primary-care specialties: 33.3%

University of Health Sciences College of Osteopathic Medicine[1]
1750 Independence Avenue
Kansas City, MO 64106-1453
http://www.uhs.edu
Private
Admissions: (800) 234-4847
E-mail: admissions@uhs.edu
Financial aid: (816) 283-2000
Tuition: N/A
Room/board/expenses: N/A
Enrollment: N/A

NEW JERSEY

UMDNJ–School of Osteopathic Medicine
1 Medical Center Drive
Stratford, NJ 08084-1501
http://som.umdnj.edu
Public
Admissions: (856) 566-7050
E-mail: somadm@umdnj.edu
Financial aid: (856) 566-6008
Application deadline: 02/01
In-state tuition: $25,783
Out-of-state tuition: $38,850
Room/board/expenses: $13,650
Average student indebtedness at graduation: $118,039
Enrollment: 413
men: 41%; women: 59%; minorities: 47%; underrepresented minorities: 24%; in state: 99%
Acceptance rate: 5%
Average MCAT: 8.9
Average GPA: 3.47
Most popular undergraduate majors: biological sciences: 44%; physical sciences: 8%; nonsciences: 13%; other: 35%
Percent of graduates entering primary-care specialties: 45.6%

NEW YORK

New York College of Osteopathic Medicine
Old Westbury
Northern Boulevard
Long Island, NY 11568
http://www.nyit.edu
Private
Admissions: (516) 686-3747
E-mail: rzaika@nyit.edu
Financial aid: (516) 686-7960
Application deadline: 02/01
Tuition: $38,965
Room/board/expenses: $21,000
Percent receiving grants: 34%
Average student indebtedness at graduation: $158,600
Enrollment: 1,202
men: 47%; women: 53%; minorities: N/A; underrepresented minorities: N/A; in state: 85%
Acceptance rate: 12%
Most popular undergraduate majors: biological sciences: N/A; physical sciences: N/A; nonsciences: N/A; other: N/A
Percent of graduates entering primary-care specialties: N/A

OHIO

Ohio University
Grosvenor and Irvine Halls
Athens, OH 45701
http://www.oucom.ohiou.edu
Public
Admissions: (740) 593-4313
E-mail: admissions@oucom.ohiou.edu
Financial aid: (740) 593-2158
Application deadline: 02/01
In-state tuition: $25,476
Out-of-state tuition: $35,809
Room/board/expenses: $10,071
Percent receiving grants: 30%
Average student indebtedness at graduation: $143,771
Enrollment: 438
men: 49%; women: 51%; minorities: 26%; underrepresented minorities: 18%; in state: 98%
Acceptance rate: 5%
Average MCAT: 8.4
Average GPA: 3.57
Most popular undergraduate majors: biological sciences: 70%; physical sciences: 14%; nonsciences: 6%; other: 10%
Percent of graduates entering primary-care specialties: 50.0%

OKLAHOMA

Oklahoma State University
1111 W. 17th Street
Tulsa, OK 74107-1898
http://healthsciences.okstate.edu
Public
Admissions: (918) 561-8421
E-mail: sarah.quinten@okstate.edu
Financial aid: (918) 561-1228
Application deadline: 02/01
In-state tuition: $18,325
Out-of-state tuition: $34,686
Room/board/expenses: $7,300
Percent receiving grants: 42%
Average student indebtedness at graduation: $142,791
Enrollment: 342
men: 53%; women: 47%; minorities: 26%; underrepresented minorities: 19%; in state: 90%
Acceptance rate: 22%
Average MCAT: 8.7

Average GPA: 3.64
Most popular undergraduate majors: biological sciences: 51%; physical sciences: 15%; nonsciences: 10%; other: 24%
Percent of graduates entering primary-care specialties: 53.7%

PENNSYLVANIA

Lake Erie College of Osteopathic Medicine
1858 W. Grandview Boulevard
Erie, PA 16509
http://www.lecom.edu
Private
Admissions: (814) 866-6641
E-mail: admissions@lecom.edu
Financial aid: (814) 866-6641
Application deadline: 04/01
Tuition: $25,950
Room/board/expenses: $11,550
Percent receiving grants: 25%
Average student indebtedness at graduation: $159,000
Enrollment: 1,567
men: 53%; women: 47%; minorities: 24%; underrepresented minorities: 8%; in state: 36%
Acceptance rate: 12%
Average MCAT: 8.7
Average GPA: 3.40

biological sciences: 68%; physical sciences: 6%; nonsciences: 15%; other: 11%
Percent of graduates entering primary-care specialties: 67.0%

Philadelphia College of Osteopathic Medicine[1]
4170 City Avenue
Philadelphia, PA 19131
http://www.pcom.edu
Private
Admissions: (800) 999-6998
E-mail: admissions@pcom.edu
Financial aid: (215) 871-6170
Tuition: N/A
Room/board/expenses: N/A
Enrollment: N/A

TEXAS

U. of North Texas Health Sci. Center (Texas Col. of Osteopathic Medicine)
3500 Camp Bowie Boulevard
Fort Worth, TX 76107-2699
http://www.hsc.unt.edu
Public
Admissions: (800) 535-8266

E-mail: TCOMAdmissions@hsc.unt.edu
Financial aid: (800) 346-8266
Application deadline: 10/01
In-state tuition: $13,950
Out-of-state tuition: $29,700
Room/board/expenses: $14,070
Percent receiving grants: 65%
Average student indebtedness at graduation: $114,000
Enrollment: 593
men: 50%; women: 50%; minorities: 40%; underrepresented minorities: 13%; in state: 95%
Acceptance rate: 20%
Average MCAT: 9.1
Average GPA: 3.56
Most popular undergraduate majors: biological sciences: 55%; physical sciences: 11%; nonsciences: 6%; other: 28%
Percent of graduates entering primary-care specialties: 76.0%

VIRGINIA

Edward Via Virginia College of Osteopathic Medicine
2265 Kraft Drive
Blacksburg, VA 24060
http://www.vcom.vt.edu
Private
Admissions: (540) 231-6138

E-mail: mprice@vcom.vt.edu
Financial aid: (540) 231-6021
Application deadline: 02/01
Tuition: $31,000
Room/board/expenses: $25,300
Percent receiving grants: 21%
Enrollment: 617
men: 47%; women: 53%; minorities: 26%; underrepresented minorities: 16%; in state: 37%
Acceptance rate: 11%
Average MCAT: 8.0
Average GPA: 3.53
Most popular undergraduate majors: biological sciences: 56%; physical sciences: 15%; nonsciences: 11%; other: 18%
Percent of graduates entering primary-care specialties: 60.0%

WEST VIRGINIA

West Virginia School of Osteopathic Medicine
400 N. Lee Street
Lewisburg, WV 24901
http://www.wvsom.edu
Public
Admissions: (800) 356-7836
E-mail: admissions@wvsom.edu
Financial aid: (800) 356-7836
Application deadline: 02/15
In-state tuition: $20,030
Out-of-state tuition: $49,273

Room/board/expenses: N/A
Percent receiving grants: 16%
Average student indebtedness at graduation: $158,372
Enrollment: 598
men: 51%; women: 49%; minorities: 17%; underrepresented minorities: 4%; in state: 36%
Acceptance rate: 19%
Average MCAT: 7.8
Average GPA: 3.44
Most popular undergraduate majors: biological sciences: 58%; physical sciences: 20%; nonsciences: 6%; other: 16%
Percent of graduates entering primary-care specialties: 84.5%

BUSINESS

EDUCATION

LAW